PEARSON

ALWAYS LEARNING

Teresa Audesirk • Gerald Audesirk • Bruce E. Byers

Biology: Life on Earth

Second Custom Edition for Saint Paul College

Taken from:
Biology: Life on Earth, Tenth Edition
by Teresa Audesirk, Gerald Audesirk, and Bruce E. Byers

Cover Images: Courtesy of Photodisc/Getty Images.

Taken from:

Biology: Life on Earth, Tenth Edition
by Teresa Audesirk, Gerald Audesirk and Bruce E. Byers
Copyright © 2014, 2011, 2008 by Pearson Education, Inc.
Published by Pearson Education, Inc.
Glenview, IL 60025

This special edition published in cooperation with Pearson Learning Solutions.

Pearson Learning Solutions, 501 Boylston Street, Suite 900, Boston, MA 02116
A Pearson Education Company
www.pearsoned.com

Printed in the United States of America

 3 4 5 6 7 8 9 10 V092 16 15 14

000200010271776475

TS

ISBN 10: 1-269-32567-1
ISBN 13: 978-1-269-32567-7

About the Authors

TERRY AND GERRY AUDESIRK grew up in New Jersey, where they met as undergraduates, Gerry at Rutgers University and Terry at Bucknell University. After marrying in 1970, they moved to California, where Terry earned her doctorate in marine ecology at the University of Southern California and Gerry earned his doctorate in neurobiology at the California Institute of Technology. As postdoctoral students at the University of Washington's marine laboratories, they worked together on the neural bases of behavior, using a marine mollusk as a model system.

They are now emeritus professors of biology at the University of Colorado Denver, where they taught introductory biology and neurobiology from 1982 through 2006. In their research, funded primarily by the National Institutes of Health, they investigated the mechanisms by which neurons are harmed by low levels of environmental pollutants and protected by estrogen.

Terry and Gerry are long-time members of many conservation organizations, and share a deep appreciation of nature and of the outdoors. They enjoy hiking in the Rockies, walking and horseback riding near their home outside Steamboat Springs, and singing in the community chorus. They are delighted that their daughter Heather is pursuing solar energy research as a doctoral student at her dad's alma mater. Keeping up with the amazing and endless stream of new discoveries in biology provides them with a continuing source of fascination and stimulation.

BRUCE E. BYERS is a midwesterner transplanted to the hills of western Massachusetts, where he is a professor in the biology department at the University of Massachusetts, Amherst.

He has been a member of the faculty at UMass (where he also completed his doctoral degree) since 1993. Bruce teaches courses in evolution, ornithology, and animal behavior, and does research on the function and evolution of bird vocalizations.

With love to Jack and Lori and in loving memory of Eve and Joe

T. A. & G. A.

To Maija

B. E. B.

Brief Contents

Detailed Contents

UNIT 2

Inheritance 138

Y chromosome

X chromosome

UNIT 3

Evolution and Diversity of Life   257

Preface

THE CASE FOR SCIENTIFIC LITERACY

Climate change, biofuels vs. food and forests, bioengineering, stem cells in medicine, potential flu pandemics, the plight of polar bears and pandas, human population growth and sustainability—our students are bombarded with biology-related information and misinformation as well. The concerns that are sweeping our increasingly connected human societies are very real, urgent, and interrelated. Never have scientifically literate societies been more important to humanity's future. As educators, we feel humbled before this massive challenge. As authors, we feel hopeful that the Tenth Edition of *Biology: Life on Earth* will help lead introductory biology students along paths to understanding.

Scientific literacy requires a foundation of factual knowledge that provides a solid and accurate cognitive framework into which new information can be integrated. But more importantly, it endows people with the mental tools to apply that knowledge to their lives. Scientifically literate citizens can better understand and evaluate information from the press and Internet, distinguish fact from fiction, and make informed choices in both their personal lives and in the political arena.

This Tenth Edition of *Biology: Life on Earth* continues our tradition of:

- Helping instructors present biological information in a way that will foster scientific literacy among their students.
- Helping to inspire students with a sense of wonder about the natural world, fostering an attitude of inquiry and appreciation for the knowledge gained through science.
- Helping students to appreciate how science illuminates life, and to recognize the importance of what they are learning to their future roles in our rapidly changing world.

WHAT'S NEW IN THIS EDITION?

Each new edition gives the authors a fresh opportunity to ponder: "What can we do better?" With extensive help from reviewers, developmental editors, and our coauthors, we've answered this question with the following major changes:

- **NEW Learning Goals and Learning Outcomes** Learning Goals now begin each chapter, alerting students to the major concepts within the chapter and the expectations for student learning. Learning Outcomes at the end of each chapter restate the Learning Goals, serving as a recap of the chapter's coverage. References to the relevant Learning Outcomes are provided for each Fill-in-the-Blank and Review Question. The Learning Outcomes also correlate with those found on MasteringBiology.
- **NEW Check Your Learning self-assessment questions** Following each major chapter section, a list of questions prompts students to evaluate their understanding of the material within the section.

- **INCREASED emphasis on human health** In this edition, we have incorporated more information about health issues—which are both inherently interesting and important to students—into our nonphysiology chapters. For example, Chapter 2 now includes a discussion of radiation therapy in cancer treatment, Chapter 5 now relates membrane fluidity to "Why Your Fingers Fumble and Go Numb in the Cold," and Chapter 9 features a new Case Study, "Body, Heal Thyself."
- **CUTTING-EDGE biotechnology** The tenth edition covers important advances in this exploding and crucial area of biological research. These advances include medical applications of stem cells, the importance of epigenetics, and the use of DNA barcoding for species identification.
- **SEVEN NEW "Case Studies"** Our tenth edition features seven entirely new Case Studies that highlight topics of emerging relevance in today's world. An example is the timely "Unstable Atoms Unleashed," which explores radioactivity through the events of the 2011 tsunami that devastated Japan's Fukushima power plant.
- **MORE flexibility for users** Our former "A Closer Look" essays are now entitled "In Greater Depth" to highlight their usefulness for those instructors who wish to cover complex topics in more detail. These essays are specifically designed to be assigned by the instructor—or not—providing flexibility in the depth of coverage. The In Greater Depth topics include, for example, step-by step reactions of cellular respiration and revised descriptions of C_4 and CAM photosynthesis. This feature will support instructors who want to teach a more challenging course or cover specific topics in greater depth, and it will also satisfy students who wish to investigate a topic more thoroughly.

BIOLOGY: LIFE ON EARTH, TENTH EDITION

. . . Is Organized Clearly and Uniformly

Navigational aids help students explore each chapter. An important goal of this organization is to present biology as a hierarchy of closely interrelated concepts rather than as a compendium of independent topics.

- In addition to the new Learning Goals, each chapter opens with "At a Glance" features, which allow users to see how the chapter topics are organized.
- Major sections are introduced as broad questions that stimulate thinking about the material to follow; subheadings are statements that summarize their specific content.
- A "Summary of Key Concepts" section ends each chapter, providing a concise, efficient review of the chapter's major topics.

. . . Engages and Motivates Students

Scientific literacy cannot be imposed on students—they must actively participate in acquiring the necessary information and skills. To be inspired to accomplish this, they must first recognize that biology is about their own lives. For example, we help students acquire a basic understanding and appreciation of how their own bodies function by including information about diet and weight, drugs (including tobacco and alcohol), and birth control options and how each works.

We fervently hope that students who use this text will come to see their world through keener eyes, for example, perceiving forests, fields, and ponds as vibrant and interconnected ecosystems brimming with diverse life-forms rather than as mundane features of their everyday surroundings. If we have done our job, students will also gain the interest, insight, and information they need to look at how humanity has intervened in the natural world. If they ask the question: "Is this activity sustainable?" and then use their new knowledge and critical thinking skills to seek some answers, we can be optimistic about the future.

In support of these goals, the Tenth Edition continues to offer these revised and updated features:

- **Case Studies** Each chapter opens with an attention-grabbing Case Study directly relevant to the chapter topic. Case Studies, including "Flesh-Eating Bacteria" (Chapter 36), "Bionic Ears" (Chapter 39), "Mussels Muscle In" (Chapter 27), and "Some Like it Hot—And Stinky!" (Chapter 44), are based on news events, personal interest stories, or particularly fascinating biological topics. Discussion of each Case Study continues throughout each chapter in boxed features that relate the topic to appropriate sections of the text. The "Case Study Revisited" at each chapter's end explores the topic further in light of what the chapter has covered.
- **Boxed Essays** Four categories of essays enliven this text. "Earth Watch" essays explore pressing environmental issues; "Health Watch" essays cover important or intriguing medical topics, and "Science in Action" essays explain how scientific knowledge is acquired. Although the main body of the text always provides a clear, general explanation of each topic, our "In Greater Depth" essays make this text versatile for different levels of instruction.
- **Engaging "Have You Ever Wondered" Questions and "Links to Everyday Life" Boxes** These short features explore questions that students might ask their instructors and illustrate the real-world applications of the text material to the students' lives.
- **BioEthics Questions** Many topics explored in the text are controversial and have ethical implications for human society. These include human cloning, genetically modified crops, and human impacts on other species. The BioEthics icon BioEthics alerts students and instructors to the possibility for further discussion and investigation.
- **Critical Thinking Questions** At the end of each "Case Study Revisited" section, in selected figure captions, and in the "Applying the Concepts" section at the end of each chapter, our critical thinking questions stimulate students to think about science rather than to simply memorize facts.
- **End-of-Chapter Questions** The questions that conclude each chapter allow students to review the material in different formats—fill-in-the-blank, essay, and critical thinking questions—that help them to study and test what they have learned. Additional critical thinking questions at the end of each Case Study and in selected figure captions stimulate students to think about and apply science to possible real-life situations. Answers to the fill-in-the-blank and figure caption questions are included in the back of the book. Answers or hints for the essay and critical thinking questions are included on the MasteringBiology Web site. Multiple choice type questions can be found in the reading quizzes and practice quizzes in MasteringBiology, as well as in the Instructor Test Bank.
- **Key Terms and a Complete Glossary** Boldfaced key terms are defined clearly within the text as they are introduced. These terms are also listed at the end of each chapter, providing users with a quick reference to the chapter's important vocabulary. The glossary, carefully written by the authors, provides exceptionally complete definitions for all key terms, as well as for many other important biological terms.

. . . Is a Comprehensive Learning Package

The Tenth Edition of *Biology: Life on Earth* is a complete learning package, providing updated and innovative teaching aids for instructors and learning aids for students.

Chapter-by-Chapter Summary of Important Changes

Following the revision of chapters in response to reviews by instructors and experts, the text and artwork were carefully reviewed by each of the other two authors and a developmental editor. The coauthors provided valuable insights to one another, integrating the chapters more thoroughly, improving consistency between chapters, and explaining complex concepts more clearly. Our developmental editors brought trained eyes for order and detail to our work, helping us make the writing even more student friendly. Following this intense scrutiny, each initial revision underwent a second, sometimes extensive revision. Specific changes include the following:

- **Chapter 1: An Introduction to Life on Earth** has undergone a major reorganization and now introduces the concept of life and how it evolved before delving into how scientists study life. A new "Links to Everyday Life: A Solar-Powered Big Mac?" explains how sunlight ultimately provides the calories in all the foods we eat. Another new "Links to Everyday Life: When Your Car Won't Start" applies the scientific method to a familiar problem. Many new photos illustrate this chapter. Figure 1-11 illustrating the tree of life has been revised for consistency with later chapters.

Unit 1: The Life of the Cell

- **Chapter 2: Atoms, Molecules, and Life** includes a timely new Case Study that explores radioactivity through the events of the 2011 tsunami that devastated Japan's Fukushima power plant. Radioactivity is further highlighted in the new "Science in Action: Radioactive Medicine" essay. An explanation of oxidative stress, including identification of some diseases caused by it, is now offered in the Health Watch essay.

- **Chapter 3: Biological Molecules** includes new art and text about the structure of silk protein. The methyl group was added to Table 3-1; adding this important functional group to DNA is described in Chapter 12 as a major epigenetic modification that alters gene expression. "What Makes Hair Curl?" is now revised, somewhat simplified, and presented as a "Links to Everyday Life" feature.

- **Chapter 4: Cell Structure and Function** has a Case Study Revisited section that discusses a cutting-edge product that promises to provide a revolutionary way to regrow skin on burn victims.

- **Chapter 5: Cell Membrane Structure and Function** now provides more information about how membrane fluidity influences membrane function, including a new Have You Ever Wondered feature that relates membrane fluidity to why fingers get numb in cold weather. The In Greater Depth essay now includes the relationship between phospholipid tail kinks and membrane fluidity. The section on membrane proteins has been substantially revised and reorganized. The figures illustrating cell attachment and communication have been combined and are now easier to interpret.

- **Chapter 6: Energy Flow in the Life of a Cell** includes a new Earth Watch essay, "Step on the Brakes and Recharge Your Battery," that uses principles of energy conversion to explain regenerative braking in some modern, fuel-efficient cars. Section 6.5 concerning enzyme regulation has undergone reorganization and rewriting. The Health Watch essay on lactose intolerance has been revised.

- **Chapter 7: Capturing Solar Energy: Photosynthesis** has had its Case Study featuring the asteroid impact that probably ended the reign of the dinosaurs extensively revised. The explanations of C4 and CAM photosynthesis also have been revised and placed in an In Greater Depth essay.

- **Chapter 8: Harvesting Energy: Glycolysis and Cellular Respiration** includes several figures illustrating chemical reactions, which have been changed to show all the carbon atoms. Talking boxes now improve the clarity of the two In Greater Depth essays explaining the details of glycolysis and the mitochondrial matrix reactions of cellular respiration. A new section explains how cellular respiration can obtain energy from a variety of molecules in addition to glucose.

Unit 2: Inheritance

- **Chapter 9: The Continuity of Life: Cellular Reproduction** opens with a new Case Study showing how physicians can use the body's own methods of controlling cell division to stimulate faster and more complete healing of injuries. The Health Watch describing how faulty control of cell division causes cancer has been streamlined and simplified. The discussion of cloning has been moved to Chapter 13, Biotechnology.

- **Chapter 10: Patterns of Inheritance** has been reorganized for improved clarity. A new Links to Everyday Life explores the impact of the sickle-cell allele on the health and performance of athletes who carry the allele.

- **Chapter 12: Gene Expression and Regulation** now describes epigenetic control of gene expression. Genomic imprinting and the possibility that epigenetic regulation may be inherited across generations are described in a new Health Watch.

- **Chapter 13: Biotechnology** has been updated with current information, including recently developed methods for diagnosing both inherited diseases and infections; a new gene therapy that may be able to alleviate and possibly cure AIDS; and new successes in gene therapy for severe combined immune deficiency. The discussion of cloning plants and animals has been moved from Chapter 9 to this chapter. We describe the use of DNA barcoding in species identification, and how barcoding might be used to reduce trafficking in endangered species. We have substantially revised the description of how genetically modified organisms are made.

Unit 3: Evolution and Diversity of Life

- **Chapter 14: Principles of Evolution** includes a new segment on the evolution of herbicide resistance in "superweeds." The Earth Watch on how people promote high-speed evolution includes a new example (color changes in tawny owls) of one impact of climate change on evolution.

ACKNOWLEDGMENTS

Biology: Life on Earth enters its 10th edition invigorated by the oversight of the excellent team at Benjamin Cummings. Beth Wilbur, our Editor-in-Chief, continues to oversee the huge enterprise with the warmth and competence that makes her such an excellent leader. Deborah Gale, Executive Director of Development, again coordinated this complex and multi-faceted endeavor. Senior Acquisitions Editor Star MacKenzie did a great job of helping us form a revision plan that even further expands the text's appeal and its ability to convey fascinating information in a user-friendly manner. She listened and responded helpfully to our questions and suggestions—all while traveling extensively to share her enthusiasm for the text and its ancillary resources with educators across the country. Nicole George-OBrien has worked closely with us from the start. As Project Editor, she has done a marvelous job of keeping everything—especially the authors—on track and on schedule, not to mention helping us through the complexities of a rigorously upgraded permissions process. Her unfailingly kind and sympathetic requests and reminders made this huge project as painless as possible. As we worked with artists and developmental editors, Nicole was also a constant, behind-the-scenes presence, making sure all went smoothly. Our developmental editors, Susan Teahan and Debbie Hardin, carefully reviewed every word of the manuscripts, making sure the sometimes extensive revisions and rearrangements flowed smoothly into the existing text. Their attention to detail and numerous, thoughtful, gently worded suggestions have contributed significantly to the text's organization and clarity. Lorretta Palagi, our outstanding copyeditor, not only negotiated the intricacies of grammar and formatting, but also caught things that we had all overlooked. Susan, Debbie, and Lorretta also looked carefully at the art, checking each piece for consistency with the text and helping us with instructions to the artists. The book boasts a large number of excellent new photos, tracked down with skill and persistence by Kristin Piljay. Kristin was always cheerfully responsive to our requests for still more photos when nothing in the first batch would do.

We are grateful to Imagineering Media Services, under the direction of Project Manager Alicia Elliot, for deciphering our art instructions and patiently making new adjustments to already outstanding figures. We owe our beautifully redesigned text to Integra Software Inc. and whimsical new cover to Marilyn Perry.

The production of this text would not have been possible without the considerable efforts of Camille Herrera, Production Project Manager, and Michael Early, Managing Editor. Roxanne Klaas, Project Editor, of S4Carlisle Publishing Services, brought the art, photos, and manuscript together into a seamless and beautiful whole, graciously handling last-minute changes. We thank Lauren Harp, Executive Marketing Manager, for making sure the finished product reached your desk.

In his role as Manufacturing Buyer, Michael Penne's expertise has served us well. The ancillaries are an endeavor fully as important as the text itself. Susan Berge, Sylvia Rebert, and Frances Sink skillfully coordinated the enormous effort of producing a truly outstanding package that complements and supports the text, while David Chavez took the lead on the Instructor's Resource CD-ROM. Finally, thanks to Laura Tommasi and Daniel Ross for their efforts in developing the outstanding MasteringBiology Web site that accompanies this text.

We are extremely fortunate to be working with the Pearson Benjamin Cummings team. This Tenth Edition of **Biology: Life on Earth** reflects their exceptional abilities and dedication.

With gratitude,

TERRY AUDESIRK, GERRY AUDESIRK,
AND BRUCE BYERS

Tenth Edition Reviewers

Kammy Algiers,
  Ventura College
Erin Baumgartner,
  Western Oregon University
Bruno Borsari,
  Winona State University
Jamie Burchill,
  Troy University
Anne Casper,
  Eastern Michigan University
Mary Colavito,
  Santa Monica College
Kimberly Demnicki,
  Thomas Nelson Community College
Gerald Farr,
  Texas State University
Sandra Gibbons,
  Moraine Valley Community College
Mary Rose Grant,
  St. Louis University
Anjali Gray,
  Lourdes College
Ida Greidanus,
  Passaic Community College
Rebecca Hare,
  Cleveland County Community College
Harriette Howard-Lee Block,
  Prairie View A&M University
Adam Hrincevich,
  Louisiana State University
Kesmic Jackson,
  Georgia State University
A. J. Karpoff,
  University of Louisville
Michael Koban,
  Morgan State University
Mary Lipscomb,
  Virginia Polytechnic Institute and State University

Fordyce Lux,
Metropolitan State College of Denver
Liz Nash,
California State University, Long Beach
David Rosen,
Lee College
Jack Shurley,
Idaho State University
Bill Simcik,
Lonestar College
Anna Bess Sorin,
University of Memphis
Anthony Stancampiano,
Oklahoma City University
Theresa Stanley,
Gordon College
Mary-Pat Stein,
California State University, Northridge
Julienne Thomas-Hall,
Kennedy King College
Lisa Weasel,
Portland State University
Janice Webster,
Ivy Tech Community College
Marty Zahn,
Thomas Nelson Community College

Previous Edition Reviewers

Mike Aaron,
Shelton State Community College
W. Sylvester Allred,
Northern Arizona University
Judith Keller Amand,
Delaware County Community College
William Anderson,
Abraham Baldwin Agriculture College
Steve Arch,
Reed College
George C. Argyros,
Northeastern University
Kerri Lynn Armstrong,
Community College of Philadelphia
Ana Arnizaut-Vilella,
Mississippi University for Women
Dan Aruscavage,
State University of New York, Potsdam
G. D. Aumann,
University of Houston
Vernon Avila,
San Diego State University
J. Wesley Bahorik,
Kutztown University of Pennsylvania
Peter S. Baletsa,
Northwestern University
Isaac Barjis
New York City College of Technology
John Barone,
Columbus State University
Bill Barstow,
University of Georgia–Athens

Mike Barton,
Centre College
Michael C. Bell,
Richland College
Colleen Belk,
University of Minnesota, Duluth
Robert Benard,
American International College
Heather Bennett,
Illinois College
Gerald Bergtrom,
University of Wisconsin
Arlene Billock,
University of Southwestern Louisiana
Brenda C. Blackwelder,
Central Piedmont Community College
Melissa Blamires,
Salt Lake Community College
Karen E. Bledsoe,
Western Oregon University
Raymond Bower,
University of Arkansas
Robert Boyd,
Auburn University
Michael Boyle,
Seattle Central Community College
Marilyn Brady,
Centennial College of Applied Arts and Technology
David Brown,
Marietta College
Virginia Buckner,
Johnson County Community College
Arthur L. Buikema, Jr.,
Virginia Polytechnic Institute
Diep Burbridge,
Long Beach City College
J. Gregory Burg,
University of Kansas
William F. Burke,
University of Hawaii
Robert Burkholter,
Louisiana State University
Matthew R. Burnham,
Jones County Junior College
Kathleen Burt-Utley,
University of New Orleans
Linda Butler,
University of Texas–Austin
W. Barkley Butler,
Indiana University of Pennsylvania
Jerry Button,
Portland Community College
Bruce E. Byers,
University of Massachusetts–Amherst
Sara Chambers,
Long Island University
Judy A. Chappell,
Luzerne County Community College
Nora L. Chee,
Chaminade University

Joseph P. Chinnici,
Virginia Commonwealth University
Dan Chiras,
University of Colorado–Denver
Nicole A. Cintas,
Northern Virginia Community College
Bob Coburn,
Middlesex Community College
Joseph Coelho,
Culver Stockton College
Martin Cohen,
University of Hartford
Jay L. Comeaux,
Louisiana State University
Walter J. Conley,
State University of New York at Potsdam
Mary U. Connell,
Appalachian State University
Art Conway,
Randolph-Macon College
Jerry Cook,
Sam Houston State University
Sharon A. Coolican,
Cayuga Community College
Clifton Cooper,
Linn-Benton Community College
Joyce Corban,
Wright State University
Brian E. Corner,
Augsburg College
Ethel Cornforth,
San Jacinto College–South
David J. Cotter,
Georgia College
Lee Couch,
Albuquerque Technical Vocational Institute
Donald C. Cox,
Miami University of Ohio
Patricia B. Cox,
University of Tennessee
Peter Crowcroft,
University of Texas–Austin
Carol Crowder,
North Harris Montgomery College
Mitchell B. Cruzan,
Portland State University
Donald E. Culwell,
University of Central Arkansas
Peter Cumbie,
Winthrop University
Robert A. Cunningham,
Erie Community College, North
Karen Dalton,
Community College of Baltimore County–Catonsville Campus
Lydia Daniels,
University of Pittsburgh
David H. Davis,
Asheville-Buncombe Technical Community College
Jerry Davis,
University of Wisconsin, LaCrosse
Douglas M. Deardon,
University of Minnesota

Lewis Deaton,
University of Louisiana–Lafayette
Lewis Deaton,
University of Southwestern Louisiana
Fred Delcomyn,
University of Illinois–Urbana
Joe Demasi,
Massachusetts College
David M. Demers,
University of Hartford
Lorren Denney,
Southwest Missouri State University
Katherine J. Denniston,
Towson State University
Charles F. Denny,
University of South Carolina–Sumter
Jean DeSaix,
University of North Carolina–Chapel Hill
Ed DeWalt,
Louisiana State University
Daniel F. Doak,
University of California–Santa Cruz
Christy Donmoyer,
Winthrop University
Matthew M. Douglas,
University of Kansas
Ronald J. Downey,
Ohio University
Ernest Dubrul,
University of Toledo
Michael Dufresne,
University of Windsor
Susan A. Dunford,
University of Cincinnati
Mary Durant,
North Harris College
Ronald Edwards,
University of Florida
Rosemarie Elizondo,
Reedley College
George Ellmore,
Tufts University
Joanne T. Ellzey,
University of Texas–El Paso
Wayne Elmore,
Marshall University
Thomas Emmel,
University of Florida
Carl Estrella,
Merced College
Nancy Eyster-Smith,
Bentley College
Gerald Farr,
Southwest Texas State University
Rita Farrar,
Louisiana State University
Marianne Feaver,
North Carolina State University
Susannah Feldman,
Towson University
Linnea Fletcher,
Austin Community College–Northridge

Doug Florian,
  Trident Technical College
Charles V. Foltz,
  Rhode Island College
Dennis Forsythe,
  The Citadel
Douglas Fratianne,
  Ohio State University
Scott Freeman,
  University of Washington
Donald P. French,
  Oklahoma State University
Harvey Friedman,
  University of Missouri–St. Louis
Don Fritsch,
  Virginia Commonwealth University
Teresa Lane Fulcher,
  Pellissippi State Technical Community College
Michael Gaines,
  University of Kansas
Cynthia Galloway,
  Texas A&M University–Kingsville
Irja Galvan,
  Western Oregon University
Gail E. Gasparich,
  Towson University
Janet Gaston,
  Troy University
Farooka Gauhari,
  University of Nebraska–Omaha
John Geiser,
  Western Michigan University
George W. Gilchrist,
  University of Washington
David Glenn-Lewin,
  Iowa State University
Elmer Gless,
  Montana College of Mineral Sciences
Charles W. Good,
  Ohio State University–Lima
Joan-Beth Gow,
  Anna Maria College
Margaret Green,
  Broward Community College
Mary Ruth Griffin,
  University of Charleston
Wendy Grillo,
  North Carolina Central University
David Grise,
  Southwest Texas State University
Martha Groom,
  University of Washington
Lonnie J. Guralnick,
  Western Oregon University
Martin E. Hahn,
  William Paterson College
Madeline Hall,
  Cleveland State University
Georgia Ann Hammond,
  Radford University
Blanche C. Haning,
  North Carolina State University

Richard Hanke,
  Rose State College
Helen B. Hanten,
  University of Minnesota
John P. Harley,
  Eastern Kentucky University
Robert Hatherill,
  Del Mar College
William Hayes,
  Delta State University
Kathleen Hecht,
  Nassau Community College
Stephen Hedman,
  University of Minnesota
Jean Helgeson,
  Collins County Community College
Alexander Henderson,
  Millersville University
Wiley Henderson,
  Alabama A&M University
Timothy L. Henry,
  University of Texas–Arlington
James Hewlett,
  Finger Lakes Community College
Alison G. Hoffman,
  University of Tennessee–Chattanooga
Kelly Hogan,
  University of North Carolina–Chapel Hill
Leland N. Holland,
  Paso-Hernando Community College
Laura Mays Hoopes,
  Occidental College
Dale R. Horeth,
  Tidewater Community College
Michael D. Hudgins,
  Alabama State University
David Huffman,
  Southwest Texas State University
Joel Humphrey,
  Cayuga Community College
Donald A. Ingold,
  East Texas State University
Jon W. Jacklet,
  State University of New York–Albany
Rebecca M. Jessen,
  Bowling Green State University
J. Kelly Johnson,
  University of Kansas
James Johnson,
  Central Washington University
Kristy Y. Johnson,
  The Citadel
Ross Johnson,
  Chicago State University
Florence Juillerat,
  Indiana University–Purdue University at Indianapolis
Thomas W. Jurik,
  Iowa State University
Ragupathy Kannan,
  University of Arkansas, Fort Smith
Arnold Karpoff,
  University of Louisville

L. Kavaljian,
California State University
Joe Keen,
Patrick Henry Community College
Jeff Kenton,
Iowa State University
Hendrick J. Ketellapper,
University of California, Davis
Jeffrey Kiggins,
Blue Ridge Community College
Aaron Krochmal,
University of Houston–Downtown
Harry Kurtz,
Sam Houston State University
Kate Lajtha,
Oregon State University
Tom Langen,
Clarkson University
Patrick Larkin,
Sante Fe College
Stephen Lebsack,
Linn-Benton Community College
Patricia Lee-Robinson,
Chaminade University of Honolulu
David E. Lemke,
Texas State University
William H. Leonard,
Clemson University
Edward Levri,
Indiana University of Pennsylvania
Graeme Lindbeck,
University of Central Florida
Jerri K. Lindsey,
Tarrant County Junior College–Northeast
Mary Lipscomb,
Virginia Polytechnic and State University
Richard W. Lo Pinto,
Fairleigh Dickinson University
Jonathan Lochamy,
Georgia Perimeter College
Jason L. Locklin,
Temple College
John Logue,
University of South Carolina–Sumter
Paul Lonquich,
California State University Northridge
William Lowen,
Suffolk Community College
Ann S. Lumsden,
Florida State University
Steele R. Lunt,
University of Nebraska–Omaha
Daniel D. Magoulick,
The University of Central Arkansas
Bernard Majdi,
Waycross College
Cindy Malone,
California State University–Northridge
Paul Mangum,
Midland College
Richard Manning,
Southwest Texas State University

Mark Manteuffel,
St. Louis Community College
Barry Markillie,
Cape Fear Community College
Ken Marr,
Green River Community College
Kathleen A. Marrs,
Indiana University–Purdue University Indianapolis
Michael Martin,
University of Michigan
Linda Martin-Morris,
University of Washington
Kenneth A. Mason,
University of Kansas
Daniel Matusiak,
St. Charles Community College
Margaret May,
Virginia Commonwealth University
D. J. McWhinnie,
De Paul University
Gary L. Meeker,
California State University, Sacramento
Thoyd Melton,
North Carolina State University
Joseph R. Mendelson III,
Utah State University
Karen E. Messley,
Rockvalley College
Timothy Metz,
Campbell University
Steven Mezik,
Herkimer County Community College
Glendon R. Miller,
Wichita State University
Hugh Miller,
East Tennessee State University
Neil Miller,
Memphis State University
Jeanne Minnerath,
St. Mary's University of Minnesota
Christine Minor,
Clemson University
Jeanne Mitchell,
Truman State University
Lee Mitchell,
Mt. Hood Community College
Jack E. Mobley,
University of Central Arkansas
John W. Moon,
Harding University
Nicole Moore,
Austin Peay University
Richard Mortenson,
Albion College
Gisele Muller-Parker,
Western Washington University
James Mulrooney,
Central Connecticut State University
Kathleen Murray,
University of Maine
Robert Neill,
University of Texas

Russell Nemecek,
Columbia College, Hancock
Harry Nickla,
Creighton University
Daniel Nickrent,
Southern Illinois University
Jane Noble-Harvey,
University of Delaware
Murad Odeh,
South Texas College
David J. O'Neill,
Community College of Baltimore County–Dundalk Campus
James T. Oris,
Miami University of Ohio
Marcy Osgood,
University of Michigan
C. O. Patterson,
Texas A&M University
Fred Peabody,
University of South Dakota
Charlotte Pedersen,
Southern Utah University
Harry Peery,
Tompkins-Cortland Community College
Luis J. Pelicot,
City University of New York, Hostos
Rhoda E. Perozzi,
Virginia Commonwealth University
Gary B. Peterson,
South Dakota State University
Bill Pfitsch,
Hamilton College
Ronald Pfohl,
Miami University of Ohio
Larry Pilgrim,
Tyler Junior College
Therese Poole,
Georgia State University
Robert Kyle Pope,
Indiana University South Bend
Bernard Possident,
Skidmore College
Ina Pour-el,
DMACC–Boone Campus
Elsa C. Price,
Wallace State Community College
Marvin Price,
Cedar Valley College
Kelli Prior,
Finger Lakes Community College
Jennifer J. Quinlan,
Drexel University
James A. Raines,
North Harris College
Paul Ramp,
Pellissippi State Technical College
Robert N. Reed,
Southern Utah University
Wenda Ribeiro,
Thomas Nelson Community College
Elizabeth Rich,
Drexel University

Mark Richter,
University of Kansas
Robert Robbins,
Michigan State University
Jennifer Roberts,
Lewis University
Frank Romano,
Jacksonville State University
Chris Romero,
Front Range Community College
Paul Rosenbloom,
Southwest Texas State University
Amanda Rosenzweig,
Delgado Community College
K. Ross,
University of Delaware
Mary Lou Rottman,
University of Colorado–Denver
Albert Ruesink,
Indiana University
Cameron Russell,
Tidewater Community College
Connie Russell,
Angelo State University
Marla Ruth,
Jones County Junior College
Christopher F. Sacchi,
Kutztown University
Eduardo Salazar,
Temple College
Doug Schelhaas,
University of Mary
Brian Schmaefsky,
Kingwood College
Alan Schoenherr,
Fullerton College
Brian W. Schwartz,
Columbus State University
Edna Seaman,
University of Massachusetts, Boston
Tim Sellers,
Keuka College
Patricia Shields,
George Mason University
Marilyn Shopper,
Johnson County Community College
Rick L. Simonson,
University of Nebraska, Kearney
Howard Singer,
New Jersey City University
Anu Singh-Cundy,
Western Washington University
Linda Simpson,
University of North Carolina–Charlotte
Steven Skarda,
Linn-Benton Community College
Russel V. Skavaril,
Ohio State University
John Smarelli,
Loyola University
Mark Smith,
Chaffey College

Dale Smoak,
Piedmont Technical College
Jay Snaric,
St. Louis Community College
Phillip J. Snider,
University of Houston
Shari Snitovsky,
Skyline College
Gary Sojka,
Bucknell University
John Sollinger,
Southern Oregon University
Sally Sommers Smith,
Boston University
Jim Sorenson,
Radford University
Mary Spratt,
University of Missouri, Kansas City
Bruce Stallsmith,
University of Alabama–Huntsville
Anthony Stancampiano,
Oklahoma City Community College
Benjamin Stark,
Illinois Institute of Technology
William Stark,
Saint Louis University
Barbara Stebbins-Boaz,
Willamette University
Kathleen M. Steinert,
Bellevue Community College
Barbara Stotler,
Southern Illinois University
Nathaniel J. Stricker,
Ohio State University
Martha Sugermeyer,
Tidewater Community College
Gerald Summers,
University of Missouri–Columbia
Marshall Sundberg,
Louisiana State University
Bill Surver,
Clemson University
Eldon Sutton,
University of Texas–Austin
Peter Svensson,
West Valley College
Dan Tallman,
Northern State University
Jose G. Tello,
Long Island University
David Thorndill,
Essex Community College
William Thwaites,
San Diego State University
Professor Tobiessen,
Union College
Richard Tolman,
Brigham Young University
Sylvia Torti,
University of Utah
Dennis Trelka,
Washington and Jefferson College

Richard C. Tsou,
Gordon College
Sharon Tucker,
University of Delaware
Gail Turner,
Virginia Commonwealth University
Glyn Turnipseed,
Arkansas Technical University
Lloyd W. Turtinen,
University of Wisconsin, Eau Claire
Robert Tyser,
University of Wisconsin, La Crosse
Robin W. Tyser,
University of Wisconsin, La Crosse
Kristin Uthus,
Virginia Commonwealth University
Rani Vajravelu,
University of Central Florida
Jim Van Brunt,
Rogue Community College
F. Daniel Vogt,
State University of New York–Plattsburgh
Nancy Wade,
Old Dominion University
Susan M. Wadkowski,
Lakeland Community College
Jyoti R. Wagle,
Houston Community College–Central
Jerry G. Walls,
Louisiana State University, Alexandria
Holly Walters,
Cape Fear Community College
Winfred Watkins,
McLennan Community College
Lisa Weasel,
Portland State University
Michael Weis,
University of Windsor
DeLoris Wenzel,
University of Georgia
Jerry Wermuth,
Purdue University–Calumet
Diana Wheat,
Linn-Benton Community College
Richard Whittington,
Pellissippi State Technical Community College
Jacob Wiebers,
Purdue University
Roger K. Wiebusch,
Columbia College
Carolyn Wilczynski,
Binghamton University
Lawrence R. Williams,
University of Houston
P. Kelly Williams,
University of Dayton
Roberta Williams,
University of Nevada–Las Vegas
Emily Willingham,
University of Texas–Austin
Sandra Winicur,
Indiana University–South Bend

Bill Wischusen,
Louisiana State University
Michelle Withers,
Louisiana State University
Chris Wolfe,
North Virginia Community College
Stacy Wolfe,
Art Institutes International
Colleen Wong,
Wilbur Wright College
Wade Worthen,
Furman University
Robin Wright,
University of Washington
Taek H. You,
Campbell University

Brenda L. Young,
Daemen College
Cal Young,
Fullerton College
Tim Young,
Mercer University
Martin Zahn,
Thomas Nelson Community College
Izanne Zorin,
Northern Virginia Community College–Alexandria
Michelle Zurawski,
Moraine Valley Community College

CHAPTER 1

An Introduction to Life on Earth

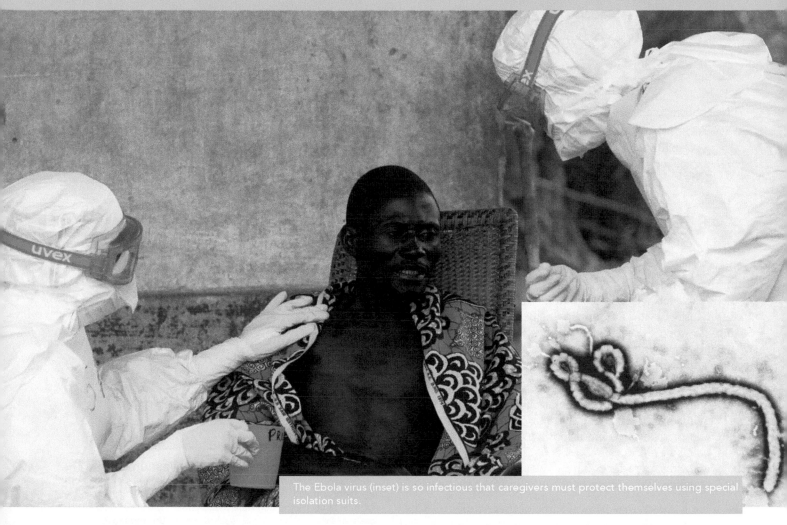

The Ebola virus (inset) is so infectious that caregivers must protect themselves using special isolation suits.

CASE STUDY

The Boundaries of Life

IN 1996 IN GABON, Africa, a hunting party discovered a newly dead chimpanzee in the bush and butchered it for food. Within a month, the hunters' village was devastated. Thirty-seven residents, including the hunters and many of their family members, had fallen ill. Before the scourge ended, more than half had died.

The villagers had fallen victim to one of Earth's most deadly pathogens—the Ebola virus (see the inset photo). The threat of Ebola hemorrhagic fever ("Ebola") strikes fear in anyone familiar with its symptoms, which begin with fever, headache, joint and muscle aches, and stomach pains, and progress to severe vomiting, bloody diarrhea, and organ failure. Internal hemorrhaging can leave victims bleeding

from every orifice. Death usually occurs within 7 to 16 days after the onset of symptoms, and there is no cure. Ebola is so contagious and deadly that caregivers wear "moonsuits" to avoid contact with any body fluids from their patients (see the chapter opener photo).

Ebola, which occurs sporadically in Africa, is one of many diseases caused by viruses. Although some viral diseases, such as smallpox and polio, have been largely eradicated, others, like the common cold and influenza, continue to make us miserable. Most alarming are viruses such as the human immunodeficiency virus (HIV), which causes acquired immunodeficiency syndrome (AIDS) and kills about 1.8 million people annually. An emerging threat is the avian influenza virus (H5N1 or "bird flu"). Although it does not spread readily from person to person,

bird flu has a very high mortality rate, and health officials are concerned that it may mutate into a far more infectious form that could cause a worldwide epidemic.

No matter how you measure it, viruses are enormously successful. Although many consist only of a small amount of genetic material surrounded by protein, viruses infect every known form of life and are the most abundant biological entity on the planet. Viruses can spread from one organism to another, rapidly increase in numbers, and mutate (undergo changes in their hereditary material). Yet in spite of these lifelike qualities, scientists disagree about whether to classify viruses as organisms or as inert parasitic biological particles. The basis for this argument may surprise you; there is no universally accepted scientific definition of life. Think about it—what is life, anyway?

AT A GLANCE

LEARNING GOALS

LG1 Describe the characteristics of living things.

LG2 Explain evolution and how three natural processes make evolution inevitable.

LG3 Explain the concept of levels of biological organization, and list the levels.

LG4 Identify the three domains of life, and describe the types of cells that make up each domain.

LG5 Explain how the three kingdoms of eukaryotic organisms are distinguished from one another.

LG6 Describe the scientific method, and provide an example of how it could be applied to an everyday problem.

LG7 Explain why experiments include control groups.

LG8 Explain how a hypothesis differs from a scientific theory.

1.1 WHAT IS LIFE?

The word **biology** comes from the Greek roots "bio" meaning "life" and "logy" meaning "the study of" (see Appendix I for more word roots). But what is life? If you look up "life" in a dictionary, you will find definitions such as "the quality that distinguishes a vital and functioning being from a dead body," but you won't discover what that "quality" is. Life is intangible and defies simple definition, even by biologists. However, most will agree that living things, or **organisms,** all share certain characteristics that, taken together, define life:

- Organisms acquire and use materials and energy.
- Organisms actively maintain organized complexity.
- Organisms perceive and respond to stimuli.
- Organisms grow.
- Organisms reproduce.
- Organisms, collectively, have the capacity to evolve.

Nonliving objects may possess some of these attributes. Crystals can grow, a desk lamp acquires energy from electricity and converts it to heat and light, but only life-forms can do it all.

Scientists in the early 1800s, observing life with simple microscopes, concluded that the **cell** is the basic unit of life (**Fig. 1-1**). A membrane separates the cell from its surroundings, enclosing a huge variety of structures and chemicals in a fluid environment. The components within the cell are precisely organized. This organization allows a staggering number of chemical reactions to occur in the proper order, at the proper location, and at the proper time so that the cell can maintain and reproduce itself.

Although the most abundant organisms on Earth exist as single cells, the qualities of life are more easily visualized in multicellular organisms such as the water flea in **Figure 1-2,** an animal smaller than this letter "o." In the sections below, we explore the characteristics of life in more depth.

Organisms Acquire and Use Materials and Energy

Organisms require both materials and energy to perform the functions of life. They obtain the materials that make up their bodies—such as minerals, water, and other simple

▲ FIGURE 1-1 **The cell is the smallest unit of life** This artificially colored micrograph of a plant cell (a eukaryotic cell) shows a supporting cell wall (blue) that surrounds plant (but not animal) cells. Just inside the cell wall, the plasma membrane (found in all cells) has control over which substances enter and leave. Cells also contain several types of specialized organelles, including the nucleus, suspended within a fluid environment (orange).

nucleus

cell wall

plasma membrane

organelles

chemical building blocks—from the air, water, soil, and from the bodies of other living things. Because life neither creates nor destroys matter, materials are continuously exchanged and recycled among organisms and their nonliving surroundings (**Fig. 1-3**).

Organisms use energy continuously to remain alive. For example, energy is required to move and to construct the complex molecules that make up an organism's body. Ultimately, the energy that sustains life comes from sunlight. Certain organisms directly capture and store solar energy using a process called **photosynthesis.** Photosynthetic organisms trap and store energy for their own use, but the energy stored in their bodies also powers all other forms of life, such as fungi and animals (ourselves included). Thus, energy flows in a one-way path from the sun through all forms of life. Eventually, it is released back to the environment as heat. The continuous flow of energy through organisms is illustrated in Figure 1-3.

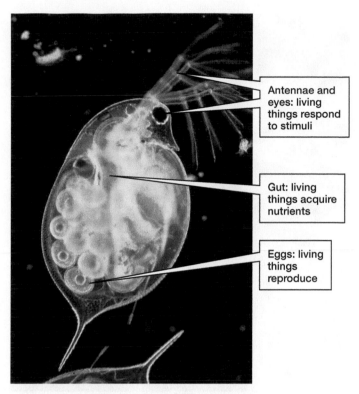

A Solar-Powered Big Mac?

If you've just eaten a hamburger for lunch, you may be surprised to learn that all the energy in it comes from sunlight. The bun is made from wheat, a photosynthetic organism, so it's clear that the energy in the bun comes from the sun. But how does a cow pack solar energy into its fat and muscle? To understand, think about what the cow eats. A cow's energy comes from grass and other plant material. The plants, in turn, harvested their energy via photosynthesis. Thus, the energy powering a cow is one step removed from the sunlight that energizes the plant. So, when you eat a hamburger, you consume energy that is only two steps removed from its original source: the sun.

▲ FIGURE 1-2 **Properties of life** The water flea uses energy from photosynthetic organisms (seen as green material in its gut) to maintain its amazing complexity. Eyes and antennae respond to stimuli. This adult female is reproducing, and she herself has grown from an egg like those she now carries. All the adaptations that allow this water flea to survive, grow, and reproduce have been molded by evolution.

Organisms Actively Maintain Organized Complexity

Whether we consider the books and papers on your desk or the components of a cell, organization tends to disintegrate into chaos unless energy is used to maintain it. (We explore this further in Chapter 6.) Living things, which are far more complex than anything people might organize, must use energy continuously to maintain themselves. For the appropriate chemical reactions to occur within a cell, for example, its

membrane constantly pumps some chemicals in and others out. People and other mammals use energy to keep their internal organs at a warm, constant temperature that allows the proper reactions to occur in their cells. To prevent body temperature from rising too much during hot weather or vigorous exercise, we sweat and we might douse ourselves with cool water (**Fig. 1-4**). When it is cold, our bodies and those of other mammals metabolize more food than usual to generate heat. Life, then, requires very precise internal conditions that organisms must expend energy constantly to maintain.

Organisms Perceive and Respond to Stimuli

To obtain energy and nutrients and to stay alive, organisms must perceive and respond to their environments. Animals use specialized cells to detect light, temperature, sound, gravity, touch, chemicals, and many other stimuli from their external and internal surroundings. For example, when your brain detects low levels of sugar in your blood (an internal stimulus), it causes your mouth to water at the smell of food (an external stimulus). Animals have nervous and muscular systems that perceive and respond to stimuli, but plants,

◀ FIGURE 1-3 **The flow of energy and the recycling of nutrients** Energy is acquired from sunlight (yellow arrow) by photosynthetic organisms, is transferred through organisms that consume other forms of life (red arrows), and is lost as heat (orange arrows) in a one-way flow. In contrast, nutrients (purple arrows) are recycled among organisms and the nonliving environment.

▲ FIGURE 1-4 **Organisms maintain relatively constant internal conditions** Evaporative cooling by water, both from sweat and from a bottle, helps this athlete maintain his body temperature during vigorous exercise.

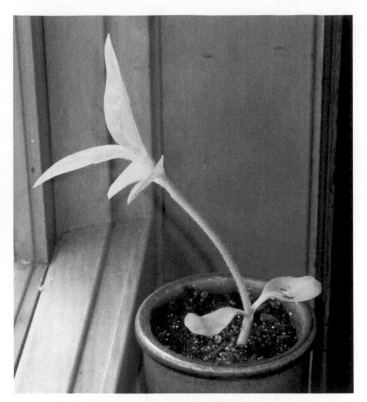

▲ FIGURE 1-5 **Bending toward the light** Plants perceive and respond to light, which provides them with energy.

fungi, and single-celled organisms use very different mechanisms that are equally effective for their needs. Think of a plant on a windowsill sensing and then bending toward sunlight that provides energy (**Fig. 1-5**). Even many bacteria, the smallest and simplest life-forms, can move toward favorable conditions and away from harmful substances.

Organisms Grow

At some time in its life, every organism becomes larger—that is, it grows. The water flea in Figure 1-2 originally was the size of one of the eggs you see in its body. Growth requires that organisms obtain material and energy from the outside world. Single-celled organisms such as bacteria grow to about double their original size, copy their genetic material, and then divide in half to reproduce. Animals and plants use a similar process to produce more cells within their bodies, repeating the sequence until growth stops. Individual cells can also contribute to the growth of an organism by increasing in size, as occurs in muscle and fat cells in animals, and in food storage cells in plants.

Organisms Reproduce

Organisms reproduce in a variety of ways that include dividing in half, producing seeds, bearing live young (**Fig. 1-6**), and laying eggs (see Fig. 1-2). The end result is always the same: new versions of the parent organisms. Be it bacterium, slug, mushroom, or person, offspring inherit from their parents the instructions for producing and maintaining their particular forms of life. These instructions—copied in every cell and passed on to offspring—are carried in the unique structure of the hereditary molecule **deoxyribonucleic acid,** or **DNA** (**Fig. 1-7**). The complete set of DNA molecules contained in each cell of an organism can be compared to an architectural blueprint or a detailed instruction manual for life.

Organisms, Collectively, Have the Capacity to Evolve

Evolution is the process by which modern organisms have descended from earlier and different forms of life. Over the course of generations, changes in DNA within any **population** (a group of the same type of organism inhabiting the same area) are inevitable, and result in evolution. Such changes in Earth's populations of organisms, accumulating over the history of life, have resulted in the evolution of the amazing diversity of organisms that now share this planet. The next section provides a brief introduction to evolution—the most important concept in biology.

(a) Dividing *Streptococcus* bacterium   (b) Dandelion producing seeds   (c) Panda with its baby

▲ FIGURE 1-6 **Organisms reproduce**

▲ FIGURE 1-7 **DNA** A model of DNA, the molecule of heredity. As James Watson, its codiscoverer, put it: "A structure this pretty just had to exist."

CASE STUDY c o n t i n u e d

The Boundaries of Life

How lifelike is a virus? Viruses release their genetic material inside cells, and hijack the infected cell's energy supplies and biochemical machinery, turning the cell into a kind of factory that churns out many copies of viral parts. These parts assemble into an army of virus particles, in a process called *replication*. The newly formed viruses then emerge from the host cell, often rupturing it in the process. Some, including HIV and the Ebola virus, acquire an outer envelope made of the host's plasma membrane. Viruses do not obtain or use their own energy or materials, they don't maintain themselves, nor do they grow. In fact, they possess only a few of the characteristics of life: Viruses respond to stimuli by binding to specific sites on the cells they attack, they evolve, and some scientists consider viral replication to be reproduction, another characteristic of life.

CHECK YOUR LEARNING
Can you describe the characteristics that define life?

1.2 WHAT IS EVOLUTION?

Evolution explains why Earth has such a huge diversity of life. At the same time, evolution accounts for the remarkable similarities among different types of organisms. For example, people have many physical features in common with chimpanzees, and our DNA differs from that of chimps by less than 5%. This is strong evidence that people and chimps descended from a common ancestor (**Fig. 1-8**), but the obvious differences reflect the differences in our evolutionary paths. How does evolution occur?

Three Natural Processes Underlie Evolution

Evolution is an automatic and inevitable outcome of three natural occurrences: (1) differences in DNA among members of a population, (2) inheritance of these differences by their offspring, and (3) *natural selection*, the increased ability of offspring that inherit certain forms and combinations of DNA molecules to survive and reproduce. Let's take a closer look at these three factors.

Mutations Are the Original Source of Differences in DNA

Look around at your classmates and notice how different they are, or observe differences among dogs in their sizes and shapes, and in the color, length, and texture of their coats. Although some of this variation (particularly among your classmates) is due to differences in environment and lifestyle, much of it is due to differences in their genes. **Genes,** which are segments of DNA, are the basic units of heredity. Before a cell divides, all of its DNA must be copied so its genes can be passed along. Just as you would make mistakes if you tried

▲ FIGURE 1-8 **Chimps and people are closely related**

to copy a blueprint by hand, cells make some errors as they copy their DNA. Changes in genes, such as those caused by these random copying errors, are called **mutations.** Mutations can also result from damage to DNA, caused for example by ultraviolet rays from sunlight, radiation released from a damaged nuclear power plant, or toxic chemicals from cigarette smoke. Just as mistakes in a blueprint will make a difference in the structure built from it, so a new cell constructed from altered DNA is likely to differ from its parent cell.

Some Mutations Are Inherited

Inherited mutations are those that occur in sperm or egg cells, thereby allowing altered DNA to pass from parent to offspring. Each cell in the offspring will carry the inherited mutation, giving the offspring traits that differ, either subtly or obviously, from its parents. Some mutations are harmful, for example, those that cause human genetic disorders such as hemophilia, sickle cell anemia, or cystic fibrosis. Many mutations have no observable effect or may change the organism in a way that is neither harmful nor beneficial, for example, by producing a different coat color on a dog. Almost all of the natural variability among traits in individuals is caused by neutral mutations that occurred in the

distant past and have been passed along through numerous generations. On rare occasions, however, an inherited mutation helps offspring to survive and reproduce more successfully than those lacking the mutation. Such infrequent events provide the raw material for evolution.

Some Inherited Mutations Help Individuals Survive and Reproduce

The most important process in evolution is natural selection, which acts on the natural variability in traits among members of a population. **Natural selection** is the process by which organisms with certain inherited traits survive and reproduce better than others in a given environment. Inherited traits that help organisms produce more healthy offspring become increasingly common in the population over many generations. Because these traits are caused by differences in genes, the genetic makeup of the population as a whole will change over time; that is, the population evolves. How might this work?

Consider a likely scenario of natural selection. Imagine that ancient beavers had short front teeth like most other mammals. If a mutation caused one beaver's offspring to grow longer front teeth, these offspring would have gnawed down trees more efficiently, built bigger dams and lodges, and eaten more bark than could beavers that lacked the mutation. Because these long-toothed beavers would obtain more food and better shelter, they would be better able to survive when times got tough, and to raise more offspring who would have inherited the genes for longer front teeth. Over time, long-toothed beavers would have become increasingly common; after many generations, all beavers would have long front teeth.

Structures, physiological processes, or behaviors that help an organism survive and reproduce in a particular environment are called **adaptations.** Most of the features that we admire so much in other life-forms, such as the long limbs of deer, the broad wings of eagles, and the mighty trunks of redwood trees, are adaptations. Adaptations help organisms escape predators, capture prey, reach the sunlight, or accomplish other feats that help ensure their survival and reproduction. The huge array of adaptations found in living things today were molded by millions of years of natural selection acting on random mutations.

What helps an organism survive today may become a liability in the future. If environments change—for example, as global climate change occurs—the genetic traits that best adapt organisms to their environments will change as well. In the case of global climate change, if a random mutation helps an organism survive and reproduce in a warmer climate, the mutation will be favored by natural selection and will increase within the population with each new generation.

Populations of the same species (organisms of the same type that can interbreed) that live in different environments will be subjected to different types of natural selection. If these differences are great enough and continue for long enough, natural selection may eventually cause the populations to become sufficiently different from one another to prevent interbreeding—a new species will have evolved.

If mutations that help an organism to adapt do not occur, a changing environment may doom a species to

▲ FIGURE 1-9 **A fossil *Tyrannosaurus rex*** The most widely accepted hypothesis for the extinction of dinosaurs is a massive meteorite strike that rapidly and radically altered their environment. This *Tyrannosaurus rex* (dubbed "Thomas" and displayed at the Natural History Museum of Los Angeles County) was excavated in Montana between 2003 and 2005. Weighing in at 7,000 pounds and 34 feet long, Thomas was 17 years old when he died roughly 68 million years ago.

extinction—the complete elimination of this form of life. Dinosaurs flourished for 100 million years, but they did not evolve fast enough to adapt to rapidly changing conditions, so they became extinct (**Fig. 1-9**). In recent decades, human activities such as burning fossil fuels and converting tropical forests to farmland have drastically accelerated the rate of environmental change. Mutations that better adapt organisms to their environments are quite rare, and consequently the rate of extinction has increased dramatically (described in Chapter 30).

CASE STUDY continued

The Boundaries of Life

One lifelike property of viruses is their capacity to evolve. Through evolution, viruses sometimes become more infectious or more deadly, or they may gain the ability to infect new hosts. Certain types of viruses, which include Ebola, HIV, and influenza, are very sloppy in copying their genetic material and mutate about 1,000 times as often as the average animal cell. As a result, nearly every new virus carries a mutation. One consequence is that viruses such as flu can rapidly evolve into new forms, so you need a new flu shot every year. Antiviral drugs act as agents of natural selection and cause drug-resistant populations of viruses to evolve. HIV, for example, may produce 10 billion new viruses daily in an infected individual, making drug resistance inevitable. For this reason, people with AIDS are given "cocktails" of three or four different drugs, because resistance to all of them would require multiple specific mutations to occur in the same virus, an enormously unlikely event.

In the words of biologist Theodosius Dobzhansky, "Nothing in biology makes sense except in the light of evolution." The theory of evolution was formulated in the mid-1800s by two English naturalists, Charles Darwin and Alfred Russel Wallace. Since that time, it has been supported by fossils, geological studies, radioactive dating of rocks, genetics, molecular biology, biochemistry, and breeding experiments. As you will learn in the next section, people who call evolution "just a theory" profoundly misunderstand the concept of a scientific theory.

CHECK YOUR LEARNING

Can you explain how three natural processes lead inevitably to evolution?

1.3 HOW DO SCIENTISTS STUDY LIFE?

The science of biology encompasses many different areas of inquiry, each requiring different types of specialized knowledge. One way to get a sense of the scope of biology is to look at the levels of organization that occur within the living world (**Fig. 1-10**). At a large university, you may find biologists conducting research at every level, from the study of complex biological molecules (for example, how changes in DNA affect specific traits) to the biosphere (for example, how the distribution of organisms on Earth may be altered by climate change).

Life Can Be Studied at Different Levels

Figure 1-10 illustrates different levels of inquiry that make up the study of life. Starting at the bottom, each level provides the foundation for the one above it, and each higher level has new, more inclusive properties. Nearly all biological inquiry encompasses more than one of these levels, which we explore in the sections that follow.

All matter consists of **elements,** substances that cannot be broken down or converted to a simpler substance. An **atom** is the smallest particle of an element that retains all the properties of that element. For example, a diamond is a form of the element carbon. The smallest possible unit of a diamond is an individual carbon atom. Atoms may combine in specific ways to form **molecules;** for example, one oxygen atom can combine with two hydrogen atoms to form a molecule of water. Complex biological molecules containing carbon atoms—such as proteins and DNA—form the building blocks of cells, which are the basic units of life. Although many organisms exist as single cells, in multicellular organisms, cells of a similar type may combine to form **tissues,** such as the epithelial tissue that lines the stomach. Different types of tissues, in turn, unite to form functional units called **organs,** such as the entire stomach. The grouping of two or more organs that work together to perform a specific body function is called an **organ system;** for example, the stomach is part of the digestive system. Organ systems combine within complex multicellular organisms to carry out the activities of life.

Biosphere	All life on Earth and the nonliving portions of Earth that support life	Earth's surface
Ecosystem	A community together with its nonliving surroundings	snake, antelope, hawk, bushes, grass, rocks, stream
Community	Populations of different species that live in the same area and interact with one another	snake, antelope, hawk, bushes, grass
Species	All organisms that are similar enough to interbreed	herd of pronghorn antelope
Population	All the members of a species living in the same area	herd of pronghorn antelope
Multicellular organism	An individual living thing composed of many cells	pronghorn antelope
Organ system	Two or more organs working together in the execution of a specific bodily function	the digestive system
Organ	A structure usually composed of several tissue types that form a functional unit	the stomach
Tissue	A group of similar cells that perform a specific function	epithelial tissue
Cell	The smallest unit of life	red blood cell epithelial cell nerve cell
Molecule	A combination of atoms	water glucose DNA
Atom	The smallest particle of an element that retains the properties of that element	hydrogen carbon nitrogen oxygen

▲ FIGURE 1-10 **Levels of biological organization** Each lower level provides building blocks for the one above it, which has new properties that emerge from the interplay of the levels beneath.

QUESTION What current, ongoing environmental change is likely to affect the entire biosphere?

Levels of organization also extend to groups of organisms. A population is a group of organisms of the same type (the same species) that live in a well-defined area where they can interact and interbreed with one another. A **species** consists of all organisms that are similar enough to interbreed, no matter where they are found.

A **community** is formed by populations of different species that live in the same area and interact with one another. An **ecosystem** consists of a community and the nonliving environment that surrounds it. Finally, the **biosphere** includes all life on Earth and the nonliving portions of Earth that support life.

Biologists Classify Organisms Based on Their Evolutionary Relationships

Although all forms of life share certain characteristics, evolution has produced an amazing variety of life-forms. Scientists classify organisms based on their evolutionary relatedness, placing them into three major groups, or **domains:** Bacteria, Archaea, and Eukarya (**Fig. 1-11**).

This classification reflects fundamental differences among their cell types. Members of both the Bacteria and the Archaea consist of a single, simple cell. At the molecular level, however, there are fundamental differences between them that indicate that they are only distantly related.

In contrast, members of the Eukarya have bodies composed of one or more extremely complex cells. The domain Eukarya includes a diverse collection of organisms collectively known as *protists*, and three major subdivisions called **kingdoms,** which are the fungi, plants, and animals. (You will learn far more about life's incredible diversity and how it evolved in Unit 3.)

The classification of a given organism into a domain and kingdom is based on three characteristics: the organism's cell type (simple or complex), whether the organism is **unicellular** (a single cell) or **multicellular** (composed of many cells), and how the organism acquires its energy (**Table 1-1**).

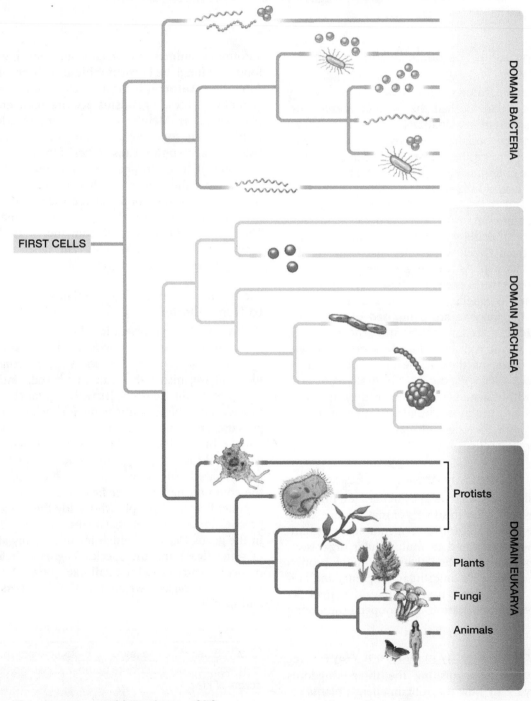

FIRST CELLS

DOMAIN BACTERIA

DOMAIN ARCHAEA

Protists

Plants

Fungi

Animals

DOMAIN EUKARYA

▲ FIGURE 1-11 **The domains and kingdoms of life**

TABLE 1-1	Some Characteristics Used in Classification of Organisms			
Domain	Kingdom	Cell Type	Cell Number	Energy Acquisition
Bacteria	Not applicable	Prokaryotic	Unicellular	Autotrophic or heterotrophic
Archaea	Not applicable	Prokaryotic	Unicellular	Autotrophic or heterotrophic
Eukarya	Fungi	Eukaryotic	Multicellular	Heterotrophic, absorb food
	Plants	Eukaryotic	Multicellular	Autotrophic
	Animals	Eukaryotic	Multicellular	Heterotrophic, ingest food
	Protists*	Eukaryotic	Unicellullar or multicellular	Autotrophic or heterotrophic

*Protists are a diverse collection of organisms; their classification is under discussion in the scientific community.

Cell Type Distinguishes the Bacteria and Archaea from the Eukarya

Cells all share certain features. All cells are surrounded by a thin sheet of molecules called the **plasma membrane.** All contain the hereditary material DNA. Cells also contain **organelles,** structures specialized to carry out specific functions such as helping to synthesize large molecules, digesting food molecules, or obtaining energy (see Fig. 1-1).

There are two fundamentally different types of cells: eukaryotic and prokaryotic. **Eukaryotic** cells are extremely complex and contain a variety of organelles, many of which are surrounded by membranes. The term "eukaryotic" comes from Greek words meaning "true" ("eu") and "nucleus" ("kary"). As the name suggests, one of their most striking features is the **nucleus** (see Fig. 1-1), a membrane-enclosed organelle that contains the cell's DNA. All members of the Eukarya are composed of eukaryotic cells. **Prokaryotic** cells are far simpler and generally much smaller than eukaryotic cells, and they lack organelles enclosed by membranes. As their name—meaning "before" ("pro") the nucleus—suggests, the DNA of prokaryotic cells is not confined within a nucleus. Although they are invisible to the naked eye, the most abundant forms of life are found in the domains Bacteria and Archaea, which consist entirely of prokaryotic cells.

Multicellularity Occurs Only Among the Eukarya

Members of the domains Bacteria and Archaea are unicellular. Although a few types live in strands or mats of cells, there is relatively little communication, cooperation, or organization among them compared to multicellular organisms, which are only found among the Eukarya. Although protists are eukaryotic and many are unicellular, all plants and animals, and nearly all fungi, are multicellular; their lives depend on intimate communication and cooperation among numerous specialized cells.

The Eukarya Acquire Energy in Different Ways

One simple way of distinguishing the three kingdoms within the Eukarya is by how they obtain energy; plants are autotrophs, animals are heterotrophs and ingest (eat) their food, and fungi are heterotrophic and absorb their food (see Table 1-1). **Autotroph** means "self" ("auto") and "feeding" ("trophic"); these organisms acquire their energy through photosynthesis. Members of the plant kingdom are autotrophs (as are some archaea, some bacteria, and some protists). **Heterotroph** means "other" ("hetero") and "feeding" ("trophic"); heterotrophs cannot photosynthesize and so they rely on the bodies of other organisms for food. Some heterotrophs digest food outside their bodies and absorb the simpler molecules through their plasma membranes. These include the fungi (and many members of the domains Archaea and Bacteria). Animals (and heterotrophic protists) usually ingest chunks of food.

Biologists Use the Binomial System to Name Organisms

Biologists place organisms in a hierarchy of categories, each more inclusive than the one below it. The smallest two categories are the *genus* and *species*. A species consists of nearly identical organisms that can interbreed, and a genus includes many different species with similar characteristics. To provide a unique scientific name for each form of life, biologists use a **binomial system,** based on Latin words meaning "two" ("bi") and "names" ("nomial"), which consists of the genus and species. The genus name is capitalized, and both are italicized. The animal in Figure 1-2, for example, has the common name "water flea," but there are many types of water fleas, and people who study them need to be more precise. So *Daphnia longispina* (the water flea in Fig. 1-2) is in the genus *Daphnia* (which includes many similar species of water fleas) and the species *longispina* (referring to this particular water flea's long, tail-like spine). People are classified as *Homo sapiens*; we are the only members of this genus and species.

CHECK YOUR LEARNING

Can you describe the levels of biological organization? Can you explain how scientists name and categorize diverse forms of life?

CASE STUDY continued

The Boundaries of Life

Viruses are not included in the classification scheme of life. Viruses appear to be very ancient, although their evolutionary relationships to living things remain obscure and controversial. Some scientists hypothesize that viruses may be remnants of a precellular stage of evolution. Others suggest that viruses may have evolved from molecules of genetic material that escaped from living cells. Some scientists argue that viruses could have evolved from cells, losing virtually all cellular structures and functions. Viruses show such diversity that all of these scenarios could be possible.

1.4 WHAT IS SCIENCE?

Science can be defined as the systematic inquiry—through observation and experiment—into the origins, structure, and behavior of our living and nonliving surroundings.

Science Is Based on the Principle That All Events Have Natural Causes

Early in human history, most people operated on the premise that supernatural forces were responsible for natural events. Ancient Greeks believed that the god Zeus hurled lightning bolts from the sky, and that epileptic seizures were evidence of a visitation from the gods. It was common in the Middle Ages to believe that life arose spontaneously (*spontaneous generation*) from nonliving matter; for example, that maggots came from rotting meat.

Science, in contrast, is based on the principle that all events can be traced to natural causes that people can study objectively. Today, we realize that lightning is a massive electrical discharge, that epilepsy is a brain disorder caused by uncontrolled firing of nerve cells, and that maggots are the larval form of flies.

The Scientific Method Is an Important Tool of Scientific Inquiry

The principle that the events we observe have natural causes, even if we do not yet understand them, underlies all scientific inquiry. To learn about the world, scientists in many disciplines, including biology, use some version of the **scientific method.** This consists of six interrelated elements: *observation, question, hypothesis, prediction, experiment,* and *conclusion.* Scientific inquiry begins with an **observation** of a specific phenomenon. The observation, in turn, leads to a **question:** "What caused this?" Then, after careful study of earlier investigations, conversations with colleagues, and often after long, hard thought, a hypothesis is formed. A **hypothesis** is a proposed explanation for the phenomenon, often based on limited evidence. To be useful, the hypothesis must lead to a **prediction,** which is the expected outcome of testing if the hypothesis is correct. The prediction is tested by carefully designed additional observations or carefully controlled manipulations called **experiments.** Experiments produce results that either support or refute the hypothesis, allowing the scientist to reach a **conclusion** about whether the hypothesis is valid or not. For the conclusion to be valid, the experiment and its results must be repeatable not only by the original researcher but also by others. Like scientists, we use versions of the scientific method, although far less rigorous, in our daily lives (see "Links to Everyday Life: When Your Car Won't Start").

Biologists Test Hypotheses Using Controlled Experiments

In controlled experiments, two types of situations are established. One is a baseline or **control** situation, in which all possible variables are held constant. The other is the experimental situation, where one factor, the **variable,** is manipulated to test the hypothesis that this variable is the cause of an observation. Often the manipulation inevitably causes more than one factor to vary. For example, in "Links to Everyday Life: When Your Car Won't Start," jump starting the car might have knocked some corrosion off the battery terminal that was preventing the battery from delivering power—your battery might be fine! In real experiments, scientists must control for all the effects of any manipulation they perform, so frequently more than one control is needed. You will find a good example of this in Malte Andersson's experiments, described in "Science in Action: Controlled Experiments, Then and Now."

Valid scientific experiments must be repeatable by the researcher and by other scientists. To help ensure this, the researcher performs multiple repetitions of any experiment, often simultaneously, by setting up several replications of each control situation (*control group*) and each experimental situation (*experimental group*), all as identical as possible.

Science must also be communicated or it is useless. Good scientists publish their results, explaining their methods in detail, so others can repeat them and build on them. Francesco Redi recognized this in the 1600s when he carefully recorded the methods of his classic controlled experiment testing the hypothesis that flies caused maggots to appear on rotting meat (see "Science in Action: Controlled Experiments, Then and Now").

⟩⟩ **LINKS** TO EVERYDAY LIFE

When Your Car Won't Start

You probably use some variation of the scientific method to solve everyday problems. For example, late for an important date, you rush to your car, turn the ignition key, and make the *observation* that the car won't start. Your *question* "Why won't the car start?" leads to a *hypothesis:* The battery is dead. This leads to the *prediction* that a jump start will solve the problem. You *experiment* by attaching jumper cables from your roommate's car battery to your own. The result? Your car starts immediately, allowing the *conclusion* that your hypothesis was correct. If jump starting didn't work, what hypothesis would you test next?

SCIENCE IN ACTION Controlled Experiments, Then and Now

A classic experiment by the Italian physician Francesco Redi (1621–1697) beautifully demonstrates the scientific method and helps to illustrate the scientific principle that events can be traced to natural causes. Redi investigated why maggots (the larva of flies) appear on spoiled meat. In Redi's time, refrigeration was unknown, and meat was stored in the open. Many people of that time believed that the appearance of maggots on meat was evidence of **spontaneous generation,** the emergence of life from nonliving matter.

Redi *observed* that flies swarm around fresh meat and that maggots appear on meat left out for a few days. He *questioned* where the maggots came from. He then formed a testable *hypothesis*: Flies produce maggots. This led to the *prediction* that keeping flies off the meat would prevent maggots from appearing. In his *experiment*, Redi wanted to test one variable—the access of flies to the meat. Therefore, he placed similar pieces of meat in each of two clean jars. He left one jar open (the control jar) and covered the other with gauze to keep out flies (the experimental jar). He did his best to keep all the other conditions the same (for example, the type of jar, the type of meat, and the temperature). After a few days, he observed maggots on the meat in the open jar but saw none on the meat in the covered jar. Redi *concluded* that his hypothesis was correct and that maggots are produced by flies, not by the nonliving meat (Fig. E1-1). Only through this and other controlled experiments could the age-old belief in spontaneous generation be laid to rest.

Today, more than 300 years later, the scientific method is still used. Consider the recent experiments of Malte Andersson, who investigated the mating choices of female widowbirds. Andersson *observed* that male, but not female, widowbirds have extravagantly long tails, which they display while flying across African grasslands. Andersson asked the *question*: Why do male birds have such long tails? His *hypothesis* was that females prefer to mate with long-tailed males, and so these males have more offspring, who inherit their genes for long tails.

Observation:	Flies swarm around meat left in the open; maggots appear on the meat.
Question:	Where do maggots on the meat come from?
Hypothesis:	Flies produce the maggots.
Prediction:	IF the hypothesis is correct, THEN keeping the flies away from the meat will prevent the appearance of maggots.

Experiment:

Obtain identical pieces of meat and two identical jars

Place meat in each jar

Leave the jar uncovered	**Experimental variable:** gauze prevents the entry of flies	Cover the jar with gauze
Leave exposed for several days	**Controlled variables:** time, temperature, place	Leave covered for several days
Flies swarm around and maggots appear	**Results**	Flies are kept from the meat; no maggots appear

Control situation   **Experimental situation**

Conclusion:	The experiment supports the hypothesis that flies are the source of maggots and that spontaneous generation of maggots does not occur.

▲ FIGURE E1-1 **The experiment of Francesco Redi illustrates the scientific method**

QUESTION Redi's experiment falsified spontaneous generation of maggots, but did his experiment convincingly demonstrate that flies produce maggots? What kind of follow-up experiment would be needed to more conclusively determine the source of maggots?

Andersson *predicted* that if his hypothesis were true, more females would build nests on the territories of males with artificially lengthened tails than on the territories of males with artificially shortened tails. To test this, he captured some males, trimmed their tails to about half their original length, and released them (*experimental* group 1). He took another group of males and glued on the tail feathers that he had removed from the first group, creating exceptionally long tails (*experimental* group 2). Finally, Andersson had two control groups. In one, the tail was cut and then glued back in place (to control for the effects of capturing the birds and manipulating their feathers). In the other control group, he simply captured and released the male birds to control for any behavioral changes caused by the stress of being caught and handled. Later, Andersson counted the number of nests that females had built on each male's territory (this indicated how many females had mated with that male). He found that males with lengthened tails had the most nests on their territories, males with shortened tails had the fewest, and control males (with normal-length tails, either untouched or cut and glued together) had an intermediate number (**Fig. E1-2**). Andersson *concluded* that his results supported the hypothesis that female widowbirds prefer to mate with long-tailed males.

▲ FIGURE E1-2   **The experiment of Malte Andersson**

Experimentation using variables and controls is powerful, but it is important to recognize its limitations. In particular, scientists can seldom be sure that they have controlled for *all* possible variables, or made all the observations that could possibly refute their hypothesis. Therefore, science mandates that conclusions are always subject to revision if new experiments or observations contradict them.

Scientific Theories Have Been Thoroughly Tested

Scientists use the word "theory" in a way that differs from its everyday usage. If Dr. Watson asked Sherlock Holmes, "Do you have a theory as to the perpetrator of this foul deed?", in scientific terms, he would be asking Holmes not for a theory, but for a hypothesis—a proposed explanation based on clues that provide incomplete evidence. A **scientific theory,** in contrast, is a general and reliable explanation of important natural phenomena that has been developed through extensive and reproducible observations and experiments. In short, a scientific theory is best described as a **natural law,** a basic principle derived from the study of nature that has never been disproven by scientific inquiry. For example, scientific theories such as the atomic theory (that all matter is composed of atoms) and the theory of gravitation (that objects exert attraction for one another) are fundamental to the science of physics. Likewise, the **cell theory** (that all living organisms are composed of cells) and the theory of evolution (discussed in Section 1.2) are fundamental to the study of biology. Scientists describe these fundamental principles as "theories" rather than "facts" because a basic premise of scientific inquiry is that it must be performed with an open mind; if compelling evidence arises that renders a scientific theory invalid, that theory must be modified or discarded.

A modern example of the need to modify basic principles in the light of new scientific evidence is the discovery of prions, which are infectious proteins (see the case study for Chapter 3). Before the early 1980s, all known infectious disease agents, including viruses, copied themselves using instructions from genetic material, such as DNA. Then in 1982, neurologist Stanley Prusiner from the University of California at San Francisco published evidence that scrapie (an infectious disease of sheep that results in brain degeneration) is actually caused and transmitted by a protein that has no genetic material. Interestingly, Prusiner's original hypothesis was that scrapie was caused by a virus, but none of his experiments supported this conclusion. Infectious proteins were unknown to science, and Prusiner's results were met with widespread disbelief. It took nearly two decades of further experiments by Prusiner and many other scientists working with him to convince most of the scientific community that a protein by itself could, indeed, act as a disease agent. Finally, in 1997, Stanley Prusiner was awarded the Nobel Prize in Physiology or Medicine for his pioneering work, which introduced an entirely new biological principle.

Prions are now recognized as the agent causing mad cow disease (also called BSE for "bovine spongiform encephalitis"), which has killed not only cattle but also about 200 people who ate infected beef. Prions also cause Creutzfeldt-Jakob disease (CJD), a fatal degenerative human brain disorder. In this example, because of their willingness to modify a scientific principle in response to new data, scientists maintained the integrity of the scientific process while expanding our understanding of how diseases can occur.

Scientific Theories Involve Both Inductive and Deductive Reasoning

Scientific theories arise through **inductive reasoning,** the process of creating a broad generalization based on many observations that support it and none that contradict it. For example, the theory that Earth exerts gravitational forces on objects began from repeated observations of objects falling downward toward Earth and from no observations of objects falling upward away from Earth. The cell theory arises from the observation that all organisms that possess the characteristics of life as described in this chapter are composed of one or more cells and that nothing that is not composed of cells shares all of these attributes.

Once a scientific theory has been formulated, it then can be used to support deductive reasoning. In science, **deductive reasoning** starts with a well-supported generalization such as a scientific theory and uses it to generate hypotheses about how a specific experiment or observation will turn out. For example, based on the cell theory, if a scientist discovers a new entity that exhibits all the characteristics of life, she can confidently hypothesize that it will be made up of cells. Of course, the new organism must then be carefully examined to confirm its cellular structure.

Scientific Theories Are Formulated in Ways That Can Potentially Be Disproved

Scientists refer to the basic principles of science as "theories" because theories have the potential to be disproved, or falsified. The possibility of being falsified is a major difference between scientific theories and beliefs based on faith, which are impossible to either prove or disprove. Faith-based beliefs—for example, that each creature on Earth was separately created—cannot be subjected to scientific inquiry. Thus, such beliefs do not fall within the scope of science.

Science Is a Human Endeavor

Scientists are people, driven by the pride, fears, and ambition common to humanity. Ambition played an important role in the discovery of the structure of DNA by James Watson and Francis Crick (described in Chapter 11). Accidents, lucky guesses, controversies with competing scientists, and, of course, the intellectual curiosity of individual scientists all contribute to scientific advances. Even mistakes can play a role. Let's consider an actual case.

Microbiologists often study pure cultures—a single type of bacterium grown in sterile, covered dishes free from contamination by other bacteria and molds. At the first sign of contamination, a culture is usually thrown out, often with mutterings about sloppy technique. In the late 1920s, however, Scottish bacteriologist Alexander Fleming turned a ruined bacterial culture into one of the greatest medical advances in history.

One of Fleming's cultures became contaminated with a mold (a type of fungus) called *Penicillium*. But instead

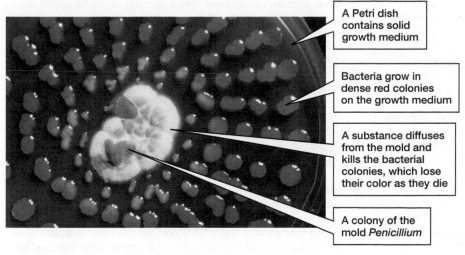

A Petri dish contains solid growth medium

Bacteria grow in dense red colonies on the growth medium

A substance diffuses from the mold and kills the bacterial colonies, which lose their color as they die

A colony of the mold *Penicillium*

▲ FIGURE 1-12 **Penicillin kills bacteria**

of just discarding the dish, Fleming looked at it carefully and observed that no bacteria were growing near the mold (**Fig. 1-12**). He asked the question: "Why aren't bacteria growing in this region?" Fleming then formulated the hypothesis that *Penicillium* releases a substance that kills bacteria, and he predicted that a solution in which the mold had grown would contain this substance and kill bacteria. To test this hypothesis, Fleming performed an experiment. First, he grew *Penicillium* in a liquid nutrient broth. Then he filtered out the mold and poured some of the mold-free broth on a plate with a pure bacterial culture. Sure enough, something in the liquid killed the bacteria, supporting his hypothesis. This (and more experiments that confirmed his results) led to the conclusion that *Penicillium* secretes a substance that kills bacteria. Further research into these mold extracts resulted in the production of the first antibiotic—penicillin.

Fleming's experiments are a classic example of the scientific method, but they would never have happened without the combination of a mistake, an observation, and the curiosity to explore it. The outcome has saved millions of lives. As French microbiologist Louis Pasteur said, "Chance favors the prepared mind."

Knowledge of Biology Illuminates Life

Some people regard science as a dehumanizing activity, thinking that too deep an understanding of the world robs us of wonder and awe. Nothing could be further from the truth. For example, let's look at lupine flowers. Their two lower petals form a tube surrounding both male and female reproductive parts (**Fig. 1-13**). In young flowers, the weight of a bee on this tube forces pollen (carrying sperm) out of the tube onto the bee's abdomen. In older lupine flowers that are ready to be fertilized, the female part grows and emerges through the end of the tube. When a pollen-dusted bee visits, it usually deposits some pollen containing sperm on the exposed female organ. This allows the lupine to produce the seeds of its next generation.

Do these insights into lupines detract from our appreciation of them? Far from it. There is added delight in understanding the intertwined form and function of bee and flower that resulted as these organisms evolved together.

Once, as two of the authors of this text crouched beside a wild lupine, an elderly man stopped to ask what they were looking at so intently. He listened with interest as they explained what they were seeing, and immediately he went to observe another patch of lupines where bees were foraging. He, too, felt the increased sense of wonder that comes with understanding.

Throughout this text, we try to convey to you the wonder that comes with understanding, and we hope that you, too, will experience it. We also emphasize that biology is not a completed work but an ongoing exploration. We urge you to follow the journey of biological discoveries throughout your life. Don't think of biology as just another set of facts to memorize, but rather as a pathway to a new understanding of yourself and the life around you.

CHECK YOUR LEARNING

Can you outline the scientific method and explain why scientific principles are called theories?

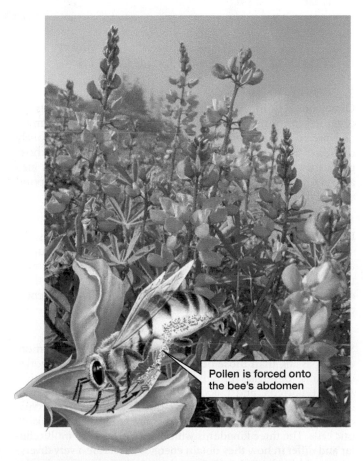

Pollen is forced onto the bee's abdomen

▲ FIGURE 1-13 **Adaptations in lupine flowers**
Understanding life helps people notice and appreciate the small wonders at their feet. (Inset) A lupine flower deposits pollen on a foraging bee's abdomen.

CASE STUDY revisited

The Boundaries of Life

If viruses aren't forms of life, then what are they? A virus by itself is an inert particle that doesn't approach the complexity of a cell. The simplest virus, such as that causing smallpox (Fig. 1-14), consists of a protein coat that surrounds genetic material. The uncomplicated structure of viruses, coupled with amazing advances in biotechnology, have allowed researchers to synthesize viruses in the laboratory. They have accomplished this using the blueprint contained in viral genetic material and readily purchased chemicals. The first virus to be synthesized was the small, relatively simple poliovirus. This feat was accomplished in 2002 by Eckard Wimmer and coworkers at Stony Brook University, who titled their work "The Test-Tube Synthesis of a Chemical Called Poliovirus."

Protein coat

Genetic material

▲ FIGURE 1-14 **A smallpox virus**

Did these researchers create life in the laboratory?

A few scientists would say "yes," defining life by its ability to copy itself and to evolve. Wimmer himself describes viruses as entities that switch between a nonliving phase outside the cell and a living phase inside. The more stringent definition of life presented in this chapter explains why most scientists agree that viruses aren't alive. As virologist Luis Villarreal of the University of California at Irvine states, "Viruses are parasites that skirt the boundaries between life and inert matter."

Consider This

BioEthics   When Wimmer and his coworkers announced that they had synthesized the poliovirus, they created considerable controversy both within and outside of the scientific community. Some people were concerned that this research jeopardized the eradication of polio, which has been nearly eliminated by widespread vaccination. They feared that deadly and highly contagious viruses might now be synthesized by bioterrorists. The researchers responded that they were merely applying current knowledge and techniques to demonstrate the principle that viruses are basically chemical entities that can be synthesized in the laboratory. Do you think scientists should synthesize viruses? What are the implications of forbidding such research?

CHAPTER REVIEW

Summary of Key Concepts

1.1 What Is Life?
Organisms acquire and use materials and energy. Materials are obtained from other organisms or the nonliving environment and are continuously recycled. Energy must be continuously captured from sunlight by photosynthetic organisms, whose bodies supply energy to all other organisms. Organisms also actively maintain organized complexity, perceive and respond to stimuli, grow, reproduce, and, collectively, evolve.

1.2 What Is Evolution?
Evolution is the scientific theory that modern organisms descended, with changes, from earlier life-forms. Evolution occurs as a consequence of (1) genetic differences, originally arising as mutations, among members of a population; (2) inheritance of these differences by offspring; and (3) natural selection of the differences that produce the best adaptations to the organisms' environment.

1.3 How Do Scientists Study Life?
Scientists identify a hierarchy of levels of organization, each more encompassing than those beneath (see Fig. 1-10). To categorize organisms, biologists group them into three major domains: Archaea, Bacteria, and Eukarya. The Archaea and Bacteria both consist of single, prokaryotic cells, but fundamental molecular differences distinguish them. Eukarya are composed of eukaryotic cells. The three kingdoms within the Eukarya are multicellular and differ in how they obtain energy. Protists are a very diverse group within the Eukarya. Some important features of the domains and kingdoms are summarized in Table 1-1. The scientific names of organisms are formed from their genus and species.

1.4 What Is Science?
Science is based on the principle that all events can be traced to natural causes that people can study objectively. Knowledge in biology is acquired through the scientific method, in which an observation leads to a question that leads to a hypothesis. The hypothesis generates a prediction that is then tested by controlled experiments. The experimental results, which must be repeatable, either support or refute the hypothesis, leading to a conclusion about the validity of the hypothesis. A scientific theory is a general explanation of natural phenomena developed through extensive and reproducible experiments and observations.

Key Terms

adaptation *6*
atom *7*
autotroph *10*
binomial system *10*
biology *2*
biosphere *8*
cell *2*
cell theory *14*
community *8*
conclusion *11*
control *11*
deductive reasoning *14*
deoxyribonucleic acid (DNA) *4*
domain *9*
ecosystem *8*
element *7*

eukaryotic *10*
evolution *4*
experiment *11*
extinction *7*
gene *5*
heterotroph *10*
hypothesis *11*
inductive reasoning *14*
kingdom *9*
molecule *7*
multicellular *9*
mutation *6*
natural law *14*
natural selection *6*
nucleus *10*
observation *11*

Learning Outcomes

In this chapter, you have learned to . . .

LO1 Describe the characteristics of living things.

LO2 Explain evolution and how three natural processes make evolution inevitable.

LO3 Explain the concept of levels of biological organization, and list the levels.

LO4 Identify the three domains of life, and describe the types of cells that make up each domain.

LO5 Explain how the three kingdoms of eukaryotic organisms are distinguished from one another.

LO6 Describe the scientific method, and provide an example of how it could be applied to an everyday problem.

LO7 Explain why experiments include control groups.

LO8 Explain how a hypothesis differs from a scientific theory.

Thinking Through the Concepts

Fill-in-the-Blank

1. Organisms respond to _Stimuli_. Organisms acquire and use _Materials_ and _energy_ from the environment. Organisms are composed of cells whose structure is both _____ and _____. Collectively, organisms _____ over time. **LO1 LO2**

2. The smallest particle of an element that retains all the properties of that element is a(n) _____. The smallest unit of life is the _____. Cells of a specific type within multicellular organisms combine to form _____. A(n) _____ consists of all of the same type of organism within a defined area. A(n) _____ consists of all the interacting populations within the same area. A(n) _____ consists of the community and its nonliving surroundings. **LO3**

3. A(n) _____ is a general explanation of natural phenomena supported by extensive, reproducible tests and observations. In contrast, a(n) _____ is a proposed explanation for observed events. To answer specific questions about life, biologists use a general process called the _____. **LO6 LO8**

4. An important scientific theory that explains why organisms are at once so similar and also so diverse is the theory of _____. This theory explains life's diversity as having originated primarily through the process of _____. **LO2**

5. The molecule that guides the construction and operation of an organism's body is called (complete term) _____, abbreviated as _____. This large molecule contains discrete segments with specific instructions; these segments are called _____. **LO1 LO2**

Review Questions

1. What properties are shared by all forms of life? **LO1**
2. Why do organisms require energy? Where does the energy come from? **LO1**
3. Define *evolution*, and explain the three natural occurrences that make evolution inevitable. **LO2**
4. What are the three domains of life? **LO4**
5. What are some differences between prokaryotic and eukaryotic cells? In which domain(s) is each found? **LO4**
6. Which kingdom(s) are heterotrophic? Which are autotrophic? **LO5**
7. What basic principle underlies all scientific inquiry? **LO6**
8. What is the difference between a scientific theory and a hypothesis? Why do scientists refer to basic scientific principles as "theories" rather than "facts"? **LO8**
9. What factors did Redi control for in his open jar of meat? What factors did Andersson control for? **LO7**
10. Explain the differences between inductive and deductive reasoning, and provide an example (real or hypothetical) of each. **LO8**
11. List the steps in the scientific method with a brief description of each step. **LO6**

Applying the Concepts

1. What properties of life does your computer possess? Which ones does it lack?
2. How would this textbook's definition of life need to be changed to allow viruses to qualify as life-forms? For prions to be considered alive?
3. Review Alexander Fleming's experiment that led to the discovery of penicillin. What would be an appropriate control for the experiment in which Fleming applied filtered medium from a *Penicillium* culture to plates of bacteria?
4. Explain an instance in which your own understanding of a phenomenon enhances your appreciation of it.
5. Provide an example (different from that in the text) of how the scientific method is used in everyday life.

Answers to Figure Caption questions and Fill-in-the-Blank questions can be found in the Answers section at the back of the book.

(MB) *Go to MasteringBiology for practice quizzes, activities, eText, videos, current events, and more.*

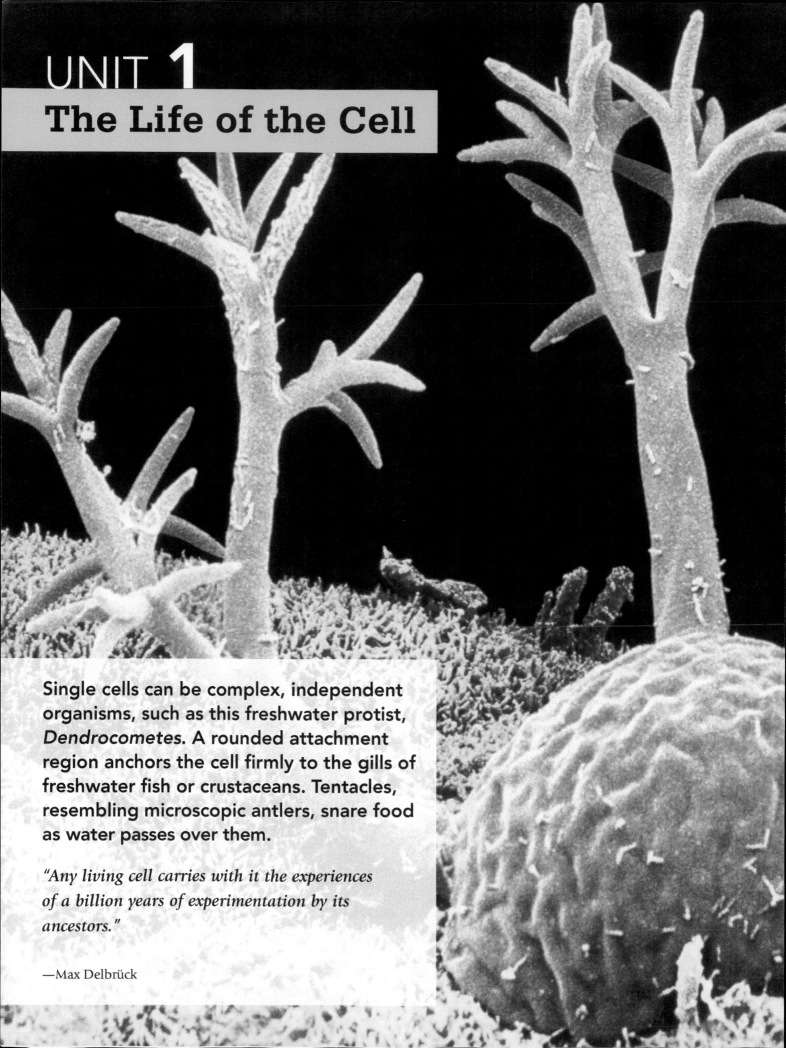

UNIT 1
The Life of the Cell

Single cells can be complex, independent organisms, such as this freshwater protist, *Dendrocometes*. A rounded attachment region anchors the cell firmly to the gills of freshwater fish or crustaceans. Tentacles, resembling microscopic antlers, snare food as water passes over them.

"Any living cell carries with it the experiences of a billion years of experimentation by its ancestors."

—Max Delbrück

The aftermath of explosions at the Fukushima nuclear power plant in Japan.

CASE STUDY

Unstable Atoms
Unleashed

ON MARCH 11, 2011, an earthquake of epic magnitude—9.0 on the Richter scale—occurred off the northeast coast of Japan. It was the most violent earthquake in Japan's history, and one of the most powerful ever recorded anywhere in the world. Soon after, a tsunami caused by the quake slammed into the Fukushima Daiichi nuclear power plant on Japan's eastern coast. The waves, towering up to 46 feet, flooded the plant and knocked out its main electrical power supply and backup generators, which caused its cooling system to fail.

The cores of nuclear reactors like those in the Fukushima plant consist of large numbers of fuel rods, metal tubes filled with pellets of uranium fuel. Two thick steel containment vessels surround the nuclear core. Water is pumped continuously around the fuel rods within the inner containment vessel, absorbing the intense heat generated by the nuclear reactions within the rods. The heated water produces steam, which then expands to drive turbines that generate electricity. When loss of power shut down the plant's water pumps, operators used firefighting equipment to inject seawater into the inner containment vessel in a desperate attempt to cool it. But their efforts failed; heat and pressure cracked the inner vessel, allowing water and steam to escape. The core temperature rose to over 1,800°F (about 1,000°C), melting the tubes of the zirconium metal alloy that enclosed the fuel rods and releasing the radioactive fuel into the inner vessel.

Because of the incredibly high temperatures, the zirconium reacted with the steam to generate hydrogen gas. As the pressure of the steam and hydrogen gas increased, it threatened to rupture the outer containment vessel. To prevent this, plant operators vented the mixture—which also contained radioactive elements from the melted fuel rods—into the atmosphere. As the hot hydrogen gas encountered oxygen in the atmosphere, the two combined explosively, destroying parts of the buildings housing the containment vessels (see the chapter opener photo). Despite venting, the intense heat and the pressure it generated eventually caused the outer containment structure to leak and disgorge contaminated water into the ocean for months following the disaster. Officials evacuated tens of thousands of people living within 12 miles of the plant.

Why were people evacuated from their homes when radioactive gases were released into the atmosphere? How do the atoms of radioactive elements differ from those that are not radioactive? And what are atoms composed of?

AT A GLANCE

2.1 What Are Atoms?

2.2 How Do Atoms Interact to Form Molecules?

2.3 Why Is Water So Important to Life?

LEARNING GOALS

LG1 Describe the relationship between elements and atoms.

LG2 Describe the structure of atoms, including identification of the three subatomic particles and the characteristics of each.

LG3 Define isotopes and explain what causes some isotopes to be radioactive and how people may be helped or harmed by radioactivity.

LG4 Explain how atoms form molecules.

LG5 Describe the characteristics of the three types of chemical bonds, and provide examples of molecules in which each type of bond is found.

LG6 Describe the special properties of water and how these properties allow water to play key roles in life on Earth.

LG7 Explain the pH scale, and describe the properties of acids, bases, and buffers.

2.1 WHAT ARE ATOMS?

If you write "atom" with a pencil, you are forming the letters with graphite, a form of carbon. Now imagine cutting up the carbon into finer and finer particles. Each particle would remain graphite until the substance was eventually split into its basic subunits: individual carbon atoms. Each carbon atom is so small that 100 million of them placed in a row would span less than half an inch (1 centimeter). The structure of each atom would be identical and unique to the element carbon.

Atoms Are the Basic Structural Units of Elements

Carbon is an example of an **element**—a substance that cannot be separated into simpler substances, and cannot be converted into another substance by ordinary chemical reactions. Elements, both alone and combined with other elements, form all matter. An **atom** is the smallest unit of an element, and each atom retains all the chemical properties of that element.

Ninety-two different elements occur in nature. Each is given an abbreviation, its *atomic symbol*, based on its name (sometimes in Latin; e.g., lead is Pb, for *plumbum*). Most elements are present in only small quantities in the biosphere, and relatively few are essential to life on Earth. **Table 2-1** lists the most common elements in living things.

Atoms Are Composed of Still Smaller Particles

Atoms are composed of *subatomic particles*: **neutrons** (n), which have no charge; **protons** (p^+), which each carry a single positive charge; and **electrons** (e^-), which each carry a single negative charge. An atom as a whole is uncharged, or *neutral*, because it contains equal numbers of protons and electrons, whose positive and negative charges electrically cancel each other. Subatomic particles are so small that they are assigned their own unit of mass, measured in *atomic mass units*. As you can see in **Table 2-2**, each proton and neutron

TABLE 2-1	Common Elements in Living Organisms		
Element	Atomic Number[1]	Mass Number[2]	% by Weight in the Human Body
Oxygen (O)	8	16	65
Carbon (C)	6	12	18.5
Hydrogen (H)	1	1	9.5
Nitrogen (N)	7	14	3.0
Calcium (Ca)	20	40	1.5
Phosphorus (P)	15	31	1.0
Potassium (K)	19	39	0.35
Sulfur (S)	16	32	0.25
Sodium (Na)	11	23	0.15
Chlorine (Cl)	17	35	0.15
Magnesium (Mg)	12	24	0.05
Iron (Fe)	26	56	Trace
Fluorine (F)	9	19	Trace
Zinc (Zn)	30	65	Trace

[1]Atomic number: number of protons in the atomic nucleus.
[2]Mass number: total number of protons and neutrons.

TABLE 2-2	Mass and Charge of Subatomic Particles	
Subatomic Particle	Mass (in atomic mass units)	Charge
Neutron (n)	1	0
Proton (p^+)	1	+1
Electron (e^-)	0.00055	−1

has a mass unit of 1, while the mass of an electron is negligible compared to these larger particles. The **mass number** of an atom is the total number (which equals the total mass) of the protons and neutrons in its nucleus.

Protons and neutrons cluster together in the center of the atom, forming the **atomic nucleus.** The tiny electrons are in continuous rapid motion around the nucleus within a large, three-dimensional space, as illustrated by the two simplest atoms, hydrogen and helium, in **Figure 2-1.** *Orbital models* of atomic structure, like that shown in Figure 2-1, are extremely simplified to make atoms easy to imagine. Atoms are never drawn to scale; if they were, and if you visualize this • to be the nucleus, the electrons would be somewhere in the next room—roughly 30 feet away!

Elements Are Defined by Their Atomic Numbers

The number of protons in the nucleus—called the **atomic number**—is the feature that defines each element, making it distinct from all others. For example, every hydrogen atom has one proton, every carbon atom has six, and every oxygen atom has eight, giving these atoms atomic numbers of 1, 6, and 8, respectively. The periodic table in Appendix II organizes the elements according to their atomic numbers (rows) and their general chemical properties (columns).

Isotopes Are Atoms of the Same Element with Different Numbers of Neutrons

Although every atom of an element has the same number of protons, the atoms of that element may have different numbers of neutrons. Atoms of the same element with different numbers of neutrons are called **isotopes.** Isotopes can be distinguished from one another because each has a different mass number, which is written as a superscript preceding the atomic symbol.

Some Isotopes Are Radioactive

Most isotopes are stable, that is, their nuclei do not change spontaneously. A few, however, are **radioactive,** meaning that their nuclei spontaneously break apart, or decay. Radioactive decay emits subatomic particles (such as neutrons) that carry large amounts of energy. Earlier, we stated that

one element cannot be converted into another by ordinary chemical reactions; these do not alter atomic nuclei. The decay of radioactive nuclei, in contrast, may form different elements. For example, nearly all carbon exists as stable ^{12}C. But a radioactive isotope called carbon-14 (^{14}C; 6 protons + 8 neutrons; comprising one in every trillion carbon atoms) is produced continuously by atmospheric reactions involving cosmic rays. Over thousands of years, the ^{14}C atoms spontaneously break down, forming nitrogen atoms. The ^{14}C is captured and stored in the bodies of organisms, where it exists in a fixed ratio with ^{12}C. After an organism dies, its ^{14}C disintegrates at a constant rate, reducing the ratio of ^{14}C to ^{12}C. By measuring this ratio, scientists can determine the age of formerly living artifacts up to about 50,000 years old (described in Chapter 17). This includes mummies, ancient trees and skeletons, or tools made of wood or bone.

In laboratory research, scientists often expose organisms to radioactive isotopes and trace the isotopes' movements during physiological processes. For example, experiments with radioactively labeled DNA and protein allowed scientists to conclude that DNA is the genetic material of cells (described in Chapter 11). Although they must be handled with caution, modern medicine makes extensive use of radioactive isotopes, as described in "Science in Action: Radioactive Medicine."

Some Radioactive Isotopes Damage Cells

Some radioactive isotopes release particles with enough energy that they can damage DNA, causing mutations (described in Chapter 1). People near the Fukushima power plant are being exposed to radiation in food, water, and air, increasing their risk of developing cancer. Japanese authorities have arranged to perform regular cancer screenings on hundreds of thousands of exposed children.

Nuclei and Electrons Play Complementary Roles in Atoms

Nuclei and electrons play complementary roles in atoms. Nuclei (unless they are radioactive) provide stability by resisting disturbance by outside forces; ordinary sources of energy such as heat, electricity, and light hardly affect them at all. Because its nucleus is stable, a carbon atom (^{12}C)

(a) Hydrogen (H)   (b) Helium (He)

▲ **FIGURE 2-1 Atomic models** Orbital models of **(a)** hydrogen (the only atom with no neutrons) and **(b)** helium. In these simplified models, the electrons (pale blue) are represented as miniature planets, orbiting around a nucleus that contains protons (gold) and neutrons (dark blue).

CASE STUDY c o n t i n u e d

Unstable Atoms Unleashed

The uranium in nuclear reactor fuel rods is mostly in the nonradioactive form (^{238}U), with about 4% radioactive uranium (^{235}U). When each ^{235}U atom splits into smaller atoms, it releases heat, which is harnessed to generate electricity, and it ejects two or three fast-moving neutrons. Neutrons hitting other ^{235}U atoms cause them to split, continuing the process. Neutrons hitting the more abundant ^{238}U atoms produce plutonium-239 (^{239}Pu). This plutonium isotope also splits apart when hit by neutrons, forming smaller atoms and releasing more heat energy that contributes to the electrical output of the power plant.

SCIENCE IN ACTION Radioactive Medicine

One medically important use of radioactive isotopes is in positron emission tomography (PET) scans. For example, a solution of sugar molecules tagged with a radioactive isotope might be injected into a patient's bloodstream. More metabolically active regions of the body use more sugar for energy and accumulate larger amounts of radioactivity. The person's body is moved through a ring of detectors that respond to the energetic particles emitted as the isotope decays (Fig. E2-1a). A powerful computer uses these data to calculate precisely where the decays occur. It then generates a color-coded map of the frequency of decays within each "slice" of body passing through the detector ring. PET can be used to study the working brain, because regions activated by a specific mental task—such as a math problem—will have increased energy needs and will "light up" as they accumulate more radioactive glucose. Tumors from cancer can be detected by PET because they grow rapidly and use large amounts of glucose, showing up in PET scans as "hot spots" (Fig. E2-1b).

Radiation therapy is used to treat about half of all cancer patients. DNA is easily damaged by radiation, so rapidly dividing cancer cells (which require intact DNA to copy themselves) are particularly vulnerable. The radioactive isotope may be introduced into the bloodstream, implanted in the body near the cancer, or radiation may be directed into the tumor by an external device (Fig. E2-2). Radiation exposure slightly increases the chance that the patient will develop cancer again in the future, but most patients consider a possible cure for a present and potentially fatal cancer to be well worth the risk.

detector ring

The subject's head is placed within a ring of detectors

Red indicates the highest radioactivity and blue the least; a malignant brain tumor shows clearly in red

(a) The subject is placed in a scanner

(b) The resulting computer image

▲ FIGURE E2-1 How positron emission tomography works

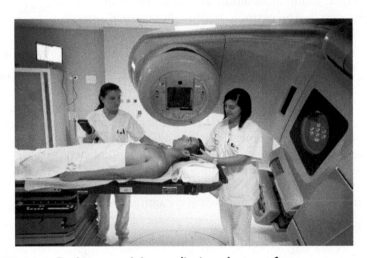

▲ FIGURE E2-2 Patient receiving radiation therapy for cancer

CASE STUDY continued

Unstable Atoms Unleashed

Months after the meltdown, engineers at the Fukushima power plant discovered hot spots of radiation so intense that a person exposed for an hour would be dead within a few weeks. How could death come so fast? Extremely high doses of radiation damage DNA and other biological molecules so much that cells—particularly those that divide rapidly—can no longer function. Skin cells are destroyed. Cells lining the stomach and intestine break down, leading to nausea and vomiting. Bone marrow, where blood cells are produced, is destroyed. Lack of white blood cells allows infections to flourish, and the loss of platelets crucial for blood clotting leads to internal bleeding. Fortunately, the hot spots inside Fukushima were detected from outside the building using special cameras, so no one was exposed to such extreme levels of radioactivity.

remains carbon whether it is part of a diamond, graphite, carbon dioxide, or sugar. Electrons, in contrast, are dynamic; they can capture and release energy, and they form bonds that link atoms together, as described later.

Electrons Occupy Complex Regions Around the Nucleus

Electrons occupy complex three-dimensional regions, called **electron shells,** around the nucleus. For simplicity, we will depict these shells as increasingly large, concentric rings around the nucleus where electrons travel like planets orbiting the sun (Fig. 2-2). Each shell has a specific energy associated with it; the farther away from the nucleus, the higher the energy of the electrons occupying the shell. Imagine each shell as a step on a ladder. Climbing each step takes energy. The higher you climb, the more energy that is stored in your

▲ FIGURE 2-2 **Electron shells in atoms** Most biologically important atoms have two or more shells of electrons. The first shell, the orbit closest to the nucleus, can hold two electrons; the next three shells each contain a maximum of eight electrons.

QUESTION Why do atoms that tend to react with other atoms have outer shells that are not full?

body, the more unstable you are, and the harder you would hit the ground if you fell off. Like a person on the ladder's lowest rung, electrons in the shell nearest the nucleus are in their most stable state and have the lowest energy. Electrons that occupy shells farther from the nucleus, like a person higher up a ladder, are at a higher energy state.

Electrons Can Capture and Release Energy

When an atom is excited by energy, such as heat or light, this energy can cause an electron to jump from a lower-energy electron shell to a higher-energy shell. Soon afterward, the electron spontaneously falls back into its original electron shell and releases its extra energy, often as light (**Fig. 2-3**).

We make use of this property of electrons every time we switch on a light bulb. Although fast becoming obsolete, the incandescent bulb is the easiest to understand. Electricity flows through a very thin wire, heating it to around 4,500°F (about 2,500°C) for a 100-watt bulb. The heat energy bumps some electrons in the wire into higher-energy electron shells. As the electrons drop back down into their original shells, they emit some of the energy as light. Unfortunately, about 90% of the energy absorbed by the wire of an incandescent bulb is reemitted as heat rather than light, so it's a very inefficient light source.

As Atomic Number Increases, Electrons Fill Shells Increasingly Distant from the Nucleus

Each electron shell can hold a specific number of electrons; the shell nearest the nucleus can hold only two, and the larger, more distant shells (in those atoms discussed here) hold eight. Electrons always first fill the shell nearest the nucleus and then fill the higher shells, keeping as close to the nucleus—and as stable—as possible. Elements with larger numbers of protons in their nuclei require more electrons to balance these protons, so their electrons will occupy shells at increasing distances from the nucleus.

The single electron in a hydrogen atom (H) and the two electrons in helium (He) occupy the first electron shell (see Fig. 2-1). The second shell, corresponding to a higher energy level, can hold up to eight electrons. Thus, a carbon atom (C) with six electrons will have two electrons filling its first shell and four occupying its second shell (see Fig. 2-2).

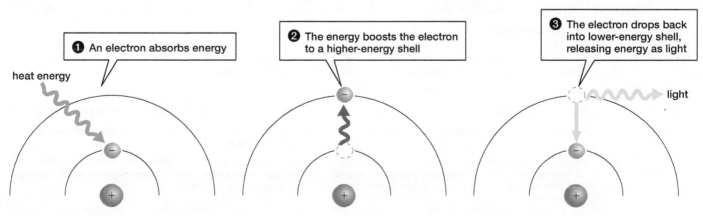

▲ FIGURE 2-3 **Energy capture and release**

Can you define an *element*, an *atom*, and the *subatomic particles* that make up the atom? Do you understand atomic number and mass number? Can you explain radioactivity and its dangers and benefits?

2.2 HOW DO ATOMS INTERACT TO FORM MOLECULES?

Most forms of matter that we encounter in our daily lives consist of atoms of the same or different elements linked together to form **molecules.** Simple examples are oxygen gas (O_2; two atoms of oxygen) or water (H_2O; two atoms of hydrogen and one of oxygen). How and why do molecules form?

Atoms Form Molecules to Fill Vacancies in Their Outer Electron Shells

Just as electrons are most stable in shells nearest the atomic nucleus, they are also most stable and less likely to interact with other atoms in shells that are completely full. For most elements, the number of electrons needed to balance the number of protons will fill one or more inner shells, but will not completely fill the outer shell. Atoms generally behave according to two basic principles:

- An atom will not react with other atoms when its outermost electron shell is completely full. Such an atom (e.g., helium in Fig. 2-1b) is extremely stable and is described as *inert*.
- An atom will react with other atoms if its outermost electron shell is only partially full (e.g., hydrogen in Fig. 2-1a). Such an atom is described as *reactive*.

Chemical Bonds Hold Atoms Together in Molecules

Chemical bonds are attractive forces that hold atoms together in molecules. Bonds are formed when reactive atoms gain, lose, or share electrons to gain stability and become less reactive. There are three major types of bonds: *ionic bonds, covalent bonds,* and *hydrogen bonds* (**Table 2-3**).

Ionic Bonds Form Among Ions

Atoms, including those that are reactive, have equal numbers of protons and electrons. This gives them an overall neutral charge. An atom with an almost empty outermost electron shell can become more stable by losing electrons and completely emptying its shell. An atom with a nearly full outer shell can become more stable by gaining electrons and filling its shell completely. When an atom gains an electron, it has more electrons than protons and becomes negatively charged. When an atom loses an electron, it has fewer electrons than protons, and becomes positively charged. An atom that has acquired an overall positive or negative charge is no longer called an atom; it has become an **ion.** Ions with opposite charges attract one another, and the electrical attraction between positively and negatively charged ions forms **ionic bonds.** For example, the white crystals in your salt shaker are molecules of sodium chloride linked by ionic bonds. Sodium (Na) has only one electron in its outermost electron shell, so it can become stable by losing this electron. Chlorine (Cl) has seven electrons in its outer shell, so it can become stable by gaining an electron (**Fig. 2-4a**). To form sodium chloride, then, sodium loses an electron to chlorine, forming Na^+, and chlorine picks up the electron, becoming Cl^- (**Fig. 2-4b**). The ionic bonds between sodium and chloride ions result in crystals composed of a repeating, orderly array of the two ions (**Fig. 2-4c**). As we will see later, water can break ionic bonds, as happens when water dissolves salt. Biological molecules must function in a watery environment and most are formed with covalent, rather than ionic, bonds.

Covalent Bonds Form by Sharing Electrons

Atoms with partially full outermost electron shells can become stable by sharing electrons with one another, filling both of their outer shells and forming **covalent bonds** (**Fig. 2-5**). The atoms in most biological molecules, such as proteins, sugars, and fats, are joined by covalent bonds (**Table 2-4**).

TABLE 2-3 Common Types of Bonds in Biological Molecules		
Type	**Type of Interaction**	**Example**
Ionic bond	An electron is transferred between atoms creating positive and negative ions that attract one another.	Occurs between the sodium (Na^+) and chloride (Cl^-) ions of table salt (NaCl)
Covalent bond	Electrons are shared between atoms.	
Nonpolar	Electrons are shared equally between atoms.	Occurs between the two hydrogen atoms in hydrogen gas (H_2)
Polar	Electrons are shared unequally between atoms.	Occurs between hydrogen and oxygen atoms of a water molecule (H_2O)
Hydrogen bond	Attractions occur between polar molecules in which H is bonded to O or N. The slightly positive hydrogen attracts the slightly negative O or N of a nearby polar molecule.	Occurs between water molecules, where slightly positive charges on hydrogen atoms attract slightly negative charges on oxygen atoms of nearby molecules

(a) Neutral atoms

(b) Ions

(c) An ionic compound: NaCl

▲ FIGURE 2-4 **The formation of ions and ionic bonds**
(a) Sodium has only one electron in its outer electron shell; chlorine has seven. (b) Sodium can become stable by losing an electron, and chlorine can become stable by gaining an electron. Sodium then becomes a positively charged ion and chlorine a negatively charged ion. (c) Because oppositely charged particles attract one another, the resulting sodium and chloride ions nestle closely together in a crystal of salt, NaCl. The arrangement of ions in salt causes it to form cubic crystals.

Covalent Bonds May Produce Nonpolar or Polar Molecules

All atoms of the same element, and certain atoms of different elements, will share electrons equally. This creates **nonpolar covalent bonds** in which there is no charge on any part of the molecule. For example, two hydrogen atoms can become more stable if they share their outer electrons, allowing each to behave almost as if it had two electrons

(a) Nonpolar covalent bonding in hydrogen gas (H$_2$)

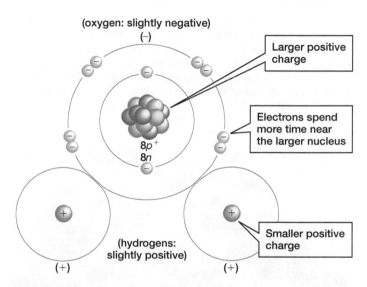

(b) Polar covalent bonding in water (H$_2$O)

▲ FIGURE 2-5 **Covalent bonds involve shared electrons**
(a) In hydrogen gas, an electron from each hydrogen atom is shared equally, forming a single nonpolar covalent bond. (b) Oxygen lacks two electrons to fill its outer shell, so oxygen can form polar covalent bonds with two hydrogen atoms, creating water. Oxygen exerts a greater pull on the electrons than does hydrogen, so the "oxygen end" of the molecule has a slight negative charge and the "hydrogen end" has a slight positive charge.

	TABLE 2-4 Electrons and Bonds in Atoms Common in Biological Molecules		
Atom	Capacity of Outer Electron Shell	Electrons in Outer Shell	Number of Covalent Bonds Usually Formed
Hydrogen	2	1	1
Carbon	8	4	4
Nitrogen	8	5	3
Oxygen	8	6	2
Sulfur	8	6	2

Health|Watch

Watch Out for Free Radicals

Partially full outer electron shells are reactive, but this reactivity increases dramatically if the unfilled shell also contains an uneven number of electrons. Like people, electrons like to pair up. Free radicals have unpaired electrons in their outer shells. As a result they react vigorously with other molecules, capturing or releasing electrons to achieve a more stable arrangement. But in stealing or donating an electron, a free radical often leaves an unpaired electron in the molecule it attacks, creating a new free radical. This can lead to chain reactions that destroy biological molecules such as DNA that are crucial to life. Our bodies continuously produce oxygen-containing free radicals. One of these is hydrogen peroxide (H_2O_2), whose ability to break down other molecules is revealed when it bleaches hair by destroying hair pigment.

Free radicals can be formed when radiation (from sunlight, X-rays, and radioactive isotopes), chemicals in automobile exhaust and cigarette smoke, and industrial metals such as mercury and lead enter our bodies. Damage to cells caused by free radicals, called *oxidative stress*, is linked to many disorders, among them heart disease, cancer, Parkinson's disease, Alzheimer's disease, and cataracts. The gradual deterioration of the body that accompanies aging is believed by many scientists to result, at least in part, from oxidative stress accumulating over a lifetime of exposure to free radicals (Fig. E2-3). Fortunately our bodies produce many different molecules, collectively called **antioxidants,** that react with free radicals and render them harmless.

There is strong evidence that diets high in the natural antioxidants found in fruits and vegetables are correlated with a lower incidence of cardiovascular disease. But did you know that dark chocolate (Fig. E2-4) might actually be a type of health food? Recent large studies that correlate chocolate consumption and health have found that participants who regularly consumed chocolate were less likely to suffer strokes and heart attacks. Cocoa powder (the dark, bitter powder made from the seeds inside cacao pods; see Fig. E2-4, inset) contains high concentrations of flavonols, which are powerful antioxidants.

Although no controlled studies have been yet done to determine whether eating large quantities of chocolate actually reduces the risk of cancer, strokes, neurological disorders, or heart disease, there would certainly be no shortage of volunteers for this research. Before you begin an uncontrolled study on yourself, however, be aware that the most sinfully delicious chocolates are also high in fat and sugar. But—in moderation—"chocoholics" with a taste for dark chocolate have reason to relax and enjoy!

▲ FIGURE E2-3 **Free-radical damage** Ultraviolet radiation from sunlight can generate free radicals in skin, damaging molecules that give skin its elasticity and contributing to wrinkles as we age.

▲ FIGURE E2-4 **Chocolate** Cocoa is derived from cacao beans found inside pods (inset) on trees native to South America.

in its outer shell (see Fig. 2-5a). This reaction forms hydrogen gas (H_2). Because the two H nuclei are identical, their electrons spend equal time near each, and so neither end, or *pole*, of the molecule is charged. Other examples of nonpolar molecules include oxygen gas (O_2), nitrogen gas (N_2), carbon dioxide (CO_2), and biological molecules such as oils and fats

(described in Chapter 3). In each of these examples, the nuclei exert an equal or very similar pull on the shared electrons.

Some atoms share electrons unequally, because one attracts the electrons more strongly than the other. Unequally shared electrons produce **polar covalent bonds** (see Fig. 2-5b). Although the molecule as a whole is electrically neutral, a polar covalent molecule has charged poles. In water (H_2O), for example, an electron is shared between each hydrogen atom and the central oxygen atom. The oxygen exerts a stronger attraction on the electrons than do the hydrogens, so the shared electrons spend more time near the oxygen atom. By attracting electrons, the oxygen pole of a water molecule becomes slightly negative, leaving each hydrogen atom slightly positive (see Fig. 2-5b).

Among atoms and molecules with unfilled outer shells, some—called **free radicals**—are so reactive that they can tear other molecules apart. Free radicals are produced in large numbers in the body by reactions that make energy available to cells. Although these reactions are essential for life, over time, the stress that free radicals place on living cells may contribute to aging and eventual death. Learn more in "Health Watch: Watch Out for Free Radicals."

Hydrogen Bonds Are Attractive Forces Between Certain Polar Molecules

Biological molecules, including sugars, proteins, and nucleic acids, often have many polar covalent bonds, between either hydrogen and oxygen or hydrogen and nitrogen. In these cases, the hydrogen is slightly positive and the oxygen or nitrogen is slightly negative. As you know, opposite charges attract. A **hydrogen bond** is the attraction between a slightly positive hydrogen and a slightly negative oxygen or nitrogen located in a nearby molecule or in another part of the same molecule. The simplest example of hydrogen bonding occurs in water. Water molecules form hydrogen bonds with one another between

▲ FIGURE 2-6 **Hydrogen bonds in water** The slight charges on different parts of water molecules produce attractive forces called hydrogen bonds (dotted lines) between the oxygen and hydrogen atoms in adjacent water molecules. As water flows, these bonds are constantly breaking and re-forming.

their slightly positive hydrogen poles and slightly negative oxygen poles, linking the water molecules into a loosely connected network (**Fig. 2-6**). As you will see shortly, hydrogen bonds among water molecules give water several unusual properties. In the following chapter, we will describe how hydrogen bonding—within different parts of a single biological molecule, between nearby biological molecules, and between biological molecules and water—is crucial for life on Earth.

2.3 WHY IS WATER SO IMPORTANT TO LIFE?

As naturalist Loren Eiseley eloquently stated, "If there is magic on this planet, it is contained in water." Water has many special properties that all result from the polarity of its molecules and the hydrogen bonds that form among them. What makes water unique?

Water Molecules Attract One Another

Hydrogen bonds interconnect water molecules. But, like square dancers continually moving from one partner to the next—joining and releasing hands as they go—hydrogen bonds in liquid water constantly break and re-form, allowing the water to flow. In water, hydrogen bonds cause **cohesion,** the tendency for molecules of a single type to stick together. The cohesion of water plays a crucial role in the life of land plants. How does water absorbed by a plant's roots ever reach its leaves, especially if the plant is a 300-foot-tall redwood tree (**Fig. 2-7a**)? Water fills tiny tubes that connect the roots, stem, and leaves. Water evaporates from leaves, and just before it enters the atmosphere, each molecule pulls the one below it to the leaf's surface. Thus water's cohesiveness allows it to be pulled upward much like a chain being dragged up from the top. This works because the hydrogen bonds that link water molecules are stronger than the weight of the water in the tube, so the water chain doesn't break. Without the cohesion of water, there could be no large land plants.

? HAVE **YOU** EVER WONDERED ...

Why It Hurts So Much to Do a Belly Flop?

The slap of a belly flop provides firsthand experience of the power of cohesion among water molecules. Because of the hydrogen bonds that interconnect its molecules, the water surface resists being broken. When you suddenly force water molecules apart over a large area using your belly, the result can be a bit painful. Do you think that belly-flopping into a pool of nonpolar vegetable oil would hurt as much?

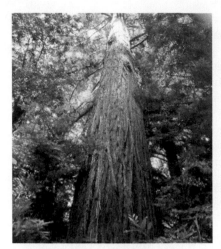

(a) Cohesion helps water to reach treetops

(b) Cohesion causes surface tension

◄ FIGURE 2-7 **Cohesion among water molecules (a)** Cohesion caused by hydrogen bonding allows water evaporating from the leaves of plants to pull water up from the roots. **(b)** A basilisk lizard uses surface tension as it races across the water's surface to escape a predator.

Cohesion among water molecules also produces **surface tension,** the tendency for a water surface to resist being broken. Surface tension can support fallen leaves, some spiders and water insects, and even a running basilisk lizard (**Fig. 2-7b**).

Water Interacts with Many Other Molecules

A **solvent** is a substance that **dissolves** some other substance; in other words, a solvent completely surrounds and disperses the individual atoms or molecules of another substance. A solvent containing one or more dissolved substances is called a **solution.** Because of its polar nature, water is an excellent solvent for other polar molecules and for ions. Water dissolves many molecules that are important to life, including proteins, salts, sugars, oxygen, and carbon dioxide. Watery solutions allow them to move around freely and meet one another, allowing reactions to occur.

Let's see how table salt dissolves in water. A crystal of table salt is held together by the electrical attraction between positively charged sodium ions (Na^+) and negatively charged chloride ions (Cl^-; see Fig. 2-4c). When a salt crystal is dropped into water, the positively charged hydrogen poles of water molecules are attracted to the Cl^-, and the negatively charged oxygen poles are attracted to the Na^+. As water molecules surround the sodium and chloride ions, shielding them from interacting with each other, the ions separate from the crystal and drift away in the water—thus, the salt dissolves (**Fig. 2-8**).

Water dissolves polar molecules because its positive and negative poles are attracted to their oppositely charged poles. Because of their electrical attraction for water molecules, ions and polar molecules are described as **hydrophilic** (from the Greek "hydro," meaning "water," and "philic" meaning "loving"). Many biological molecules are hydrophilic and dissolve readily in water.

Gases such as oxygen and carbon dioxide are essential for biochemical reactions but are nonpolar—so how do they dissolve? These molecules are sufficiently small that they can fit into the spaces between water molecules without

▲ FIGURE 2-8 **Water as a solvent** When a salt crystal (NaCl) is dropped into water, the water surrounds the sodium and chloride ions. The positive poles of water molecules face the Cl^-, and the negative poles face the Na^+. The ions disperse as the surrounding water molecules isolate them from one another, and the salt crystal gradually dissolves.

QUESTION If you placed a salt crystal in a nonpolar liquid (like oil), would it dissolve?

disrupting the hydrogen bonds that link the water molecules. Fish swimming below the ice on a frozen lake rely on oxygen that dissolved before the ice formed, and the CO_2 they release dissolves into the water.

Larger molecules with nonpolar covalent bonds, such as fats and oils, do not dissolve in water and hence are called **hydrophobic** (Greek for "water-fearing"). Nevertheless, water has an important effect on such molecules. In sticking together, water molecules—like high school cliques—exclude oil molecules. The nonpolar oil molecules are forced into clusters, surrounded by water molecules that form hydrogen bonds with one another but not with the oil (**Fig. 2-9**). The tendency of oil molecules to clump together in water is

▲ FIGURE 2-9 **Oil and water don't mix** Yellow oil poured into water remains in discrete droplets as it rises to the surface. Oil floats because it is less dense than water.

QUESTION Why is this oil forming droplets?

Water's high specific heat protects sunbathers

▲ FIGURE 2-10 **Water moderates body temperature and cools the body** Because of water's high specific heat, sunbathers can absorb a great deal of heat without their body temperatures skyrocketing. Water vaporizing from perspiration also helps cool their bodies.

QUESTION Why is the skin on these sunbathers beginning to redden? Why is this dangerous?

described as a **hydrophobic interaction.** The membranes of living cells owe much of their structure to both hydrophilic and hydrophobic interactions (discussed in Chapter 5).

Water Moderates the Effects of Temperature Changes

The hydrogen bonds among polar water molecules (see Fig. 2-6) allow water to moderate temperature changes, as described in the sections that follow.

It Takes a Lot of Energy to Heat Water

The energy required to heat 1 gram of a substance by 1°C is called its **specific heat.** Water has a very high specific heat, meaning that it takes more energy to heat water than to heat most other substances. Why?

At any temperature above absolute zero (−459°F or −273°C), the atoms or molecules of a substance are in constant motion because of the heat they contain. More heat produces faster motion. Increasing the temperature of water requires the water molecules to move faster. However, because water molecules are linked by hydrogen bonds, the molecules can only move faster if the hydrogen bonds are broken more often and more rapidly. Breaking hydrogen bonds uses up a considerable amount of heat energy, which is then not available to raise the water's temperature. The same amount of heat energy could raise the temperature of nonpolar substances much more. For example, the energy needed to heat a given weight of water by 1°C would raise the temperature of an equal weight of granite rock by about

5.3°C. The high specific heat of water helps organisms, whose bodies are mostly water, to inhabit hot, sunny environments without overheating as much as they would if their bodies were mostly composed of nonpolar substances (**Fig. 2-10**). Overheating still poses a real threat, however, because the molecules in our bodies function only within a narrow range of temperatures.

It Takes a Lot of Energy to Evaporate Water

Sunbathers are cooled as water evaporates from perspiration on their skin. Water has an extremely high **heat of vaporization,** which is the amount of heat needed to cause a substance to evaporate (to change from a liquid to a vapor). Because of the polar nature of water molecules, water must absorb enough energy to break the hydrogen bonds that interconnect its molecules before the molecules can evaporate into the air. Evaporation has a cooling effect because the fastest-moving (warmest) molecules are those that vaporize, leaving cooler molecules behind.

CASE STUDY c o n t i n u e d

Unstable Atoms Unleashed

The high specific heat of water makes it an ideal coolant for nuclear power plants. Compared to nonpolar liquids like alcohol, a great deal of heat is required to raise the temperature of water. The tsunami that hit the Fukushima power plant disrupted the electrical supply running the pumps that kept water circulating over the fuel rods. Without enough water to absorb the excess heat, the zirconium alloy tubes surrounding the fuel rods melted.

Water Forms an Unusual Solid: Ice

Even solid water is unusual. Most liquids become denser when they solidify, but ice is actually less dense than liquid water. When water freezes, each molecule forms stable hydrogen bonds with four other water molecules, creating an open, hexagonal (six-sided) arrangement. This keeps the water molecules further apart than their average distance in liquid water, so ice is less dense than liquid water (**Fig. 2-11**).

When a pond or lake starts to freeze in winter, the ice floats on top, forming an insulating layer that delays the freezing of the rest of the water. This insulation allows fish and other aquatic animals to survive in the liquid water below (**Fig. 2-12**). If ice were to sink, many ponds and lakes around the world would freeze solid from the bottom up during the winter, killing plants, fish, and other underwater organisms. The ocean floor at higher latitudes would be covered with extremely thick layers of ice that would never melt.

Water-Based Solutions Can Be Acidic, Basic, or Neutral

At any given time, a tiny fraction of water molecules (H_2O) will have split into hydroxide ions (OH^-) and hydrogen ions (H^+) (**Fig. 2-13**). Pure water contains equal concentrations of OH^- and H^+. When ion-forming substances that release OH^- or H^+ are added to water, the solution may no longer have equal concentrations of OH^- and H^+ although it has a neutral charge overall. If the concentration of H^+ exceeds the concentration of OH^-, the solution is **acidic.** An **acid** is a substance that releases hydrogen ions when it dissolves in water. For example, when hydrochloric acid (HCl) is added to pure water, almost all of the HCl molecules separate into H^+ and Cl^-. Therefore, the concentration of H^+ exceeds the concentration of OH^-, and the resulting solution is acidic. Acidic substances—think lemon juice (containing citric acid) or vinegar (acetic acid)—taste sour because sour receptors on your tongue respond to excess H^+. Dental cavities are caused by bacteria that break down trapped food particles and release acid.

If the concentration of OH^- is greater than the concentration of H^+, the solution is **basic.** A **base** is a substance that combines with hydrogen ions, reducing their number. If, for instance, sodium hydroxide (NaOH) is added to water, the NaOH molecules separate into Na^+ and OH^-. Some

▲ FIGURE 2-12 **Ice floats**

OH^- ions combine with H^+ to produce H_2O, reducing the number of H^+ ions and creating a basic solution. Bases are used in many cleaning solutions. They are also in antacids like Tums™ to neutralize heartburn caused by excess hydrochloric acid in the stomach and esophagus.

▲ FIGURE 2-11 **Liquid water (left) and ice (right)**

water (H_2O) hydroxide ion (OH^-) hydrogen ion (H^+)

▲ FIGURE 2-13 **Some water is always ionized**

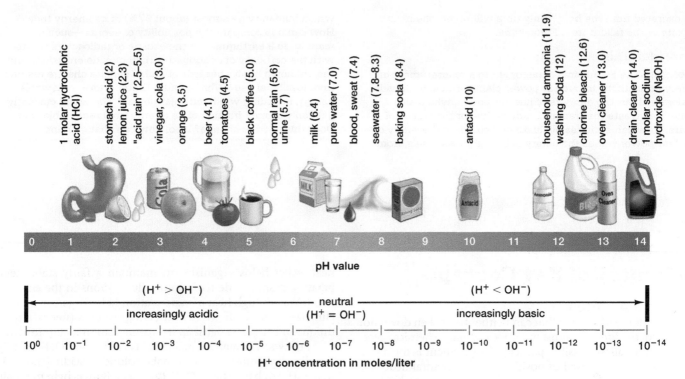

▲ FIGURE 2-14 **The pH scale** The pH scale reflects the concentration of hydrogen ions in a solution. Notice that pH (upper scale; 0–14) is the negative log of the H⁺ concentration (lower scale). Each unit on the scale represents a tenfold change. Lemon juice, for example, is about 10 times more acidic than orange juice, and the most severe acid rain in the northeastern United States is almost 1,000 times more acidic than normal rainfall.

The **pH scale** of 0 to 14 measures how acidic or basic a solution is (**Fig. 2-14**). Neutral pH (equal concentrations of H^+ and OH^-) is 7. Acids have a pH below 7, pure water has a pH of 7, and bases have a pH above 7. Each unit on the pH scale represents a tenfold change in the concentration of H^+. Thus, a soft drink with a pH of 3 has a concentration of H^+ that is 10,000 times that of pure water, which has a pH of 7.

A **buffer** is a type of molecule that tends to maintain a solution at a constant pH by accepting or releasing H^+ in response to small changes in H^+ concentration. In the presence of excess H^+, a buffer combines with the H^+, reducing its concentration. In the presence of excess OH^-, buffers release H^+, which combines with the OH^- to form H_2O. Mammals, including humans, maintain a pH in body fluids that is just slightly basic (pH about 7.4). If your blood became as acidic as 7.0 or as basic as 7.8, you would die because even small changes in pH cause drastic changes in both the structure and function of biological molecules. Nevertheless, living cells seethe with chemical reactions that take up or give off H^+. The pH of the body fluid remains constant because it is controlled by several different buffers.

CHECK YOUR LEARNING

Are you familiar with the unique properties of water and the importance of these properties to life? Can you explain how polar covalent and hydrogen bonds contribute to the unique properties of water? Do you understand how acids, bases, and buffers affect solutions?

CASE STUDY revisited

Unstable Atoms Unleashed

Scientists believe that the isotopes of uranium were forged in the explosion of a star and became incorporated into Earth when our solar system formed. Today the radioactive form of this rare element is mined and concentrated to help satisfy humanity's unquenchable desire for energy.

The chain reaction that generates heat in nuclear power plants begins when neutrons are released from radioactive uranium. These bombard other uranium atoms and cause them to split, in a self-sustaining chain reaction. When the tsunami struck the Fukushima plant, special neutron-absorbing rods were immediately lowered around the fuel, halting the chain reaction. But many of the atoms that result from the breakdown of uranium are also radioactive isotopes, and these continued to spontaneously decay and generate heat. This caused the unstoppable and disastrous rise in temperature and pressure that eventually burst through the containment vessels, releasing these isotopes into the environment. One isotope of particular concern is radioactive iodine (^{131}I).

Iodine enters the body through air and food and is concentrated in the thyroid gland, where it is used to synthesize thyroid hormone. Unfortunately, the thyroid does not distinguish between radioactive and nonradioactive iodine. Children exposed to ^{131}I are at increased risk for thyroid cancer, which may occur decades after exposure. Japanese authorities distributed iodine tablets to children near the failed reactor. This reduces the danger from ^{131}I, because the nonradioactive iodine in the tablets competes with ^{131}I in the thyroid and displaces it, allowing most of it to be excreted from the body. Only time will reveal the health effects of the fallout from Fukushima.

Consider This

BioEthics The Fukushima disaster led to a reassessment of safety precautions in nuclear power plants, and a worldwide dialogue about the dangers of nuclear power, which also generates waste that remains radioactive for thousands of years. How can societies evaluate and compare the safety of nuclear power versus the safety of burning fossil fuels, from which humanity gets most (about 87%) of its energy today? How can one compare the possibility of events—such as a magnitude 9 earthquake or the escape or radioactive waste—with the certainty of continued carbon dioxide emissions and the unknown health hazards of global climate change resulting from fossil fuel use? What about a third option—renewable energy, including wind and solar power? The world currently gets only a small fraction of its energy from renewable sources. Does this need to change? If so, how can change happen?

CHAPTER REVIEW

Summary of Key Concepts

2.1 What Are Atoms?

An element is a substance that can neither be broken down nor converted to different substances by ordinary chemical reactions. The smallest possible particle of an element is the atom, which is itself composed of positive protons, neutral neutrons, and negative electrons. All atoms of a given element have the same unique number of protons. Neutrons cluster with protons in atomic nuclei (except hydrogen), contributing to the mass number of the nucleus. Electrons orbit the nucleus within specific regions called electron shells. Shells at increasing distances from the nucleus contain electrons with increasing amounts of energy. Each shell can contain a fixed maximum number of electrons. An atom is most stable when its outermost shell is full. Isotopes are atoms of the same element with different numbers of neutrons. Some isotopes are radioactive; their nuclei spontaneously break down, forming new elements. This releases energy and often releases subatomic particles.

2.2 How Do Atoms Interact to Form Molecules?

Atoms gain stability by filling or emptying their outer electron shells. They do this by acquiring, losing, or sharing electrons during chemical reactions. This produces attractive forces called chemical bonds, which link atoms, forming molecules.

There are three types of bonds: ionic, covalent, and hydrogen bonds. Atoms that have lost or gained electrons are called ions. Ionic bonds are electrical attractions between negatively and positively charged ions that hold them together in the form of crystals. Covalent bonds form when atoms fill their outer electron shells by sharing electrons. In a nonpolar covalent bond, the two atoms share electrons equally. In a polar covalent bond, one atom attracts the electron more strongly than the other atom does, giving the molecule slightly positive and negative poles. Polar covalent bonds allow hydrogen bonding, the attraction between the slightly positive hydrogen on one molecule and the slightly negative regions of other polar molecules.

2.3 Why Is Water So Important to Life?

Water has many unique properties that allowed life as we know it to evolve. Water is polar and dissolves polar substances and ions. Water forces nonpolar substances, such as oil, to form clumps. Water molecules cohere to each other using hydrogen bonds, producing surface tension. Because of its high specific heat, water helps organisms to maintain a fairly stable temperature despite wide temperature fluctuations in the environment. Water's high heat of vaporization helps organisms in dry climates to cool off while conserving water. Water is almost unique in being less dense in its frozen than in its liquid state.

Pure water contains equal numbers of H^+ and OH^- (pH 7), but dissolved substances can make solutions acidic (more H^+ than OH^-) or basic (more OH^- than H^+). Buffers help maintain a constant pH.

Key Terms

acid 30	hydrophilic 28
acidic 30	hydrophobic 28
antioxidant 26	hydrophobic interaction 29
atom 20	ion 24
atomic nucleus 21	ionic bond 24
atomic number 21	isotope 21
base 30	mass number 21
basic 30	molecule 24
buffer 31	neutron 20
chemical bond 24	nonpolar covalent bond 25
cohesion 27	pH scale 31
covalent bond 24	polar covalent bond 26
dissolve 28	proton 20
electron 20	radioactive 21
electron shell 22	solution 28
element 20	solvent 28
free radical 27	specific heat 29
heat of vaporization 29	surface tension 28
hydrogen bond 27	

Learning Outcomes

In this chapter, you have learned to . . .

LO1 Describe the relationship between elements and atoms.

LO2 Describe the structure of atoms, including identification of the three subatomic particles and the characteristics of each.

LO3 Define isotopes and explain what causes some isotopes to be radioactive and how people may be helped or harmed by radioactivity.

LO4 Explain how atoms form molecules.

LO5 Describe the characteristics of the three types of chemical bonds, and provide examples of molecules in which each type of bond is found.

LO6 Describe the special properties of water and how

these properties allow water to play key roles in life on Earth.

LO7 Explain the pH scale, and describe the properties of acids, bases, and buffers.

Thinking Through the Concepts

Fill-in-the-Blank

1. An atom consists of an atomic nucleus composed of positively charged _____ and uncharged _____. The number of positively charged particles in the nucleus determines the _____ of the element. Orbiting around the nucleus are _____ that occupy confined spaces called _____. **LO2**

2. An atom that has lost or gained one or more electrons is called a(n) _____. If an atom loses an electron it takes on a(n) _____ charge. If it gains an electron it takes on a(n) _____ charge. Atoms with opposite charges attract one another, forming _____ bonds. **LO5**

3. Atoms of the same element that differ in the number of neutrons in their nuclei are called _____ of one another. Some of these forms of atoms spontaneously break apart, releasing _____ particles that carry large amounts of _____. In the process, they may become different _____. Atoms that behave this way are described as being _____. **LO3**

4. An atom with an outermost electron shell that is either completely full or completely empty is described as _____. Atoms with partially full outer electron shells are _____. Covalent bonds are formed when atoms _____ electrons, filling their outer shells. **LO4 LO5**

5. Water is described as _____ because each water molecule has slightly negative and positive poles. This property allows water molecules to form _____ bonds with one another. The bonds between water molecules give water a high _____ that produces surface tension. **LO6**

Review Questions

1. Based on Table 2-1 how many neutrons are there in oxygen? In hydrogen? In nitrogen? **LO2**

2. Distinguish between atoms and molecules; between elements and compounds; and among protons, neutrons, and electrons. **LO1 LO2 LO4**

3. Define *isotopes* and describe the properties of radioactive isotopes. **LO3**

4. Compare and contrast covalent bonds and ionic bonds. **LO5**

5. Explain how polar covalent bonds allow hydrogen bonds to form, and provide an example. **LO5 LO6**

6. Why can water absorb a great amount of heat with little increase in its temperature? What is this property of water called? **LO6**

7. Describe how water dissolves a salt. **LO5 LO6**

8. Define *pH scale, acid, base,* and *buffer.* How do buffers reduce changes in pH when hydrogen ions or hydroxide ions are added to a solution? Why is this phenomenon important in organisms? **LO7**

Applying the Concepts

1. Detergents and soaps help clean by dispersing fats and oils in water so that they can be rinsed away. From your knowledge of the structure of water and the hydrophobic nature of fats, what general chemical structures (for example, polar or nonpolar parts) must a soap or detergent have, and why?

2. What do people mean when they say: "It's not the heat, it's the humidity"? What disadvantages would there be to sweating if water had a lower heat of vaporization?

Answers to Figure Caption questions and Fill-in-the-Blank questions can be found in the Answers section at the back of the book.

(MB) Go to MasteringBiology for practice quizzes, activities, eText, videos, current events, and more.

Friends don't eat friends. Mad cow disease emerged as a result of feeding cows chow made with protein from sheep, some of whom were infected with scrapie.

CASE STUDY
Puzzling Proteins

"YOU KNOW, LISA, I think something is wrong with me," Charlene Singh told her sister. It was 2001 when the vibrant, 22-year-old scholarship winner began to lose her memory and experience mood swings. During the next 3 years, her symptoms worsened. Singh's hands shook, she was subject to uncontrollable episodes of biting and striking people, and she became unable to walk or swallow. In June 2004, Charlene Singh became the first U.S. resident to die of the human form of mad cow disease, which she had almost certainly contracted more than 10 years earlier while living in England.

It was not until the mid-1990s that health officials recognized that mad cow disease, or bovine spongiform encephalitis (BSE), could spread to people who ate meat from infected cattle. Although millions of people may have eaten this tainted beef, fewer than 200 people worldwide have died from the human version of BSE, called variant Creutzfeldt-Jakob disease (vCJD). For those infected, however, the disease is always fatal, riddling the brains of both humans with vCJD and cows with BSE with microscopic holes, giving the brain a spongy appearance.

Where did mad cow disease come from? For centuries, it has been known that sheep can suffer from scrapie, a disease that causes similar symptoms. A leading hypothesis is that a mutated form of scrapie became capable of infecting cattle, perhaps in the early 1980s. At that time, cattle feed was often formulated with sheep parts, some of which may have harbored scrapie. BSE was first identified in British cattle in 1986, and sheep parts were banned from cattle feed in 1988. However, it was 1996 before beef exports from Britain were banned, when experts confirmed that the disease could spread to people through consumption of infected meat. As a precautionary measure at that time, more than 4.5 million cattle in Britain were slaughtered and their bodies were burned.

Why is mad cow disease particularly fascinating to scientists? In the early 1980s, Dr. Stanley Prusiner, a researcher at the University of California–San Francisco, startled the scientific world by providing evidence that a protein, which lacks genetic material (DNA or RNA), was the cause of scrapie, and that this protein could transmit the disease to experimental animals in the laboratory. He dubbed the infectious proteins "prions" (pronounced PREE-ons).

What are proteins? How do they differ from DNA and RNA? How can a protein with no hereditary material infect another organism, increase in number, and produce a fatal disease? Is vCJD still a threat? Read on to find out.

AT A GLANCE

LEARNING GOALS

LG1 Explain why carbon is important in biological molecules.

LG2 Describe dehydration synthesis and hydrolysis and explain the roles they play in forming and breaking down large biological molecules.

LG3 Describe the molecular structure, physical properties, and biological functions of the major groups of carbohydrates and include examples of each.

LG4 Describe the molecular structure, physical properties, and biological functions of the major groups of lipids and include examples of each.

LG5 Describe protein subunits and how they are joined to form proteins.

LG6 Describe the four levels of protein structure and discuss how protein structure relates to the six major functions of proteins.

LG7 Describe the molecular structure, physical properties, and biological functions of the major types of nucleotides and nucleic acids and include examples of each.

3.1 WHY IS CARBON SO IMPORTANT IN BIOLOGICAL MOLECULES?

You have probably seen fruits and vegetables grown without synthetic fertilizers or pesticides labeled as "organic." But in chemistry, the word **organic** describes molecules that have a carbon backbone bonded to hydrogen atoms. The term is derived from the ability of organisms to synthesize and use this general type of molecule. **Inorganic** molecules lack carbon atoms (examples are water and salt) or lack hydrogen atoms (carbon dioxide). Inorganic molecules are far less diverse and generally much simpler than organic molecules.

Life is characterized by an amazing variety of molecules interacting in ways that are dazzlingly complex. Interactions among molecules are governed by their structures and the chemical properties that arise from these structures. As molecules within cells interact with one another, their structures and chemical properties change. Collectively, these precisely orchestrated changes give cells the ability to acquire and use nutrients, to eliminate wastes, to move and grow, and to reproduce. As we explain below, this complexity is made possible by the versatile carbon atom.

The Unique Bonding Properties of Carbon Are Key to the Complexity of Organic Molecules

Atoms are unstable when their outermost electron shells are only partially filled (as described earlier in Chapter 2). Atoms in this state react with one another, and in so doing gain stability by sharing electrons to fill their outer shells, forming covalent bonds. Depending on the number of vacancies in their shells, two atoms can share two, four, or six electrons—forming a single, double, or triple covalent bond. The bonding patterns in the four most common types of atoms found in biological molecules

▲ **FIGURE 3-1 Bonding patterns** The bonding patterns of the four most common atoms in biological molecules. A single line indicates a single covalent bond (two shared electrons) with another atom. Two parallel lines indicate a double covalent bond (four shared electrons), and three parallel lines indicate a triple covalent bond (six shared electrons) between the atom shown and another atom.

are shown in **Figure 3-1**. The versatile carbon atom is the key to the tremendous variety of organic molecules that make life on Earth possible. The carbon atom has four electrons in its outermost shell, which can accommodate eight electrons. Therefore, a carbon atom can become stable by bonding with up to four other atoms or with fewer atoms by forming double or even triple bonds. As a result, organic molecules can assume complex shapes, including branched chains, rings, sheets, and helices.

Attached to the carbon backbone of organic molecules are **functional groups,** which are commonly occurring combinations of atoms; seven important examples are shown in **Table 3-1**. Functional groups are less stable than the carbon backbone and more likely to participate in chemical reactions, and so they are mainly responsible for the properties and chemical reactivity of organic molecules.

CHECK YOUR LEARNING

Can you define *organic* and explain why carbon is so important to life? Can you name and describe the properties of several functional groups and explain why functional groups are important in biological molecules?

TABLE 3-1   Important Functional Groups in Biological Molecules

Group	Structure	Properties	Found In
Hydroxyl	—O—H	Polar; involved in dehydration and hydrolysis reactions; forms hydrogen bonds	Sugars, polysaccharides, nucleic acids, alcohols, some amino acids, steroids
Carbonyl	$\overset{O}{\underset{}{\parallel}}$ C	Polar; makes parts of molecules hydrophilic (water soluble)	Sugars (linear forms), steroid hormones, some vitamins
Carboxyl (ionized form)	$\overset{O}{\underset{O^-}{}}$ C	Polar and acidic; the negatively charged oxygen may bond H^+, forming carboxylic acid (–COOH); involved in peptide bonds	Amino acids, fatty acids, carboxylic acids (such as acetic and citric acids)
Amino	$\overset{H}{\underset{H}{}}$ N	Polar and basic; may become ionized by binding a third H^+; involved in peptide bonds	Amino acids, nucleic acids, some hormones
Sulfhydryl	—S—H	Nonpolar; forms disulfide bonds in proteins	Cysteine (an amino acid); many proteins
Phosphate (ionized form)	$\overset{O}{\underset{O^-}{O—P—O^-}}$	Polar and acidic; links nucleotides in nucleic acids; forms high-energy bonds in ATP (ionized form occurs in cells)	Phospholipids, nucleotides, nucleic acids
Methyl	$\overset{H}{\underset{H}{H—C}}$	Nonpolar; may be attached to nucleotides in DNA (methylation), changing gene expression	Steroids, methylated nucleotides in DNA

3.2 HOW ARE ORGANIC MOLECULES SYNTHESIZED?

Although a complex molecule could be made by laboriously attaching one atom after another, the machinery of life works far more efficiently by preassembling molecular subunits and hooking them together. Just as trains are made by joining a series of train cars, small organic molecules (for example, sugars or amino acids) are joined to form longer molecules (for example, starches or proteins). The individual subunits are called **monomers** ("mono" means "one"); chains of monomers are called **polymers** ("poly" means "many").

Biological Polymers Are Formed by Removing Water and Split Apart by Adding Water

The subunits of large biological molecules are usually joined by a chemical reaction called **dehydration synthesis.** In dehydration synthesis, a hydrogen ion (H^+) is removed from one subunit and a hydroxyl ion (OH^-) is removed from a second subunit, leaving openings in the outer electron shells of atoms in the two subunits. These openings are filled when the subunits share electrons, creating a covalent bond that links them. The hydrogen ion and the hydroxyl ion combine

▲ FIGURE 3-2 **Dehydration synthesis**

to form a molecule of water (H_2O), as shown in **Figure 3-2.** This explains the literal translation of dehydration synthesis: "removing water to put together."

The reverse reaction is hydrolysis ("hydro" means "water" and "lysis" means "to break apart"). **Hydrolysis** breaks apart the molecule into its original subunits, with water donating a hydrogen ion to one subunit and a hydroxyl ion to the other (**Fig. 3-3**). Digestive enzymes use hydrolysis to

▲ FIGURE 3-3 **Hydrolysis**

TABLE 3-2   Principal Types of Biological Molecules

Type and Structure of Molecule	Principal Subtypes and Structures	Examples
Carbohydrate: primarily carbon, oxygen, and hydrogen, in the approximate formula $(CH_2O)_{n*}$	*Monosaccharide:* Simple sugar, often with the formula $C_6H_{12}O_6$	Glucose, fructose, galactose
	Disaccharide: Two monosaccharides bonded together	Sucrose
	Polysaccharide: Chain of monosaccharides (usually glucose)	Starch, glycogen, cellulose
Lipid: Contains a high proportion of carbon and hydrogen; most lipids are nonpolar and insoluble in water	*Triglyceride:* three fatty acids bonded to glycerol	Oil, fat
	Wax: Variable numbers of fatty acids bonded to a long-chain alcohol	Wax in plant cuticle
	Phospholipid: Polar phosphate group and two fatty acids bonded to glycerol	Phospholipids in cell membranes
	Steroid: Four fused rings of carbon atoms with functional groups attached	Cholesterol, estrogen, testosterone
Protein: Consists of one or more chains of amino acids; may have up to four levels of structure that determine its function	*Peptide:* Short chain of amino acids	Oxytocin
	Polypeptide: Long chain of amino acids	Hemoglobin, keratin
Nucleotide/Nucleic acid:	*Nucleotide:* Composed of a five-carbon sugar (ribose or deoxyribose), a nitrogen-containing base, and a phosphate group	Adenosine triphosphate (ATP), cyclic adenosine monophosphate (cAMP)
	Nucleic acid: A polymer of nucleotide subunits joined by covalent bonds between their phosphate and sugar groups	Deoxyribonucleic acid (DNA), ribonucleic acid (RNA)

*n signifies the number of carbons in the molecule's backbone.

break down food. For example, the starch in a cracker consists of a series of glucose (simple sugar) molecules (see Fig. 3-8). Enzymes in our saliva and small intestines promote hydrolysis of the starch into individual sugar molecules that can be absorbed into the body.

Although there is a tremendous diversity of biological molecules, most fall into one of four general categories: carbohydrates, lipids, proteins, and nucleotides/nucleic acids (**Table 3-2**).

CHECK YOUR LEARNING

Can you name and describe the reactions that create biological polymers?

3.3 WHAT ARE CARBOHYDRATES?

Carbohydrate molecules are composed of carbon, hydrogen, and oxygen in the approximate ratio of 1:2:1. This ratio explains the origin of the word "carbohydrate," which literally translates to "carbon plus water." All carbohydrates are either small, water-soluble **sugars** or polymers of sugar, such as starch. If a carbohydrate consists of just one sugar molecule, it is called a **monosaccharide** ("saccharide" means "sugar"). When two monosaccharides are linked, they form a **disaccharide** ("di" means "two"). Both mono- and disaccharides are called sugars. If you've stirred sugar into coffee, you know that sugar dissolves in water; it is hydrophilic

("water loving"). This is because the hydroxyl functional groups of sugars are polar and form hydrogen bonds with polar water molecules (**Fig. 3-4**).

A polymer of many monosaccharides is called a **polysaccharide.** Most polysaccharides do not dissolve in water at body temperatures. Starches are polysaccharides that serve as energy storage molecules in cells. Other polysaccharides strengthen the cell walls of plants, fungi, and bacteria, or form a supportive armor over the bodies of insects, crabs, and their relatives.

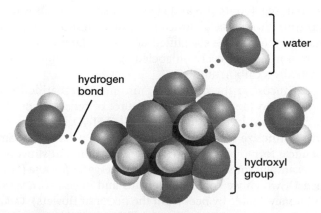

▲ FIGURE 3-4 **Sugar dissolving in water** Glucose dissolves as the polar hydroxyl groups of each sugar molecule form hydrogen bonds with nearby water molecules.

$C_6H_{12}O_6$

(a) Chemical formula

(b) Linear, ball and stick

(c) Ring, ball and stick

(d) Ring, simplified

▲ FIGURE 3-5 **Depictions of glucose structure**
Chemists draw the same molecule in different ways. **(a)** The chemical formula for glucose; **(b)** the linear form, which occurs when glucose is in its crystal state; **(c, d)** two depictions of the ring form of glucose, which forms when glucose dissolves in water. In (d), each unlabeled joint is a carbon atom; the carbons are numbered for easy reference. Figure 3-4 depicts the space-filling ring structure of glucose.

There Are Several Monosaccharides with Slightly Different Structures

Monosaccharides have a backbone of three to seven carbon atoms. Most of these carbon atoms have both a hydrogen (–H) and a hydroxyl group (–OH) attached to them; therefore, carbohydrates generally have the approximate chemical formula $(CH_2O)_n$, where n is the number of carbons in the backbone. When a sugar molecule is dissolved in water, such as inside a cell, its carbon backbone usually forms a ring. **Figure 3-5** and Figure 3-4 show various ways of depicting the chemical structure of the common sugar **glucose.** When you see simplified depictions later in this text, keep in mind that every unlabeled "joint" in a ring or chain is actually a carbon atom.

Glucose is the most common monosaccharide in organisms and the primary energy source of cells. Glucose has six carbons, so its chemical formula is $C_6H_{12}O_6$. Many organisms synthesize other monosaccharides that have the same chemical formula as glucose but slightly different structures. For example, some plants may store energy in *fructose* ("fruit sugar"), which we consume in fruits and juices, corn syrup, and honey (made by bees from the nectar of flowers). *Galactose* (part of lactose, or "milk sugar") is secreted by mammals in their milk as an energy source for their young (**Fig. 3-6**).

fructose   galactose

▲ FIGURE 3-6 **Some six-carbon monosaccharides**

Fructose and galactose must be converted to glucose before cells can use them as a source of energy.

Other common monosaccharides, such as ribose and deoxyribose (found in the nucleic acids of RNA and DNA, respectively), have five carbons. Notice in **Figure 3-7** that deoxyribose ("deoxy" means "without oxygen") has one fewer oxygen atom than ribose because one of the hydroxyl groups in ribose is replaced by a hydrogen atom in deoxyribose.

Disaccharides Consist of Two Monosaccharides Linked by Dehydration Synthesis

Monosaccharides can be linked by dehydration synthesis to form disaccharides or polysaccharides (**Fig. 3-8**). Disaccharides are often used for short-term energy storage, especially in plants. When energy is required, the disaccharides are broken apart by hydrolysis into their monosaccharide subunits (see Fig. 3-3) and converted to glucose, which is broken down further to release energy stored in its chemical bonds. Perhaps you had toast and coffee with cream and sugar at breakfast. You stirred *sucrose* (glucose plus fructose, an energy storage molecule in sugarcane and sugar beets) into your coffee, and added cream containing *lactose* (glucose plus galactose). The disaccharide *maltose* (glucose plus glucose) is rare in nature, but it is formed when enzymes in your digestive tract hydrolyze starch, such as the starch in your toast. Other digestive enzymes then hydrolyze each maltose into two glucose molecules that cells can absorb and break down to liberate energy.

If you are on a diet, you may have used an artificial sugar substitute in your coffee. These interesting molecules are described in "Links to Everyday Life: Fake Foods."

ribose   deoxyribose

Note "missing" oxygen atom

▲ FIGURE 3-7 **Some five-carbon monosaccharides**

glucose   fructose   sucrose

CH_2OH CH_2OH

$HOCH_2$ $HOCH_2$

dehydration
synthesis

CH_2OH CH_2OH

$H O H$

▲ FIGURE 3-8 **Synthesis of a disaccharide** Sucrose is synthesized by a dehydration reaction in which a hydrogen is removed from glucose and a hydroxyl group is removed from fructose. This forms a water molecule and leaves the two monosaccharide rings joined by single bonds to the remaining oxygen atom.

QUESTION Describe hydrolysis of this molecule.

Polysaccharides Are Chains of Monosaccharides

If you take a bite of bagel and chew on it for a few minutes, do you notice that it gradually tastes sweeter? This is because enzymes in saliva cause hydrolysis of the **starch** (a polysaccharide) in a bagel into its component glucose molecules (monosaccharides), which taste sweet. Plants often use starch (Fig. 3-9) as an energy-storage molecule. Animals commonly store **glycogen,** a similar polysaccharide. Both starch and glycogen are polymers of glucose molecules.

Starch, which is commonly formed in roots and seeds, consists of branched chains of up to half a million glucose subunits. Glycogen, stored in the liver and muscles of animals (including people), is also a chain of glucose subunits, but is more highly branched than starch.

Many organisms use polysaccharides as structural materials. One of the most important structural polysaccharides is **cellulose,** which makes up most of the walls of the living cells of plants, the fluffy white bolls of cotton plants, and about half the bulk of tree trunks (Fig. 3-10). Scientists estimate that

⟫ LINKS TO EVERYDAY LIFE

Fake Foods

In societies blessed with an overabundance of food, obesity is a serious health problem. To address this problem, food scientists have modified biological molecules to make them noncaloric. Thus, we can now purchase foods or beverages made with artificial sweeteners or the artificial oil olestra (Fig. E3-1). How are these "nonbiological food molecules" made?

The sweetener sucralose is a modified sucrose molecule in which three hydroxyl groups are replaced with chlorine atoms. Sucralose tastes about 600 times as sweet as table sugar (sucrose) and provides no calories because we can't digest it. Aspartame, a combination of two amino acids (aspartic acid and phenylalanine; see Fig. 3-19a, b), tastes 200 times as sweet as sugar. Although both sweeteners have been tested extensively and found safe by the Food and Drug Administration (FDA), people with the rare genetic disorder phenylketonuria cannot break down phenylalanine and should avoid aspartame.

The artificial oil olestra tastes and feels similar to oil, and has been approved by the FDA for use in snack foods like potato chips. The olestra molecule is based on sucrose, with six to eight fatty acids attached to its carbon atoms. The fatty acid chains—which extend outward from the sucrose molecule like the arms of an octopus—prevent digestive enzymes from breaking it down. Because fat-soluble vitamins (A, D, E, and K) dissolve in olestra, foods containing olestra are supplemented with small amounts of these vitamins to compensate for those

lost as olestra moves through the digestive tract. Olestra also interferes with the absorption of carotenoids, which give fruits and vegetables their red, orange, and yellow colors and are widely believed to be part of a healthy diet. This is a possible drawback to eating olestra frequently.

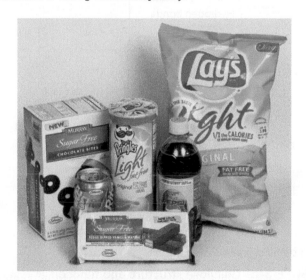

▲ FIGURE E3-1 **Artificial foods** Artificial sweeteners and olestra are marketed to people trying to control their weight.

(a) Potato cells

(b) A starch molecule

(c) Detail of a starch molecule

▲ **FIGURE 3-9 Starch structure and function (a)** Starch grains inside potato cells store energy that will allow the potato to generate new plants in the spring. **(b)** A section of a single starch molecule. Starches consist of branched chains of up to half a million glucose subunits. **(c)** The precise structure of the circled portion of the starch molecule in (b). Notice the linkage between the individual glucose subunits for comparison with cellulose (Fig. 3-10).

(a) Cellulose is a major component of wood

(b) A plant cell with a cell wall

(c) A close-up of cellulose fibers in a cell wall

Hydrogen bonds cross-linking cellulose molecules

bundle of cellulose molecules

cellulose fiber

Alternating bond configuration differs from starch

(d) Detail of a cellulose molecule

▲ **FIGURE 3-10 Cellulose structure and function (a)** Wood in this 3,000-year-old bristlecone pine is primarily cellulose. **(b)** Cellulose forms the cell wall that surrounds each plant cell. **(c)** Plant cell walls often consist of cellulose fibers in layers that run at right angles to each other to resist tearing in both directions. **(d)** Cellulose is composed of up to 10,000 glucose subunits. Compare this structure with Figure 3-9c and notice that every other glucose molecule in cellulose is "upside down."

▲ FIGURE 3-11 **Chitin structure and function** Chitin has the same glucose bonding configuration as cellulose does. In chitin, however, the glucose subunits have a nitrogen-containing functional group (green) replacing one of the hydroxyl groups. Tough, flexible chitin supports the otherwise soft bodies of arthropods (such as the spider in the photograph, insects, crabs, and their relatives) and most fungi.

plants synthesize about a trillion tons of cellulose each year, making it the most abundant organic molecule on Earth.

Cellulose, like starch, is a polymer of glucose, but in cellulose, every other glucose is "upside down" as you will see when you compare Figure 3-9c with Figure 3-10d. Although most animals easily digest starch, no vertebrates synthesize an enzyme that can attack the bonds between glucose molecules in cellulose. A few animals, such as cows and termites, harbor cellulose-digesting microbes in their digestive tracts and can benefit from the glucose subunits the microbes release. In humans, cellulose fibers pass intact through the digestive system, supplying no nutrients but providing the "roughage" that helps prevent constipation.

The supportive outer coverings (exoskeletons) of insects, crabs, and spiders are made of **chitin,** a polysaccharide in which the glucose subunits bear a nitrogen-containing functional group (**Fig. 3-11**). Chitin also stiffens the cell walls of many fungi, including mushrooms.

Carbohydrates may also form parts of larger molecules; for example, the plasma membrane that surrounds each cell is studded with proteins to which carbohydrates are attached. Nucleic acids (discussed later) also contain sugar molecules.

CHECK YOUR LEARNING

Can you describe the major classes of carbohydrates and provide examples of each type and how organisms use them?

3.4 WHAT ARE LIPIDS?

Lipids are a diverse group of molecules that contain regions composed almost entirely of hydrogen and carbon, with nonpolar carbon–carbon and carbon–hydrogen bonds. These nonpolar regions make lipids insoluble in water, or hydrophobic ("water fearing"). Some lipids are used to store energy, some form waterproof coverings on plant or animal bodies, some serve as the primary component of cellular membranes, and still others are hormones. Lipids fall into three major groups: (1) oils, fats, and waxes; (2) phospholipids; and (3) steroids.

Oils, Fats, and Waxes Are Lipids Containing Only Carbon, Hydrogen, and Oxygen

Oils, fats, and waxes are built from only three types of atoms: carbon, hydrogen, and oxygen. Each contains one or more **fatty acid** subunits, which are long chains of carbon and hydrogen with a carboxylic acid group (−COOH) at one end. Fats and oils are formed by dehydration synthesis linking three fatty acid subunits to one molecule of *glycerol*, a three-carbon molecule (**Fig. 3-12**). This structure gives fats and oils their chemical name: **triglycerides.**

▲ FIGURE 3-12 **Synthesis of a triglyceride** Dehydration synthesis links a single glycerol molecule with three fatty acids to form a triglyceride and three water molecules.

QUESTION What kind of reaction breaks this molecule apart?

(a) Fat

(b) Wax

▲ FIGURE 3-13 **Lipids in nature** (a) A fat grizzly bear ready to hibernate. If this bear stored the same amount of energy in carbohydrates instead of fat, he probably would be unable to walk. **(b)** Wax is a highly saturated lipid that remains very firm at normal outdoor temperatures. Its rigidity allows it to be used to form the strong but thin-walled hexagons of this honeycomb.

Fats and **oils** are used primarily as energy-storage molecules; they contain more than twice as many calories per gram as do carbohydrates and proteins (9 Cal/gram for fats; 4 Cal/gram for carbohydrates and proteins). For example, the bear in **Figure 3-13a** has accumulated enough fat to last him through his winter hibernation. To avoid accumulating excess fat, some people turn to foods manufactured with fat substitutes such as olestra, as described earlier in "Links to Everyday Life: Fake Foods."

Fats (such as butter and lard) are produced primarily by animals, whereas oils (such as corn, canola, and soybean oil) are found primarily in the seeds of plants. The difference between a fat, which is solid at room temperature, and an oil, which is liquid at room temperature, lies in the structure of their fatty acid subunits. In fats, the carbons of fatty acids are joined by single bonds, with hydrogen atoms at all the other bonding sites. Such fatty acids are described as **saturated,** because they contain as many hydrogen atoms as possible. Saturated fatty acid chains are straight and can pack closely together, thus forming a solid at room temperature (**Fig. 3-14a**).

If there are double bonds between some of the carbons, and consequently fewer hydrogens, the fatty acid is **unsaturated.** The double bonds in the unsaturated fatty acids of oils produce kinks in the fatty acid chains (**Fig. 3-14b**). Oils are liquid at room temperature because these kinks prevent oil molecules from packing closely together. The commercial process of hydrogenation—which breaks some of the double bonds and adds hydrogens to the carbons—can convert liquid oils to solids, but with health consequences (see "Health Watch: Cholesterol, Trans Fats, and Your Heart").

Although **waxes** are chemically similar to fats, humans and most other animals do not have the appropriate enzymes to break them down. Waxes are highly saturated and therefore solid at normal outdoor temperatures. Waxes form a waterproof coating over the leaves and stems of land

(a) A fat

(b) An oil

▲ FIGURE 3-14 **Fats and oils** (a) Fats have straight chains of carbon atoms in their fatty acid tails. **(b)** The fatty acid tails of oils have double bonds between some of their carbon atoms, creating kinks in the chains. Oils are liquid at room temperature because their kinky tails keep the molecules farther apart.

plants. Animals synthesize waxes as waterproofing for mammalian fur and insect exoskeletons. Honey bees use waxes to build elaborate honeycomb structures where they store honey and lay their eggs (**Fig. 3-13b**).

Health|Watch

Cholesterol, Trans Fats, and Your Heart

Why are so many foods advertised as "cholesterol free" or "low in cholesterol"? Although cholesterol is crucial to life, people with high levels of certain forms of cholesterol-containing particles in their blood are at increased risk for heart attacks and strokes. These particles, often called "bad cholesterol," can cause obstructions called *plaques* to form in arteries (Fig. E3-2). Plaques, in turn, may stimulate the formation of blood clots. If a clot breaks loose and blocks an artery supplying blood to the heart muscle or brain, it can cause a heart attack or a stroke. What makes cholesterol turn bad?

▲ FIGURE E3-2 **Plaque** A plaque deposit (rippled structure) partially blocks this carotid artery.

Cholesterol molecules are nonpolar, so they are transported in the blood (which is mostly water) surrounded by polar carrier molecules consisting of phospholipids and proteins. These particles are called *lipoprotein* (lipid plus protein) and they differ considerably in the percentage of cholesterol and protein they contain. Those with less cholesterol and more protein are described as *high-density lipoprotein* (HDL), because protein is denser than lipid. HDL is the good guy, because HDL transports excess cholesterol from cells to the liver, where the cholesterol is metabolized (used in bile synthesis, for example), and to organs that use it to produce steroid hormones. The particles with more lipids and less protein are *low-density lipoprotein* (LDL). These particles are carried in the blood from the liver, where most cholesterol is synthesized, to cells where cholesterol is stored or used to produce cell membranes. When there is excess LDL, it becomes the bad guy, entering cells in the artery walls, where it can build up and stimulate plaque formation.

Our diet provides only about 15% to 20% of the cholesterol in our blood, and this comes from animal-derived foods such egg yolks, sausages, bacon, whole milk, and butter. Genetic differences cause some people to regulate their LDL cholesterol at safe levels regardless of diet and others to produce far more LDL cholesterol than they need, even on a low-cholesterol diet. Saturated fats (such as those in red meat and whole-milk products) stimulate the liver to churn out more LDL cholesterol. Diets in which unsaturated fats (found in fish, nuts, and most vegetable oils) replace saturated fats and carbohydrates are associated with a decreased risk of heart disease. Lifestyle also contributes; exercise tends to increase HDL, whereas obesity and smoking increase LDL cholesterol levels. A high ratio of LDL to HDL is correlated with an increased risk of heart disease.

The worst fats are **trans fats,** which are made artificially when hydrogen atoms are added to oils to make them solid at room temperature. This process alters the attachment points of hydrogen near the remaining double bonds, causing the kinky tails of oil to straighten. Trans fats are not metabolized in the same way as naturally occurring fats; for unknown reasons they actually decrease HDL while increasing LDL, and they are likely to place consumers at a higher risk of heart disease.

Until recently, artificially produced trans fats were abundant in commercial food products such as margarine, cookies, crackers, and French fries, because they extended the shelf life and helped retain the flavor of packaged products. Since January 2006, the FDA has required food labels to list the trans fat content, but a loophole allows up to 0.5 gram per serving to be labeled "no trans fat" in products that contain partially hydrogenated oil or vegetable shortening. Fortunately, most food manufacturers and fast-food chains are reducing or eliminating trans fats from their products.

Phospholipids Have Water-Soluble "Heads" and Water-Insoluble "Tails"

The plasma membrane that surrounds each cell contains several types of **phospholipids.** A phospholipid is similar to an oil, except that one of the three fatty acids is replaced by a phosphate group attached to any of several polar functional groups that typically contain nitrogen (Fig. 3-15). A phospholipid has two dissimilar ends. At one end are the two nonpolar fatty acid "tails," which are insoluble in water. At the other end is the phosphate–nitrogen "head" that is polar and water soluble. (These properties of phospholipids are crucial to the structure and function of cell membranes; see Chapter 5.)

Steroids Contain Four Fused Carbon Rings

All **steroids** are composed of four rings of carbon atoms. As shown in **Figure 3-16**, the rings share one or more sides, with various functional groups protruding from them. One steroid, *cholesterol,* is a vital component of the membranes of animal cells (Fig. 3-16a). It makes up about 2% of the human brain, where it is an important component of the lipid-rich membranes that insulate nerve cells. Cholesterol is also used by cells to synthesize other steroids, such as the female and male sex hormones *estrogen* and *testosterone* (Figs. 3-16b, c). Too much of the wrong form of cholesterol can contribute to cardiovascular disease, as explained in "Health Watch: Cholesterol, Trans Fats, and Your Heart."

variable
functional phosphate
group   group

polar head   glycerol   fatty acid tails
                backbone
(hydrophilic)   (hydrophobic)

▲ FIGURE 3-15 **Phospholipids** Phospholipids have two hydrophobic fatty acid tails attached to the glycerol backbone. The third (here, the upper) position on glycerol is occupied by a polar "head" consisting of a phosphate group to which a second (usually nitrogen-containing) variable functional group is attached. The phosphate group bears a negative charge, and the nitrogen-containing functional group bears a positive charge, making the head hydrophilic.

(a) Cholesterol   **(b) Estrogen**   **(c) Testosterone**

▲ FIGURE 3-16 **Steroids** All steroids have a similar, nonpolar molecular structure with four fused carbon rings. Differences in steroid function result from differences in functional groups attached to the rings. **(a)** Cholesterol, the molecule from which other steroids are synthesized; **(b)** the female sex hormone, estrogen (estradiol); **(c)** the male sex hormone, testosterone. Note the similarities in structure between the sex hormones.

QUESTION Why are steroid hormones able to diffuse through cell membranes to exert their effects?

CHECK YOUR LEARNING

Can you compare and contrast the structure and synthesis of fats and oils? Can you describe the functions of fats, oils, and waxes? Do you recall two reasons why cholesterol is important in the body?

3.5 WHAT ARE PROTEINS?

Proteins are molecules composed of chains of amino acids. Scientists estimate that the human body has about 100,000 different types of proteins that play important and diverse roles (**Table 3-3**). Most cells contain hundreds of different **enzymes,** which are proteins that promote

TABLE 3-3	Functions of Proteins
Function	Examples
Structural	Keratin (forms hair, nails, scales, feathers, and horns); silk (forms webs and cocoons)
Movement	Actin and myosin (found in muscle cells; allow contraction)
Defense	Antibodies (found in the bloodstream; fight disease organisms, some neutralize venoms); venoms (found in venomous animals; deter predators and disable prey)
Storage	Albumin (in egg white; provides nutrition for an embryo)
Signaling	Insulin (secreted by the pancreas; promotes glucose uptake into cells)
Catalyzing reactions	Amylase (found in saliva and the small intestine; digests carbohydrates)

specific chemical reactions. Other proteins are structural. Keratin, for example, forms hair, horns, nails, scales, and feathers (**Fig. 3-17**). Silk proteins are secreted by silk moths and spiders to make cocoons and webs. Nutritional proteins, such as albumin in egg white and casein in milk, provide amino acids to developing animals. The protein hemoglobin transports oxygen in the blood. Actin and myosin in muscle are contractile proteins that allow animal bodies to move. Some proteins are hormones (insulin and growth hormone, for example), others are antibodies (which help fight disease and infection), and a few are toxins (such as rattlesnake venom).

Proteins Are Formed from Chains of Amino Acids

Proteins are polymers of **amino acids** joined by peptide bonds. All amino acids have the same fundamental structure: a central carbon bonded to a hydrogen atom, a

(a) Hair

(b) Horn

(c) Silk

▲ FIGURE 3-17 **Structural proteins** Keratin is a common structural protein. It is the predominant protein found in **(a)** hair, **(b)** horn, and **(c)** the silk of a spider web.

variable group (R)

amino group

carboxylic acid group

hydrogen

▲ FIGURE 3-18 **Amino acid structure**

nitrogen-containing amino group (–NH$_2$), a carboxylic acid group (–COOH), and an "R" group that varies among different amino acids (Fig. 3-18).

Twenty amino acids are commonly found in the proteins of organisms. The R group gives each amino acid distinctive properties (Fig. 3-19). Some amino acids are hydrophilic and water soluble because their R groups are polar. Others are hydrophobic, with nonpolar R groups that are insoluble in water. The amino acid cysteine (Fig. 3-19c) has a sulfur-containing (sulfhydryl) R group that can form covalent **disulfide bonds** with the sulfur of another cysteine molecule. Disulfide bonds play important roles in proteins, as described later.

Amino Acids Are Joined by Dehydration Synthesis

Proteins are formed by dehydration synthesis, as are polysaccharides and lipids. In proteins, the nitrogen in the amino group (–NH$_2$) of one amino acid is joined to the carbon in the carboxylic acid group (–COOH) of another amino acid by a single covalent bond, and water is liberated (Fig. 3-20). This bond is called a **peptide bond,** and the resulting chain of two amino acids is called a **peptide,** a term used for relatively short chains of amino acids (up to 50 or so). Additional amino acids are added, one by one, until a long *polypeptide* chain is completed. Polypeptide chains in cells can range up to thousands of amino acids in length. A protein consists of one or more polypeptide chains.

A Protein Can Have As Many As Four Levels of Structure

Interactions among amino acid R groups cause twists, folds, and interconnections that give proteins their three-dimensional structure. Up to four organized levels of protein structure are possible: primary, secondary, tertiary, and quaternary (Fig. 3-21). The sequence of amino acids in a protein is described as its **primary structure** (Fig. 3-21a)

glutamic acid (glu)   aspartic acid (asp)   phenylalanine (phe)   leucine (leu)   cysteine (cys)

(a) Hydrophilic functional groups

(b) Hydrophobic functional groups

(c) Sulfur-containing functional group

▲ FIGURE 3-19 **Amino acid diversity** The diversity of amino acids is caused by the variable R functional group (blue backgrounds), which may be **(a)** hydrophilic or **(b)** hydrophobic. **(c)** The R group of cysteine has a sulfur atom that can form covalent bonds with the sulfur in other cysteines.

dehydration
synthesis   peptide   water

amino
group   carboxylic acid   amino
group   group   peptide
bond

▲ FIGURE 3-20 **Protein synthesis** A dehydration reaction forms a peptide bond between
the carbon of the carboxylic acid group of one amino acid and the nitrogen of the amino group of
a second amino acid.

of protein. The amino acid sequence of each protein is specified by genetic instructions in a cell's DNA. The specific amino acid sequences cause polypeptides to assume simple, repeating **secondary structures:** a helix or a pleated sheet. Secondary structures are maintained by hydrogen bonds between the polar portions of amino acids. Keratin protein in hair and the subunits of the hemoglobin molecule in blood provide examples of the coiled, spring-like secondary structure called a **helix** (Fig. 3-21b).

Hydrogen bonds that form between the oxygen atoms of the carbonyl functional groups (with slightly negative charges) and the hydrogens of the amino functional groups (with slightly positive charges) hold the turns of the coils together. Other proteins, such as silk, contain polypeptide chains that repeatedly fold back upon themselves, with hydrogen bonds holding adjacent segments of the polypeptide together in a secondary **pleated sheet** arrangement (**Fig. 3-22a**).

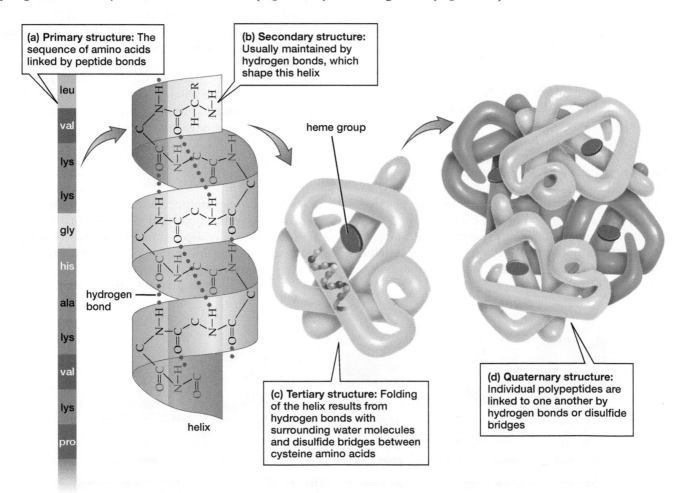

(a) **Primary structure:** The sequence of amino acids linked by peptide bonds

(b) **Secondary structure:** Usually maintained by hydrogen bonds, which shape this helix

heme group

hydrogen bond

helix

(c) **Tertiary structure:** Folding of the helix results from hydrogen bonds with surrounding water molecules and disulfide bridges between cysteine amino acids

(d) **Quaternary structure:** Individual polypeptides are linked to one another by hydrogen bonds or disulfide bridges

▲ FIGURE 3-21 **The four levels of protein structure** Hemoglobin (illustrated) is the oxygen-carrying protein in red blood cells. The red disks represent the iron-containing heme group that binds oxygen.

QUESTION Why do most proteins, when heated excessively, lose their ability to function?

(a) Pleated sheet

hydrogen bond

stack of pleated sheets

disordered segment

strand of silk

(b) Structure of silk

▲ FIGURE 3-22 **The pleated sheet and the structure of silk protein (a)** In a pleated sheet, a single polypeptide chain is folded back upon itself repeatedly (loops of peptide connecting the ends of the chains in the sheet are not shown). Adjacent segments of the folded polypeptide are linked by hydrogen bonds (dotted lines), creating a folded (pleated) sheet-like configuration. The R groups (green) project alternately above and below the sheet. **(b)** Silk protein contains stacks of pleated sheets connected by disordered protein segments. Pleated sheets do not stretch, but the disordered segments do, so a strand of silk is stretchy.

CASE STUDY continued

Puzzling Proteins

Infectious prions are misfolded versions of a normal protein found throughout the body. The secondary structure of the normal prion protein is primarily helical. Infectious prions, however, fold into pleated sheets. The pleated sheets are so stable that they cannot be destroyed by high temperatures or most chemical agents, so it is very difficult to sterilize equipment contaminated by prions. More important, the altered secondary structure of prions is unaffected by the enzymes that break down normal prion protein. Because they are so stable, infectious prions accumulate destructively in the brain.

In addition to their secondary structures, many proteins are contorted into **tertiary structures (Fig. 3-21c)**. Their origami folds are determined both by the protein's secondary structure and by its environment. A protein in water, for example, one dissolved in the watery interior of a cell, folds in a way that exposes its hydrophilic amino acids to the water and hides its hydrophobic amino acids deep within the molecule. In contrast, portions of a protein embedded in the phospholipid cell membrane expose their hydrophobic functional groups to the surrounding hydrophobic tails of the phospholipids. Disulfide bonds can also contribute to tertiary structure by linking together the sulfur-containing R groups of cysteines in different regions of the polypeptide, as in keratin (see Figs. E3-3 and E3-4).

A fourth level of protein organization, called **quaternary structure,** occurs in certain proteins that contain individual polypeptides linked by hydrogen bonds, disulfide bonds, or by attractions between oppositely charged portions of different amino acids. Hemoglobin, for example, consists of four polypeptide chains held together by hydrogen bonds (**Fig. 3-21d**). Each of the four polypeptides holds an iron-containing organic molecule called a heme group (red disks in Figs. 3-21c, d), which can bind one molecule (two atoms) of oxygen.

Most proteins, such as enzymes and hormones, work in close association with other molecules. Because they have very precise roles to play, their highly organized three-dimensional structures help ensure that they interact only with other molecules of particular shapes—much like a key fits a lock. However, scientists are now discovering that many proteins are quite flexible, and only the primary structure is fixed. These *disordered proteins* or *disordered segments* of proteins can fold in a variety of ways, allowing some of them to interact with several different molecules—more like master keys that fit several locks. Some structural proteins, such as silk (**Fig. 3-22b**), have disordered segments linking sections of pleated sheets. These disordered segments allow the silk to stretch. Although the exact structure of most proteins has not yet been determined, some experts now estimate that one-third of all human proteins are disordered or include disordered segments.

The Functions of Proteins Are Related to Their Three-Dimensional Structures

Within a protein, the exact position and number of amino acids bearing specific R groups determine both the structure of the protein and its biological function. In hemoglobin, for example, amino acids bearing specific R groups must be present in precisely the right places to hold the iron-containing heme group that binds oxygen. In contrast, the polar amino acids on the outside of a hemoglobin molecule mainly keep it dissolved in the fluid of a red blood cell. Therefore, a mutation that changes the identity of one of these amino acids will not significantly alter the protein's function, as long as the substituted amino acid is also hydrophilic. A mutation that replaces a hydrophilic with a hydrophobic amino acid, however, can have catastrophic effects on the hemoglobin molecule (causing the painful and sometimes life-threatening disorder called sickle-cell anemia; see Chapters 10 and 12).

The importance of higher level protein structure becomes obvious when a protein is **denatured,** meaning that its normal three-dimensional structure is altered while leaving the primary structure intact. A denatured protein has different properties and will no longer perform its function. For example, the white of an egg consists of the protein albumin. If you fry it, the heat rips hydrogen bonds apart, destroying the protein's secondary and tertiary structure, which causes the egg white to become opaque and solid. The albumin could no longer nourish a developing chick in this denatured form. Keratin in hair is denatured by the chemicals in a permanent wave, as described in "Links to Everyday Life: What Makes Hair Curl?" Bacteria and viruses are often destroyed by denaturing their proteins using heat, ultraviolet radiation, or solutions that are highly salty or acidic. For example, canned foods are sterilized by heating them, water is sometimes sterilized with ultraviolet light, and dill pickles are preserved from bacterial attack by their salty, acidic brine.

CHECK YOUR LEARNING

Can you describe protein subunits and how proteins are synthesized? Do you understand the four levels of protein structure and why the three-dimensional structure of proteins is important? Can you list several functions of proteins and provide examples of proteins that perform each function?

3.6 WHAT ARE NUCLEOTIDES AND NUCLEIC ACIDS?

A **nucleotide** is a molecule with a three-part structure: a five-carbon sugar, a phosphate functional group, and a nitrogen-containing **base.** Bases all have carbon and nitrogen atoms linked in rings, with functional groups attached to some of the carbon atoms. Nucleotides fall into two general classes: deoxyribose nucleotides and ribose nucleotides,

▲ FIGURE 3-23 **Deoxyribose nucleotide**

depending on which type of sugar they contain (see Fig. 3-7). The bases in deoxyribose nucleotides are adenine, guanine, cytosine, and thymine. The bases in ribose nucleotides are adenine, guanine, cytosine, and uracil. Adenine and guanine have double rings, whereas cytosine, thymine, and uracil have single rings (see Fig. 3-25 and Fig. 11-3). A nucleotide with the adenine base is illustrated in **Figure 3-23.** Nucleotides may function as energy-carrier molecules, intracellular messenger molecules, or as subunits of polymers called nucleic acids, described below.

Nucleotides Act as Energy Carriers and Intracellular Messengers

Adenosine triphosphate (ATP) is a ribose nucleotide with three phosphate functional groups (**Fig. 3-24**). This molecule is formed in cells by reactions that release energy, such as the reaction that breaks down a sugar molecule. ATP stores energy in bonds between its phosphate groups, and releases energy when the bond linking the last phosphate to the ATP molecule is broken. This energy is then available to drive energy-demanding reactions such as linking amino acids to form proteins.

The ribose nucleotide cyclic adenosine monophosphate (cAMP) acts as a messenger molecule in cells. Many hormones exert their effects by stimulating cAMP to form within cells, where it initiates a series of biochemical reactions (see Chapter 37).

Other nucleotides (NAD^+ and FAD) are known as *electron carriers* because they transport energy in the form of

▲ FIGURE 3-24 **The energy-carrier molecule adenosine triphosphate (ATP)**

high-energy electrons. Their energy and electrons are used in ATP synthesis, for example, when cells break down sugar. (You will learn more about these nucleotides in Chapters 6, 7, and 8.)

DNA and RNA, the Molecules of Heredity, Are Nucleic Acids

Single nucleotides (monomers) may be strung together in long chains by dehydration synthesis, forming polymers called **nucleic acids.** In nucleic acids, an oxygen atom in the phosphate functional group of one nucleotide is covalently bonded to the sugar of the next. The polymer of deoxyribose nucleotides, called **deoxyribonucleic acid (DNA),** can contain millions of nucleotides (**Fig. 3-25**). DNA is found in the chromosomes of all cells. A DNA molecule consists of two strands of nucleotides entwined in the form of a double helix and linked by hydrogen bonds (see Fig. 3-24). Its sequence

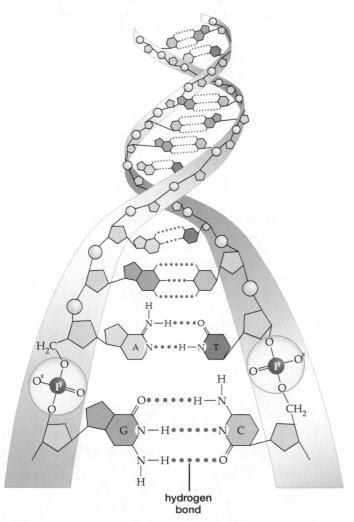

hydrogen
bond

▲ FIGURE 3-25 **Deoxyribonucleic acid** Like a twisted ladder, the double helix of DNA is formed by chains of nucleotides that spiral around one another, linked by hydrogen bonds between the bases of the nucleotides in the two adjacent chains. The bases are identified by their initials: A: adenine; C: cytosine; T: thymine; G: guanine.

CASE STUDY continued

Puzzling Proteins

All cells use DNA as a blueprint for producing more cells, and viruses use either DNA or RNA. Before the discovery of prions, however, no infectious agent had ever been discovered that completely lacked genetic material composed of nucleic acids. Scientists were extremely skeptical of the hypothesis that proteins could effectively "reproduce themselves" until repeated studies found no trace of genetic material associated with prions.

of nucleotides, like the letters of a biological alphabet, spells out the genetic information needed to construct the proteins of each organism. Single-stranded chains of ribose nucleotides, called **ribonucleic acid (RNA),** are copied from the DNA and direct the synthesis of proteins (see Chapters 11 and 12).

CHECK YOUR LEARNING

Can you describe the structure and provide three different functions of nucleotides? Can you explain how nucleic acids are synthesized and give two examples of nucleic acids and their functions?

CASE STUDY revisited

Puzzling Proteins

Stanley Prusiner and his associates identified the prion, a misfolded version of a protein found throughout the animal kingdom. This protein, with no trace of genetic material, is the culprit in scrapie, BSE, and vCJD. But how do prions replicate themselves and build up in the body over time? Prusiner and other researchers have strong experimental evidence supporting a radical hypothesis: The infectious prions interact with normal helical prion proteins and cause them to change their configuration into the pleated sheet configuration of the infectious form. These new "infectious prion converts" then go on to transform other normal prion proteins in an ever-expanding chain reaction. As in Charlene Singh's case, it can be a decade or more after infection before enough of the proteins have been transformed to cause disease symptoms. Fortunately, the actions taken to prevent new infections appear successful; as of mid 2012, there were no surviving vCJD victims and no new confirmed cases of vCJD; only four people in the world were known to be living with the disorder.

The emergence of vCJD has focused attention on the role of the normal prion protein. It is found in cell membranes throughout the body, so it is likely to have a variety of functions, most of which are still unknown. Normal prion protein is found in relatively high levels in the brain, a prime target of infectious prions.

Prusiner's efforts led to the recognition of a totally new disease process. A major strength of the scientific method is that hypotheses can be tested experimentally. If repeated experiments support the hypothesis, then even well-established scientific principles—for example, that all infectious agents must have genetic material—must be reexamined and sometimes discarded. Prusiner's startling revision of how infectious diseases can be transmitted was recognized when he was awarded a Nobel Prize in 1997.

Consider This

A disorder called "chronic wasting disease" (CWD) of deer and elk, first identified in the late 1960s, has now been reported in at least 15 U.S. states. Like scrapie and BSE, CWD is a fatal brain disorder caused by prions. The disease spreads readily between animals in herds, apparently by contact with saliva, urine, and feces of infected animals, which all may contain prions. These infectious proteins have also been found in the muscles of deer with CWD. The U.S. Centers for Disease Control and Prevention states, "To date, no strong evidence of CWD transmission to humans has been reported." If you were a hunter in an affected region, would you eat deer or elk meat? Explain why or why not.

►► LINKS TO EVERYDAY LIFE

What Makes Hair Curl?

Each of the roughly 125,000 hairs on your head has a remarkable structure; **Figure E3-3** shows its assemblage of bundles within bundles, which consist mostly of keratin protein. To understand what makes hair curl, we'll focus on hydrogen and disulfide bonds. Hydrogen bonds give keratin its helical, spring-like secondary structure. When you stretch hair or get it wet, these bonds break and the hair lengthens slightly. The bonds re-form when the tension is released or the hair dries. Keratin has lots of cysteines, which can form covalent disulfide bonds with other cysteines. Whether your hair is naturally straight or curly is determined by the locations of the cysteines in your keratin, which is determined by your genes. In curly hair, disulfide bonds occur in places that contort the otherwise straight keratin molecules (**Fig. E3-4**).

Now let's curl some straight hair. We'll start by putting wet hair on curlers. The water causes keratin's hydrogen bonds to break and re-form with surrounding water molecules. As hair dries, the curlers force new hydrogen bonds to form in different places on the keratin that hold the hair in a curl. But if it's rainy or even humid outside, you can say goodbye to your curls as water breaks the new bonds and hair reverts to its natural straightness.

First the hair is soaked in a solution that breaks the disulfide bonds linking keratin molecules. The hair is then wrapped around curlers and saturated with a second solution. This solution counteracts the effects of the first, allowing disulfide bonds to re-form. The bonds form in new locations, however, because the curlers have shifted the positions of the keratin helices relative to one another. These new covalent bonds link the keratin molecules in a way that permanently maintains the curl (see Fig. E3-4). Genetically straight hair has been transformed into artificially curly hair.

single hair

enlargement of single hair

helix of single keratin molecule

S–S disulfide bonds in straight hair

hydrogen bonds

▲ FIGURE E3-3 **The structure of hair** At the microscopic level, a single hair is organized into bundles within larger bundles, all consisting primarily of keratin. Individual keratin molecules are held in a helical shape by hydrogen bonds, and adjacent keratin molecules are cross-linked by disulfide bonds. These bonds give hair both elasticity and strength. Straight hair is depicted here.

▲ FIGURE E3-4 **Curly hair is contorted by disulfide bonds**

CHAPTER REVIEW

Summary of Key Concepts

3.1 Why Is Carbon So Important in Biological Molecules?

Organic molecules have a carbon backbone. They are so diverse because the carbon atom is able to form bonds with up to four other molecules. This allows organic molecules to form complex shapes, including branched chains, helices, pleated sheets, and rings. The presence of functional groups produces further diversity among biological molecules (see Table 3-1).

3.2 How Are Organic Molecules Synthesized?

Most large biological molecules are polymers synthesized by linking many smaller monomer subunits using dehydration synthesis. Hydrolysis reactions break these polymers apart. The most important organic molecules fall into four classes: carbohydrates, lipids, proteins, and nucleotides/nucleic acids (see Table 3-2).

3.3 What Are Carbohydrates?

Carbohydrates include sugars, starches, cellulose, and chitin. Sugars include monosaccharides and disaccharides. They are used for temporary energy storage and the construction of other molecules. Starches and glycogen are polysaccharides that provide longer-term energy storage in plants and animals, respectively. Cellulose forms the cell walls of plants, and chitin strengthens the exoskeletons of many invertebrates and the cell walls of fungi.

3.4 What Are Lipids?

Lipids are nonpolar, water-insoluble molecules. Oils, fats, waxes, and phospholipids all contain fatty acids, which are chains of carbon and hydrogen atoms with a carboxylic acid group at the end. Steroids all have four fused rings of carbon atoms with functional groups attached. Lipids are used for energy storage (oils and fats), as waterproofing for the outside of many plants and animals (waxes), as the principal component of cellular membranes (phospholipids and cholesterol), and as hormones (steroids).

3.5 What Are Proteins?

Proteins consist of one or more amino acid chains called polypeptides with up to four levels of structure. Primary structure is the sequence of amino acids; secondary structure consists of helices or pleated sheets. These may fold to produce tertiary structure. Proteins in which two or more polypeptides are linked have quaternary structure. Some proteins or parts of proteins are disordered and lack a stable structure. The function of a protein is determined by its shape and by how its amino acids interact with their surroundings and with each other. Proteins can be enzymes; structural molecules such as hair, silk, or horn; hormones such as insulin; or transport molecules such as hemoglobin.

3.6 What Are Nucleotides and Nucleic Acids?

A nucleotide is composed of a phosphate group, a five-carbon sugar (ribose or deoxyribose), and a nitrogen-containing base. Molecules formed from single nucleotides include energy-carrier molecules, such as ATP, and messenger molecules such as cyclic AMP. Nucleic acids are chains of nucleotides. DNA carries the hereditary blueprint, and RNA is copied from DNA and directs the synthesis of proteins.

Key Terms

adenosine triphosphate (ATP) 48	nucleic acid 49
amino acid 44	nucleotide 48
base 48	oil 42
carbohydrate 37	organic 35
cellulose 39	peptide 45
chitin 41	peptide bond 45
dehydration synthesis 36	phospholipid 43
denatured 48	pleated sheet 46
deoxyribonucleic acid (DNA) 49	polymer 36
disaccharide 37	polysaccharide 37
disulfide bond 45	primary structure 45
enzyme 44	protein 44
fat 42	quaternary structure 47
fatty acid 41	ribonucleic acid (RNA) 49
functional group 35	saturated 42
glucose 38	secondary structure 46
glycogen 39	starch 39
helix 46	steroid 43
hydrolysis 36	sugar 37
inorganic 35	tertiary structure 47
lipid 41	trans fat 43
monomer 36	triglyceride 41
monosaccharide 37	unsaturated 42
	wax 42

Learning Outcomes

In this chapter, you have learned to . . .

LO1 Explain why carbon is important in biological molecules.

LO2 Describe dehydration synthesis and hydrolysis and explain the roles they play in forming and breaking down large biological molecules.

LO3 Describe the molecular structure, physical properties, and biological functions of the major groups of carbohydrates and include examples of each.

LO4 Describe the molecular structure, physical properties, and biological functions of the major groups of lipids and include examples of each.

LO5 Describe protein subunits and how they are joined to form proteins.

LO6 Describe the four levels of protein structure and discuss how protein structure relates to the six major functions of proteins.

LO7 Describe the molecular structure, physical properties, and biological functions of the major types of nucleotides and nucleic acids and include examples of each.

Thinking Through the Concepts

Fill-in-the-Blank

1. In organic molecules made of chains of subunits, each subunit is called a(n) _____, and the chains are called _____. Carbohydrates consisting of long chains of sugars are called _____. These sugar chains can be broken down by _____reactions. Three types of carbohydrates consisting of long glucose chains are _____, _____, and _____. Three examples of disaccharides are _____, _____, and _____. LO2 LO3

2. Fill in the following with the appropriate type of lipid: Unsaturated, liquid at room temperature: _____; bees use to make honeycombs: _____; stores energy in animals: _____; sex hormones are synthesized from these: _____; the LDL form of this contributes to heart disease: _____; a major component of cell membranes that has polar heads: _____. LO4

3. Proteins are synthesized by a reaction called _____ synthesis, which releases _____. Subunits of proteins are called _____. The sequence of protein subunits is called the _____ structure of the protein. Two regular configurations of secondary protein structure are _____ and _____. Which of these secondary structures is characteristic of infectious prion proteins? _____ When a protein's secondary or higher-order structure is destroyed, the protein is said to be _____. LO5 LO6

4. Fill in the following with the most specific term describing the bonds involved: Create kinks in the carbon chains of fatty acids in oils: _____; maintain the helical structure of many proteins: _____; link polypeptide chains and can cause proteins to bend: _____ and _____; join the two strands of the double helix of DNA: _____; link amino acids to form the primary structure of proteins: _____. LO4 LO5 LO6

5. A nucleotide consists of three parts: _____, _____, and _____. A nucleotide that acts as an energy carrier is _____. The four bases found in deoxyribose nucleotides are _____, _____, _____, and _____. Two important nucleic acids are _____ and _____. The functional group that joins nucleotides in nucleic acids is _____. LO7

Review Questions

1. What does the term "organic" mean to a chemist? LO1

2. List the four principal types of biological molecules and give an example of each. LO3 LO4 LO6 LO7

3. What roles do nucleotides play in living organisms? LO7

4. How are fats and oils similar? How do they differ, and how do their differences explain whether they are solid or liquid at room temperature? LO4

5. Describe and compare dehydration synthesis and hydrolysis. Give an example of a substance formed by each chemical reaction, and describe the specific reaction in each instance. LO2 LO3 LO5

6. Distinguish among the following: monosaccharide, disaccharide, and polysaccharide. Give two examples of each. LO3

7. Describe the synthesis of a protein from amino acids. Then describe the primary, secondary, tertiary, and quaternary structures of a protein. LO6

8. Where in nature do we find cellulose? Where do we find chitin? In what way(s) are these two polymers similar? Different? LO3

9. Which kinds of bonds between keratin molecules are altered when hair is (a) wet and allowed to dry on curlers and (b) given a permanent wave? LO6

Applying the Concepts

1. In this chapter, you read that a phospholipid has a hydrophilic head and hydrophobic tails. Predict how phospholipids would organize themselves in water.

2. Fat contains twice as many calories per unit weight as carbohydrate. Compare the way fat and carbohydrates interact with water, and explain why this interaction gives fat an extra advantage for weight-efficient energy storage.

3. Some people think that consuming fat and sugar substitutes is a good way to reduce weight, whereas others object to these artificial dietary shortcuts. Explain and justify one of these two positions.

4. Saliva from infected deer can transmit chronic wasting disease, caused by misfolded prion proteins. The infectious prions can persist in soil. How might the disease pass from an infected animal to others in the herd?

5. In an alternate universe where people could digest cellulose molecules, how might this affect our way of life?

Answers to Figure Caption questions and Fill-in-the-Blank questions can be found in the Answers section at the back of the book.

(MB) *Go to MasteringBiology for practice quizzes, activities, eText, videos, current events, and more.*

CASE STUDY
Spare Parts for Human Bodies

"I DON'T THINK I've ever screamed so loud in my life." Jennifer looks back on the terrible day when boiling oil from a deep-fat fryer spilled onto her 10-month-old baby, burning more than 70% of his body. "The 911 operator said to get his clothes off, but they'd melted onto him. I pulled his socks off and the skin came right with them." A few decades ago, Zachary Jenkins' burns would have been fatal. Now, the only evidence of the burn is slightly crinkled skin. Zachary was saved by the bioengineering marvel of artificial skin.

Skin consists of several specialized cell types with complex interactions. The outer cells of skin are masters of multiplication, allowing superficial burns to heal without a trace. However, if the deeper layers of the skin are damaged, as occurs with spilled boiling oil, healing is significantly slower. Deep burns are often treated by grafting skin (including some of the deeper layer) from other sites on the body. This creates a new and painful wound where the skin for the graft is removed. In addition, for burns covering a large portion of the body, the lack of healthy skin for grafting makes this approach impossible. Although cells from a piece of the patient's skin can be grown in culture and placed over the affected area, traditional methods of growing enough cells to cover extensive burns can take weeks. Until recently, the only other option was to use skin from human cadavers or pigs. At best, these tissues serve as temporary biological bandages because the victim's body eventually rejects them. Extensive and disfiguring scars are a common legacy.

Bioengineered skin has radically changed the prognosis for burn victims. The child in this chapter's opening photograph was treated with a bioengineered artificial skin that uses skin cells obtained from the donated foreskins of infants who were circumcised at birth. This tissue, which would otherwise be discarded, provides a source of rapidly dividing cells. Cultured in the laboratory on nylon mesh, the cells secrete growth factors and protein fibers. When used for skin grafting, the foreskin cells die, but the growth factors and protein fibers remaining in the mesh stimulate the victim's own cells to grow and multiply. Therefore, new skin and blood vessels regenerate far more rapidly than with burn coverings of cadaver or pig skin.

Bioengineered artificial skin demonstrates our expanding ability to manipulate cells, the fundamental units of life. What structures make up cells? What new techniques using cells to treat burns are under development? Might medical researchers also manipulate cells into forming other replacement organs? We will explore these questions in this chapter.

Just 6 months before this photo was taken, this child's chest was severely burned (inset). Because he was treated with bioartificial skin, his healing time was radically reduced, and scarring from the burn is almost nonexistent.

AT A GLANCE

LEARNING GOALS

LG1 Summarize the cell theory.

LG2 Compare and contrast prokaryotic and eukaryotic cells.

LG3 Describe the major structures of animal cells and their functions.

LG4 Describe the structure and function of organelles that are found in plant, but not animal, cells.

LG5 Explain the structure, function, and movement of eukaryotic cilia and flagella.

LG6 Describe the structure and function of the nucleus, and compare it to the nucleoid region of prokaryotic cells.

LG7 List the parts of the endomembrane system and explain how they are interconnected.

LG8 Describe the structure and function of both the surface and the internal features of bacterial cells.

4.1 WHAT IS THE CELL THEORY?

Because cells are so small, no one had ever seen them until the first microscope was invented in the mid-1600s (see "Science in Action: The Search for the Cell"). But seeing cells was only the first step toward understanding their importance. In 1838, the German botanist Matthias Schleiden concluded that cells and substances produced by cells form the basic structure of plants, and that plant growth occurs by adding new cells. In 1839, German biologist Theodor Schwann (Schleiden's friend and collaborator) drew similar conclusions about animal cells. The work of Schleiden and Schwann provided a unifying theory of cells as the fundamental units of life. In 1855, the German physician Rudolf Virchow completed the **cell theory**—a fundamental concept of biology—by concluding that all cells come from previously existing cells.

The cell theory consists of three principles:

- Every organism is made up of one or more cells.
- The smallest organisms are single cells, and cells are the functional units of multicellular organisms.
- All cells arise from preexisting cells.

CHECK YOUR LEARNING

Can you list the three precepts of the cell theory?

4.2 WHAT ARE THE BASIC ATTRIBUTES OF CELLS?

All living things, from microscopic bacteria to the human body to a giant sequoia tree, are composed of cells. Cells perform an enormous variety of functions, including obtaining energy and nutrients, synthesizing biological molecules, eliminating wastes, interacting with other cells, and reproducing.

Most cells range in size from about 1 to 100 micrometers (μm; millionths of a meter) in diameter (Fig. 4-1). Why are most cells so small? The answer lies in the need for cells to exchange nutrients and wastes with their external environment through the plasma membrane. Many nutrients and wastes move into, through, and out of cells by diffusion. **Diffusion** is the process by which molecules dissolved in fluids disperse from regions where their concentration is higher to regions where concentration is lower (described in Chapter 5). Diffusion is a relatively slow process. Therefore, to meet the constant demands of cells, the interior of the cell must remain close to the external environment, keeping the cell small.

All Cells Share Common Features

All cells arose from a common ancestor at the dawn of evolution. Modern cells include the simple prokaryotic cells of bacteria and archaea, as well as the far more complex eukaryotic cells of protists, fungi, plants, and animals. All cells share important features, as described in the following sections.

The Plasma Membrane Encloses the Cell and Allows Interactions Between the Cell and Its Environment

Each cell is surrounded by an extremely thin, rather fluid membrane called the **plasma membrane** (Fig. 4-2). The plasma membrane and the other membranes within cells consist of a double layer (a bilayer) of phospholipids and cholesterol molecules, with many different proteins embedded within the bilayer. Important functions of the plasma membrane include:

- selectively isolating the cell's contents from the external environment;
- regulating the flow of materials into and out of the cell; and
- allowing communication with other cells and with the extracellular environment.

The phospholipid and protein components of cellular membranes have very different roles. The phospholipid bilayer helps isolate the cell from its surroundings, allowing the cell to maintain essential differences in concentrations of materials inside and outside. In contrast, proteins embedded in the plasma membrane facilitate communication between the cell and its environment. Some proteins allow passage of specific molecules or ions, while others respond to signals from molecules outside the cell and promote chemical reactions inside the cell. (The structure of the plasma membrane is covered in detail in Chapter 5.)

Size

100 m —

10 m —

1 m —

10 cm —

1 cm —

1 mm —

100 μm —

10 μm —

1 μm —

100 nm —

10 nm —

1 nm —

0.1 nm —

tallest trees

visible with unaided human eye

adult human

chicken egg

frog embryo

visible with light microscope

most eukaryotic cells

mitochondrion

visible with conventional electron microscope

most prokaryotic cells

virus

visible with special electron microscope

proteins

diameter of DNA double helix

atoms

Units of measurement:
    1 meter (m) = 39.37 inches
    1 centimeter (cm) = 1/100 m
    1 millimeter (mm) = 1/1,000 m
    1 micrometer (μm) = 1/1,000,000 m
    1 nanometer (nm) = 1/1,000,000,000 m

▲ FIGURE 4-1 **Relative sizes** Dimensions commonly encountered in biology range from about 100 meters (the height of the tallest redwood trees) through a few micrometers (the diameter of most cells) to a few nanometers (the diameter of many large molecules).

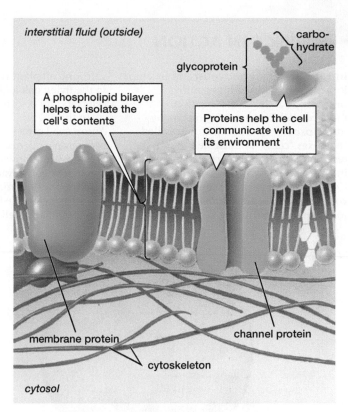

▲ FIGURE 4-2 **The plasma membrane** The plasma membrane encloses the cell. Like all cellular membranes, it consists of a double layer of phospholipid molecules in which a variety of proteins is embedded. The membrane is supported by the cytoskeleton.

All Cells Contain Cytoplasm

The **cytoplasm** consists of all the fluid and structures that lie inside the plasma membrane but outside of the nucleus (see Figs. 4-3 and 4-4). The fluid portion of the cytoplasm in both prokaryotic and eukaryotic cells, called the **cytosol,** contains water, salts, and an assortment of organic molecules, including proteins, lipids, carbohydrates, sugars, amino acids, and nucleotides (described in Chapter 3). Most of the cell's metabolic activities—the biochemical reactions that support life—occur in the cell cytoplasm. Protein synthesis is one example. Cells must

CASE STUDY continued

Spare Parts for Human Bodies

Why is skin from cadavers and pigs eventually rejected by the bodies of burn victims? The plasma membranes of all human cells bear surface molecules called glycoproteins (shown in Fig. 4-2). Each individual has unique glycoproteins that allow the person's immune system to recognize the cells as belonging to that person's own body, and not attack them as it would foreign, invading cells. But skin cells grafted from a different person or other animal bear glycoproteins that differ from those of the burn victim. This difference causes the victim's immune system to treat the skin as foreign, attack it, and eventually reject it. Fortunately, the response is gradual enough that the transplanted skin can still help the burn heal before the graft is rejected. Synthetic skin substitutes—although produced by donated human skin cells—are preferable because by the time the skin substitutes are grafted, no donor cells remain to stimulate an immune response.

SCIENCE IN ACTION The Search for the Cell

In 1665, the English scientist and inventor Robert Hooke aimed his primitive microscope at an "exceeding thin . . . piece of Cork" and saw "a great many little Boxes" (Fig. E4-1a). Hooke called the boxes "cells," because he thought they resembled the rooms occupied by monks in a monastery, which were called cells. Cork comes from the dry outer bark of the cork oak, and we now know that he was looking at the nonliving cell walls that surround all plant cells. Hooke wrote that in the living oak and other plants, "These cells [are] fill'd with juices."

In the 1670s, Dutch microscopist Anton van Leeuwenhoek constructed his own simple microscopes and observed a previously unknown world. A self-taught amateur scientist, van Leeuwenhoek's descriptions of myriad "animalcules" (mostly single-celled organisms) in rain, pond, and well water caused quite an uproar because, in those days, water was consumed without being treated. Eventually, van Leeuwenhoek made careful observations of an enormous range of microscopic specimens, including blood cells, sperm cells, and the eggs of small insects such as aphids and fleas. His discoveries struck a blow to the idea of spontaneous generation; at that time, fleas were believed to emerge spontaneously from sand or dust, and weevils were

(a) Robert Hooke's light microscope and his drawing of cork cells

(b) van Leeuwenhoek's light microscope

(c) Electron microscope

▲ FIGURE E4-1 **Microscopes yesterday and today** (a) Robert Hooke saw the walls of cork cells through his elegant light microscope, and drew them with great skill. (b) Hooke and van Leeuwenhoek were contemporaries. Hooke admitted that van Leeuwenhoek's microscopes produced better images, but described these extremely simple microscopes as "offensive to my eye." (c) This elaborate machine can perform as both a transmission electron microscope (TEM) and a scanning electron microscope (SEM).

believed to spring from grain. Although Leeuwenhoek's microscopes appear much more primitive than Hooke's, because of better lenses, they actually provided much clearer images and higher magnification (Fig. E4-1b).

Ever since the pioneering efforts of Hooke and van Leeuwenhoek, biologists, physicists, and engineers have collaborated in the development of a variety of advanced microscopes to view the cell and its components. *Light microscopes* use lenses made of glass or quartz to bend, focus, and transmit light rays that have passed through or been bounced off a specimen. Light microscopes provide a wide range of images, depending on how the specimen is illuminated and whether

it has been stained (Fig. E4-2a). The resolving power of light microscopes— that is, the smallest structure that can be distinguished under ideal conditions— is about 200 nanometers (200 nm, or 0.2 micrometers; a nanometer is a billionth of a meter). This power is sufficient to see most prokaryotic cells, and some of the internal structures of eukaryotic cells. Light microscopes can be used to observe living cells—a swimming *Paramecium*, for example.

Instead of light, electron microscopes (Fig. E4-1c) use beams of electrons, which are focused by magnetic fields rather than by lenses. All objects viewed using electron microscopes must be dead and sliced, dried, or coated to allow viewing.

Transmission electron microscopes pass electrons through a thin specimen and can reveal the details of interior cell structure (Fig. E4-2c). Some modern transmission electron microscopes can resolve structures as small as 0.05 nanometer, allowing scientists to see molecules such as DNA. *Scanning electron microscopes* bounce electrons off specimens that are dry and hard (such as shells) or that have been covered with an ultrathin coating of metal such as gold. Scanning electron microscopes can be used to view the three-dimensional surface details of structures that range in size from entire small insects down to cells and their components, with a maximum resolution of about 1.5 nm (Figs. E4-2b, d).

(a) Light micrograph

(b) Scanning electron micrograph

(c) Transmission electron micrograph

(d) Scanning electron micrograph

▲ FIGURE E4-2 **A comparison of microscope images** (a) A living *Paramecium* (a single-celled freshwater organism) photographed through a light microscope. (b) A scanning electron micrograph (SEM) of several *Paramecium*. (c) A transmission electron micrograph (TEM) showing mitochondria. (d) An SEM showing mitochondria and smooth endoplasmic reticulum Any colors you see in electron micrographs (SEMs or TEMs) have been added artificially.

synthesize a variety of proteins, such as those of the cytoskeleton (described later in this chapter), proteins in the plasma membrane, and all the enzymes that promote biochemical reactions.

All Cells Use DNA as a Hereditary Blueprint and RNA to Copy the Blueprint and Guide Construction of Cell Parts

The genetic material in cells is **deoxyribonucleic acid (DNA),** an inherited blueprint that stores the instructions for making all the parts of the cell and for producing new cells. This fascinating molecule (discussed in Chapters 3 and 11) contains genes consisting of precise sequences of nucleotides. During cell division, the original, or parent, cells pass exact copies of their DNA to their newly formed offspring, or daughter cells. **Ribonucleic acid (RNA),** which is chemically similar to DNA, copies the genes on DNA and helps construct proteins based on this genetic blueprint. All cells contain both DNA and RNA.

There Are Two Basic Types of Cells: Prokaryotic and Eukaryotic

All forms of life are composed of only two different types of cells. **Prokaryotic** cells ("prokaryotic" means "before the nucleus"; see Fig. 4-19) form the bodies of **bacteria** and **archaea,** the simplest forms of life. **Eukaryotic** cells ("eukaryotic" means "true nucleus"; see Figs. 4-3 and 4-4) are far more complex and make up the bodies of animals, plants, fungi, and protists. As their names suggest, one striking difference between prokaryotic and eukaryotic cells is that the genetic material of eukaryotic cells is contained within a membrane-enclosed nucleus. In contrast, the genetic material of prokaryotic cells is not enclosed within a membrane. The nucleus and other membrane-enclosed structures, collectively called **organelles,** contribute to the far greater structural complexity of eukaryotic cells. Table 4-1 summarizes the features of eukaryotic and prokaryotic cells, which we discuss further in the sections that follow.

TABLE 4-1   Functions and Distribution of Cell Structures

Structure	Function	Prokaryotes	Eukaryotes: Plants	Eukaryotes: Animals
Cell Surface				
Cell wall	Protects and supports the cell	Present	Present	Absent
Cilia	Move the cell through fluid or move fluid past the cell surface	Absent	Absent (in most)	Present
Flagella	Move the cell through fluid	Present[1]	Absent (in most)	Present
Plasma membrane	Isolates the cell contents from the environment; regulates movement of materials into and out of the cell; allows communication with other cells	Present	Present	Present
Organization of Genetic Material				
Genetic material	Encodes the information needed to construct the cell and to control cellular activity	DNA	DNA	DNA
Chromosomes	Contain and control the use of DNA	Single, circular, no proteins	Many, linear, with proteins	Many, linear, with proteins
Nucleus*	Contains chromosomes and nucleoli	Absent	Present	Present
Nuclear envelope	Encloses the nucleus; regulates movement of materials into and out of the nucleus	Absent	Present	Present
Nucleolus	Synthesizes ribosomes	Absent	Present	Present
Cytoplasmic Structures				
Ribosomes	Provide sites for protein synthesis	Present	Present	Present
Mitochondria*	Produce energy by aerobic metabolism	Absent	Present	Present
Chloroplasts*	Perform photosynthesis	Absent	Present	Absent
Endoplasmic reticulum*	Synthesizes membrane components, proteins, and lipids	Absent	Present	Present
Golgi apparatus*	Modifies, sorts, and packages proteins and lipids	Absent	Present	Present
Lysosomes*	Contain digestive enzymes; digests food and worn-out organelles	Absent	Absent (in most)	Present
Plastids*	Store food, pigments	Absent	Present	Absent
Central vacuole*	Contains water and wastes; provides turgor pressure to support the cell	Absent	Present	Absent
Other vesicles and vacuoles*	Transport secretory products; contain food obtained through phagocytosis	Absent	Present	Present
Cytoskeleton	Gives shape and support to the cell; positions and moves cell parts	Present	Present	Present
Centrioles	Produce the basal bodies of cilia and flagella	Absent	Absent (in most)	Present

[1]Some prokaryotes have structures called flagella, which lack microtubules and move in a fundamentally different way than do eukaryotic flagella.
*All of these structures are organelles, surrounded by membranes and found only in eukaryotic cells.

How Many Cells Form the Human Body?

Scientists through the years have wondered how many cells form the human body—and they don't yet agree. Estimates range from 10 trillion to 100 trillion. Interestingly, there seems to be a consensus that there are far more bacterial cells in the body than there are human cells—at least 10 times as many. Does that make us primarily prokaryotic? Hardly. Most of the bacteria are guests that reside in our digestive tracts.

CHECK YOUR LEARNING

Can you describe the structures and features shared by all cells? Can you distinguish prokaryotic from eukaryotic cells?

4.3 WHAT ARE THE MAJOR FEATURES OF EUKARYOTIC CELLS?

Eukaryotic cells make up the bodies of animals, plants, protists, and fungi; as you might imagine, these cells are extremely diverse. The single cells that make up the entire body of some protists are sufficiently complex to perform all the necessary activities of life. Within the body of any multicellular organism there exists a huge variety of eukaryotic cells specialized to perform different functions. In this section we will focus on plant and animal cells.

The cytoplasm of all eukaryotic cells includes a variety of organelles, such as the nucleus and mitochondria, that perform specific functions within the cell; organelles are indicated by an asterisk in Table 4-1. **Figure 4-3** illustrates a generalized animal cell and **Figure 4-4** illustrates a generalized plant cell. Animal cells have structures (centrioles, lysosomes, cilia, and flagella) not found in plant cells, and plant cells have structures (central vacuoles, cell walls, and plastids including chloroplasts) not found in animal cells.

Some Eukaryotic Cells Are Supported by Cell Walls

The outer surfaces of plants, fungi, and some protists are covered with nonliving, relatively stiff coatings called **cell walls** that are secreted outside the plasma membrane. Protists may have cell walls made of cellulose, protein, or glassy silica (see Chapter 20). Plant cell walls (see Fig. 4-4) are composed primarily of cellulose, whereas fungal cell walls

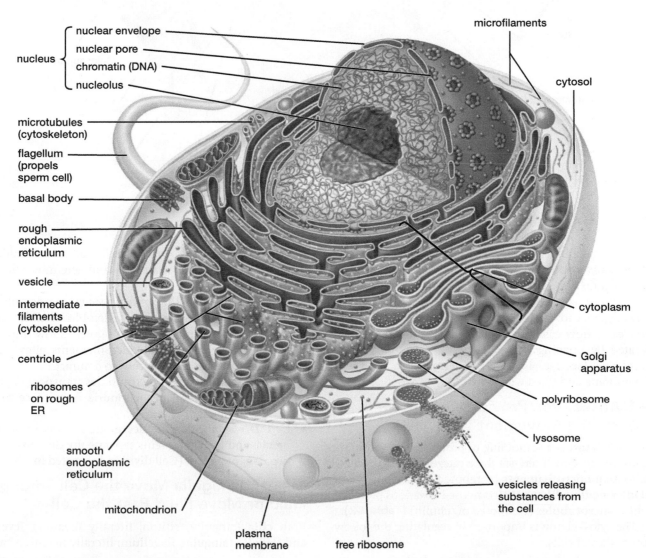

▲ FIGURE 4-3 **A generalized animal cell**

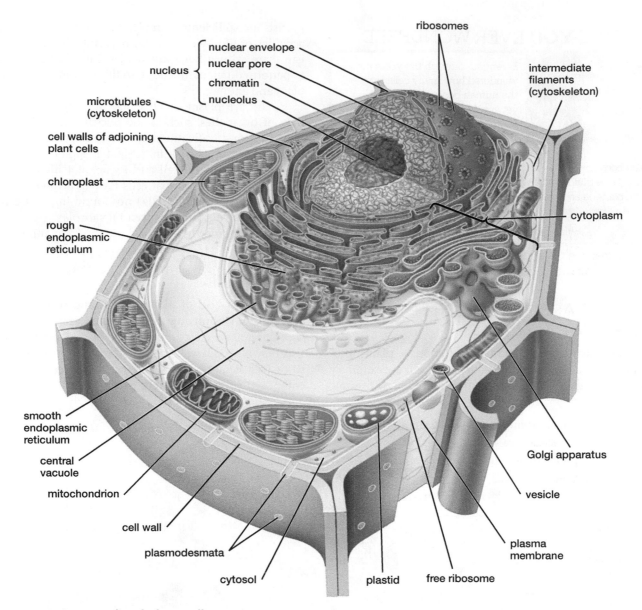

▲ FIGURE 4-4 **A generalized plant cell**

are usually made of chitin (see Chapter 3). Prokaryotic cells have cell walls made of different polysaccharides.

Cell walls protect the delicate plasma membrane and its cytoplasmic contents. Cell walls are usually porous, allowing oxygen, carbon dioxide, and water carrying dissolved molecules to flow easily through them. Plant cell walls are perforated by openings called *plasmodesmata* that connect adjacent cells (see Fig. 4-4). Plasmodesmata are lined with cell membrane and filled with cytosol.

The Cytoskeleton Provides Shape, Support, and Movement

The **cytoskeleton** is a scaffolding of protein fibers within the cytoplasm (Fig. 4-5). There are three categories of cytoskeletal proteins: thin **microfilaments** (composed of actin), medium-sized **intermediate filaments** (composed of various proteins), and thick **microtubules** (composed of tubulin) (Table 4-2).

The cytoskeleton is important in regulating the following properties of cells:

- **Cell Shape** In cells without cell walls, a scaffolding of intermediate filaments supports and determines the shape of the cell.
- **Cell Movement** Cell movement occurs as microfilaments or microtubules assemble, disassemble, or slide past one another. For example, microtubules allow movement of cilia and flagella, and microfilaments allow cells to change shape and muscle cells to contract.
- **Organelle Movement** Microtubules transport organelles such as vesicles and mitochondria from place to place within a cell.
- **Cell Division** Microtubules guide chromosome movements, and microfilaments separate the dividing cell into two daughter cells. (Cell division is covered in Chapter 9.)

Cilia and Flagella Move the Cell Through Fluid or Move Fluid Past the Cell

Both **cilia** (singular, cilium; literally meaning "eyelash") and **flagella** (singular, flagellum; literally meaning "whip")

(a) Cytoskeleton

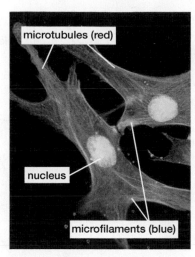

(b) Light micrograph showing the cytoskeleton

▲ FIGURE 4-5 **The cytoskeleton (a)** The eukaryotic cytoskeleton consists of three types of proteins: microfilaments, intermediate filaments, and microtubules. **(b)** In this light micrograph, cells treated with fluorescent stains reveal microtubules and microfilaments, as well as nuclei.

are hair-like structures that propel cells through fluids or move fluids past cells. In mammals, cilia are found lining the respiratory tract and female reproductive tract; flagella are found only on sperm cells. Both are common in protists. Cilia and flagella are both covered by extensions of the plasma membrane and supported internally by microtubules of the cytoskeleton. Each cilium and flagellum contains a ring of nine fused pairs of microtubules, with an unfused pair in the center of the ring (**Fig. 4-6**).

Cilia and flagella undulate almost continuously; the energy to power this motion is supplied by mitochondria that cluster near their bases just beneath the plasma membrane. How do cilia and flagella move? In both structures, tiny sidearms of protein attach neighboring pairs of microtubules (see Fig. 4-6). These sidearms flex, using energy from adenosine triphosphate (ATP) to power their movement. Flexing of the sidearms slides the pair of microtubules past one another, causing the cilium or flagellum to bend.

In general, cilia are shorter and more numerous than flagella. Cilia produce a force on the surrounding fluid that is similar to that created by oars on the sides of a rowboat (**Fig. 4-7a**). Flagella are longer than cilia, and cells with flagella usually have only one or two of these structures.

TABLE 4-2	Major Components of the Eukaryotic Cytoskeleton		
Structure	**Appearance**	**Protein Type**	**Major Functions**
Microfilaments	Twisted double strands of protein subunits; about 7 nm in diameter	Actin	Allow muscle cell contraction; help cells change shape; separate daughter cells during cell division
Intermediate filaments	Helical subunits twisted around one another and bundled into clusters of four, which may be further twisted together; about 10 nm in diameter	Proteins differ depending on function and cell type	Provide supportive internal scaffolding that helps maintain cell shape
Microtubules	Tubes consisting of spirals of two-part protein subunits; about 25 nm in diameter	Tubulin	Transport organelles within the cell; components of cilia and flagella; guide chromosome movements during cell division

section of cilium

protein sidearms

central pair of microtubules

fused microtubule pair

0.1 micrometer

Paramecium — cilium

plasma membrane

basal body (extends into cytoplasm)

▲ FIGURE 4-6 **Cilia and flagella** Both cilia and flagella contain an outer ring of nine fused pairs of microtubules surrounding a central unfused pair. The outer pairs have sidearms made of protein that interact with adjacent pairs to provide the force for bending. Cilia and flagella arise from basal bodies, triplets of microtubules located just beneath the plasma membrane. (Only a cilium is illustrated here.)

The flagellum propels the cell through water, acting somewhat like the propeller on a motorboat (**Fig. 4-7b**).

Some unicellular organisms, such as *Paramecium* (see Figs. E4-2a, b), use cilia to swim through water; others use flagella. Flagella also propel the sperm cells of nearly all animals (see Fig. 4-7b, right). In animals, cilia usually move fluids and suspended particles past a surface. Ciliated cells line such diverse structures as the gills of oysters (over which cilia circulate water rich in food and oxygen), the female reproductive tract of vertebrates (where cilia transport the egg cell to the uterus), and the respiratory tracts of most land vertebrates (where cilia convey mucus that carries debris and microorganisms out of the air passages; see Fig. 4-7a, right).

The microtubules of each cilium and flagellum arise from a **basal body,** which consists of a ring of nine fused triplets of microtubules located just beneath the plasma membrane (see Fig. 4-6). Basal bodies are produced by **centrioles,** which are identical in structure to basal bodies. A single pair of centrioles is found near the nucleus of animal cells (see Fig. 4-3). Centrioles appear to play a role in organizing the proteins of the cytoskeleton that are active during cell division.

The Nucleus, Containing DNA, Is the Control Center of the Eukaryotic Cell

A cell's DNA stores all the information needed to construct the cell and direct the countless chemical reactions necessary for life and reproduction. Only part of the instructions in DNA is used by a cell at any given time, depending on its stage of development, its environment, and the function of the cell in a multicellular body. In eukaryotic cells, DNA is housed within the nucleus.

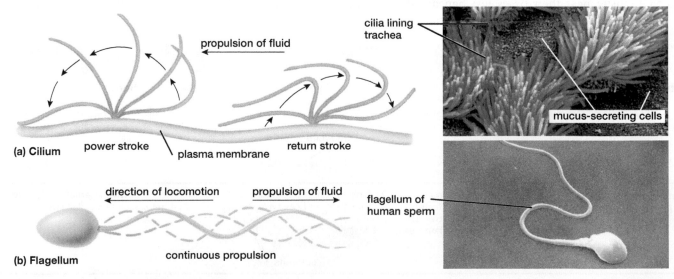

propulsion of fluid

(a) Cilium   power stroke   return stroke
plasma membrane

direction of locomotion   propulsion of fluid

(b) Flagellum   continuous propulsion

cilia lining trachea

mucus-secreting cells

flagellum of human sperm

▲ FIGURE 4-7 **How cilia and flagella move (a)** (Left) Cilia usually "row," providing force parallel to the plasma membrane. The "power stroke" propels the fluid past the membrane, and the "return stroke" restores the cilium to its original position; this movement is much like the arms of a swimmer doing the breast stroke. (Right) SEM of cilia lining the trachea (the tube which conducts air to the lungs); these cilia sweep out mucus and trapped particles. **(b)** (Left) Flagella move in an undulating wavelike motion, providing continuous propulsion perpendicular to the plasma membrane. Thus, a sperm's flagellum propels it forward. (Right) SEM of a human sperm cell.

QUESTION What problems would arise if the trachea were lined with flagella instead of cilia?

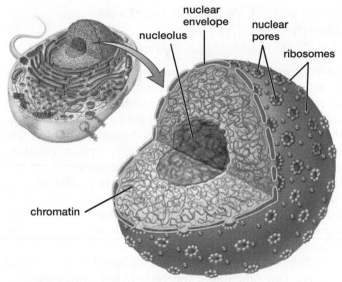

(a) The nucleus

nuclear envelope
nucleolus
nuclear pores
ribosomes
chromatin

nucleus

nuclear pores with nuclear pore complex

(b) Nucleus of a yeast cell

▲ FIGURE 4-8 **The nucleus (a)** The nucleus is bounded by a double outer membrane perforated by pores. Inside the membrane are chromatin and one or more nucleoli. **(b)** SEM of the nucleus of a yeast cell. The "gatekeeper proteins" of the nuclear pore complex are colored pink. These proteins line the nuclear pores.

The **nucleus** is a large organelle with three major parts: the nuclear envelope, chromatin, and the nucleolus, shown in **Figure 4-8** (see also Fig. 4-3) and described in the following sections.

The Nuclear Envelope Allows Selective Exchange of Materials

The nucleus is isolated from the rest of the cell by a double membrane, the **nuclear envelope,** which is perforated by protein-lined nuclear pores. Water, ions, and small molecules can pass freely through the pores, but the passage of large molecules—particularly proteins, parts of ribosomes, and RNA—is regulated by specialized gatekeeper proteins called the **nuclear pore complex** (see Fig. 4-8b) that line each nuclear pore. Ribosomes stud the outer nuclear membrane, which is continuous with membranes of the rough endoplasmic reticulum, described later (see Figs. 4-3 and 4-4).

Chromatin Consists of Strands of DNA Associated with Proteins

Early observers of the nucleus noted that it was darkly colored by the stains used in light microscopy, and named the nuclear material **chromatin** (meaning "colored substance"). Biologists have since learned that chromatin consists of **chromosomes** (literally, "colored bodies") made of DNA molecules and their associated proteins. When a cell is not dividing, the chromosomes are extended into extremely long strands that are so thin that they cannot be distinguished from one another with a light microscope. During cell division, the individual chromosomes become compacted and condensed so they are easily visible with a light microscope (**Fig. 4-9**).

The genes on DNA, consisting of specific sequences of nucleotides, provide a molecular blueprint for the synthesis of a huge variety of proteins. Some of these proteins form structural components of the cell. Others regulate the movement of materials through cell membranes, and still others are enzymes that promote chemical reactions within the cell.

Proteins are synthesized in the cytoplasm, but DNA is confined to the nucleus. This means that copies of the code for proteins must be ferried out through the nuclear membrane into the cytoplasm. To accomplish this, the genetic information is copied from DNA into molecules of *messenger RNA* (mRNA). The mRNA then moves out of the nucleus and into the cytosol through the nuclear pores. In the cytosol, the sequence of nucleotides in mRNA is used to direct protein synthesis, a process that occurs on ribosomes (see Fig. 4-10). (Protein synthesis is described in Chapter 12.)

The Nucleolus Is the Site of Ribosome Assembly

Eukaryotic nuclei contain at least one **nucleolus** (plural, nucleoli; meaning "little nuclei"; see Fig. 4-8a). The nucleolus is the

chromatin

chromosome

▲ FIGURE 4-9 **Chromosomes** Chromosomes, seen here in a light micrograph of a dividing cell (center) in an onion root tip. The chromatin that you see in adjacent nondividing cells consists of uncondensed chromosomes.

QUESTION Why do the chromosomes in chromatin condense in dividing cells?

Spare Parts for Human Bodies

Replacing the skin cells killed by a deep burn requires a tremendous proliferation of new cells. Without special treatments, this regeneration can take up to a year and leave significant scars. But a new product may soon minimize recovery time and scars. Medical personnel remove a microscopically thin slice of healthy skin about the size of a postage stamp from the patient. Enzymes are then used to separate the skin cells from one another. These cells are suspended in liquid, sucked into a syringe-like applicator, and sprayed over the burn, covering up to 80 times the area of skin that provided the cells. This remarkably simple process takes about 20 minutes. The healthy skin cells grow and begin multiplying rapidly, spreading over the burned area to form a new layer of skin in about a week, with very little scarring. Because the patient's own skin cells are used, there is no danger of rejection. Already in use in Australia and Europe—and in clinical trials in the United States as of 2011—this product could become a standard treatment for burns and other injuries to the skin.

site of ribosome synthesis. It consists of *ribosomal RNA* (rRNA), proteins, ribosomes in various stages of synthesis, and the portions of chromosomes that carry genes that code for rRNA.

A **ribosome** is a small particle composed of a type of RNA unique to ribosomes, called ribosomal RNA, combined with proteins. Each ribosome serves as a kind of workbench for the synthesis of proteins within the cell cytoplasm. Just as a workbench can be used to construct many different objects, a ribosome can be used to synthesize a multitude of different proteins (depending on the mRNA to which it attaches). In electron micrographs of cells, ribosomes appear as dark granules, either singly or studding the membranes of the nuclear envelope and rough endoplasmic reticulum (see Fig. 4-11), or as *polyribosomes* ("many ribosomes") strung along strands of mRNA within the cytoplasm (Fig. 4-10).

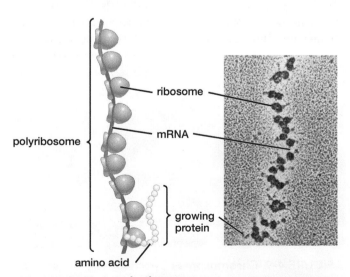

▲ FIGURE 4-10 **A polyribosome** Ribosomes are strung along a messenger RNA molecule, forming a polyribosome. In the TEM (right) individual ribosomes are synthesizing multiple copies of a protein, the small strands projecting horizontally from some of the ribosomes.

Eukaryotic Cytoplasm Contains Membranes That Form the Endomembrane System

All eukaryotic cells contain internal membranes that create loosely connected compartments within the cytoplasm. These membranes, collectively called the **endomembrane system,** segregate molecules from the surrounding cytosol and ensure that biochemical processes occur in an orderly fashion. The endomembrane system creates specialized regions within the cytoplasm where an enormous variety of molecules are synthesized. The fluid property of membranes permits them to fuse with one another. In so doing they empty their contents into different compartments for various types of processing, transfer pieces of membrane among themselves, and also shuttle materials into and out of the cell.

Small temporary sacs made of membrane are called **vesicles.** One function of vesicles is to ferry biological molecules among various regions of the endomembrane system. Vesicles may also fuse with the plasma membrane, exporting their contents outside the cell (see Fig. 4-14), a process called *exocytosis* (described in Chapter 5). Conversely, the plasma membrane may extend and surround material just outside the cell, then fuse and pinch off to form a vesicle inside the cell (see Fig. 4-13), a process called *endocytosis* (see Chapter 5). How do the vesicles know where to go? Researchers have discovered that specific molecules embedded in membranes serve as "mailing labels" that provide the address for delivery of the vesicle and its payload.

The cell's endomembrane system functions to synthesize, transport, and export biological molecules, and to break down defective cellular structures. The endomembrane system includes the nuclear envelope and vesicles described earlier, as well as the endoplasmic reticulum, Golgi apparatus, and lysosomes, described in the sections that follow.

The Endoplasmic Reticulum Forms Membrane-Enclosed Channels Within the Cytoplasm

The **endoplasmic reticulum (ER)** is a series of interconnected membranes that form a labyrinth of flattened sacs and channels within the cytoplasm (reticulum translates to "network" and endoplasmic to "within the cytoplasm"; Fig. 4-11). The ER membrane typically makes up at least 50% of the total membrane of the cell. The ER plays a major role in synthesizing, modifying, and transporting biological molecules throughout the cell. For example, the ER synthesizes phospholipids and proteins for most of the membrane found within the cell. Bits of ER membrane are constantly pinched off when vesicles surround molecules such as proteins or lipids. From the ER, vesicles travel to destinations that include the Golgi apparatus, lysosomes (organelles in which digestion occurs), and the plasma membrane. As the vesicles fuse with these structures, membrane is transferred from the ER to other sites in the cell.

Rough Endoplasmic Reticulum Rough ER emerges from the ribosome-covered outer nuclear membrane (see Fig. 4-3). It is studded with ribosomes on the surface facing the cytosol, and so appears rough under the electron microscope. The

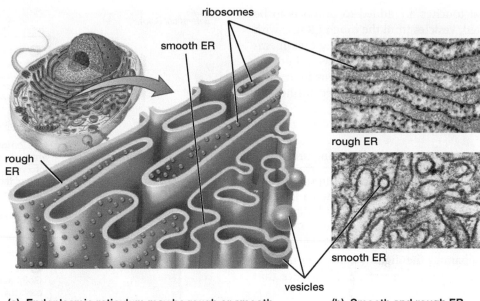

(a) Endoplasmic reticulum may be rough or smooth   (b) Smooth and rough ER

▲ FIGURE 4-11 **Endoplasmic reticulum** **(a)** Ribosomes (depicted as orange dots) stud the side of the rough ER membrane that faces the cytosol. Rough ER membrane is continuous with the outer nuclear envelope. Smooth ER is less flattened and more cylindrical than rough ER, and may be continuous with rough ER. **(b)** A TEM of smooth and rough ER with vesicles.

rough ER is the most important site of protein synthesis in the cell, and it also serves to modify and transport proteins. As they are synthesized, proteins destined either for secretion outside the cell or to be used elsewhere within the cell are inserted into the interior of the ER. Here they are chemically modified and folded into their proper three-dimensional structures (see Chapter 3). Eventually the proteins accumulate in pockets of ER membrane that pinch off as vesicles, which in turn carry their protein cargo to the Golgi apparatus. Some of these proteins become membrane components such as channels through which molecules or ions can pass. Others are digestive enzymes used in the cell or exported. In cells of the pancreas, rough ER synthesizes the protein hormone insulin; in white blood cells, rough ER produces antibodies that help fight infections.

Smooth Endoplasmic Reticulum Smooth ER lacks ribosomes and is scarce in most cells. In certain cells, however, smooth ER is abundant and specialized. In some cells, smooth ER manufactures large quantities of lipids such as steroid hormones. For example, steroid sex hormones are produced by smooth ER in mammalian reproductive organs. Smooth ER is also abundant in liver cells, where it contains enzymes that detoxify harmful drugs such as alcohol and metabolic wastes such as ammonia. In muscle cells, smooth ER is enlarged and specialized to store calcium ions, the release of which allows muscle contraction.

The Golgi Apparatus Modifies, Sorts, and Packages Important Molecules

Named for the Italian physician and cell biologist Camillo Golgi, who discovered it in 1898, the **Golgi apparatus** (or simply **Golgi**) is a specialized set of membranes resembling a stack of flattened and interconnected sacs (**Fig. 4-12**). The compartments of the Golgi act like the finishing rooms of

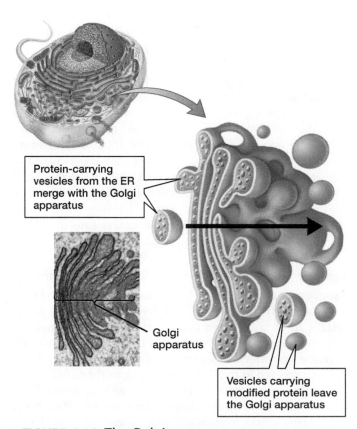

Protein-carrying vesicles from the ER merge with the Golgi apparatus

Golgi apparatus

Vesicles carrying modified protein leave the Golgi apparatus

▲ FIGURE 4-12 **The Golgi apparatus** The Golgi apparatus is a stack of flattened membranous sacs. Vesicles transport both cell membrane and the enclosed material from the ER to the Golgi. The arrow shows the direction of movement of materials through the Golgi as they are modified and sorted. Vesicles bud from the face of the Golgi opposite the ER.

a factory, where final touches are added to products to be packaged and exported. Vesicles from the rough ER fuse with the receiving side of the Golgi apparatus, adding their membranes to the Golgi and emptying their contents into the Golgi sacs. Within the Golgi compartments, some of the proteins synthesized in the rough ER are modified further. Finally, vesicles bud off from the "shipping" face of the Golgi, carrying away finished products for use in the cell or export out of the cell.

The Golgi apparatus performs the following functions:

- The Golgi modifies some molecules; an important role of the Golgi is to add carbohydrates to proteins to make glycoproteins.
- The Golgi separates various proteins received from the ER according to their destinations. For example, the Golgi apparatus separates the digestive enzymes that are bound for lysosomes from the protein hormones that the cell will secrete.
- The Golgi packages the finished molecules into vesicles that are then transported to other parts of the cell or to the plasma membrane for export.

Secreted Proteins Are Modified as They Move Through the Cell

To understand how some of the components of the endomembrane system work together, let's look at the manufacture and export of antibodies (**Fig. 4-13**). Antibodies are glycoproteins produced by white blood cells that bind to foreign invaders (such as disease-causing bacteria) and help destroy them. Antibody proteins are synthesized on ribosomes of the rough ER within white blood cells, and they are packaged into vesicles formed from ER membrane. These vesicles travel to the Golgi, where their membranes fuse with the Golgi membranes and release the antibodies into the Golgi apparatus. Within the Golgi, carbohydrates are attached to the antibodies, which are then repackaged into vesicles formed from membrane acquired from the Golgi. The vesicle containing the completed antibody travels to the plasma membrane and fuses with it, releasing the antibody outside the cell, where it will make its way into the bloodstream to help defend the body against infection.

Lysosomes Serve as the Cell's Digestive System

Lysosomes are membrane-bound sacs that digest food ranging from individual proteins to microorganisms such as bacteria. Lysosomes contain dozens of different enzymes that can break down almost any type of biological molecule. The digestive enzymes of lysosomes are manufactured in the ER and transported to the Golgi in vesicles. In the Golgi, the enzymes are sorted from other proteins and repackaged into vesicles that transport the enzymes to lysosomes (**Fig. 4-14**).

Many cells of animals and protists "eat" by endocytosis—that is, by engulfing particles just outside the cell. The plasma membrane with its enclosed food then pinches off inside the cytosol and forms a vesicle called a **food vacuole** (see **Fig. 4-14**). Lysosomes merge with these food vacuoles,

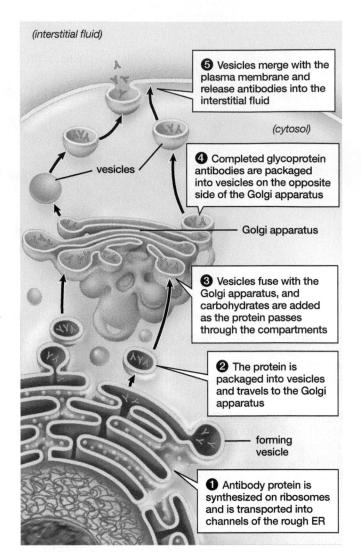

(interstitial fluid)

(cytosol)

5 Vesicles merge with the plasma membrane and release antibodies into the interstitial fluid

vesicles

4 Completed glycoprotein antibodies are packaged into vesicles on the opposite side of the Golgi apparatus

Golgi apparatus

3 Vesicles fuse with the Golgi apparatus, and carbohydrates are added as the protein passes through the compartments

2 The protein is packaged into vesicles and travels to the Golgi apparatus

forming vesicle

1 Antibody protein is synthesized on ribosomes and is transported into channels of the rough ER

▲ FIGURE 4-13 **A protein is manufactured and exported via the endomembrane system** The formation of an antibody is an example of the process of protein manufacture and export.

and the lysosomal enzymes digest the food into small molecules such as amino acids, monosaccharides, and fatty acids. Lysosomes also digest worn-out or defective organelles within the cell, breaking them down into their component molecules. Small biological molecules are released into the cytosol through the lysosomal membrane, where they are used in the cell's metabolic processes.

Vacuoles Serve Many Functions, Including Water Regulation, Storage, and Support

Some vacuoles are temporary large vesicles, such as food vacuoles (see Fig. 4-14). In the following sections, we describe some permanent vacuoles found in some freshwater protists and in plant cells.

Freshwater Protists Have Contractile Vacuoles

Freshwater protists such as *Paramecium* possess **contractile vacuoles**, each composed of collecting ducts, a central

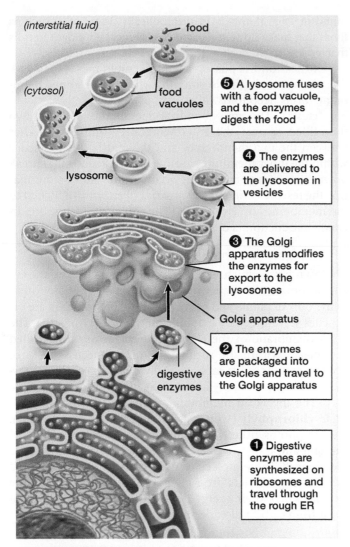

5 A lysosome fuses with a food vacuole, and the enzymes digest the food

4 The enzymes are delivered to the lysosome in vesicles

3 The Golgi apparatus modifies the enzymes for export to the lysosomes

Golgi apparatus

2 The enzymes are packaged into vesicles and travel to the Golgi apparatus

digestive enzymes

1 Digestive enzymes are synthesized on ribosomes and travel through the rough ER

▲ FIGURE 4-14 **Formation and function of lysosomes and food vacuoles via the endomembrane system**
QUESTION Why is it advantageous for all membranes associated with the cell to have a fundamentally similar composition?

substances into the water that fills the central vacuole. Some plants store substances in central vacuoles that deter animals from munching on their otherwise tasty leaves. Vacuoles may also store sugars and amino acids not immediately needed by the cell. Blue or purple pigments stored in central vacuoles are responsible for the colors of many flowers.

Central vacuoles also provide support for plant cells. Dissolved substances in the vacuole attract water into its interior. The resulting water pressure, called *turgor pressure*, within the vacuole pushes the fluid portion of the cytoplasm up against the cell wall with considerable force. Cell walls are usually somewhat flexible, so both the overall shape and the rigidity of the cell depend on turgor pressure within the cell. Turgor pressure thus provides support for the non-woody parts of plants. (Look ahead to Fig. 5-8 to see what happens when you forget to water your houseplants.)

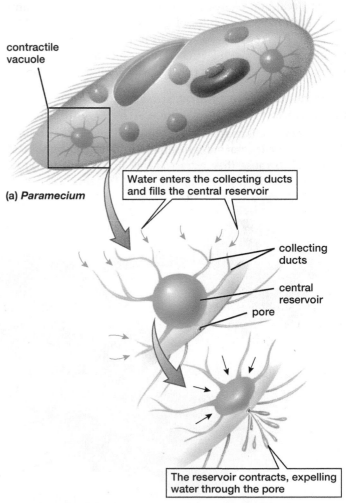

contractile vacuole

Water enters the collecting ducts and fills the central reservoir

collecting ducts

central reservoir

pore

The reservoir contracts, expelling water through the pore

(a) *Paramecium*

(b) Contractile vacuole

▲ FIGURE 4-15 **A contractile vacuole** Many freshwater protists contain contractile vacuoles. **(a)** The single-celled protist *Paramecium* lives in freshwater ponds and lakes. **(b)** An enlargement of the contractile vacuole showing its structure and activity as it collects and expels water.

reservoir, and a tube leading to a pore in the plasma membrane (**Fig. 4-15**). Fresh water constantly leaks into contractile vacuoles through the protists' plasma membranes. (We describe this process, called osmosis, in Chapter 5.) The influx of water would soon burst the fragile organism if it did not have a mechanism to excrete the water. Cellular energy is used to pump salts from the cytoplasm of the protist into collecting ducts. Water follows by osmosis and drains into the central reservoir. When the reservoir of the contractile vacuole is full, it contracts, squirting the water out through a pore in the plasma membrane.

Plant Cells Have Central Vacuoles

A large **central vacuole** occupies three-quarters or more of the volume of most mature plant cells (see Fig. 4-4) and serves several functions. Its membrane helps to regulate the ion content of the cytosol, and secretes wastes and toxic

Mitochondria Extract Energy from Food Molecules and Chloroplasts Capture Solar Energy

All eukaryotic cells have mitochondria that produce high-energy ATP molecules from energy-storage molecules such as sugar. The cells of plants and some protists also have chloroplasts, which can capture energy directly from sunlight and store it in sugar molecules.

Most biologists accept the **endosymbiont hypothesis** (discussed in more detail in Chapter 17), which holds that both mitochondria and chloroplasts evolved from prokaryotic bacteria. Roughly 1.7 billion years ago, these prokaryotes took up residence within other prokaryotic cells, a process called endosymbiosis (literally "living together inside"). Both mitochondria and chloroplasts are surrounded by a double membrane; the outer membrane may have come from the original host cell and the inner membrane from the guest cell. Mitochondria and chloroplasts resemble each other and both resemble prokaryotic cells in several ways. They are both the size of a typical prokaryotic cell (1 to 5 micrometers in diameter). Both have assemblies of enzymes that synthesize ATP, as would have been needed by an independent cell. Finally, both possess their own DNA and ribosomes that more closely resemble prokaryotic than eukaryotic DNA and ribosomes.

Mitochondria Use Energy Stored in Food Molecules to Produce ATP

All eukaryotic cells contain **mitochondria** (singular, mitochondrion), organelles that are sometimes called the "powerhouses" of the cell because they extract energy from food molecules and store it in the high-energy bonds of ATP. Mitochondria are found in large numbers in metabolically active cells, such as those that make up muscle, and they are less abundant in cells that are less active, such as those that make up cartilage.

Mitochondria possess a pair of membranes (Fig. 4-16). The outer membrane is smooth, whereas the inner membrane forms deep folds called cristae (singular, crista; meaning "crest"). The mitochondrial membranes enclose two fluid-filled spaces: the intermembrane compartment lies between the two membranes and the matrix fills the space within the inner membrane. Some of the reactions that break down high-energy molecules occur in the fluid of the matrix; the rest are conducted by a series of enzymes attached to the membranes of the cristae. (The role of mitochondria in energy production is described in detail in Chapter 8.)

Chloroplasts Are the Sites of Photosynthesis

Photosynthesis, which captures sunlight and provides the energy to power life, occurs in the chloroplasts that are found in the cells of plants and some protists. **Chloroplasts** are organelles surrounded by a double membrane (Fig. 4-17). The inner membrane of the chloroplast encloses a fluid called the *stroma*. Within the stroma are interconnected stacks of hollow, membranous sacs. An individual sac is called a *thylakoid*, and a stack of thylakoids is a *granum* (plural, grana).

The thylakoid membranes contain the pigment molecule **chlorophyll** (which gives plants their green color). During photosynthesis, chlorophyll captures the energy of sunlight and transfers it to other molecules in the thylakoid membranes. These molecules transfer the energy to ATP and other energy carriers. The energy carriers diffuse into the stroma, where their energy is used to drive the synthesis of sugar from carbon dioxide and water.

outer membrane
inner membrane
intermembrane space
matrix
cristae

0.1 micrometer

▲ FIGURE 4-16 **A mitochondrion** Mitochondria contain two membranes enclosing two fluid compartments: the intermembrane compartment between the outer and inner membranes and the matrix within the inner membrane. The outer membrane is smooth, but the inner membrane forms deep folds called cristae. Some structures are visible in the TEM on the right.

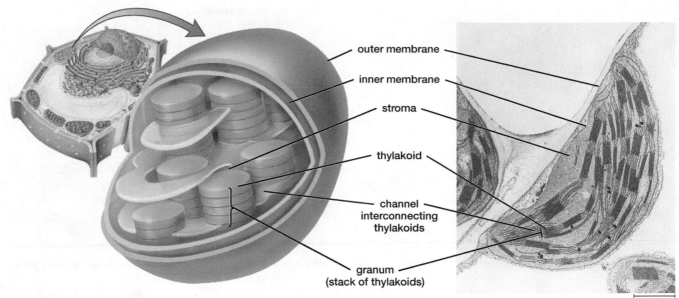

outer membrane
inner membrane
stroma
thylakoid
channel interconnecting thylakoids
granum (stack of thylakoids)

1 micrometer

▲ **FIGURE 4-17 A chloroplast** Chloroplasts are surrounded by a double membrane. The fluid stroma is enclosed by the inner membrane; within the stroma are stacks of thylakoid sacs called grana. Chlorophyll is embedded in the membranes of the thylakoids.

Plants Use Some Plastids for Storage

Chloroplasts are highly specialized **plastids,** organelles found only in plants and photosynthetic protists (**Fig. 4-18**). Plants and photosynthetic protists use nonchloroplast types of plastids as storage containers for various molecules, including pigments that give ripe fruits their yellow, orange, or red colors. In plants that continue growing from one year to the next, plastids store photosynthetic products produced during the growing season. Most plants convert the sugars made during photosynthesis into starch, which is stored in plastids. Potatoes, for example, are composed almost entirely of cells stuffed with starch-filled plastids (see Fig. 4-18, upper right).

CHECK YOUR LEARNING

Can you define *organelles*? Do you recall which structures are found in animal but not plant cells and which are found in plant but not animal cells? Can you describe each major structure found in eukaryotic cells, including its function?

4.4 WHAT ARE THE MAJOR FEATURES OF PROKARYOTIC CELLS?

Most prokaryotic cells are small, generally less than 5 micrometers in diameter (most eukaryotic cells are from 10 to 100 micrometers in diameter) with an internal structure that is simple compared to that of eukaryotic cells (**Fig. 4-19;** compare this to Figs. 4-3 and 4-4). In general, prokaryotes lack the membrane-surrounded organelles that are the most prominent internal features of eukaryotic cells.

Members of the domains Archaea and Bacteria have bodies that consist of single prokaryotic cells. The Archaea superficially resemble bacteria, but recent research has revealed that they differ in many important molecular features, and they are

plastid
starch globules

0.5 micrometer

▲ **FIGURE 4-18 A plastid** Plastids, found in the cells of plants and photosynthetic protists, are surrounded by a double outer membrane. Chloroplasts are the most familiar plastid; other types of plastids store various materials, such as the starch filling these plastids in the potato cells seen at the upper right in a TEM.

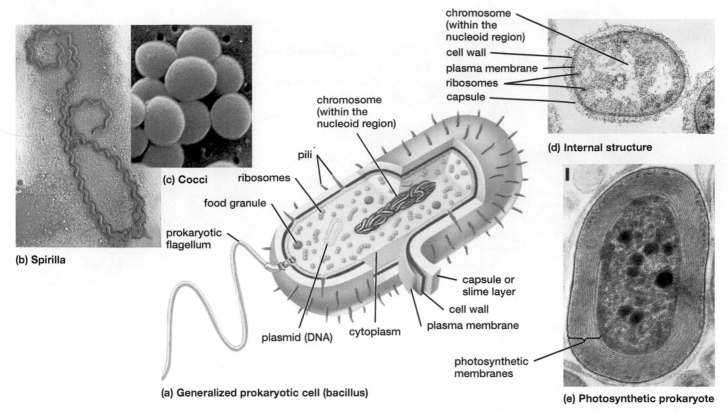

▲ FIGURE 4-19 **Prokaryotic cells are simpler than eukaryotic cells** Prokaryotes assume a variety of shapes, including **(a)** rod-shaped bacilli, **(b)** spiral-shaped spirilla, and **(c)** spherical cocci. Internal structures are revealed in the TEMs in **(d)** and **(e)**. Some photosynthetic bacteria have internal membranes where photosynthesis occurs, as shown in **(e)**.

now considered an entirely different form of life. Archaea inhabit extreme environments, such as hot springs and cow stomachs, but are increasingly being discovered in more familiar locales, such as the soil and oceans. None are known to cause disease. In this chapter we focus on the more familiar bacteria.

Prokaryotic Cells Possess Specialized Surface Features

Nearly all prokaryotic cells are surrounded by a stiff cell wall; in bacteria this is composed of *peptidoglycan* (a unique molecule consisting of short peptides linking chains of sugar molecules bearing amino groups). The cell wall protects the cell and helps the cell retain its shape. Most prokaryotes are rod-shaped *bacilli* (**Fig. 4-19a**), spiral-shaped *spirilla* (**Fig. 4-19b**), or spherical *cocci* (**Fig. 4-19c**). Several types of antibiotics, including penicillin, fight bacterial infections by interfering with cell wall synthesis, causing the bacteria to rupture. Although no prokaryotic cells possess cilia, some bacteria and archaea are propelled by flagella, the structure of which differs from that of eukaryotic flagella (see Chapter 19).

Many bacteria secrete polysaccharide coatings called *capsules* and *slime layers* outside their cell walls. Capsules and slime layers are very similar except that capsules have a more organized structure and are more difficult to remove. In bacteria such as those that cause tooth decay, diarrhea, pneumonia, or urinary tract infections, capsules and slime

layers help them adhere to specific host tissues, such as the lining of the small intestine, lungs, or bladder, or the surface of a tooth (see "Links to Everyday Life: Unwanted Guests"). Capsules and slime layers allow some bacteria to form surface films (such as may coat unwashed toilet bowls). They also protect bacteria and help prevent them from drying out.

Pili (singular, pilus; meaning "hairs") are surface proteins that project from the cell walls of many bacteria (see Fig. 4-19a). There are two types of pili: attachment pili and sex pili. *Attachment pili* are short and abundant. Like slime layers and capsules, attachment pili help bacteria adhere to structures. In some disease-causing bacteria, these pili attach to human tissues. Some types of bacteria form *sex pili*, which are few in number and quite long. A single sex pilus from one bacterium binds to a nearby bacterium of the same type and draws them together. This allows them to form a pore linking their cytoplasm through which they transfer pieces of DNA called plasmids (see Fig. 19-8). (The features of prokaryotic cells are covered in more detail in Chapter 19.)

Prokaryotic Cells Have Fewer Specialized Cytoplasmic Structures Than Do Eukaryotic Cells

The cytoplasm of a typical prokaryotic cell contains a distinctive region called the **nucleoid** (meaning "like a nucleus"; see Fig. 4-19a), consisting primarily of DNA, with some

⟫⟫ **LINKS** TO EVERYDAY LIFE

Unwanted Guests

You may think you have "yuck mouth" in the morning, but imagine the mouths of people in the late 1600s, when dental hygiene was virtually nonexistent. It was then that the Dutch scientist Anton van Leeuwenhoek scraped white matter from his teeth. Viewing the gunk through a microscope that he had built himself, he saw swarms of cells that he called "animalcules," and which we now recognize as bacteria. Disturbed by these life-forms in his mouth, he attempted to kill them with vinegar and hot coffee—with little success. The warm, moist environment of the human mouth, particularly the crevices of the teeth and gums, is an ideal habitat for a variety of bacteria. Some produce slime layers that help them and others adhere to teeth. Thick layers of bacteria, slime, and glycoproteins from saliva make up the white substance, called plaque, which van Leeuwenhoek scraped from his teeth. Sugar in foods and beverages nourishes the bacteria, which break down the sugar into lactic acid. The acid eats away at the tooth enamel, producing tiny crevices in which the bacteria multiply, eventually producing a cavity. So, although he didn't know why, van Leeuwenhoek was right to be concerned about the "animalcules" in his mouth!

RNA and protein. The DNA within the nucleoid takes the form of a single, circular chromosome consisting of a long coiled strand of DNA that carries essential genetic information. The nucleoid is not separated from the cytoplasm by a membrane, as is the nucleus of eukaryotic cells. Most prokaryotic cells also contain small rings of DNA called **plasmids,** located outside the nucleoid. Plasmids usually carry genes that give the cell special properties; for example, some disease-causing bacteria possess plasmids that allow them to inactivate antibiotics, making the bacteria much more difficult to kill.

Bacterial cytoplasm includes ribosomes (see Fig. 4-19a). Although their role in protein synthesis is similar to that of eukaryotic ribosomes, bacterial ribosomes are smaller and contain different RNA and proteins. These ribosomes resemble those found in eukaryotic mitochondria and chloroplasts, providing support for the endosymbiont hypothesis described earlier. Prokaryotic cytoplasm also may contain food granules that store energy-rich molecules, such as glycogen, but these are not enclosed by membranes.

Although prokaryotic cells lack membrane-enclosed organelles, some bacteria use membranes to organize the enzymes responsible for a series of biochemical reactions. Such enzymes are situated in a particular sequence along the membrane to promote reactions in the proper order. For example, photosynthetic bacteria possess extensive internal membranes in which light-capturing proteins and enzymes that guide the synthesis of high-energy molecules are embedded in a specific order (**Fig. 4-19e**). Recent research has revealed that bacteria contain an extensive cytoskeleton. Although bacterial cytoskeletal proteins differ from those of the eukaryotic cytoskeleton, they play some of the same roles as in eukaryotic cells, for example, in cell division.

You might wish to go back and look at Table 4-1 at this point to review the differences between prokaryotic and eukaryotic cells.

CHECK YOUR LEARNING

Can you explain the major differences between prokaryotic and eukaryotic cells? Are you able to describe the structure and function of the major surface features of bacteria? Can you describe the internal features of bacteria, and include how some bacteria utilize internal membranes?

CASE STUDY revisited

Spare Parts for Human Bodies

Bioengineering of tissues and organs such as skin requires the coordinated efforts of biochemists, biomedical engineers, cell biologists, and physicians—experts who rarely communicated in the past. But now teams of scientists are working together to grow not only skin but also windpipes, bone, cartilage, heart valves, bladders, and breast tissue in laboratories around the world. To heal broken bones, researchers are working to develop biodegradable plastic scaffolds that incorporate protein growth factors. These molecules encourage nearby bone cells and tiny blood vessels to invade the plastic as it degrades, eventually replacing the artificial scaffold with the patient's own bone. Bioartificial blood vessels are currently being tested in animals. These are composed of a matrix of proteins deposited by cells grown on scaffolding. Replacement bladders have been created using bladder cells from patients seeded onto a bladder-shaped scaffold, incubated for about 7 weeks, and then transplanted into a patient. Some of these bladders have performed successfully in patients for years and are now in human clinical trials in preparation for the medical marketplace.

Recently the first bioartificial organ using stem cells was successfully transplanted into a man suffering from inoperable cancer that was blocking his windpipe (**Fig. 4-20**). Scientists built a Y-shaped scaffold based on three-dimensional (3-D) scans of the patient's own windpipe. They then seeded the scaffold with stem cells, which can develop into a wide range of cell types. The stem cells were taken from the patient's own bone marrow, so there was no danger of tissue rejection. The structure was bathed in special growth factors that prodded the stem cells to mature into cell types found in the windpipe.

▲ FIGURE 4-20 **A laboratory-grown windpipe**

An exciting new development in tissue engineering is bioprinting, which eliminates the need for scaffolding. Gabor Forgacs, a biophysicist at the University of Missouri–Columbia, cofounded a biotech firm that created a machine that has just reached the research market. This distant relative of the familiar ink-jet printer is designed to print organs in three dimensions. Its 3-D printer head, controlled by sophisticated computer software, ejects tiny droplets containing 10,000 or more cells onto a gel-like "paper" within which the cells can migrate and interact with one another. Layers of paper and cells are stacked and fuse together.

The bioprinting technique relies on the inherent ability of cells to communicate with one another using physical and chemical signals and to organize themselves into functional units. Forgacs and his team are currently working on printing blood vessels using droplets composed of the three types of cells that make up a blood vessel. The droplets are deposited around a central core of protein that will eventually be removed to allow blood to flow through. Over time, the three cell types spontaneously organize themselves around the core just as they do in a natural vessel. Such bioprinted blood vessels should be available in the near future. Bioprinting also offers the possibility of one day building a complete organ from a patient's own cells.

Consider This

BioEthics Forgacs foresees one of the first uses of his cell-printing technique to be the production of tissues from human cells on which to test new drugs. What do you think are the advantages of this approach compared to testing drugs on laboratory animals?

CHAPTER REVIEW

Summary of Key Concepts

4.1 What Is the Cell Theory?

The principles of the cell theory are that every living organism is made up of one or more cells, the smallest organisms are single cells, cells are the functional units of multicellular organisms, and all cells arise from preexisting cells.

4.2 What Are the Basic Attributes of Cells?

Cells are small because they must exchange materials with their surroundings by diffusion, a slow process that requires the interior of the cell to be close to the plasma membrane. All cells are surrounded by a plasma membrane that regulates the interchange of materials between the cell and its environment. All cells use DNA as a genetic blueprint and RNA to direct protein synthesis based on DNA. There are two fundamentally different types of cells: Prokaryotic cells are small and lack membrane-enclosed organelles. Eukaryotic cells have a variety of organelles, including a nucleus.

4.3 What Are the Major Features of Eukaryotic Cells?

Cells of plants, fungi, and some protists are supported by porous cell walls outside the plasma membrane. Eukaryotic cells have an internal cytoskeleton of protein filaments that shapes the cell, transports and anchors organelles, and allows cells to move. Some eukaryotic cells have cilia or flagella, extensions of the plasma membrane that contain microtubules in a characteristic pattern. These structures move fluids past the cell or move the cell through a fluid environment.

Genetic material (DNA) is contained within the nucleus, surrounded by the double membrane of the nuclear envelope. Pores in the nuclear envelope regulate the movement of molecules between nucleus and cytoplasm. The genetic material is organized into strands called chromosomes, which consist of DNA and proteins. The nucleolus consists of rRNA and ribosomal proteins, as well as the genes that code for ribosome synthesis. Ribosomes, composed of rRNA and protein, are the sites of protein synthesis.

The endomembrane system within eukaryotic cells includes the nuclear envelope, endoplasmic reticulum (ER), Golgi apparatus, and lysosomes and other vesicles. The ER forms a series of interconnected membranous compartments. The ER is a major site of new membrane production. Rough ER, continuous with the outer nuclear envelope, bears ribosomes where proteins are manufactured. These proteins are modified, folded, and transported within the ER channels. Smooth ER, which lacks ribosomes, manufactures lipids such as steroid hormones, detoxifies drugs and metabolic wastes, and stores calcium. The Golgi apparatus is a series of flattened membranous sacs. The Golgi processes and modifies materials that are synthesized in the rough ER and transported in vesicles to the Golgi. Substances modified in the Golgi are sorted and packaged into vesicles for transport elsewhere in the cell. Lysosomes are vesicles that contain digestive enzymes that digest food particles after merging with vesicles called food vacuoles. Lysosomes also digest defective organelles.

Some freshwater protists have contractile vacuoles that collect and expel excess water. Plants use central vacuoles to support the cell and may also use it to store nutrients, pigments, wastes, and toxic materials.

All eukaryotic cells contain mitochondria, which are organelles that use oxygen to complete the metabolism of food molecules, capturing some of their energy in ATP. Cells of plants and some protists contain plastids. Chloroplasts are specialized plastids that capture solar energy during photosynthesis, allowing plant cells to manufacture sugar from water and carbon dioxide. Storage plastids store pigments or starch. The endosymbiont hypothesis states that both mitochondria and chloroplasts originated from prokaryotic cells.

4.4 What Are the Major Features of Prokaryotic Cells?

All members of the domains Archaea and Bacteria consist of prokaryotic cells. Prokaryotic cells are generally smaller than eukaryotic cells and have a simpler internal structure that lacks membrane-enclosed organelles. Some bacteria have flagella. Most bacteria are surrounded by a cell wall made of peptidoglycan. Some bacteria, including many that cause disease, attach to surfaces such as human tissue using external capsules or slime layers. Others use short, numerous, hair-like protein strands called attachment pili. Sex pili, which are long and few in number, draw bacteria together to allow transfer of plasmids. Plasmids are small rings of DNA that confer special features such as antibiotic resistance. Most bacterial DNA is in a single chromosome in the nucleoid region. Bacterial cytoplasm includes ribosomes and a cytoskeleton (differing in structure from those of eukaryotic cells). Photosynthetic bacteria may have extensive internal membranes where the reactions of photosynthesis occur.

Key Terms

archaea 58	flagellum (plural,
bacteria 58	flagella) 60
basal body 62	food vacuole 66
cell theory 54	Golgi apparatus 65
cell wall 59	intermediate filament 60
central vacuole 67	lysosome 66
centriole 62	microfilament 60
chlorophyll 68	microtubule 60
chloroplast 68	mitochondrion (plural,
chromatin 63	mitochondria) 68
chromosome 63	nuclear envelope 63
cilium (plural, cilia) 60	nuclear pore complex 63
contractile vacuole 66	nucleoid 70
cytoplasm 55	nucleolus (plural,
cytoskeleton 60	nucleoli) 63
cytosol 55	nucleus 63
deoxyribonucleic acid	organelle 58
(DNA) 58	pilus (plural, pili) 70
diffusion 54	plasma membrane 54
endomembrane system 64	plasmid 71
endoplasmic reticulum	plastid 69
(ER) 64	prokaryotic 58
endosymbiont	ribonucleic acid (RNA) 58
hypothesis 68	ribosome 64
eukaryotic 58	vesicle 64

Learning Outcomes

In this chapter, you have learned to . . .

LO1   Summarize the cell theory.

LO2   Compare and contrast prokaryotic and eukaryotic cells.

LO3   Describe the major structures of animal cells and their functions.

LO4   Describe the structure and function of organelles that are found in plant, but not animal, cells.

LO5   Explain the structure, function, and movement of eukaryotic cilia and flagella.

LO6   Describe the structure and function of the nucleus, and compare it to the nucleoid region of prokaryotic cells.

LO7   List the parts of the endomembrane system and explain how they are interconnected.

LO8   Describe the structure and function of both the surface and the internal features of bacterial cells.

Thinking Through the Concepts

Fill-in-the-Blank

1. The plasma membrane is composed of two major types of molecules, _____ and _____. Which type of molecule is responsible for each of the following functions? Isolation from the surroundings: _____; interactions with other cells: _____. **LO2 LO3**

2. The _____ is composed of a network of protein fibers. The three types of cytoskeleton fibers are _____, _____, and _____. Which of these supports cilia? _____. Moves organelles? _____. Allows muscle contraction? _____. Provides a supporting framework for the cell? _____. **LO2 LO3 LO5**

3. After each description, fill in the appropriate term: "workbenches" of the cell: _____; comes in rough and smooth forms: _____; site of ribosome production: _____; a stack of flattened membranous sacs: _____; outermost layer of plant cells: _____; ferries blueprints for protein production from the nucleus to the cytoplasm: _____. **LO3 LO4**

4. Antibody proteins are synthesized on ribosomes associated with the _____. The antibody proteins are packaged into membranous sacs called _____ and are then transported to the _____. Here, what type of molecule is added to the protein? _____ After the antibody is completed, it is packaged into vesicles that fuse with the _____. **LO3 LO7**

5. After each description, fill in the appropriate structure: "powerhouses" of the cell: _____; capture solar energy: _____; outermost structure of plant cells: _____; region of prokaryotic cell containing DNA: _____; propel fluid past cells: _____; consists of the cytosol and the organelles within it: _____. **LO2 LO3 LO4 LO5 LO8**

6. Two organelles that are believed to have evolved from prokaryotic cells are _____ and _____. Evidence for this hypothesis is that both have _____ membranes, both have groups of enzymes that synthesize _____, and their _____ is similar to that of prokaryotic cells. LO2 LO3 LO4 LO8

7. What structure in bacterial cells is composed of peptidoglycan? _____. What structure in prokaryotic cells serves a similar function to the nucleus in eukaryotic cells? _____. Short segments of DNA that confer special features such as antibiotic resistance on bacteria are called _____. Bacterial structures called _____ pull bacterial cells together so they can transfer DNA. LO2 LO8

Review Questions

1. What are the three principles of the cell theory? LO1

2. Which cytoplasmic structures are common to both plant and animal cells, and which are found in one type but not the other? LO3 LO4

3. Name the proteins of the eukaryotic cytoskeleton; describe their relative sizes and major functions. LO3

4. Describe the nucleus and the function of each of its components, including the nuclear envelope, chromatin, chromosomes, DNA, and the nucleolus. LO6

5. What are the functions of mitochondria and chloroplasts? Why do scientists believe that these organelles arose from prokaryotic cells? What is this hypothesis called? LO2 LO4 LO5 LO8

6. What is the function of ribosomes? Where in the cell are they found? Are they limited to eukaryotic cells? LO2 LO3

7. Describe the structure and function of the endoplasmic reticulum (smooth and rough) and the Golgi apparatus and how they work together. LO3 LO8

8. How are lysosomes formed? What is their function? LO3

9. Diagram the structure of eukaryotic cilia and flagella. Describe how each moves and what their movement accomplishes. LO3

10. List the structures of bacterial cells that have the same name and function as some eukaryotic structures, but a different molecular composition. LO2 LO8

Applying the Concepts

1. If samples of muscle tissue were taken from the legs of a world-class marathon runner and a sedentary individual, which would you expect to have a higher density of mitochondria? Why?

2. One of the functions of the cytoskeleton in animal cells is to give shape to the cell. Plant cells have a fairly rigid cell wall surrounding the plasma membrane. Does this mean that a cytoskeleton is unnecessary for a plant cell?

3. What problems would an enormous round cell encounter? What adaptations might help a very large cell survive?

Answers to Figure Caption questions and Fill-in-the-Blank questions can be found in the Answers section at the back of the book.

(MB) *Go to MasteringBiology for practice quizzes, activities, eText, videos, current events, and more.*

CHAPTER 5

Cell Membrane Structure and Function

CASE STUDY
Vicious Venoms

THIRTEEN-YEAR-OLD JUSTIN SCHWARTZ was having a great time during his 3-week stay at a summer camp near Yosemite National Park. But that all changed after a 4.5-mile hike as Justin rested on some sunny rocks, hands hanging loosely at his sides. Suddenly, he felt a piercing pain in his left palm. A 5-foot rattlesnake—probably feeling threatened by Justin's dangling arm—had struck without warning.

His campmates stared in alarm as the snake slithered into the undergrowth, but Justin focused on his hand, where the pain was becoming agonizing and the palm was beginning to swell. He suddenly felt weak and dizzy. As counselors and campmates spent the next 4 hours carrying him down the trail, pain and discoloration spread up Justin's arm, and his hand felt as if it were going to burst. A helicopter whisked him to a hospital, where he fell unconscious. A day later, he regained consciousness at the University of California Davis Medical Center. There, Justin spent more than a month undergoing 10 surgeries. These relieved the enormous pressure from swelling in his arm, removed dead muscle tissue, and began the long process of repairing the extensive damage to his hand and arm.

Diane Kiehl's ordeal began as she dressed for an informal Memorial Day celebration with her family, pulling on blue jeans that she had tossed on the bathroom floor the previous night. Feeling a sting on her right thigh, she ripped off the jeans and watched with irritation as a long-legged spider crawled out. Living in an old house in the Kansas countryside, Diane had grown accustomed to spiders—which are often harmless—but this was an exception: a brown recluse. The two small puncture wounds seemed merely a minor annoyance until the next day, when an extensive, itchy rash appeared at the site. By the third day, intermittent pain pierced like a knife through her thigh. A physician gave her painkillers, steroids to reduce the swelling, and antibiotics to combat bacteria introduced by the spider's mouthparts. The next 10 days were a nightmare of pain from the growing sore, now covered with oozing blisters and underlain with clotting blood. It took 4 months for the lesion to heal. Even after a year, Diane sometimes felt pain in the large scar that remained.

How do rattlesnake and brown recluse spider venoms cause leaky blood vessels, disintegrating skin and tissue, and sometimes life-threatening symptoms throughout the body? What do venoms have to do with cell membranes? Find out as you read this chapter.

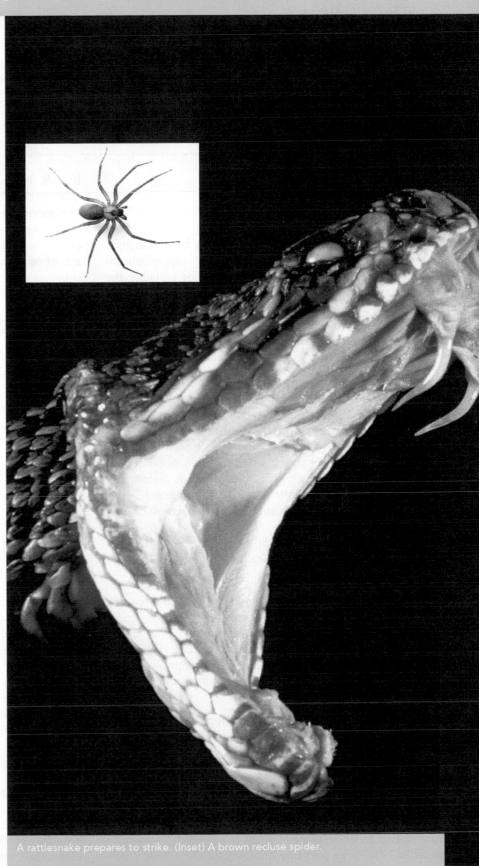

A rattlesnake prepares to strike. (Inset) A brown recluse spider.

AT A GLANCE

5.1 How Is the Structure of the Cell Membrane Related to Its Function?

5.2 How Do Substances Move Across Membranes?

5.3 How Do Specialized Junctions Allow Cells to Connect and Communicate?

LEARNING GOALS

LG1 Describe the components, structure, and function of cell membranes and explain how the different components contribute to membrane functions.

LG2 Explain how substances move across cell membranes.

LG3 Explain the basic concepts of diffusion and osmosis.

LG4 Describe the major types of junctions between cells and explain how these junctions function.

5.1 HOW IS THE STRUCTURE OF THE CELL MEMBRANE RELATED TO ITS FUNCTION?

All the membranes of a cell have a similar basic structure: proteins suspended in a double layer of phospholipids (**Fig. 5-1**). Phospholipids are responsible for isolating the cell's contents, whereas proteins are responsible for selectively exchanging substances and communicating with the environment, controlling biochemical reactions associated with the cell membrane, and forming connections between cells.

As you now know, all cells, as well as organelles within eukaryotic cells, are surrounded by membranes. Cell membranes perform several crucial functions:

- They selectively isolate the contents of membrane-enclosed organelles from the surrounding cytosol, and the cell's contents from the surrounding interstitial fluid.
- They regulate the exchange of essential substances between the cell and the interstitial fluid, or between membrane-enclosed organelles and the surrounding cytosol.
- They allow communication among the cells of multicellular organisms.
- They create attachments within and between cells.
- They regulate many biochemical reactions.

These are formidable tasks for a structure so thin that 10,000 membranes stacked atop one another would scarcely equal the thickness of this page. Membranes are not simply uniform sheets; they are complex structures whose different parts perform very distinct functions. Membranes vary from one tissue type to another, and their structures can also change dynamically in response to their surroundings.

Membranes Are "Fluid Mosaics" in Which Proteins Move Within Layers of Lipids

Before the 1970s, although cell biologists knew that cell membranes consist primarily of proteins and lipids, they did not know how these molecules create the structure of membranes. In 1972, S. J. Singer and G. L. Nicolson developed the **fluid mosaic model** of cell membranes, which is now known to be accurate. A **fluid** is any substance whose molecules can flow past one another; fluids include gases, liquids, and also cell membranes, whose molecules move quite freely within the thin layer. According to the fluid mosaic model, cell membranes consist of a fluid formed by a double layer (or *bilayer*) of phospholipids. A variety of different proteins form a kind of "mosaic," or patchwork, within the phospholipid bilayer. Both the phospholipids and the proteins are constantly shifting with respect to one another (see Fig. 5-1).

The Fluid Phospholipid Bilayer Helps to Isolate the Cell's Contents

A phospholipid consists of two very different parts: a "head" that is polar and hydrophilic (attracted to water) and a pair of fatty acid "tails" that are nonpolar and hydrophobic (not attracted to water). Membranes contain a variety of phospholipids with structures similar to that shown in **Figure 5-2**.

The arrangement of phospholipids in membranes arises from the fact that all cells are immersed in watery solutions. For example, single-celled organisms may live in fresh water or in the ocean, and water also saturates the cell walls that surround plant cells. The outer surfaces of animal plasma membranes are bathed in watery **interstitial fluid,** a weakly salty liquid resembling blood without its cells or large proteins. Inside the plasma membrane, the *cytosol* (the fluid portion of the cytoplasm) is mostly water. In these watery surroundings, phospholipids spontaneously arrange themselves into a double layer called a **phospholipid bilayer** (Fig. 5-3). Hydrogen bonds form between water and the hydrophilic phospholipid heads, causing the heads to face the water on either side. The phospholipid tails, being hydrophobic, cluster together within the bilayer.

The components of cell membranes are continually shifting position. The phospholipid molecules within each layer move relatively rapidly and the larger proteins move more slowly. To understand this movement, it is important to be aware that, at temperatures above absolute zero (−459.4°F or −273°C), atoms, molecules, and ions are in constant random motion. As the temperature increases, their rate of motion increases; at temperatures that support life, these particles move rapidly indeed. Phospholipid molecules do not bond to one another, so at body temperature, their constant random motion causes them to shift

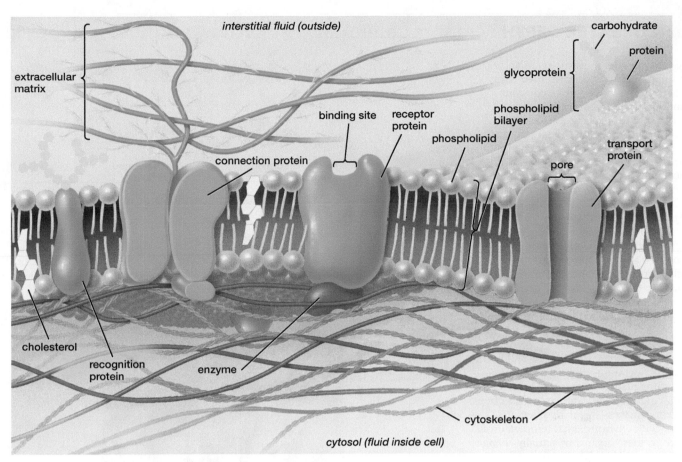

▲ FIGURE 5-1 **The plasma membrane** The plasma membrane is a bilayer of phospholipids interspersed with cholesterol molecules that form a fluid mosaic in which various proteins (blue) are embedded. Many proteins have carbohydrates attached to them, forming glycoproteins. Enzyme, recognition, connection, receptor, and transport proteins are illustrated.

about freely, although they generally maintain their orientation and only rarely flip between the two membrane layers. The flexible, fluid nature of the bilayer is very important for membrane function. As you breathe, move your eyes, and turn the pages of this book, cells in your body change shape. If plasma membranes were stiff, your cells would break open and die. This fluidity also allows

membrane-enclosed compartments to ferry substances into the cell, carry materials within the cell, and expel them to the outside, merging their membranes in the process (see Chapter 4). Most membranes maintain a consistency

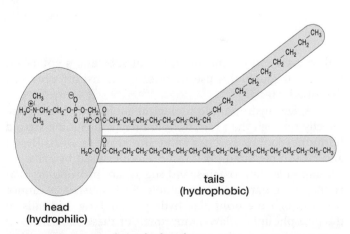

▲ FIGURE 5-2 **A phospholipid** Notice that a double bond in one of the fatty acid tails causes the tail to bend.

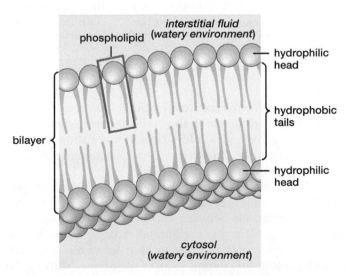

▲ FIGURE 5-3 **The phospholipid bilayer of the cell membrane**

IN GREATER DEPTH Membrane Fluidity, Function, and Phospholipids

Cell membranes must maintain an optimal fluidity to perform their many functions. Molecules are in constant random motion, and membrane phospholipids jiggle around more vigorously and maintain more distance from one another as the temperature increases. This extra space between molecules increases membrane fluidity. At cooler temperatures, membranes become less fluid as the phospholipids pack together more tightly.

Membrane fluidity is strongly influenced by the relative amounts of saturated and unsaturated fatty acid tails in membrane phospholipids. Why? Unsaturated fatty acids have one or more double bonds, causing them to kink (see Fig. 5-2). Kinked tails occupy more space and cannot pack as tightly together. Saturated fatty acid tails are straight and can pack more tightly (Fig. E5-1). But the body temperatures of many organisms—including plants, protists and bacteria, and "cold-blooded" animals such as frogs, fish, and snakes—regularly fluctuate along with environmental temperatures. To cope, these organisms actually change the composition of their membranes in response to changes in temperature, incorporating more saturated fatty acids into their membranes as the temperature rises, and replacing them with unsaturated fatty acids as the temperature falls. These molecular changes compensate for the effects of changing temperature, maintaining optimum membrane fluidity.

A few mammals have similar adaptations. For example, caribou (which live in the far north) maintain a core temperature of about 100°F (38°C), but allow the temperature of their lower legs to drop almost to freezing (32°F or 0°C),

more unsaturated
greater fluidity

more saturated
less fluidity

▲ FIGURE E5-1 **Tail kinks in phospholipids increase membrane fluidity**

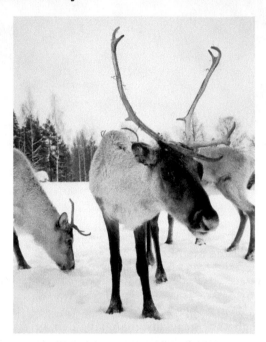

▲ FIGURE E5-2 **Caribou legs are adapted to cold**

thus conserving body heat as they stand in winter snow (Fig. E5-2). In caribou legs, the membranes of cells near the chilly hooves have lots of unsaturated fatty acids, whereas those near the warmer trunk have more saturated fatty acids. This gives cell membranes the necessary fluidity throughout the leg, despite large temperature differences from thigh to hoof.

similar to room temperature olive oil. But olive oil becomes a solid if you refrigerate it, so what happens to membranes when an organism gets cold? To learn more about how organisms adapt, see "In Greater Depth: Membrane Fluidity, Function, and Phospholipids."

All animal cell membranes contain cholesterol (see Fig. 5-1), which is especially abundant in the plasma membrane. Interactions between cholesterol and phospholipids help to stabilize the membrane, making it less fluid at higher temperatures and less solid at lower temperatures. A high cholesterol content reduces the permeability of the membrane to hydrophilic substances and small molecules that would otherwise diffuse through it. This allows the

cell to exert more control over what substances enter and leave it, through the use of selective transport proteins, described later.

A few hydrophobic biological molecules can diffuse directly through the phospholipid bilayer, including steroid hormones such as estrogen and testosterone (see Chapter 3) and fat-soluble vitamins. Most molecules used by cells, including salts, amino acids, and sugars, are hydrophilic; that is, they are polar and water soluble. Such substances cannot pass through the nonpolar, hydrophobic fatty acid tails of the phospholipid bilayer. Movement of these substances in or out of the cell relies on the "mosaic" of proteins within the membrane.

Vicious Venoms

Some of the most devastating effects of certain snake and spider venoms occur because they contain phospholipases, enzymes that break down phospholipids. You now know that phospholipids are a major component of cell membranes, which isolate the cell's contents from its surroundings. As the phospholipids degrade, the membranes become leaky, causing the cells to die. As the venom spreads, nearby tissues can be seriously damaged—as you will see later.

A Variety of Proteins Form a Mosaic Within the Membrane

Thousands of different membrane proteins are embedded within or attached to the surfaces of the phospholipid bilayer of cell membranes. Some membrane proteins bear carbohydrate groups that project from the outer membrane surface (the branched structures in Fig. 5-1). These proteins are called **glycoproteins** ("glyco" is from the Greek, meaning "sweet," and refers to the carbohydrate portion with its sugar subunits). Membrane proteins may be grouped into five major categories based on their function: enzymes, receptor proteins, recognition proteins, connection proteins, and transport proteins, described in the sections that follow.

Enzymes

Proteins that promote chemical reactions that synthesize or break apart biological molecules are called **enzymes** (described in Chapter 6). Although many enzymes are located within the cytoplasm, some span cell membranes and others are attached to membrane surfaces. For example, some plasma membrane enzymes help synthesize the *extracellular matrix*, a web of protein and glycoprotein fibers that fills spaces between animal cells (see Fig. 5-1). Plasma membrane enzymes in cells lining the small intestine complete the digestion of carbohydrates and proteins as these nutrients are taken into the cells.

Receptor Proteins

Most cells bear dozens of types of **receptor proteins** (some of which are glycoproteins; see Fig. 5-1) that span their plasma membranes. Receptor proteins allow cells to respond to specific messenger molecules (such as hormones) carried in the bloodstream. When the appropriate messenger molecule binds to a receptor protein, the receptor is activated, often by changing shape. This activation, in turn, causes a response inside the cell (**Fig. 5-4**). The response can lead to pores in the membrane opening or closing, or enzymes becoming active or inactive. Some hormones binding to receptor proteins stimulate cell division. Receptor proteins on cells of the immune system bind to molecules on the surface of invading bacteria or viruses so they can be destroyed.

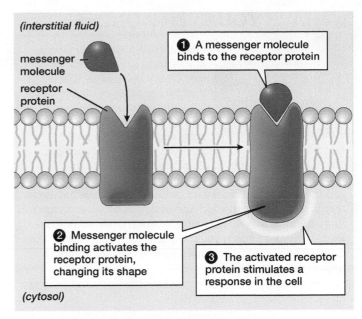

(interstitial fluid)

messenger molecule

receptor protein

❶ A messenger molecule binds to the receptor protein

❷ Messenger molecule binding activates the receptor protein, changing its shape

❸ The activated receptor protein stimulates a response in the cell

(cytosol)

▲ FIGURE 5-4 Receptor protein activation

Messenger molecules binding to receptor proteins often start a complex series of biochemical reactions in the cell. For example, the hormone epinephrine (adrenaline) is released in response to stress, such as you might experience if a mugger approached from a dark alley. Epinephrine binds to a specific receptor on muscle cells that activates an enzyme that causes formation of the messenger molecule cyclic adenosine monophosphate (cAMP; see Chapter 3). The cAMP then activates other enzymes, resulting in the breakdown of glycogen into glucose. The glucose is then broken down and its energy stored in adenosine triphosphate (ATP; see Chapter 3). ATP fuels muscle contraction, which you will need to escape the mugger!

Recognition Proteins

Recognition proteins are glycoproteins that serve as identification tags (see Fig. 5-1). The cells of each individual organism bear unique glycoproteins that identify the cells as "self." Immune cells ignore self-cells and attack invading cells, such as bacteria, that have different recognition proteins on their membranes. For successful organ transplants, the most important recognition glycoproteins of the donor must match those of the recipient so the organ won't be attacked by the recipient's immune system.

Connection Proteins

A diverse group of **connection proteins** anchors cell membranes in various ways. Some connection proteins help maintain cell shape by linking the plasma membrane to the cell's cytoskeleton. Other connection proteins span the plasma membrane, linking the cytoskeleton inside the cell with the extracellular matrix outside, which helps anchor the cell in place within a tissue (see Fig. 5-1). Connection proteins also form connections between adjacent cells, as described later in this chapter (see Fig. 5-16).

HAVE **YOU** EVER WONDERED ...

Why Your Fingers Fumble and Go Numb in the Cold?

Fingers are among the first parts of your body to suffer from the cold. That's because as your internal temperature begins to fall, your body conserves warmth for vital organs (such as your heart and brain) by reducing blood flow to your extremities. As a result, your hands get colder, the membranes in them become less fluid, their membrane channel proteins open and close more slowly, and the conduction of nerve impulses slows. Nerve impulses therefore do not reach your hand as fast as usual, and your fingers fumble as you try to zip your coat. When you can no longer feel your fingers, you know that their temperature has dropped so low that your sensory nerve cells are no longer transmitting signals.

Transport Proteins

Transport proteins (see Fig. 5-1) span the phospholipid bilayer and regulate the movement of hydrophilic molecules across the membrane. Some transport proteins form pores (channels) that can be opened or closed to allow specific substances to pass across the membrane. Other transport proteins bind substances and conduct them through the membrane, sometimes using cellular energy. Transport proteins are described later in this chapter.

CHECK YOUR LEARNING

Can you describe the components, structure, and functions of cell membranes? Are you able to explain how the different components of cell membranes contribute to their functions? Can you describe the fluid mosaic model of cell membranes?

5.2 HOW DO SUBSTANCES MOVE ACROSS MEMBRANES?

Some substances, especially individual molecules and ions, can move across membranes by diffusing through the phospholipid bilayer or traveling through specialized transport proteins.

To provide some background, we begin our study of membrane transport with a few definitions:

- A **solute** is a substance that can be dissolved (dispersed into individual atoms, molecules, or ions) in a **solvent,** which is a fluid (usually a liquid) capable of dissolving the solute. Water, in which all biological processes occur, dissolves so many different solutes that it is sometimes called the "universal solvent."
- The **concentration** of a substance defines the amount of solute in a given amount of solvent. The concentration of sugar solution, for example, is a measure of the number of molecules of sugar contained in a given volume of solution.
- A **gradient** is a difference in certain properties—such as temperature, pressure, electrical charge, or the concentration of a solute in a fluid—between two adjacent regions. Creation of a gradient requires the expenditure of energy. Over time, gradients break down unless energy is supplied to maintain them or a perfect barrier separates them. For example, a temperature gradient breaks down as heat energy is transmitted from a higher-temperature region to a lower-temperature region. Electrical gradients can drive the movement of charged ions, which are pulled toward an oppositely charged region. Gradients of concentration or pressure cause molecules or ions to move from one region to another, equalizing the difference. Cells use energy-requiring transport proteins to generate and maintain **concentration gradients,** or differences in solute concentrations across their membranes.

Molecules in Fluids Diffuse in Response to Gradients

Recall that atoms, molecules, and ions are in constant random motion. As a result of this motion, molecules and ions in solution are continuously bombarding one another and the structures surrounding them. Over time, random movements of solutes produce a net movement from regions of high concentration to regions of low concentration, a process called **diffusion.** The greater the concentration gradient, the more rapidly diffusion occurs. If nothing opposes this diffusion (such as electrical charge, pressure differences, or physical

❶ A drop of dye is placed in water

❷ Dye molecules diffuse into the water; water molecules diffuse into the dye

❸ Both dye molecules and water molecules are evenly dispersed

dye molecules

water molecule

▶ FIGURE 5-5 **Diffusion of a dye in water**

barriers), then the random movement of molecules will continue until the substance is evenly dispersed throughout the fluid. In an analogy to gravity, molecules moving from regions of high concentration to regions of low concentration are described as moving "down" their concentration gradients.

To watch diffusion in action, place a drop of food coloring in a glass of water (Fig. 5-5). Random motion propels dye molecules both into and out of the dye droplet, but there is a net transfer of dye into the water and of water into the dye, down their concentration gradients. The net movement of dye will continue until it is uniformly dispersed in the water. If you compare the diffusion of a dye in hot and cold water, you will see that heat increases the diffusion rate because heat causes molecules to move faster.

SUMMING UP Principles of Diffusion

- Diffusion is the net movement of molecules down a gradient from high to low concentration.
- The greater the concentration gradient, the faster the rate of diffusion.
- The higher the temperature, the faster the rate of diffusion.
- If no other processes intervene, diffusion will continue until the concentrations become equal throughout the solution; that is, until the concentration gradient is eliminated.

Movement Through Membranes Occurs by Passive Transport and Energy-Requiring Transport

Gradients of ions and molecules across cell membranes are crucial for life; a cell without gradients is dead. Proteins in cell membranes must constantly use energy to create and maintain these concentration gradients because gradients underlie many crucial biochemical processes. For example, neurons depend on the flow of specific ions down their concentration gradients to produce the electrical signals that underlie sensation, movement, and thought. Plasma membranes are described as **selectively permeable** because their proteins selectively allow only certain ions or molecules to pass through, or permeate. The selective permeability of the plasma membrane creates a barrier that helps maintain the gradients that characterize all cells.

A cell's plasma membrane permits substances to move through it in two different ways: passive transport and energy-requiring transport (Table 5-1). **Passive transport** involves diffusion of substances across cell membranes down their concentration gradients, whereas **energy-requiring transport** requires that the cell expend energy to move substances across membranes for example, into or out of the cell, usually against a concentration gradient.

Passive Transport Includes Simple Diffusion, Facilitated Diffusion, and Osmosis

Diffusion can occur within a fluid or across a membrane that is permeable to the diffusing substance. Many molecules cross plasma membranes by diffusion, driven by

TABLE 5-1 Transport Across Membranes	
Passive Transport	Diffusion of substances across a membrane down a gradient of concentration, pressure, or electrical charge; does not require cellular energy.
Simple diffusion	Diffusion of water, dissolved gases, or lipid-soluble molecules through the phospholipid bilayer of a membrane.
Facilitated diffusion	Diffusion of water, ions, or water-soluble molecules through a membrane via a channel or carrier protein.
Osmosis	Diffusion of water across a selectively permeable membrane from a region of higher free water concentration to a region of lower free water concentration.
Energy-Requiring Transport	Movement of substances through membranes using cellular energy, usually supplied by ATP.
Active transport	Movement of individual small molecules or ions against their concentration gradients through membrane-spanning proteins.
Endocytosis	Movement of fluids, specific molecules, or particles into a cell; occurs as the plasma membrane engulfs the substance in a membranous sac that pinches off and enters the cytosol.
Exocytosis	Movement of particles or large molecules out of a cell; occurs as a membrane within the cell encloses the material, moves to the cell surface, and fuses with the plasma membrane, allowing its contents to diffuse out.

concentration differences between the cytosol and the interstitial fluid.

Some Molecules Move Across Membranes by Simple Diffusion

Some molecules diffuse directly through the phospholipid bilayer of cell membranes, a process called **simple diffusion** (Fig. 5-6a). Very small molecules with no net charge, such as water, oxygen, and carbon dioxide, can travel across cell membranes by simple diffusion. Lipid-soluble molecules, regardless of their size, may also use this method. Such molecules include ethyl alcohol (found in alcoholic beverages), vitamins A, D, and E, and steroid hormones (described in Chapter 3). A larger concentration gradient, higher temperature, smaller molecular size, and greater solubility in lipids all increase the rate of simple diffusion.

How can water—a polar molecule—diffuse directly through the hydrophobic (literally "water-fearing") phospholipid bilayer? Because water molecules are so small and so abundant in both the cytosol and the interstitial fluid, some stray into the thicket of phospholipid tails, and the random movement of these water molecules carries them through the membrane. Because simple diffusion of water through the phospholipid bilayer is relatively slow, many cell types have specific transport proteins for water, described a bit later.

(a) Simple diffusion through the phospholipid bilayer

(b) Facilitated diffusion through carrier proteins

(c) Facilitated diffusion through channel proteins

(d) Osmosis through aquaporins or the phospholipid bilayer

▲ **FIGURE 5-6 Types of diffusion through the plasma membrane (a)** Molecules that are very small, uncharged, or lipid soluble move directly through the phospholipid bilayer by simple diffusion. Here, oxygen molecules diffuse from the interstitial fluid into the cell down their concentration gradient (red arrow). **(b)** Carrier proteins have binding sites for specific molecules (such as the glucose shown here). Binding of the transported molecule causes the carrier to change shape, shuttling the molecule across the membrane down its concentration gradient. **(c)** Facilitated diffusion through channel proteins allows ions to cross membranes. Here, chloride ions diffuse down their concentration gradient into the cell through chloride channels. **(d)** Osmosis is the diffusion of water. Water molecules can diffuse directly through the phospholipid bilayer by simple diffusion, or they can pass far more rapidly by facilitated diffusion through water channels called aquaporins.

Some Molecules Cross Membranes by Facilitated Diffusion Using Membrane Transport Proteins

The phospholipid bilayers of cell membranes are quite impermeable to larger, polar molecules (such as sugars) and to ions (for example, K^+, Na^+, Cl^-, and Ca^{2+}). The charges on these substances cause water molecules (which are polar) to cluster around them, forming an aggregation that is too large to move directly through the phospholipid bilayer. So ions and polar molecules must use specific transport proteins to move through cell membranes, a process called **facilitated diffusion.** Two types of proteins allow facilitated diffusion: carrier proteins and channel proteins. No energy is used by these transport proteins, which only facilitate diffusion down a concentration gradient either into or out of the cell.

Carrier proteins span the cell membrane and have regions that loosely bind certain ions or specific molecules such as sugars or small proteins. This binding causes carrier proteins to change shape and transfer the bound molecules across the membrane. For example, glucose carrier proteins in plasma membranes allow this sugar to diffuse from the interstitial fluid into cells, which continuously use up glucose to meet their energy needs (**Fig. 5-6b**).

Channel proteins form pores through the cell membrane. For example, the cell membranes of mitochondria and chloroplasts have pores that allow passage of a variety of water-soluble substances. In contrast, ion channel proteins (ion channels) are small and highly selective (**Fig. 5-6c**). All cells maintain gradients of several different ions across their membranes. Many ion channels help preserve these gradients by remaining closed unless they are opened by specific stimuli, such as a nerve impulse. Ion channel proteins are selective because their interior diameters limit the size of the ions that can pass through, and certain channel

protein amino acids in the pore have weak electrical charges that attract specific ions and repel others. For example, slight negative charges on some amino acids inside Na^+ channels attract Na^+ but repel Cl^-.

Many cells have specialized water channel proteins called **aquaporins** (literally, "water pores"; **Fig. 5-6d**). The narrow aquaporin channels are selective for water molecules, which are extremely small. Some amino acids within the aquaporin channel protein have slight positive charges that attract the negative poles of water but repel positive ions (see **Fig. E5-4b**). To learn more, see "Science in Action: The Discovery of Aquaporins."

Osmosis Is the Diffusion of Water Across Selectively Permeable Membranes

Osmosis is the diffusion of water across a selectively permeable membrane in response to gradients of concentration, pressure, or temperature. Here, we will focus on osmosis from a region of higher water concentration to a region of lower water concentration.

What do we mean when we describe a solution as having a "high water concentration" or a "low water concentration"? The answer is simple: Pure water has the highest possible water concentration. Any substance that dissolves in water (any solute) reduces the water concentration by displacing some of the water molecules in a given volume. Polar solutes or ions also attract water molecules, so the water molecules aren't free to move across a water-permeable membrane. Therefore, the higher the concentration of solute, the lower the concentration of water that is available to move across a membrane. Consequently, there will be a net movement of water molecules from the solution with more free water molecules (a lower solute concentration) into the solution with fewer free water molecules

(a) A sac in an isotonic solution

(b) A sac in a hypertonic solution

(c) A sac in a hypotonic solution

◄FIGURE 5-7 **The effect of solute concentration on osmosis** We start with three sacs made of membrane that is selectively permeable to water (not to sugar, represented by the red balls). We place equal volumes of the same concentration of sugar water in each sac. We then immerse each in a beaker filled with a different concentration of sugar water—**(a)** isotonic, **(b)** hypertonic, or **(c)** hypotonic—to that in the sac. The figure shows the results after an hour. The blue arrows indicate relative water movement into and out of the sac.

QUESTION If the concentration of solute in the sac were doubled, how would the size of the sac compare to its size in each of the situations shown?

(a higher solute concentration). For example, water will move by osmosis from a solution with less dissolved sugar into a solution with more dissolved sugar. Because there are more free water molecules in the less-concentrated sugar solution, more water molecules will collide with—and thus move through—the water-permeable membrane on that side. The concentration of solute in water determines the solution's *osmotic strength* or its tendency to attract water across a membrane. The greater the solute concentration, the greater the osmotic strength.

Solutions with equal concentrations of solute (and thus equal concentrations of water) are described as being **isotonic** to one another ("iso" means "same"). When isotonic solutions are separated by a water-permeable membrane, there is no net movement of water between them (**Fig. 5-7a**). When a membrane that is selectively permeable to water separates solutions with different concentrations of a solute, the solution that contains a greater concentration of solute is described as being **hypertonic** ("hyper" means "greater than") to the less concentrated solution (**Fig. 5-7b**). The more dilute solution is described as **hypotonic** ("hypo" means "below"; **Fig. 5-7c**). Water tends to move through water-permeable membranes from hypotonic solutions into hypertonic solutions.

SUMMING UP Principles of Osmosis

- Osmosis is the movement of water through a selectively water-permeable membrane by simple diffusion or by facilitated diffusion through aquaporins.
- Water moves across a selectively water-permeable membrane down its concentration gradient from the side with a higher concentration of free water molecules to the side with a lower concentration of free water molecules.
- Dissolved substances, called solutes, reduce the concentration of free water molecules in a solution.
- If two solutions are separated by a membrane that is selectively permeable to water, the solution with a higher solute concentration is hypertonic and has a higher osmotic strength; the solution with the lower solute concentration is hypotonic and has a lower osmotic strength.

Osmosis Across the Plasma Membrane Plays an Important Role in the Lives of Cells

Osmosis across plasma membranes is crucial to many biological processes, including water uptake by the roots of plants, absorption of dietary water from the intestine, and the reabsorption of water in kidneys. In addition, organisms that live in fresh water must continuously expend energy to counteract osmosis because their cells are hypertonic to the surrounding water. For example, protists such as *Paramecium* use cellular energy to pump salts from the cytosol into their contractile vacuoles. Water follows by osmosis and is squirted out through a pore in the plasma membrane (see Fig. 4-15).

Nearly every living plant cell is supported by water that enters through osmosis. Most plant cells have a large central vacuole. The membrane that encloses this vacuole is rich in aquaporins. Dissolved substances stored in the vacuole make its contents hypertonic to the surrounding cytosol, which in turn is usually hypertonic to the interstitial fluid that bathes the cells. Water therefore flows into the cytosol and then into the vacuole by osmosis, creating **turgor pressure** within the cell. Turgor pressure inflates the cell, forcing the cytosol within its surrounding plasma membrane against the cell wall (**Fig. 5-8a**). If you forget to water a houseplant, the cytosol and cell vacuole lose water, causing the cell to shrink away from its cell wall. Like a leaky balloon, the plant droops as its cells lose turgor pressure (**Fig. 5-8b**). Now you know why grocery stores are always spraying their leafy produce: to keep it looking perky and fresh with full central vacuoles.

In animals, the interstitial fluid is usually isotonic to the cell cytosol. Although the concentrations of specific solutes are rarely the same both inside and outside of cells, the total concentrations of water and solutes inside and out are equal. As a result, there is no overall tendency for water to enter or leave animal cells. To demonstrate the importance of maintaining isotonic conditions between fragile cells and their surrounding interstitial fluid, we can observe cells placed in solutions with different solute concentrations. In an isotonic salt solution, red blood cells (which have an

cytoplasm   central vacuole

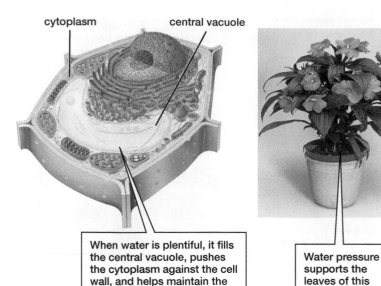

When water is plentiful, it fills the central vacuole, pushes the cytoplasm against the cell wall, and helps maintain the cell's shape

Water pressure supports the leaves of this impatiens plant

(a) Turgor pressure provides support

cell wall   plasma membrane

When water is scarce, the central vacuole shrinks and the cell wall is unsupported

Deprived of the support from water, the plant wilts

(b) Loss of turgor pressure causes the plant to wilt

▲ FIGURE 5-8 **Turgor pressure in plant cells** Aquaporins allow water to move rapidly in and out of the central vacuoles of plant cells. **(a)** The cell and the plant are supported by water turgor pressure. **(b)** The cell and the plant have lost turgor pressure and support due to dehydration.

QUESTION If a plant cell is placed in water containing no solutes, will the cell eventually burst? What about an animal cell? Explain.

abundance of aquaporins in their plasma membranes) retain their normal size (**Fig. 5-9a**). But if the salt solution is hypertonic to the cytosol of the blood cells, water leaves by osmosis, causing the cells to shrivel (**Fig. 5-9b**). Immersion in a hypotonic salt solution, in contrast, causes the cells to swell (and eventually burst) as water diffuses in (**Fig. 5-9c**).

Energy-Requiring Transport Includes Active Transport, Endocytosis, and Exocytosis

A multitude of cellular activities rely on the energy-expending activities of active transport, endocytosis, and exocytosis—all necessary to sustain life. These processes are crucial to maintaining concentration gradients, acquiring food, excreting wastes, and (in multicellular organisms) communicating with other cells.

Cells Maintain Concentration Gradients Using Active Transport

By building gradients and then allowing them to run down under specific circumstances, cells regulate their biochemical reactions, respond to external stimuli, and acquire and store chemical energy. Energy stored as concentration gradients of ions powers the electrical signals of neurons, the contraction of muscles, and the generation of ATP in mitochondria and chloroplasts (see Chapters 7 and 8). But gradients do not form spontaneously—they require active transport across a membrane.

During **active transport,** membrane proteins use cellular energy to move molecules or ions across a plasma membrane *against* their concentration gradients, which means that the substances are transported from areas of lower concentration to areas of higher concentration (**Fig. 5-10**). For example, every cell must acquire some nutrients that are less concentrated in the environment than in the cell's cytoplasm. In addition, many ions, such as sodium and calcium ions, are actively transported to maintain them at much lower concentrations in the cytosol than in the interstitial fluid. Nerve cells maintain large ion concentration gradients because generating their electrical signals requires rapid, passive flow of ions when channels are opened. After these ions diffuse into or out of the cell, their concentration gradients must be restored by active transport.

Active-transport proteins span the width of the membrane and have two binding regions. One of these loosely binds with a specific molecule or ion, such as a calcium ion (Ca^{2+}), as shown in **Figure 5-10 ❶**; the second region, on the inside of the membrane, binds ATP. The ATP donates energy to the protein, causing the protein to change shape and move the calcium ion across the membrane (**Fig. 5-10 ❷**). The energy for active transport comes from breaking the high-energy bond that links the last of the three phosphate groups in ATP. As it releases its stored energy, ATP becomes ADP (adenosine diphosphate) plus a free phosphate (**Fig. 5-10 ❸**). Active-transport proteins are often called pumps because, like pumping water into an elevated storage tank, they use energy to move ions or molecules "uphill" against a concentration gradient.

Endocytosis Allows Cells to Engulf Particles or Fluids

A cell may need to acquire materials from its extracellular environment that are too large to move directly through the membrane. These materials are engulfed by the plasma membrane and are transported within the cell inside vesicles.

(a) Red blood cells in an isotonic solution

(b) Red blood cells in a hypertonic solution

(c) Red blood cells in a hypotonic solution

▲ FIGURE 5-9 **The effects of osmosis on red blood cells** (a) The cells are immersed in an isotonic solution and retain their normal dimpled shape. **(b)** The cells shrink when placed in a hypertonic solution, as more water moves out than flows in. **(c)** The cells expand when placed in a hypotonic solution.

QUESTION A student pours some distilled water into a sample of blood. Returning later, she looks at the blood under a microscope and sees no blood cells at all. What happened?

This energy-requiring process is called **endocytosis** (Greek for "into the cell"). Here, we describe three forms of endocytosis based on the size and type of material acquired and the method of acquisition: pinocytosis, receptor-mediated endocytosis, and phagocytosis.

In **pinocytosis** ("cell drinking"), a very small patch of plasma membrane dimples inward as it surrounds interstitial fluid, and then the membrane buds off into the cytosol as a tiny vesicle (**Fig. 5-11**). Pinocytosis moves a droplet of interstitial fluid, contained within the dimpling patch of

membrane, into the cell. Therefore, the cell acquires materials in the same concentration as in the interstitial fluid.

Cells use **receptor-mediated endocytosis** to selectively take up specific molecules or complexes of molecules (for example, packets containing protein and cholesterol) that cannot move through channels or diffuse through the plasma membrane (**Fig. 5-12**). Receptor-mediated endocytosis relies on specialized receptor proteins located on the plasma membrane in thickened depressions called *coated pits*. After the appropriate molecules bind these receptors,

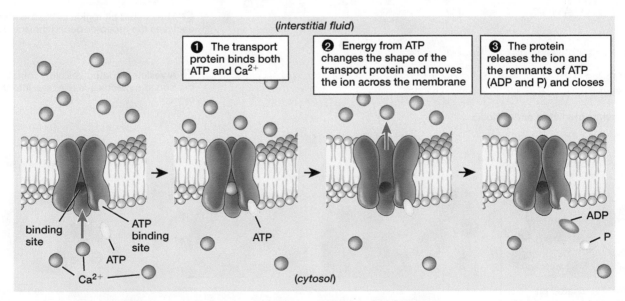

(interstitial fluid)

❶ The transport protein binds both ATP and Ca^{2+}

❷ Energy from ATP changes the shape of the transport protein and moves the ion across the membrane

❸ The protein releases the ion and the remnants of ATP (ADP and P) and closes

binding site

ATP binding site

ATP

Ca^{2+}

ATP

ADP

P

(cytosol)

▲ FIGURE 5-10 **Active transport** Active transport uses cellular energy to move molecules across the plasma membrane against a concentration gradient. A transport protein (blue) has an ATP binding site and a binding site for the molecules to be transported; in this case, calcium ions (Ca^{2+}). Notice that when ATP donates its energy, it loses its third phosphate group and becomes ADP plus a free phosphate.

(a) Pinocytosis

(b) TEM of pinocytosis

❶ A dimple forms in the plasma membrane, which ❷ deepens and surrounds the interstitial fluid. ❸ The membrane encloses the interstitial fluid, forming a vesicle.

▲ FIGURE 5-11 Pinocytosis The circled numbers correspond to both (a) the diagram and (b) the transmission electron micrograph (TEM).

the coated pit deepens into a pocket that pinches off, forming a vesicle that carries the molecules into the cytosol.

Phagocytosis (from the Greek for "cell eating") moves large particles—sometimes including whole microorganisms—into the cell (**Fig. 5-13a**). When the freshwater protist *Amoeba*, for example, senses a tasty *Paramecium*, the *Amoeba* extends parts of its surface membrane. These membrane extensions are called pseudopods (Latin for "false feet"). The pseudopods fuse around the prey, thus enclosing it inside a vesicle called a **food vacuole**, for digestion (**Fig. 5-13b**). Like *Amoeba*, white blood cells use phagocytosis followed by digestion to engulf and destroy invading bacteria, in a drama that occurs constantly within your body (**Fig. 5-13c**).

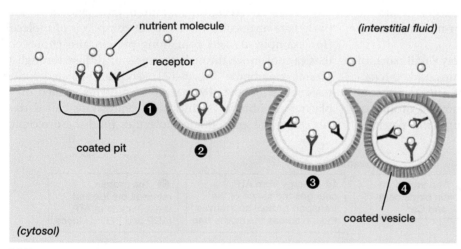

❶ Receptor proteins for specific molecules or complexes of molecules are localized at coated pit sites.

❷ The receptors bind the molecules and the membrane dimples inward.

❸ The coated pit region of the membrane encloses the receptor-bound molecules.

❹ A vesicle ("coated vesicle") containing the bound molecules is released into the cytosol.

(a) Receptor-mediated endocytosis

(b) TEM of receptor-mediated endocytosis

▲ FIGURE 5-12 Receptor-mediated endocytosis The numbers correspond to both (a) the diagram and (b) the transmission electron micrographs (TEM).

❶ The plasma membrane extends pseudopods toward an extracellular particle (for example, food). ❷ The ends of the pseudopods fuse, encircling the particle. ❸ A vesicle called a food vacuole is formed containing the engulfed particle.

(a) Phagocytosis

(b) An *Amoeba* engulfs a *Paramecium*

(c) A white blood cell engulfs a disease-causing fungal cell

▲ FIGURE 5-13 Phagocytosis (a) The mechanism of phagocytosis. (b) Amoebas use phagocytosis to feed, and (c) white blood cells use phagocytosis to engulf disease-causing microorganisms.

Exocytosis Moves Material Out of the Cell

Cells also use energy to dispose of undigested particles of waste or to secrete substances such as hormones into the interstitial fluid, a process called **exocytosis** ("out of the cell"; Fig. 5-14). During exocytosis, a membrane-enclosed vesicle carrying material to be expelled moves to the cell surface, where the vesicle's membrane fuses with the cell's plasma membrane. The vesicle's contents then diffuse into the fluid outside the cell.

Exchange of Materials Across Membranes Influences Cell Size and Shape

As you learned in Chapter 4, most cells are too small to be seen with the naked eye; they range from about 1 to 100 micrometers (millionths of a meter) in diameter (see Fig. 4-1). Why are cells so small? Assuming that a cell is roughly spherical, the larger its diameter, the farther away are its innermost contents from the plasma membrane. To acquire nutrients and eliminate wastes, all parts of the cell rely on the slow process of diffusion.

In a hypothetical giant cell 8.5 inches (20 centimeters) in diameter, oxygen molecules would take more than 200 days to diffuse to the center of the cell, but by then the cell would be long dead for lack of oxygen. In addition, as a sphere enlarges, its volume increases more rapidly than does its surface area. So a large, roughly spherical cell (which would require even more nutrients and produce more wastes than a smaller cell) would have a relatively smaller area of membrane—not enough to accomplish this exchange (Fig. 5-15).

This constraint limits the size of most cells. However, some cells, such as nerve and muscle cells, have an extremely elongated shape that increases their membrane surface area, keeping the ratio of surface area to volume relatively high.

CHECK YOUR LEARNING

Can you explain simple diffusion, facilitated diffusion, and osmosis? Can you describe active transport, endocytosis, and exocytosis? Can you explain how the need to exchange materials across membranes influences cell size and shape?

► FIGURE 5-14 Exocytosis Exocytosis is functionally the reverse of endocytosis.

QUESTION How does exocytosis differ from diffusion of materials out of a cell?

Material is enclosed in a vesicle that fuses with the plasma membrane, allowing its contents to diffuse out

0.2 micrometer

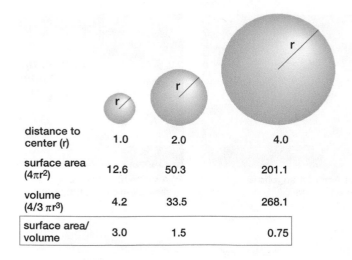

distance to center (r)	1.0	2.0	4.0
surface area ($4\pi r^2$)	12.6	50.3	201.1
volume ($4/3\ \pi r^3$)	4.2	33.5	268.1
surface area/ volume	3.0	1.5	0.75

◄FIGURE 5-15 **Surface area and volume relationships** As the size of a sphere (or a spherical cell) increases, its volume (or the amount of cytoplasm it contains) increases much more than its surface area (its plasma membrane). This means that cells with a roughly spherical shape must remain quite small to allow the cell surface to meet the metabolic needs of the amount of cytoplasm inside.

5.3 HOW DO SPECIALIZED JUNCTIONS ALLOW CELLS TO CONNECT AND COMMUNICATE?

In multicellular organisms, some specialized structures on plasma membranes hold cells together, while others provide avenues through which cells communicate with neighboring cells. Here we discuss four major types of cell-connecting structures: desmosomes, tight junctions, gap junctions, and plasmodesmata. The first three types of junctions are found only in animal cells, and plasmodesmata are restricted to plant cells.

Desmosomes Attach Cells Together

Attachment structures called **desmosomes** (Fig. 5-16a) join cells in tissues that are repeatedly stretched, such as the skin, intestines, and heart. These strong junctions prevent the forces on these tissues from pulling them apart. In a desmosome, anchoring proteins lie on the inner side of each membrane of adjacent cells. These anchoring proteins are attached to intermediate filaments of the cytoskeleton that extend through the cytoplasm. Linking proteins extend from each plasma membrane, spanning the narrow space between the adjacent cells and joining them firmly together.

Tight Junctions Make Cell Attachments Leakproof

Tight junctions are formed by proteins that span the plasma membranes at corresponding sites on adjacent cells. As illustrated in **Figure 5-16b**, tight junctions join cells almost as if the

(a) Desmosome

(b) Tight junctions

(c) Gap junctions

(d) Plasmodesmata

◄FIGURE 5-16 **Cell attachment structures** (a) Desmosomes form strong attachments. Anchoring proteins on adjacent plasma membranes are bound together by linking proteins. Protein filaments (intermediate filaments) attach to the cytoskeleton inside each cell, strengthening the connection. **(b)** Tight junction proteins of adjacent cells fuse to one another. They form a stitch-like pattern that prevents movement of substances between the plasma membranes of adjacent cells. **(c)** Gap junctions contain protein channels that interconnect the cytosol of adjacent cells, allowing small molecules and ions to pass between them. **(d)** Plasmodesmata connect the cytosol and plasma membranes of adjacent plant cells, allowing coordination of their metabolic activities.

SCIENCE IN ACTION The Discovery of Aquaporins

The French microbiologist Louis Pasteur's observation that "Chance favors the prepared mind" is as true today as it was when he first expressed it in the 1800s. Scientists have long realized that osmosis directly through the phospholipid bilayer is much too slow to account for water movement across certain cell membranes, such as those of red blood cells (see Fig. 5-9). But attempts to identify selective transport proteins for water repeatedly failed.

Then, as often happens in science, chance and prepared minds met. In the mid-1980s, Peter Agre (Fig. E5-3), then at the Johns Hopkins School of Medicine in Maryland, was attempting to determine the structure of a glycoprotein on red blood cells. The protein he isolated was contaminated, however, with large quantities of an unknown protein.

Instead of discarding the unknown protein, he and his coworkers collaborated to determine its structure. To test the hypothesis that the protein was involved with water transport, they performed an experiment using frog egg cells, whose membranes are nearly impermeable to water. Agre's team injected frog eggs with messenger RNA that coded for the mystery protein. This caused the eggs to synthesize this protein and insert it into their plasma membranes. Agre discovered that normal frog egg cells swelled only slightly when placed in a hypotonic solution, while those with the protein swelled rapidly and burst (Fig. E5-4a). Further studies revealed that no other ions or molecules could move through this channel protein, which Agre named "aquaporin." In

2000, he and other research teams reported the three-dimensional structure of aquaporin (Fig. E5-4b). Billions of water molecules can move through an aquaporin in single file every second, while larger molecules and small positively charged ions (such as hydrogen ions) cannot move through.

Many types of aquaporins have now been identified, and aquaporins have been found in all forms of life that have been

investigated. For example, the plasma membrane of the central vacuole of plant cells is rich in aquaporins, which allows the central vacuole to fill rapidly when water is available (see Fig. 5-8). In 2003, Agre shared the Nobel Prize in Chemistry for his discovery—the result of chance, careful observation, persistence, and perhaps a bit of what Agre himself describes modestly as "sheer blind luck."

(a) Frog eggs

(b) Aquaporin

▲FIGURE E5-4 Function and structure of aquaporins
(a) The frog egg on the right has aquaporins in its plasma membrane; the egg on the left does not. They have both been immersed in a hypotonic solution for 30 seconds. The egg on the right has burst, whereas that on the left has swollen only slightly. (b) An aquaporin (shown here in cross-section) is formed by a membrane-spanning protein. Within the channel, charged amino acids attract water molecules, promoting their movement in either direction while repelling other substances.

▲FIGURE E5-3 Peter Agre

two adjacent membranes had been stitched together. Interlocking tight junction proteins create barriers that prevent nearly all substances from passing between the plasma membranes of the linked cells. For example, tight junctions in the bladder prevent cellular wastes in urine from leaking back into the blood. In the digestive tract, tight junctions between the cells that line it protect the rest of the body from the acids, digestive enzymes, and bacteria found in its various compartments.

Gap Junctions and Plasmodesmata Allow Direct Communication Between Cells

The cells of many tissues in the animal body are interconnected by **gap junctions** (Fig. 5-16c), clusters of channels ranging in number from a few to thousands. The channels are formed by six-sided tubes of protein called *connexons* that span the plasma membrane. Connexons line up so that their central pores link the cytosol of adjacent cells. The small size of the pore allows small water-soluble molecules—including sugars, various ions, amino acids, and small messenger molecules such as cAMP—to pass between cells, but excludes organelles and large molecules such as proteins. Gap junctions coordinate the metabolic activities of many cells. They allow electrical signals to pass extremely rapidly among certain groups of nerve cells, and they synchronize contraction of heart muscle and of smooth muscles, such as in the walls of the digestive tract, bladder, and uterus.

Plasmodesmata are channels that link nearly all adjacent plant cells. These openings are lined with plasma membrane and filled with cytosol, so the membranes and the cytosol of adjacent cells are continuous with one another at plasmodesmata (Fig. 5-16d). Many plant cells have thousands of plasmodesmata, allowing water, nutrients, and hormones to pass quite freely from one cell to another. These connections among plant cells serve a function similar to the gap junctions of animal cells in coordinating metabolic activities.

CASE STUDY revisited

Vicious Venoms

Although the "witches' brew" of rattlesnake and spider venoms differs among species, many contain phospholipases that break down membrane phospholipids, causing cells to rupture and die. Cell death destroys the tissue around a rattlesnake or brown recluse spider bite (Fig. 5-17). When phospholipases attack the membranes of capillary cells, these tiny blood vessels rupture and release blood into the tissue surrounding the wound. In extreme cases, capillary damage can lead to internal bleeding. By attacking the membranes of red blood cells, rattlesnake venoms can cause anemia (an inadequate number of oxygen-carrying red blood cells). Rattlesnake phospholipases also attack muscle cell membranes; this attack caused extensive damage in Justin Schwartz's forearm. Justin required large quantities of antivenin, which contains specialized proteins that bind and neutralize the snake venom proteins. Unfortunately, no antivenin is available for brown recluse bites, and treatment generally consists of preventing infection, controlling pain and swelling, and waiting—sometimes for months—for the wound to heal.

Although both snake and spider bites can have serious consequences, very few of the spiders and snakes found in the Americas are dangerous to people. The best defense is to learn which of these live in your area and where they prefer to hang out. If your activities bring you to such places, wear protective clothing—and always look before you reach! Knowledge can help us coexist with spiders and snakes, avoid their bites, and keep our cell membranes intact.

Consider This

Phospholipases are found in animal digestive tracts as well as in snake venom. How does the role of phospholipase in snake venom differ from its role in the snake's digestive tract?

(a) Justin's rattlesnake bite

(b) Brown recluse spider bite

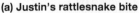

▲ FIGURE 5-17 **Phospholipases in venoms can destroy cells** Both **(a)** Justin Schwartz's hand 36 hours after the rattlesnake bite and **(b)** a brown recluse spider bite show extensive tissue destruction caused by phospholipases.

Throughout this textbook, we will return many times to the concepts of membrane structure and transport described in this chapter. Understanding the diversity of membrane lipids and proteins is the key to understanding not just the isolated cell, but also entire organs, which could not perform as they do without the specialized membrane properties of their cells.

CHAPTER REVIEW

Summary of Key Concepts

5.1 How Is the Structure of the Cell Membrane Related to Its Function?

Cell membrane consists of a bilayer of phospholipids in which a variety of proteins are embedded, often described as a fluid mosaic. The plasma membrane isolates the cytoplasm from the external environment, regulates the flow of materials into and out of the cell, allows communication between cells, allows attachments within and between cells, and regulates many biochemical reactions. There are five major types of membrane proteins: (1) enzymes, which promote chemical reactions; (2) receptor proteins, which bind molecules and trigger changes within the cell; (3) recognition proteins, which label the cell; (4) connection proteins, which anchor the plasma membrane to the cytoskeleton and extracellular matrix or bind cells to one another; and (5) transport proteins, which regulate the movement of most water-soluble substances through the membrane.

5.2 How Do Substances Move Across Membranes?

Diffusion is the movement of particles from regions of higher concentration to regions of lower concentration. In simple diffusion, water, dissolved gases, and lipid-soluble molecules diffuse through the phospholipid bilayer. During facilitated diffusion, carrier proteins or channel proteins allow water and water-soluble molecules to cross the membrane down their concentration gradients without expending cellular energy. Osmosis is the diffusion of water across a selectively permeable membrane down its concentration gradient through the phospholipid bilayer or through aquaporins.

Energy-requiring transport includes active transport, in which carrier proteins use cellular energy (ATP) to drive the movement of molecules across the plasma membrane against concentration gradients. Interstitial fluid, large molecules, and food particles may be acquired by endocytosis, which includes pinocytosis, receptor-mediated endocytosis, and phagocytosis. The secretion of substances, such as hormones, and the excretion of particulate cellular wastes are accomplished by exocytosis.

Cells exchange materials between the cytoplasm and the external environment by the slow process of diffusion through the plasma membrane. This requires that no part of the cell be too far from the plasma membrane, limiting the diameter of cells.

5.3 How Do Specialized Junctions Allow Cells to Connect and Communicate?

Animal cell junctions include (1) desmosomes, which attach adjacent cells and prevent tissues from tearing apart during ordinary movements; (2) tight junctions, which leak-proof the spaces between adjacent cells; and (3) gap junctions that connect the cytosol of adjacent cells. Plasmodesmata interconnect the cytosol of adjacent plant cells.

Key Terms

active transport 84	hypertonic 83
aquaporin 82	hypotonic 83
carrier protein 82	interstitial fluid 76
channel protein 82	isotonic 83
concentration 80	osmosis 82
concentration gradient 80	passive transport 81
connection protein 79	phagocytosis 86
desmosome 88	phospholipid bilayer 76
diffusion 80	pinocytosis 85
endocytosis 85	plasmodesmata 90
energy-requiring transport 81	receptor protein 79
enzyme 79	receptor-mediated endocytosis 85
exocytosis 87	recognition protein 79
facilitated diffusion 82	selectively permeable 81
fluid 76	simple diffusion 81
fluid mosaic model 76	solute 80
food vacuole 86	solvent 80
gap junction 90	tight junction 88
glycoprotein 79	transport protein 80
gradient 80	turgor pressure 83

Learning Outcomes

In this chapter, you have learned to . . .

LO1 Describe the components, structure, and function of cell membranes and explain how the different components contribute to membrane functions.

LO2 Explain how substances move across cell membranes.

LO3 Explain the basic concepts of diffusion and osmosis.

LO4 Describe the major types of junctions between cells and explain how these junctions function.

Thinking Through the Concepts

Fill-in-the-Blank

1. Membranes consist of a bilayer of _____. The five major categories of protein within the bilayer are: _____, _____, _____, _____, and _____ proteins. **LO1**

2. A membrane that is permeable to some substances but not to others is described as being _____. The movement of a substance through a membrane down its concentration gradient is called _____. When applied to water, this process is called _____. Channels that are specific for water are called _____. The process that moves substances through a membrane against their concentration gradient is called _____. LO2 LO3

3. Facilitated diffusion involves either _____ proteins or _____ proteins. Diffusion directly through the phospholipid bilayer is called _____ diffusion, and molecules that take this route must be soluble in _____ or be very small and have no net electrical charge. LO1 LO2 LO3

4. The three types of cell attachment structures in animal cells are: _____, _____, and _____. The structures that interconnect plant cells are called _____. LO4

5. After each molecule, place the two-word term that most specifically describes the *process* by which it moves through a plasma membrane: Carbon dioxide: _____; ethyl alcohol: _____; a sodium ion:_____; glucose: _____. LO2

6. The general process by which fluids or particles are transported into cells is called _____. Does this process require energy? _____ The specific term for engulfing fluid is _____, and the term for engulfing particles is _____. The engulfed substances are taken into the cell in membrane-enclosed sacs called _____. LO2

Review Questions

1. Describe and diagram the structure of a plasma membrane. What are the two principal types of molecules in plasma membranes, and what is the general function of each? LO1

2. Sketch the configuration that 10 phospholipid molecules would assume if placed in water. Explain why they arrange themselves this way. LO1

3. What are the five categories of proteins commonly found in plasma membranes, and what is the function of each one? LO1 LO4

4. Define *diffusion* and *osmosis*. Explain how osmosis helps plant leaves remain firm. What is the term for water pressure inside plant cells? LO2 LO3

5. Define *hypotonic*, *hypertonic*, and *isotonic*. What would be the fate of an animal cell immersed in each of these three types of solution? LO2 LO3

6. Describe the following types of transport processes in cells: simple diffusion, facilitated diffusion, active transport, pinocytosis, receptor-mediated endocytosis, phagocytosis, and exocytosis. LO2 LO4

7. Name the protein that allows facilitated diffusion of water. What experiment demonstrated the function of this protein? LO1 LO2 LO3

8. Imagine a container of glucose solution, divided into two compartments (A and B) by a membrane that is permeable to water and glucose but not to sucrose. If some sucrose is added to compartment A, how will the contents of compartment B change? Explain. LO3

9. Name four types of cell-to-cell junctions, and describe the function of each. Which are found in plants, and which in animals? LO4

Applying the Concepts

1. Different cells have somewhat different plasma membranes. The plasma membrane of a *Paramecium*, for example, is only about 1% as permeable to water as the plasma membrane of a human red blood cell. Hypothesize about why this is the case. Is *Paramecium* likely to have aquaporins in its plasma membrane? Explain your answer.

2. Predict and sketch the configuration of phospholipids that are placed in vegetable oil. Explain your prediction.

3. The fluid portion of blood, in which red blood cells are suspended, is called plasma. Is the plasma likely to be isotonic, hypertonic, or hypotonic to the red blood cells? Explain.

4. Some cells in the nervous system wrap themselves around parts of neurons, serving as insulation for the electrical signals that flow inside neurons carried by ions. Given the general roles of protein and lipids in the cell membrane, which component would you predict to be more abundant in these insulating cells? Explain.

Answers to Figure Caption questions and Fill-in-the-Blank questions can be found in the Answers section at the back of the book.

(MB) *Go to MasteringBiology for practice quizzes, activities, eText, videos, current events, and more.*

CHAPTER 6

Energy Flow in the Life of a Cell

CASE STUDY
Energy Unleashed

PICTURE THE NEW YORK MARATHON: One year, this huge throng of people from around the globe included many propelling themselves in wheelchairs using well-developed arm muscles, a woman battling cancer, a wildlife supporter running in a rhino costume, a 91-year-old man shuffling slowly, a fireman wearing full firefighting gear to honor his fallen comrades, a one-legged man using crutches, and blind people guided by the sighted. All participated in a 26-mile journey—a personal odyssey for each, and a collective testimony to human persistence, endurance, and the ability of the human body to utilize energy.

The 20,000-plus runners in the New York Marathon collectively expend more than 50 million Calories worth of energy. Once finished, they douse their overheated bodies with water and refuel themselves on snacks. Eventually, cars, buses, and airplanes—burning vast quantities of fuel and releasing enormous amounts of heat—will transport the runners back to their homes throughout the world.

What exactly is energy? Do our bodies use it according to the same principles that govern energy use in the engines of cars and airplanes? Why do our bodies generate heat, and why do we give off more heat when exercising than when watching TV?

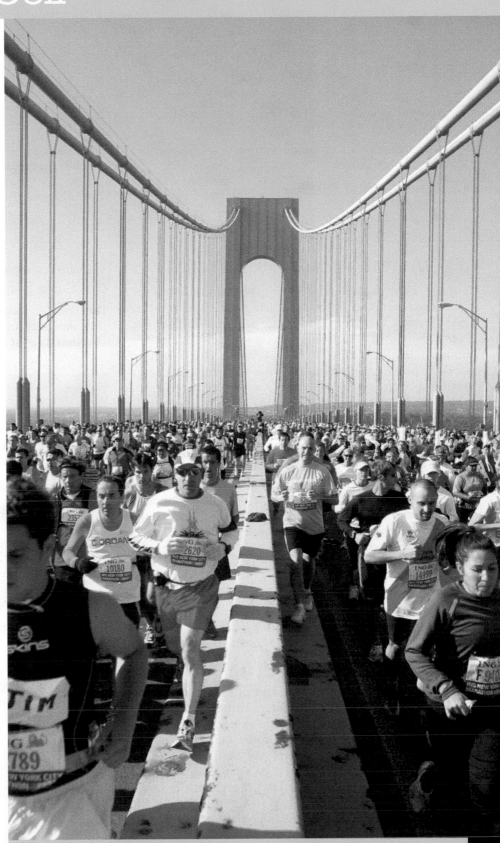

The bodies of these runners in the New York Marathon convert stored energy to the energy of movement and heat. Their pounding footsteps shake the Verrazano Narrows Bridge.

AT A GLANCE

LEARNING GOALS

LG1 Define the key terms used to describe energy and explain the forms that energy takes.

LG2 Summarize the first and second laws of thermodynamics.

LG3 Define *entropy* and explain how organisms create the low-entropy conditions of life.

LG4 Describe how energy is captured and released by chemical reactions.

LG5 Describe the energy-carrier molecules in cells and explain how they facilitate chemical reactions.

LG6 Explain how catalysts work and how enzymes in cells catalyze chemical reactions.

LG7 Describe how cells control their metabolic pathways by regulating enzyme activity.

6.1 WHAT IS ENERGY?

Energy is the capacity to do work. **Work,** in turn, is the transfer of energy to an object, causing the object to move. It is obvious that marathoners are working; their chests heave, their arms pump, and their legs stride, moving their bodies relentlessly forward for 26 miles. This muscular work is powered by **chemical energy,** which is energy available in the bonds of molecules. Molecules that provide this chemical energy—including sugar, glycogen, and fat—are stored in the cells of the runners' bodies. Cells utilize specialized molecules such as ATP to accept, briefly store, and transfer energy from one chemical reaction to the next.

There are two fundamental types of energy: potential energy and kinetic energy, each of which takes several forms. **Potential energy,** which is stored energy, includes the chemical energy available in biological molecules and other molecules such as fossil fuels, elastic energy stored in a wound clock spring or a drawn bow, and gravitational energy stored in water behind a dam or a roller-coaster car about to begin its downward plunge (**Fig. 6-1**). **Kinetic energy** is the energy of movement. It includes radiant energy (such as waves of light, X-rays, and other forms of *electromagnetic radiation*), heat or thermal energy (the motion of molecules or atoms), electrical energy (also called electricity; the flow of charged particles), and any motion of larger objects, such as the plummeting roller-coaster car or running marathoners. Under the right conditions, kinetic energy can be transformed into potential energy, and vice versa. For example, the roller-coaster car converts the kinetic energy of its downward plunge into potential gravitational energy as it coasts to the top of the next rise. At a molecular level, during photosynthesis (described in Chapter 7), the kinetic energy of light is captured and transformed into the potential energy of chemical bonds. To understand energy flow and change, we need to know more about its properties and behavior.

The Laws of Thermodynamics Describe the Basic Properties of Energy

The laws of thermodynamics describe the quantity (the total amount) and the quality (the usefulness) of energy. The **first law of thermodynamics** states that energy can

▲ FIGURE 6-1 **Converting potential energy to kinetic energy** Roller coasters convert gravitational potential energy to kinetic energy as they plummet downhill.

QUESTION Could one design a roller coaster that didn't use any motors to pull the cars uphill after the cars were released from a high point?

neither be created nor destroyed by ordinary processes. (Nuclear reactions, in which matter is converted into energy, are the exception.) This means that in a hypothetical **closed system**—where energy can neither enter nor leave—the total amount of energy before and after any process will be unchanged. For this reason, the first law of thermodynamics is often called the **law of conservation of energy.** Energy can, however, be converted from one form to another.

To illustrate this law, consider a combustion engine car. Before you turn the ignition key, the energy in the car is all potential energy, stored in the chemical bonds of its fuel. As you drive, only about 20% of this potential energy is converted into the kinetic energy of motion. According to the first law of thermodynamics, however, energy is neither created nor destroyed. So what happens to the other 80% of the energy? The burning fuel is used to set the car in motion, but it also heats up the engine, the exhaust system, and the air around the car, while friction from the tires heats the road. So, as the first law dictates, the total amount of energy remains the same, although it has changed in form—much of it to waste heat.

The **second law of thermodynamics** states that when energy is converted from one form to another, the amount of useful energy decreases. In other words, all ordinary (nonnuclear) processes cause energy to be converted from more useful into less useful forms. In our combustion example, 80% of the energy stored in gasoline was converted into waste heat, which increased the random movement of molecules in the car, the air, and the road (**Fig. 6-2**). Heat is a less usable form of energy than energy stored in chemical bonds, as discussed further in "Earth Watch: Step on the Brakes and Recharge Your Battery."

Now consider the human body. Whether running or reading, your body "burns" food to release the chemical energy stored in its molecules. Your body warmth results from the heat given off, which is radiated to your surroundings. This heat is not available to power muscle contraction or to

100 units chemical energy   80 units heat + 20 units kinetic energy
                                                        energy

▲ FIGURE 6-2 **Energy conversions result in a loss of useful energy**

help brain cells interpret written words. Thus, the second law tells us that no energy conversion process, including those that occur in the body, is 100% efficient in using energy to achieve a specific outcome.

The second law of thermodynamics also tells us something about the organization of matter. Useful energy tends to be stored in highly ordered matter, such as in the bonds of complex molecules. As a result, whenever energy is used within a closed system, there is an overall increase in the randomness and disorder of matter—be it molecules or far larger objects. We all experience this in our homes. Without energy-demanding cleaning and organizing efforts, dirty dishes accumulate, books and papers pile up, clothes collect in confusion on the floor, and the bed remains rumpled.

At the molecular level, we see the same principle at work. The chemical equation for burning gasoline is:

$$2\ C_8H_{18} + \ \ 25\ O_2\ \rightarrow\ \ \ \ \ 16\ CO_2\ \ \ \ \ + 18\ H_2O +\ \text{energy}$$
(octane) + (oxygen) → (carbon dioxide) + (water) + (energy)
(reactants)   (products)

Although you'll find the same number of atoms on both sides of the equation, notice that the 27 starting molecules on the left (*reactants*) are converted to 34 simple molecules on the right (*products*). The heat energy that is released imparts rapid random motion to the products and other nearby

Earth|Watch

Step on the Brakes and Recharge Your Battery

As we deplete Earth's stores of fossil fuels and damage ecosystems as we dig and drill for more, we are also becoming increasingly aware of the environmental hazards of adding carbon dioxide and other pollutants to the atmosphere as we burn these fuels.

In a typical combustion engine car, whenever you step on the brake, brake pads are forced against brake discs and the resulting friction converts the kinetic energy of forward motion into waste heat. Fortunately, engineers have devised a way to capture and use some of this squandered energy. Called regenerative braking, this technology (used in trolley cars since the 1930s) is now available in hybrid or all-electric cars, which are partly or entirely driven by battery-powered electric

motors. Stepping on the brake switches the motor into a generator mode, which slows down the car and simultaneously causes the motor to generate (rather than consume) electricity. This electrical energy, derived from the kinetic energy of the car's forward motion, is stored in the chemical energy of the car's battery. Here, it will help propel the car forward when you start up again. Of course, the second law of thermodynamics tells us that each of these energy conversions will generate some waste heat, but regenerative braking wastes 30% to 50% less energy than conventional friction braking. Regenerative braking, along with other innovations to increase efficiency, should allow cars of the very near future to travel much farther on less energy.

Energy Unleashed

Much like a car's engine, the marathoner's muscles are only about 25% efficient in converting chemical energy into movement; much of the other 75% is lost as heat. Highly trained marathoners completing the race in about 2 hours generate enough heat to raise their body temperatures by about 1.8°F (1°C) every 5 minutes. If they were unable to dissipate the heat, they would die of heatstroke within a half hour.

molecules. This tendency toward loss of complexity, orderliness, and useful energy—and the concurrent increase in randomness, disorder, and less useful energy—is called **entropy.** To counteract entropy, energy must be infused into the system from an outside source. When the eminent Yale scientist G. Evelyn Hutchinson stated, "Disorder spreads through the universe, and life alone battles against it," he made an eloquent reference to entropy and the second law of thermodynamics.

Living Things Use the Energy of Sunlight to Create the Low-Entropy Conditions of Life

If you think about the second law of thermodynamics, you may wonder how life can exist at all. If chemical reactions, including those inside living cells, cause the amount of unusable energy to increase, and if matter tends toward increasing randomness and disorder, how can organisms accumulate the usable energy and the complex, precisely ordered molecules that characterize life? The answer is that cells, the bodies of organisms, and Earth itself are not closed systems; they receive solar energy released by nuclear reactions occurring 93 million miles away—in the sun. These reactions not only generate light and other forms of electromagnetic energy, they also produce vast increases in entropy within the sun. These reactions liberate an almost unimaginable amount of heat; the temperature of the sun's core is estimated to be 27 million °F (16 million °C).

Living things "battle against disorder" by using a continuous influx of solar light energy to synthesize complex molecules and maintain their intricate bodies. Thus, the highly ordered (and therefore low-entropy) systems that characterize life do not violate the second law of thermodynamics because they are achieved and maintained through a continuous influx of useful energy from the sun. Because of ever-increasing entropy, the solar reactions that power life on Earth will eventually cause the sun to burn out, but fortunately, not for billions of years.

CHECK YOUR LEARNING

Can you define the key terms relating to energy and thermodynamics and provide examples that illustrate these terms? Can you summarize the first and second laws of thermodynamics?

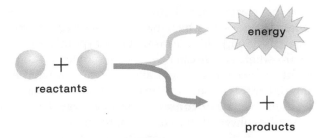

▲ FIGURE 6-3 **An exergonic reaction** The products contain less energy than the reactants.

6.2 HOW IS ENERGY TRANSFORMED DURING CHEMICAL REACTIONS?

A **chemical reaction** is a process that forms or breaks the chemical bonds that hold atoms together. Chemical reactions convert one set of chemical substances, the **reactants,** into another set, the **products.** All chemical reactions either release energy or require an overall (net) input of energy. A reaction is **exergonic** (Greek for "energy out") if it releases energy; that is, if the starting reactants contain more energy than the end products. All exergonic reactions release some of their energy as heat (**Fig. 6-3**). A reaction is **endergonic** ("energy in") if it requires a net input of energy; that is, if the products contain more energy than the reactants. Endergonic reactions require a net influx of energy from an outside source (**Fig. 6-4**).

Exergonic Reactions Release Energy

Sugar can be ignited by heat, as any cook can tell you. As it burns, sugar (glucose, for example) undergoes the same overall reaction as it does in the bodies of humans and nearly all other forms of life; sugar is combined with oxygen to produce carbon dioxide and water, generating both chemical energy and heat. The total energy in the reactant molecules (sugar and oxygen) is much higher than in the product molecules (carbon dioxide and water), so burning sugar is an exergonic reaction (**Fig. 6-5**). It may be helpful to think of exergonic reactions as running "downhill," from higher energy to lower energy.

Endergonic Reactions Require a Net Input of Energy

In contrast to what happens when sugar is burned, many reactions in living things produce products that contain more energy than do the reactants. Sugar, for example, contains far

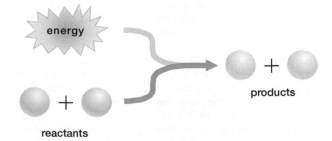

▲ FIGURE 6-4 **An endergonic reaction** The products contain more energy than the reactants.

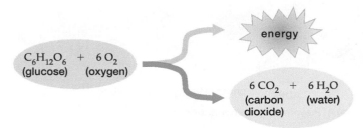

▲ **FIGURE 6-5 Reactants and products of burning glucose**
QUESTION Is this an endergonic or an exergonic reaction?

▲ **FIGURE 6-6 Photosynthesis**
QUESTION Is photosynthesis an endergonic or an exergonic reaction?

more energy than does the carbon dioxide and water from which it was formed. The proteins in a muscle cell contain more energy than the individual amino acids that were joined together to synthesize them. In other words, synthesizing complex biological molecules requires a net input of energy. These reactions are endergonic. Endergonic reactions will not happen spontaneously. We might call them "uphill" reactions, because the reactants contain less energy than the products do. Like pushing a rock up to the top of a hill, going from low-energy reactants to high-energy products requires a net input of energy. Where do living organisms get the energy to fuel endergonic reactions? Photosynthesis uses light energy from the sun to produce high-energy sugar from low-energy water and carbon dioxide (**Fig. 6-6**). Photosyn-

thetic organisms use the energy captured in sugars to synthesize proteins and all of the other complex molecules of their bodies. Virtually all other living organisms, ourselves included, use the energy captured by photosynthesis and stored in sugars and other biological molecules to power endergonic reactions, including such activities as active transport, synthesizing complex molecules, and movement.

All Chemical Reactions Require Activation Energy to Begin

All chemical reactions, even those that can continue spontaneously, require energy to get started. Think of a rock sitting at the top of a hill. It will remain there indefinitely unless a push starts it rolling down. In chemical reactions, the energy "push" is called the **activation energy** (**Fig. 6-7a**). Shells of negatively charged electrons surround all atoms (see Chapter 2); activation energy is the energy that is required to overcome the repulsive electrical forces between the electron shells so that they can move close enough together to react.

Activation energy can be provided by the kinetic energy of moving molecules. At any temperature higher than absolute zero (–460°F or –273°C), atoms and molecules are in constant motion. Reactive molecules moving with sufficient speed collide hard enough to force their electron

Energy Unleashed

Marathoners rely on glycogen stored in their muscles and liver for much of the energy to power their run. Glycogen consists of chains of glucose molecules. When energy is needed, glucose molecules are cleaved from the chain and then broken down into carbon dioxide and water. This exergonic reaction generates heat and the ATP required for muscle contraction. The carbon dioxide is exhaled as the runners breathe rapidly to supply their muscles with adequate oxygen. The water generated by glucose breakdown (and a lot more that the runners drink during the race) is lost as sweat. As the sweat evaporates, it prevents the runners' bodies from overheating by carrying away the excess heat energy released by the exergonic chemical reactions in their muscles.

▶ **FIGURE 6-7 Activation energy in an exergonic reaction (a)** An exergonic ("downhill") reaction proceeds from high-energy reactants to lower-energy products, with a net release of energy. **(b)** Sparks from a friction gas lighter ignite gas flowing from a Bunsen burner. The sparks provide the activation energy for this exergonic reaction. Heat released by the burning gas then allows the reaction to continue spontaneously.

(a) An exergonic reaction

(b) Sparks ignite gas

shells to mingle and react. Because molecules move faster as the temperature increases, most chemical reactions occur more readily at high temperatures. For example, sparks will ignite the gas from a stove or Bunsen burner (**Fig. 6-7b**) and heat from a burning match can set sugar on fire. When sugar is ignited, the initial reaction combining sugar and oxygen releases enough heat to sustain the reaction, and the sugar continues to burn.

CHECK YOUR LEARNING

Can you describe how energy is captured and released by chemical reactions? Can you explain exergonic and endergonic reactions and provide examples of each? Are you able to explain activation energy?

6.3 HOW IS ENERGY TRANSPORTED WITHIN CELLS?

Most organisms are powered by the chemical energy supplied by the exergonic breakdown of glucose illustrated earlier. This energy is used to do cellular work, such as constructing complex biological molecules and causing muscles to contract. But glucose cannot be used directly to fuel these endergonic processes. Instead, the energy released by glucose breakdown is first transferred to energy-carrier molecules. **Energy-carrier molecules** are high-energy molecules that are synthesized at the site of an exergonic reaction, where they capture some of the released energy. Energy carriers behave much like rechargeable batteries: They are charged up by an exergonic reaction, and then release the energy to drive an endergonic reaction. They can then be recharged, as described later. Energy-carrier molecules only capture and transfer energy within cells; they cannot ferry energy from cell to cell, nor are they used for long-term energy storage.

ATP and Electron Carriers Transport Energy Within Cells

Many exergonic reactions in cells, such as breaking down sugars and fats, produce **adenosine triphosphate (ATP),** the most common energy-carrier molecule in the body (described in Chapter 3). ATP is a nucleotide composed of the nitrogen-containing base adenine, the sugar ribose, and three phosphate groups (see Fig. 3-23). Because ATP provides energy to drive a wide variety of endergonic reactions, it is sometimes called the "energy currency" of cells. It is produced when energy released in cells during glucose breakdown or other exergonic reactions is used to combine the lower-energy molecules **adenosine diphosphate (ADP)** and inorganic phosphate (HPO_4^{2-}, also designated P_i) (**Fig. 6-8a**). Because it requires an input of energy, ATP synthesis is endergonic.

ATP diffuses throughout the cell, carrying energy to sites where endergonic reactions occur. There its energy is liberated as it is broken down, regenerating ADP and P_i (**Fig. 6-8b**). The life span of an ATP molecule in a living cell is very short; each molecule is recycled roughly 1,400 times every day. A marathon runner may use a pound of ATP molecules every minute,

(a) ATP synthesis: Energy is stored in ATP

(b) ATP breakdown: Energy is released   ADP   phosphate

▲ FIGURE 6-8 **The interconversion of ADP and ATP**
(a) Energy is captured when a phosphate group (P_i) is added to adenosine diphosphate (ADP) to make adenosine triphosphate (ATP). **(b)** Energy to accomplish cellular work is released when ATP is broken down into ADP and P_i.

so if this molecule were not rapidly recycled, marathon runs would not happen. As you can see, ATP is *not* a long-term energy-storage molecule. In contrast, more stable molecules such as starch in plants and glycogen and fat in animals can store energy for hours, days, or—in the case of fat—years.

ATP is not the only energy-carrier molecule within cells. In some exergonic reactions, including both glucose breakdown and the light-capturing stage of photosynthesis, some energy is transferred to electrons. These energetic electrons, along with hydrogen ions (H^+; present in the cytosol of cells), are captured by molecules called **electron carriers.** The loaded electron carriers donate their high-energy electrons to other molecules, which are often involved in pathways that generate ATP. Common electron carriers include the nucleotide nicotinamide adenine dinucleotide (NADH) and its relative, flavin adenine dinucleotide ($FADH_2$). (You will learn more about electron carriers in Chapters 7 and 8.)

Coupled Reactions Link Exergonic with Endergonic Reactions

In a **coupled reaction,** an exergonic reaction provides the energy needed to drive an endergonic reaction (**Fig. 6-9**) using ATP or electron carriers as intermediaries. During photosynthesis, for example, plants use sunlight (from exergonic reactions in the sun's core) to drive the endergonic synthesis of high-energy glucose molecules from lower-energy reactants (carbon dioxide and water). Nearly all organisms use the energy released by exergonic reactions (such as the breakdown of glucose into carbon dioxide and water) to drive endergonic reactions (such as the synthesis of proteins from amino acids). Because energy is lost as heat every time it is transformed, in coupled reactions the energy released by exergonic reactions must always exceed the energy needed to drive the endergonic reactions.

◀ FIGURE 6-9 **Coupled reactions within living cells** Exergonic reactions (such as glucose breakdown) drive the endergonic reaction that synthesizes ATP from ADP and P_i. The ATP molecule carries its chemical energy to a part of the cell where energy is needed to drive an endergonic reaction (such as protein synthesis). The ADP and P_i are rejoined in an endergonic reaction that forms ATP.

The exergonic and endergonic portions of coupled reactions often occur in different places within a cell, so there must be some way to transfer the energy from the exergonic reactions that release energy to the endergonic reactions that require it. In coupled reactions, energy is transferred from place to place by energy-carrier molecules such as ATP. In its role as an intermediary in coupled reactions, ATP is constantly being synthesized to capture the energy released during exergonic reactions and then broken down to power endergonic reactions (as shown in Fig. 6-9).

CHECK YOUR LEARNING

Can you name and describe two important energy-carrier molecules in cells? Can you explain coupled reactions?

6.4 HOW DO ENZYMES PROMOTE BIOCHEMICAL REACTIONS?

Ignite sugar and it will go up in flames as it combines rapidly with oxygen, releasing carbon dioxide and water. The same overall reaction occurs in our cells, but of course they are in no danger of catching fire. Chemical reactions that released uncontrolled blasts of heat energy would not be useful to cells. On the other hand, a single molecule of sugar contains enough energy to produce dozens of molecules of ATP if the energy is released in controlled steps that are linked to ATP synthesis.

Catalysts Reduce the Energy Required to Start a Reaction

In general, the speed at which a reaction occurs is determined by its activation energy; that is, by how much energy is required to start the reaction (see Fig. 6-7a). Some reactions, such as table salt dissolving in water (see Fig. 2-8), have low activation energies and occur readily at human body temperature (approximately 98.6°F, or 37°C). In contrast, you could store sugar at body temperature for decades and it would remain virtually unchanged.

The reaction of sugar with oxygen to yield carbon dioxide and water is exergonic, but it has a high activation energy. The heat of a flame increases the rate of movement of sugar molecules and nearby oxygen molecules, causing them to collide with one another with sufficient force to overcome their activation energy and react; the sugar burns. Promoting reactions by overcoming activation energy without added heat is the job of catalysts.

Catalysts are molecules that speed up the rate of a reaction without themselves being used up or permanently altered. A catalyst speeds up a reaction by reducing the reaction's activation energy (**Fig. 6-10**). For example, consider the catalytic converters on automobile exhaust systems. Incomplete combustion of gasoline generates poisonous carbon monoxide (CO). Carbon monoxide then reacts spontaneously but slowly with oxygen in the air to form carbon dioxide:

$$2\,CO + O_2 \rightarrow 2\,CO_2 + \text{heat energy}$$

In heavy traffic, the spontaneous reaction of CO with O_2 can't keep pace with the CO emitted, and unhealthy levels of CO accumulate. Enter the catalytic converter. Catalysts such as platinum in the converter provide a surface upon which O_2 and CO combine more readily, hastening the conversion of CO to CO_2 and reducing air pollution.

All catalysts share three important properties:

- Catalysts speed up reactions by lowering the activation energy required for the reaction to begin.

▲ FIGURE 6-10 **Catalysts such as enzymes lower activation energy** A high activation energy (red curve) means that reactant molecules must collide very forcefully to react. Catalysts lower the activation energy of a reaction (blue curve), so a much higher proportion of molecules moves fast enough to react when the molecules collide. Therefore, the reaction proceeds much more rapidly.

QUESTION Can an enzyme catalyst make an endergonic reaction occur spontaneously at body temperature?

- Catalysts can speed up both exergonic and endergonic reactions, but they cannot make an endergonic reaction occur spontaneously.
- Catalysts are not consumed or permanently changed by the reactions they promote.

Enzymes Are Biological Catalysts

Inorganic catalysts speed up a number of different chemical reactions. But indiscriminately speeding up dozens of reactions would not be useful to living organisms, and indeed would almost certainly be deadly. Instead, cells employ highly specific biological catalysts called **enzymes,** nearly all of which are proteins. A given enzyme catalyzes only a few types of chemical reactions, at most. The majority of enzymes catalyze a single reaction involving specific molecules, while leaving even very similar molecules unchanged.

Both exergonic and endergonic reactions are catalyzed by enzymes. The synthesis of ATP from ADP and P_i, for example, is catalyzed by the enzyme ATP synthase. When energy is required to drive endergonic reactions, ATP is broken down by ATPase. Enzyme names are not consistent; some add the suffix "ase" to what the enzyme does (ATP synthase), some add "ase" to the molecule upon which the enzyme acts (ATPase), and others don't use "ase" at all.

The Structure of Enzymes Allows Them to Catalyze Specific Reactions

The function of an enzyme, like the function of any protein, is determined by its structure (see Chapter 3; Fig. 3-20). Each enzyme's distinctive shape is determined by its amino acid sequence and the precise way in which the amino acid chain is twisted and folded. Enzymes use their three-dimensional structures to orient, distort, and reconfigure other molecules, causing these molecules to react, but emerging unchanged themselves.

Each enzyme has a pocket, called the **active site,** into which reactant molecules, called **substrates,** can enter. The shape of the active site, as well as the charges on the amino acids that form the active site, determine which molecules can enter. Consider the enzyme amylase, for example. Amylase breaks down starch molecules by hydrolysis, but leaves cellulose molecules intact, even though both starch and cellulose consist of chains of glucose molecules. Why? Because the bonding pattern between glucose molecules in starch fits into the active site of amylase, but the bonding pattern in cellulose does not. In the stomach, the enzyme pepsin breaks down proteins, attacking them at many sites along their amino acid chains. Certain other protein-digesting enzymes (trypsin, for example) will break bonds only between specific amino acids. Therefore, digestive systems must manufacture several different enzymes that work together to completely break down dietary protein into its individual amino acids.

How does an enzyme catalyze a reaction? You can follow the events in **Figure 6-11,** where two substrate molecules are combined into a single product. Both the shape and the charge of the active site allow substrates to enter the enzyme only in specific orientations. When appropriate

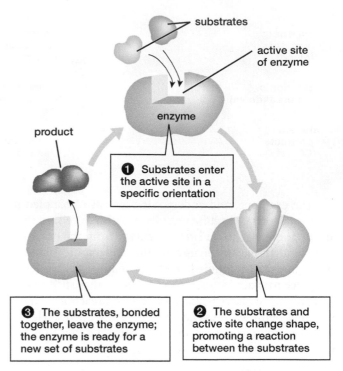

▲ FIGURE 6-11 **The cycle of enzyme–substrate interactions** Although this diagram shows two reactant substrate molecules combined to form a single product, enzymes can also catalyze the breakdown of a single substrate into two product molecules.

substrates enter the active site, both the substrates and active site change shape. Electrical interactions between the amino acids in the active site and the substrates may distort chemical bonds within the substrates. The combination of substrate selectivity, substrate orientation, temporary chemical bonds, and the distortion of existing bonds promotes the specific chemical reaction catalyzed by a particular enzyme. This holds true whether the enzyme is causing two molecules to react with one another, or breaking a single molecule into smaller products. When the reaction is complete, the product(s) no longer fits properly into the active site and diffuses away. The enzyme reverts to its original configuration, and it is then ready to accept another set of substrates. When substrate molecules are abundant, some fast-acting enzymes can catalyze tens of thousands of reactions per second, while others act far more slowly.

Enzymes, Like All Catalysts, Lower Activation Energy

The breakdown or synthesis of a molecule within a cell usually occurs in many small, discrete steps, each catalyzed by a different enzyme (see Fig. 6-12). Each of these enzymes lowers the activation energy for its particular reaction, allowing the reaction to occur readily at body temperature. Think of a rock climber ascending a steep cliff by finding a series of hand- and footholds that allow her to scale it one small step at a time. In a similar manner, a series of reaction steps, each requiring a small amount of activation energy and each catalyzed by an enzyme that lowers activation energy, allows the

What Makes a Firefly Glow?

The almost magical glow of fireflies comes from specialized cells in their abdomens that are bioluminescent, meaning that they produce "biological light." These cells are rich in ATP and the fluorescent chemical luciferin (Latin, meaning "light-bringer"). Luciferin and ATP serve as substrates for the enzyme luciferase. In the presence of oxygen, luciferase catalyzes a reaction that modifies luciferin and uses the energy from ATP to boost electrons briefly into a higher-energy electron shell. As they fall back into their original shell, the electrons emit their excess energy as light. The process produces so little heat that these beetles are often described as emitting "cold light."

overall reaction to surmount its high activation energy "cliff" and to proceed at body temperature.

CHECK YOUR LEARNING

Can you list the properties of catalysts and explain how they reduce activation energy? Can you explain how enzymes function as biological catalysts?

6.5 HOW ARE ENZYMES REGULATED?

The **metabolism** of a cell is the sum of all its chemical reactions. Many of these reactions, such as those that break down glucose into carbon dioxide and water, are linked in sequences called **metabolic pathways** (Fig. 6-12). In a metabolic pathway, a starting reactant molecule is converted, with the help of an enzyme, into a slightly different intermediate molecule, which is modified by yet another

enzyme to form a second intermediate, and so on, until an end product is produced. Photosynthesis (Chapter 7), for example, is a metabolic pathway that results in the synthesis of high-energy molecules, including glucose. Another metabolic pathway, glycolysis, begins the breakdown of glucose (Chapter 8). Different metabolic pathways often use some of the same molecules; as a result, all the thousands of metabolic pathways within a cell are directly or indirectly interconnected.

Cells Regulate Metabolic Pathways by Controlling Enzyme Synthesis and Activity

In a test tube under constant, ideal conditions, the rate of a particular reaction will depend on how many substrate molecules diffuse into the active sites of enzyme molecules in a given time period. This, in turn, will be determined by the concentrations of the enzyme and substrate molecules. Generally, increasing the concentrations of either the enzyme or the substrate (or both) will increase the reaction rate, because it will boost the chances that the two types of molecules will meet. But living cells must precisely control the rate of reactions in their metabolic pathways, creating an environment far more complex than occurs in a test tube. Cells must keep their end products within narrow limits, even when the amounts of reactants (the substrates for enzymes) fluctuate considerably. For example, when glucose molecules flood into the bloodstream after a meal, it would not be desirable to metabolize them all at once, producing far more ATP than the cell needs. Instead, some of the glucose molecules should be stored as glycogen or fat for later use. To be effective, then, metabolic reactions within cells must be precisely regulated; they must occur at the proper times and proceed at the proper rates. Cells regulate their metabolic pathways by controlling the type, quantity, and activity levels of the enzymes they produce.

Genes That Code for Enzymes May Be Turned On or Off

A very effective way for cells to regulate enzymes is to control the quantity of enzymes they synthesize by turning the genes that code for specific enzymes on or off depending on the cell's

▲ FIGURE 6-12 Simplified metabolic pathways The initial reactant molecule (A) undergoes a series of reactions, each catalyzed by a specific enzyme. The product of each reaction serves as the reactant for the next reaction in the pathway. Metabolic pathways are commonly interconnected so the product of a step in one pathway may serve as a substrate for the next enzyme in the pathway or for an enzyme in a different pathway.

Health|Watch

A Lost Enzyme Leads to Lactose Intolerance

If you enjoy ice cream and pizza, it might be hard for you to imagine life without these treats. It might even surprise you that such dairy products cannot be enjoyed by most of the world's population. Although all young children normally produce lactase (the enzyme that breaks down lactose, or "milk sugar"), about 65% of people worldwide, including 30 to 50 million people in the United States, produce less of this enzyme as they progress through childhood, a condition called *lactose intolerance*. In the worst cases of lactose intolerance, people may experience abdominal pain, flatulence, nausea, and diarrhea after consuming milk products (Fig. E6-1).

Why do people stop synthesizing the enzyme for this nutritious food? From an evolutionary perspective, it makes sense not to continue expending energy to produce a protein that has no function. In our early ancestors (who had not yet domesticated livestock)

▲ FIGURE E6-1 **Risky behavior?** For the majority of the world's adults, drinking milk invites unpleasant consequences.

lactase lost its function in very early childhood because, after weaning, these people no longer had access to milk—the main source of lactose. As a result, many modern adults cannot digest lactose because the gene that encodes lactase is turned off after weaning. Lactose intolerance is particularly prevalent in people of East Asian, West African, and Native American descent. Genetic studies have revealed that between 10,000 and 6,000 years ago, some people in northern Europe and the Middle East experienced mutations that allowed them to digest lactose throughout their lives. These mutations gradually spread because they provided better nutrition for members of agricultural societies, who could then obtain milk as well as meat from their livestock. Their descendants today continue to enjoy milk, ice cream, and extra-cheese pizzas.

changing needs. (You'll learn more about gene regulation in Chapter 12.) Gene regulation may cause enzymes to be synthesized in larger quantities when more of their substrate is available. Larger concentrations of enzyme make it more likely that substrate molecules will encounter the enzyme, speeding up the rate at which the reaction occurs. Consider marathon runners, who often eat high-carbohydrate meals before competing. The glucose that enters the bloodstream after a starchy meal triggers an elaborate series of metabolic adjustments. One of these is to cause cells of the pancreas to release insulin. This increase in insulin turns on the genes that code for the first enzyme in the metabolic pathway that breaks down glucose. Turning on these genes causes the cell to synthesize larger amounts of the enzyme (hexokinase), making more of it available. This enzyme adds a phosphate group to glucose, producing glucose-6-phosphate (G6P), which can be further broken down and its energy captured in ATP that will help fuel muscle cells.

Some enzymes are regulated by being synthesized only during specific stages in an organism's life. A mutation can alter this regulation, as described in "Health Watch: A Lost Enzyme Leads to Lactose Intolerance."

Some Enzymes Are Synthesized in Inactive Forms

Some enzymes are synthesized in an inactive form that is activated under the conditions found where the enzyme is needed. Examples are the protein-digesting enzymes pepsin and trypsin, mentioned earlier. Cells synthesize and release each of these enzymes in an inactive form, preventing the

enzyme from digesting and killing the cell that manufactures it. In the stomach, acid causes the inactive form of pepsin to break apart, exposing the active site of pepsin and allowing it to begin breaking down proteins from a meal. An inactive form of trypsin, which helps complete protein digestion, is released into the small intestine. The small intestine secretes an enzyme that removes the inactivating part of this protein, making functional trypsin.

Enzyme Activity May Be Controlled by Competitive or Noncompetitive Inhibition

It is not in the cell's best interest to have its enzymes churning out products all the time. Many enzymes need to be inhibited so that the cell does not use up all of its substrate or become overwhelmed by too much product. There are two general ways in which enzymes can be inhibited.

We know that for an enzyme to catalyze a reaction, its substrate must bind to the enzyme's active site (Fig. 6-13a). In **competitive inhibition,** a substance that is not the enzyme's normal substrate can also bind to the active site of the enzyme, competing with the substrate for the active site (Fig. 6-13b). Usually, a competitive inhibitor molecule has some structural similarities to the usual substrate, allowing it to occupy the active site. For example, during the metabolic pathway that produces ATP from glucose (see Chapter 8), the enzyme that acts on one intermediate molecule (oxaloacetate) to produce a second intermediate (citrate) is competitively inhibited by citrate. This is an example of a product inhibiting the enzyme that produced it. Both the product and the substrate diffuse in and out of the active site, and either can displace the other if its concentration is high enough. This example of competitive inhibition helps control the rate of glucose breakdown, because a high concentration of citrate molecules will reduce the rate of citrate production by inhibiting the enzyme that produces citrate. The best known examples of competitive inhibitors are drugs, described later.

In **noncompetitive inhibition,** a molecule binds to a site on the enzyme that is distinct from the active site. As a result, the enzyme's active site is distorted, making the enzyme less able to catalyze the reaction (**Fig. 6-13c**). Some

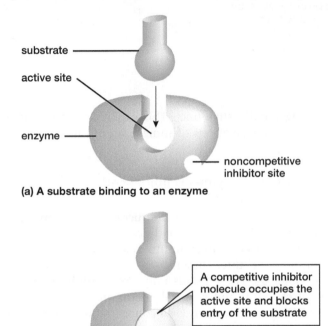

(a) A substrate binding to an enzyme

A competitive inhibitor molecule occupies the active site and blocks entry of the substrate

(b) Competitive inhibition

The active site changes shape so the substrate no longer fits when a noncompetitive inhibitor molecule binds the enzyme

noncompetitive inhibitor molecule

(c) Noncompetitive inhibition

▲ FIGURE 6-13 **Competitive and noncompetitive enzyme inhibition (a)** The normal substrate fits into the enzyme's active site when the enzyme is not being inhibited. **(b)** In competitive inhibition, a competitive inhibitor molecule that resembles the substrate enters and blocks the active site. **(c)** In noncompetitive inhibition, a molecule binds to a different site on the enzyme, distorting the active site so that the enzyme's substrate no longer fits.

noncompetitive inhibitor molecules are poisons, as described later, but many others are molecules produced by cells to regulate metabolic pathways using allosteric inhibition, as described in the following section.

Some Enzymes Are Controlled by Allosteric Regulation

An important mechanism by which cells regulate their metabolic pathways is by activating or inhibiting the activity of enzymes within the pathway. Many enzymes that participate in metabolic pathways are *allosteric enzymes*. Allosteric enzymes switch easily and spontaneously between two different configurations (allosteric literally means "other shape"). One configuration is active, while the other is inactive. Such enzymes are controlled by **allosteric regulation,** which can either activate or inhibit the enzyme. Allosteric inhibition is a form of noncompetitive inhibition in which the inhibitor molecule binds to a noncompetitive inhibition site and stabilizes the enzyme in its inactive form. Allosteric activation occurs when an activator molecule binds to a different site and stabilizes the enzyme in its active form. Activators and inhibitors bind briefly and reversibly to their allosteric regulatory sites. As a result of this temporary binding, the number of enzyme molecules being activated (or inhibited) is proportional to the numbers of activator (or inhibitor) molecules that are present at any given time.

An example of an allosteric activator molecule is ADP, which is produced by the breakdown of ATP and is then used to synthesize more ATP (see Fig. 6-8). ADP is abundant in a cell when a lot of ATP has been used up and more is needed. Under these conditions, ADP activates allosteric enzymes that function in metabolic pathways that produce ATP, stabilizing the enzymes in their active state and increasing production of ATP.

An important form of allosteric regulation is feedback inhibition. **Feedback inhibition (Fig. 6-14)** causes a metabolic pathway to stop producing its end product when the product concentration reaches an optimal level, much as a thermostat turns off a heater when a room becomes warm enough. In feedback inhibition, the activity of an enzyme near the beginning of a metabolic pathway is inhibited by the end product of that pathway; the end product acts as an allosteric inhibitor molecule.

In the metabolic pathway illustrated in Figure 6-14, a series of reactions, each catalyzed by a different enzyme, converts one amino acid to another. As the level of the end product amino acid isoleucine increases, isoleucine more frequently encounters and binds to the allosteric regulatory site on an enzyme early in the pathway, inhibiting it. Thus, when enough of the end product (isoleucine) is present, the pathway is slowed or halted. Another allosteric inhibitor is ATP, which inhibits enzymes in metabolic pathways that lead to ATP synthesis. When a cell has sufficient ATP, there is enough ATP present to block further ATP production. As ATP is used up, the pathways that produce it become active once again.

▲ FIGURE 6-14 **Allosteric regulation of an enzyme by feedback inhibition**
This metabolic pathway converts the amino acid threonine into the amino acid isoleucine via a
series of intermediate molecules (shown here as colored shapes), each acted upon by a different
enzyme (arrows). If a cell lacks isoleucine, the reactions proceed. As isoleucine builds up, it inhibits
enzyme 1, blocking the pathway. When concentrations of isoleucine drop, with less inhibitor to
block enzyme 1, isoleucine production resumes.

QUESTION If molecule B reversibly bound to the active site of enzyme 1, what kind of
enzyme regulation would this be?

Poisons, Drugs, and Environmental Conditions Influence Enzyme Activity

Poisons and drugs that act on enzymes usually inhibit them, either competitively or noncompetitively. In addition, environmental conditions can denature enzymes, distorting the three-dimensional structure that is crucial for their function.

Some Poisons and Drugs Are Competitive or Noncompetitive Inhibitors of Enzymes

Competitive inhibitors of enzymes, including nerve gases (such as sarin) and certain insecticides (such as malathion), permanently block the active site of the enzyme acetylcholinesterase, which breaks down acetylcholine (a substance that nerve cells release to activate muscles). This allows acetylcholine to build up and overstimulate muscles, causing paralysis. Death may ensue because victims become unable to breathe. Other poisons are noncompetitive inhibitors of enzymes; these include the heavy metals arsenic, mercury, and lead. The poison potassium cyanide causes rapid death by noncompetitively inhibiting an enzyme that is crucial for the production of ATP.

Many drugs work because they act as competitive inhibitors of enzymes. For example, the antibiotic penicillin destroys bacteria by competitively inhibiting an enzyme that is crucial to synthesizing bacterial cell walls. Both aspirin and ibuprofen (Advil™) act as competitive inhibitors of an enzyme that catalyzes the synthesis of molecules that contribute to swelling, pain, and fever. Some anticancer drugs are also competitive inhibitors of enzymes. Rapidly dividing cancer cells are constantly synthesizing new strands of DNA. Some anticancer drugs resemble the subunits of DNA. These drugs compete with the normal subunits, tricking enzymes into building defective DNA, which in turn prevents the cancer cells from proliferating. Unfortunately, these anticancer drugs also interfere with the growth of other rapidly dividing cells, including those in hair follicles and lining the digestive tract. This explains why hair loss and nausea are side effects of some types of cancer chemotherapy drugs.

The Activity of Enzymes Is Influenced by Their Environment

The complex three-dimensional structures of enzymes are sensitive to environmental conditions. Recall that hydrogen bonds between polar amino acids are important in determining the three-dimensional structure of proteins (see Chapter 3). These bonds only occur within a narrow range of chemical and physical conditions, including the proper pH, temperature, and salt concentration. Thus, most enzymes have a very narrow range of conditions in which they function optimally. When conditions fall outside this range, the enzyme becomes **denatured,** meaning that it loses the exact three-dimensional structure required for it to function properly.

In humans, cellular enzymes generally work best at a pH around 7.4, the level maintained in and around our cells (**Fig. 6-15a**). For these enzymes, an acid pH alters the charges on amino acids by adding hydrogen ions to them, which in turn will change the enzyme's shape and compromise its ability to function. Enzymes that operate in the human digestive tract, however, may function outside of the pH range maintained within cells. The protein-digesting enzyme pepsin, for example, requires the acidic conditions of the stomach (pH around 2). In contrast, the protein-digesting enzyme trypsin, found in the small intestine where alkaline conditions prevail, works best at a pH close to 8 (see Fig. 6-15a).

In addition to pH, temperature affects the rate of enzyme-catalyzed reactions, which are slowed by lower temperatures and accelerated by moderately higher temperatures. This is because the rate of movement of molecules affects how likely they are to encounter the active site of an enzyme (**Fig. 6-15b**). Cooling the body can drastically

(a) Effect of pH on enzyme activity

(b) Effect of temperature on enzyme activity

▲ FIGURE 6-15 Human enzymes function best within narrow ranges of pH and temperature (a) The digestive enzyme pepsin, released into the stomach, works best at an acidic pH. Trypsin, released into the small intestine, works best at a basic pH. Most enzymes within cells work best at the pH found in the interstitial fluid and cytosol (about 7.4). (b) The maximum activity of most human enzymes occurs at human body temperature.

slow human metabolic reactions. Consider the example of a young boy who fell through the ice on a lake and was rescued and survived with no permanent disability after 20 minutes under water. At normal body temperature, the brain dies after about 4 minutes without oxygen, but the boy's body temperature and metabolic rate were lowered by the icy water, drastically reducing his need for oxygen.

In contrast, when temperatures rise too high, the hydrogen bonds that regulate protein shape may be broken apart by the excessive molecular motion, denaturing the protein. Think of the protein in egg white and how its appearance and texture are completely altered by cooking. Far lower temperatures than those required to fry an egg can still be too hot to allow enzymes to function properly. Excessive heat may be fatal; every summer, many children in the United States die from heatstroke when left unattended in overheated cars.

Food remains fresh longer in the refrigerator or freezer because cooling slows the enzyme-catalyzed reactions that allow bacteria and fungi (which can spoil food) to grow and reproduce. Before the advent of refrigeration, meat was commonly preserved by using concentrated salt solutions (think of bacon or salt pork), which kill most bacteria. Salts dissociate into ions, which form bonds with amino acids in enzyme proteins. Too much (or too little) salt interferes with the three-dimensional structure of enzymes, destroying their activity. Dill pickles are very well preserved in a vinegar-salt solution, which combines both highly salty and acidic conditions. The enzymes of organisms that live in salty environments, as you might predict, have configurations that depend on a relatively high concentration of salt ions.

CHECK YOUR LEARNING

Can you describe how cells regulate the rate at which metabolic reactions proceed? Can you describe how poisons, drugs, and environmental conditions influence enzyme activity, and provide examples?

CASE STUDY revisited

Energy Unleashed

During the course of a 26-mile race, a marathoner burns a great deal of glucose to provide enough ATP to power muscles through roughly 34,000 running steps. People store glucose molecules linked together in long branched chains of glycogen, primarily in the muscles and liver. Adults typically store about 3.5 ounces (100 grams) of glycogen in the liver, and another 9.9 ounces (280 grams) in muscles. Highly trained distance athletes may have their liver glycogen storage capacity increased by more than 50%, and the ability of their muscles to store glycogen may be more than double that of nonathletes.

Glycogen storage is crucial for marathon runners. During a marathon, a runner depletes essentially all of his or her body's stored glycogen. At this point, often about 90 minutes into the

race, the runner may experience extreme muscle fatigue, loss of motivation, and occasionally even hallucinations, because both muscles and brain are starved of energy. Runners describe this sensation as "hitting the wall" or "bonking." To store the greatest possible amount of glycogen, endurance athletes practice carbo-loading by consuming large quantities of carbohydrates (starches and sugars) during the 3 days preceding the race. By packing their livers and muscles with glycogen before the race, and by consuming energy drinks during the race, some runners manage to cross the finish line before they hit the wall.

Consider This

When a runner's body temperature begins to rise, the body activates several mechanisms, including sweating and circulating more blood to the skin. Compare this response to overheating with feedback inhibition in enzymes.

CHAPTER REVIEW

Summary of Key Concepts

6.1 What Is Energy?

Energy is the capacity to do work. Potential energy is stored energy (such as chemical energy, elastic energy, or gravitational energy). Kinetic energy is the energy of movement (including radiant energy, heat energy, and the movement of objects). Potential energy can be converted to kinetic energy, and kinetic energy can be converted to potential energy. The first law of thermodynamics states that in a closed system, the total amount of energy remains constant, although the energy may change form. The second law of thermodynamics states that any use of energy causes a decrease in the quantity of useful energy and an increase in entropy (disorder or less useful forms of energy such as heat). The highly organized, low-entropy systems that characterize life do not violate the second law of thermodynamics, because they are achieved through a continuous influx of usable energy from the sun, accompanied by an enormous increase in solar entropy.

6.2 How Is Energy Transformed During Chemical Reactions?

Chemical reactions fall into two broad categories. In exergonic reactions, the reactant molecules have more energy than do the product molecules, so the reaction releases energy. In endergonic reactions, the reactants have less energy than do the products, so the reaction requires a net input of energy. Exergonic reactions can occur spontaneously, but all reactions, including exergonic ones, require an initial input of activation energy to overcome electrical repulsions between reactant molecules. Exergonic and endergonic reactions may be coupled such that the energy liberated by an exergonic reaction drives an endergonic reaction. For example, organisms couple exergonic reactions, such as breaking down sugar, with endergonic reactions, such as synthesizing organic molecules.

6.3 How Is Energy Transported Within Cells?

Energy released by chemical reactions within a cell is captured and transported within the cell by unstable energy-carrier molecules, such as ATP and the electron carriers NADH and $FADH_2$. These molecules are the major means by which cells couple exergonic and endergonic reactions occurring at different places in the cell.

6.4 How Do Enzymes Promote Biochemical Reactions?

Cells control their metabolic reactions by regulating the synthesis and the use of enzymes, which are biological catalysts that help overcome activation energy. High activation energies slow many reactions, even exergonic ones, to an imperceptible rate under normal environmental conditions. Catalysts lower the activation energy and thereby speed up chemical reactions without being permanently changed themselves. Organisms synthesize enzyme catalysts that promote one or a few specific reactions. The reactants temporarily bind to the active site of the enzyme, causing less activation energy to be needed to produce the product. Enzymes also allow the breakdown of energy-rich molecules such as glucose in a series of small steps so that energy is released gradually and can be captured in ATP for use in endergonic reactions.

6.5 How Are Enzymes Regulated?

Enzyme action is regulated by altering the rate of enzyme synthesis, activating previously inactive enzymes, competitive and noncompetitive inhibition, and allosteric regulation, which includes feedback inhibition. Many poisons, including cyanide, some nerve gases, some insecticides, and heavy metals, act as enzyme inhibitors. Penicillin, aspirin, and cancer chemotherapy drugs also act as competitive enzyme inhibitors. Environmental conditions—including pH, salt concentration, and temperature—can promote or inhibit enzyme function by altering or preserving the enzyme's three-dimensional structure.

Key Terms

activation energy   97
active site   100
adenosine diphosphate
   (ADP)   98
adenosine triphosphate
   (ATP)   98
allosteric regulation   103
catalyst   99
chemical energy   94
chemical reaction   96
closed system   95
competitive inhibition   102
coupled reaction   98
denature   104
electron carrier   98
endergonic   96
energy   94
energy-carrier molecule   98
entropy   96

enzyme   100
exergonic   96
feedback inhibition   103
first law of
   thermodynamics   94
kinetic energy   94
law of conservation of
   energy   95
metabolic pathway   101
metabolism   101
noncompetitive
   inhibition   103
potential energy   94
product   96
reactant   96
second law of
   thermodynamics   95
substrate   100
work   94

Learning Outcomes

In this chapter, you have learned to . . .

LO1 Define the key terms used to describe energy and explain the forms that energy takes.

LO2 Summarize the first and second laws of thermodynamics.

LO3 Define *entropy* and explain how organisms create the low-entropy conditions of life.

LO4 Describe how energy is captured and released by chemical reactions.

LO5 Describe the energy-carrier molecules in cells and explain how they facilitate chemical reactions.

LO6 Explain how catalysts work and how enzymes in cells catalyze chemical reactions.

LO7 Describe how cells control their metabolic pathways by regulating enzyme activity.

Thinking Through the Concepts

Fill-in-the-Blank

1. According to the first law of thermodynamics, energy can be neither _____ nor _____. Energy occurs in two major forms: _____, the energy of movement, and _____, or stored energy. LO1 LO2

2. According to the second law of thermodynamics, when energy changes forms it tends to be converted from _____ useful to _____ useful forms. This leads to the conclusion that matter spontaneously tends to become less _____. This tendency is called _____. LO2

3. Once started, some reactions release energy and are called _____ reactions. Others require a net input of energy and are called _____ reactions. Which type of reaction will continue spontaneously once it starts? _____. Which type of reaction allows the formation of complex biological molecules from simpler molecules (for example, proteins from amino acids)? _____. When the energy released from one reaction provides the energy required by another, the two reactions are described as _____ reactions. LO3

4. The abbreviation ATP stands for _____. This molecule is the principal _____ molecule in living cells. The molecule is synthesized by cells from _____ and _____. This synthesis requires an input of _____, which is temporarily stored in the ATP molecule. LO4

5. Enzymes are nearly all (type of biological molecule) _____. Enzymes promote reactions in cells by acting as biological _____ that lower the _____. Each enzyme possesses a specialized region called a(n) _____ that binds specific biological molecules. These specific molecules are described as _____ for the enzyme. LO5 LO6

6. Some poisons and drugs act by _____ enzymes. When a drug is similar to the enzyme's substrate, it acts as a (two words) _____ _____. Feedback inhibition is a form of _____ regulation. LO7

Review Questions

1. Explain why organisms do not violate the second law of thermodynamics. What is the ultimate energy source for most forms of life on Earth? LO2

2. Define *potential energy* and *kinetic energy* and provide two specific examples of each. Explain how one form of energy can be converted into another. Will some energy be lost during this conversion? If so, what form will it take? LO1 LO2

3. Define *metabolism*, and explain how reactions can be coupled to one another. LO3 LO4 LO7

4. What is activation energy? How do catalysts affect activation energy? How do catalysts affect the rate of reactions? LO3 LO5

5. Compare breaking down glucose in a cell to setting it on fire with a match. What is the source of activation energy in each case? LO3 LO5 LO7

6. Compare the mechanisms of competitive and noncompetitive inhibition of enzymes. LO7

7. Describe the structure and function of enzymes. How is enzyme activity regulated? LO6 LO7

Applying the Concepts

1. One of your nerdiest friends walks in while you are vacuuming. Trying to impress her, you casually mention that you are expending electrical energy to create a lower-entropy state in your room. She comments that, ultimately, you are taking advantage of the increase in entropy of the sun to clean your room. What is she talking about?

2. The subunits of virtually all organic molecules are joined by condensation reactions and can be broken apart by hydrolysis reactions (described in Chapter 3). Why, then, does your digestive system produce separate enzymes to digest proteins, fats, and carbohydrates?

3. Suppose someone tried to refute evolution using the following argument: "According to evolutionary theory, organisms have increased in complexity through time. However, the increase in complexity contradicts the second law of thermodynamics. Therefore, evolution is impossible." Explain why their reasoning is faulty.

4. When a bear eats a salmon, can the bear use all the energy contained in the body of the fish? Why or why not? Based on your conclusion, would you predict that a natural system (such as a forest) would have more predators or more prey animals (by weight). Explain.

Answers to Figure Caption questions and Fill-in-the-Blank questions can be found in the Answers section at the back of the book.

(MB) *Go to MasteringBiology for practice quizzes, activities, eText, videos, current events, and more.*

CASE STUDY

Did the Dinosaurs Die from Lack of Sunlight?

ABOUT 65 MILLION YEARS AGO, the Cretaceous-Tertiary (K-T) extinction event brought the Cretaceous period to a violent end, and life on Earth suffered a catastrophic blow. The fossil record indicates that a devastating mass extinction eliminated at least 50% of all forms of life known to exist at that time. The 160-million-year reign of the dinosaurs, including the massive *Triceratops* and its predator *Tyrannosaurus rex*, ended abruptly. It would be many millions of years before Earth became repopulated with a diversity of species even approaching that of the late Cretaceous.

In 1980, Luis Alvarez, a Nobel Prize–winning physicist, his geologist son Walter Alvarez, and nuclear chemists Helen Michel and Frank Asaro published a controversial hypothesis. They proposed that an invader from outer space—a massive asteroid—had brought the Cretaceous period to an abrupt and violent end. Their evidence consisted of a thin layer of clay deposited at the end of the Cretaceous period, found at sites throughout the world. Known as the "K-T boundary layer," this clay deposit contains from 30 to 160 times the iridium level typical of Earth's crust. Iridium is a silvery-white metal that is extremely rare in Earth's crust, but abundant in certain types of asteroids. How large must an iridium-rich asteroid have been to create the K-T boundary layer? The Alvarez team calculated that this iridium-enriched space rock must have been at least 6 miles (10 kilometers) in diameter. In the Alvarez scenario, as the asteroid ploughed into Earth at nearly 45,000 miles per hour, its impact released energy greater than 100 trillion tons of TNT, blasting out a plume of debris that likely extended halfway to the moon. The asteroid's fragments, plummeting back into the atmosphere in a fiery shower, ignited widespread wildfires. A shroud of dust and soot blocked the sun's rays, and cooling darkness enveloped Earth.

Although the immediate destruction from fire, earthquakes, landslides, and tsunamis must have been almost unimaginable, these paled in contrast to the prolonged effects of the collision. How could an asteroid impact have eliminated half of all forms of life? Its most damaging long-term effect would have been disruption of the most important biochemical pathway on Earth: photosynthesis. What exactly occurs during photosynthesis? What makes this process so important that interrupting it ended the age of the dinosaurs? In this chapter, we explore these questions.

A giant asteroid may have ended the reign of *Tyrannosaurus*, *Triceratops*, and the other dinosaurs of the Cretaceous period.

AT A GLANCE

LEARNING GOALS

LG1 Explain the process of photosynthesis and discuss why photosynthesis is crucial to most forms of life.

LG2 Describe the structures of plant leaves and chloroplasts and explain how these structures support the process of photosynthesis.

LG3 Identify the source of energy for photosynthesis and describe how this energy is captured and transferred during the light reactions.

LG4 Describe the inputs and products of the light reactions.

LG5 Explain how the products of the light reactions are used during the Calvin cycle and discuss how plants use the products of the Calvin cycle.

7.1 WHAT IS PHOTOSYNTHESIS?

Living things continuously expend energy to survive. For nearly all forms of life, this energy is derived from sunlight, either directly or indirectly. The only organisms capable of directly trapping solar energy are those that perform **photosynthesis,** the process by which light energy is captured and stored as chemical energy in the bonds of organic molecules such as sugar. The evolution of photosynthesis made life as we know it possible. This amazing process provides not only fuel for life but also the oxygen required to burn this fuel. In lakes and oceans, photosynthesis is performed primarily by photosynthetic protists and certain bacteria, and on land mostly by plants. Collectively, these organisms incorporate close to 100 billion tons of carbon into their bodies annually. The carbon- and energy-rich molecules of photosynthetic organisms eventually become available to feed all other forms of life. Fundamentally similar reactions occur in all photosynthetic organisms; here we will concentrate on the most familiar of these: land plants.

Leaves and Chloroplasts Are Adaptations for Photosynthesis

The leaves of plants are beautifully adapted to the demands of photosynthesis (**Fig. 7-1**). A leaf's flattened shape exposes a large surface area to the sun, and its thinness ensures that sunlight can penetrate to reach the light-trapping chloroplasts inside. Both the upper and lower surfaces of a leaf consist of a layer of transparent cells that form the **epidermis,** which protects the inner parts of the leaf while allowing light to penetrate. The outer surface of the epidermis is covered by the **cuticle,** a transparent, waxy, waterproof covering that reduces the evaporation of water from the leaf.

A leaf obtains the carbon dioxide (CO_2) necessary for photosynthesis from the air, through adjustable pores in the epidermis called stomata (singular, **stoma;** Greek for "mouth"; **Fig. 7-2**). Inside the leaf are layers of cells collectively called **mesophyll** (which translates to "middle of the leaf") where most chloroplasts are located. *Vascular bundles,* which form veins in the leaf (**Fig. 7-1b**), supply water and minerals to the leaf's cells and carry the sugars produced during photosynthesis to other parts of the plant. Cells that surround the vascular bundles are called **bundle sheath cells,** which lack chloroplasts in most plants.

Photosynthesis in plants takes place within **chloroplasts,** most of which are contained within mesophyll cells. A single mesophyll cell often contains 40 to 50 chloroplasts (**Fig. 7-1c**), which are so small (about 5 micrometers in diameter) that 2,500 of them lined up would span an average thumbnail. Chloroplasts are organelles that consist of a double outer membrane enclosing a semifluid substance, the **stroma.** Embedded in the stroma are disk-shaped, interconnected membranous sacs called **thylakoids** (**Fig. 7-1d**). Each of these sacs encloses a fluid-filled region called the thylakoid space. The chemical reactions of photosynthesis that depend on light (the light reactions) occur in and adjacent to the thylakoids. The reactions of the Calvin cycle that capture carbon from CO_2 and produce simple sugar molecules occur in the surrounding stroma.

Photosynthesis Consists of the Light Reactions and the Calvin Cycle

Starting with the simple molecules of carbon dioxide and water, photosynthesis converts the energy of sunlight into chemical energy stored in the bonds of glucose and releases oxygen as a by-product (**Fig. 7-3**). The simplest overall chemical reaction for photosynthesis is:

$$6\,CO_2 + 6\,H_2O + \text{light energy} \rightarrow C_6H_{12}O_6 \text{ (sugar)} + 6\,O_2$$

This straightforward equation obscures the fact that photosynthesis actually involves dozens of individual reactions, each catalyzed by a separate enzyme. These reactions occur in two distinct stages: the light reactions and the Calvin cycle. Each stage takes place within a different region of the

(a) Leaves

stoma

cuticle

upper epidermis

mesophyll cells

lower epidermis

stoma

chloroplasts

bundle sheath cells

vascular bundle (vein)

(b) Internal leaf structure

outer membrane
inner membrane
thylakoid
stroma

(d) Chloroplast

channel interconnecting thylakoids

(c) Mesophyll cell containing chloroplasts

▲ FIGURE 7-1 **An overview of photosynthetic structures (a)** In land plants, photosynthesis occurs primarily in the leaves. **(b)** A section of a leaf. **(c)** A light micrograph of a single mesophyll cell, packed with chloroplasts. **(d)** A single chloroplast, showing the stroma and thylakoids where photosynthesis occurs.

chloroplast, but the two are connected by an important link: energy-carrier molecules.

In the **light reactions,** chlorophyll and other molecules embedded in the membranes of the chloroplast thylakoids capture sunlight energy and convert some of it into chemical energy stored in the energy-carrier molecules ATP (adenosine triphosphate) and NADPH (nicotinamide adenine dinucleotide phosphate). Water is split apart, and oxygen gas is released as a by-product. In the reactions of the **Calvin cycle,** enzymes in the fluid stroma that surrounds the thylakoids use CO_2 from the atmosphere and chemical energy from the energy-carrier molecules to drive the synthesis of a three-carbon sugar that will be used to make glucose. Figure 7-3 shows the locations at which the light reactions and the Calvin

cycle occur, and illustrates the interdependence of the two processes. The "photo" part of photosynthesis refers to the capture of light energy by the light reactions in the thylakoid membranes. These reactions use light energy to charge up the energy-carrier molecules ADP (adenosine diphosphate) and $NADP^+$ (the energy-depleted form of NADPH) to form ATP and NADPH. The "synthesis" part of photosynthesis refers to the Calvin cycle, which captures carbon and uses it to synthesize sugar, powered by energy provided by ATP and NADPH. The depleted carriers—ADP and $NADP^+$—are then recharged by the light reactions into ATP and NADPH, which will fuel the synthesis of more sugar molecules.

In the following sections we will look more closely at each stage of photosynthesis.

(a) Stomata open

(b) Stomata closed

▲ FIGURE 7-2 **Stomata (a)** Open stomata allow CO_2 to diffuse in and oxygen to diffuse out. **(b)** Closed stomata reduce water loss by evaporation but prevent CO_2 from entering and oxygen from leaving.

CASE STUDY continued

Did the Dinosaurs Die from Lack of Sunlight?

More than 2 billion years ago, some bacterial (prokaryotic) cells, through chance mutations, acquired the ability to harness the energy of sunlight. Exploiting this abundant energy source, early photosynthetic cells filled the seas. As their numbers increased, oxygen began to accumulate in the atmosphere, radically altering Earth's environment. Later, plants evolved, made the transition to land, and eventually grew in luxuriant profusion. By the Cretaceous period, plants had become sufficiently abundant to provide enough food to support plant-eating giants, such as the 8-ton *Triceratops* on which huge meat-eaters, such as the 40-foot-long *Tyrannosaurus,* may have preyed or scavenged. Then, as now, energy harvested through photosynthesis sustained nearly all forms of life.

CHECK YOUR LEARNING

Can you explain why photosynthesis is important? Can you diagram the structure of leaves and chloroplasts and explain how these structures function in photosynthesis? Can you write out and explain the basic equation for photosynthesis? Are you able to summarize the main events of the light reactions and the Calvin cycle and explain the relationship between these two processes?

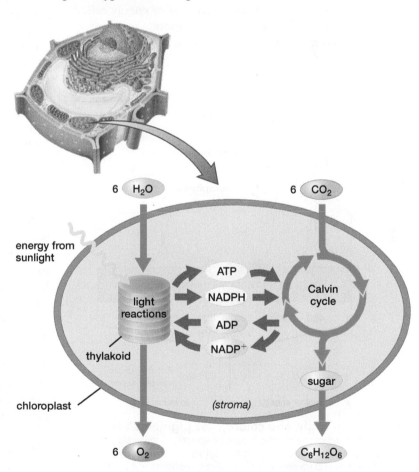

▲ FIGURE 7-3 **An overview of the relationship between the light reactions and the Calvin cycle** The simple molecules that provide the raw ingredients for photosynthesis (H_2O and CO_2) enter at different stages of the process and are used in different parts of the chloroplast. The O_2 liberated by photosynthesis is derived from H_2O, while the carbon used in the synthesis of sugar is obtained from CO_2. (In some later figures you will see smaller versions of this figure.)

7.2 THE LIGHT REACTIONS: HOW IS LIGHT ENERGY CONVERTED TO CHEMICAL ENERGY?

The light reactions capture the energy of sunlight, storing it as chemical energy in two different energy-carrier molecules: ATP and NADPH. The molecules that make these reactions possible, including light-capturing pigments and enzymes, are anchored in a precise array within the membranes of the thylakoid. As you read this section, notice how the thylakoid membranes and the spaces they enclose support the light reactions.

Light Is Captured by Pigments in Chloroplasts

The sun emits energy that spans a broad spectrum of electromagnetic radiation. The **electromagnetic spectrum** ranges from short-wavelength gamma rays, through ultraviolet, visible, and infrared light, to very long-wavelength radio waves (**Fig. 7-4**). Light and other electromagnetic waves are composed of individual packets of energy called **photons.** The energy of a photon corresponds to its wavelength: short-wavelength photons, such as gamma and

▲ FIGURE 7-4 **Light and chloroplast pigments** Visible light, a small part of the electromagnetic spectrum, consists of wavelengths that correspond to the colors of the rainbow. Chlorophyll *a* and *b* (green and blue curves, respectively) strongly absorb violet, blue, and red light, reflecting a green or yellowish-green color to our eyes. Carotenoids (orange curve) absorb blue and green wavelengths.

QUESTION Which chlorophyll would be greener and which would be more yellow-green?

X-rays, are very energetic, whereas longer-wavelength photons, such as radio waves, carry lower energies. Visible light consists of wavelengths with energies that are high enough to alter biological *pigment molecules* (light-absorbing molecules) such as chlorophyll, but not high enough to break the bonds of crucial molecules such as DNA. (It is no coincidence that these wavelengths, with just the right amount of energy, also stimulate the pigments in our eyes, allowing us to see.)

When a specific wavelength of light strikes an object such as a leaf, one of three events occurs: The light may be reflected (bounced back), transmitted (passed through), or absorbed (captured). Wavelengths of light that are reflected or transmitted can reach the eyes of an observer; these wavelengths are seen as the color of the object. Light that is absorbed can drive biological processes such as photosynthesis.

Chloroplasts contain a variety of pigment molecules that absorb different wavelengths of light. **Chlorophyll *a*,** the key light-capturing pigment molecule in chloroplasts, strongly absorbs violet, blue, and red light, but reflects green, thus giving green leaves their color (see Fig. 7-4). Chloroplasts also contain other molecules, collectively called **accessory pigments,** which absorb additional wavelengths of light energy and transfer their energy to chlorophyll *a*. Accessory pigments include chlorophyll *b*, a slightly different form of chlorophyll that absorbs some of the blue and red-orange wavelengths of light that are missed by chlorophyll *a* and reflects yellow-green light. **Carotenoids** are accessory pigments found in all chloroplasts. They absorb blue and green light and appear mostly yellow or orange because they reflect these wavelengths (see Fig. 7-4). Carotenoid accessory pigments include beta-carotene, which gives many vegetables and fruits (including carrots, squash, oranges, and cantaloupes) their orange colors. Interestingly, animals convert beta-carotene into vitamin A, which is used to synthesize the light-capturing pigment in our eyes. Thus, in a beautiful symmetry, the beta-carotene that captures light energy in plants is converted into a substance that captures light in animals as well.

Although carotenoids are present in leaves, their color is usually masked by the more abundant green chlorophyll. In temperate regions, as autumn leaves begin to die, chlorophyll breaks down before carotenoids do, revealing these bright yellow and orange pigments as fall colors (**Fig. 7-5**). (Red and purple fall leaf pigments are not involved in photosynthesis.)

The Light Reactions Occur in Association with the Thylakoid Membranes

Light energy is captured and converted into chemical energy by the light reactions that occur in and on the thylakoid membranes. These membranes contain many **photosystems,** each consisting of a cluster of chlorophyll

▲ FIGURE 7-5 **Loss of chlorophyll reveals carotenoid pigments** As winter approaches, chlorophyll in these aspen leaves breaks down, revealing yellow-to-orange carotenoid pigments.

and accessory pigment molecules surrounded by various proteins. Two photosystems—photosystem II and photosystem I—work together during the light reactions. (The photosystems are named according to the order in which they were discovered, but the light reactions use photosystem II before using photosystem I.)

Each photosystem has an electron transport chain located adjacent to it. Each **electron transport chain** consists of a series of electron-carrier molecules embedded in the thylakoid membrane. So within the thylakoid membrane, the overall path of electrons is photosystem II → electron transport chain II → photosystem I → electron transport chain I → $NADP^+$ (see Fig. 7-7).

You can think of the light reactions as a sort of pinball game: Energy is transferred from spring-driven pistons (chlorophyll molecules) to a ball (an electron). The ball is propelled upward (enters a higher-energy level). As the ball bounces back downhill, the energy it releases can be used to

? HAVE **YOU** EVER WONDERED . . .

What Color Might Plants Be on Other Planets?

Biologist Nancy Kiang and her colleagues at NASA have developed hypotheses about alien plant colors. M-type stars, the most abundant type in our galaxy, emit light that is redder and dimmer than that of our sun. If photosynthetic organisms happened to evolve on an Earth-like planet circling an M-type star, to glean enough energy, the plants very possibly would require pigments that would absorb all visible wavelengths of light. Such pigments would reflect almost no light back to our eyes, so these alien photosynthesizers would probably be black!

turn a wheel (generate ATP) or ring a bell (generate NADPH). With this overall scheme in mind, let's look more closely at the actual sequence of events in the light reactions.

Photosystem II Uses Light Energy to Create a Hydrogen Ion Gradient and to Split Water

As you read the descriptions below, match them to the numbered steps in **Figure 7-6.** The light reactions begin when photons of light are absorbed by pigment molecules clustered in photosystem II (**Fig. 7-6 ❶**). The energy hops from one pigment molecule to the next until it is funneled into the photosystem II reaction center (**Fig. 7-6 ❷**). The **reaction center** of each photosystem consists of a pair of specialized chlorophyll *a* molecules and a *primary electron acceptor* molecule embedded in a complex of proteins. When the energy from light reaches the reaction center, it boosts an electron from one of the reaction center chlorophylls to the primary electron acceptor, which captures the energized electron (**Fig. 7-6 ❸**).

The reaction center of photosystem II must be supplied continuously with electrons to replace those that are boosted out of it when energized by light. These replacement electrons come from water (see Fig. 7-6 ❷). Water molecules are split by an enzyme associated with photosystem II, liberating electrons that will replace those lost by the reaction center chlorophyll molecules. Splitting water also releases two hydrogen ions (H^+) that are used in forming the H^+ gradient that drives ATP synthesis (see Fig. 7-7). For every two water molecules split, one molecule of O_2 is produced.

Once the primary electron acceptor in photosystem II captures the electron, it passes the electron to the first molecule of electron transport chain II (**Fig. 7-6 ❹**). The electron then travels from one electron carrier molecule to the next, losing energy as it goes. Some of this energy is harnessed to pump H^+ across the thylakoid membrane and into the thylakoid space, where it will be used to generate ATP (**Fig. 7-6 ❺**; to be discussed shortly). Finally, the energy-depleted electron leaves electron transport chain II and enters the reaction center of photosystem I, where it replaces the electron ejected when light strikes photosystem I (**Fig. 7-6 ❻**).

Photosystem I Generates NADPH

Meanwhile, light has also been striking the pigment molecules of photosystem I. This light energy is passed to a chlorophyll *a* molecule in the reaction center (see Fig. 7-6 ❻). Here, it energizes an electron that is absorbed by the primary electron acceptor of photosystem I (**Fig. 7-6 ❼**). (The energized electron is immediately replaced by an energy-depleted electron from electron transport chain II.) From the primary electron acceptor of photosystem I, the energized electron is passed along electron transport chain I (**Fig. 7-6 ❽**) until it reaches $NADP^+$. When an $NADP^+$ molecule (dissolved in the fluid stroma) picks up two energetic electrons along with one hydrogen ion, the energy-carrier molecule NADPH is formed (**Fig. 7-6 ❾**).

▲ FIGURE 7-6 **Energy transfer and the light reactions of photosynthesis** Light reactions occur within or adjacent to the thylakoid membrane. The vertical axis indicates the relative energy levels of the molecules involved. ❶ Light is absorbed by photosystem II, and the energy is passed to an electron in one of the chlorophyll a molecules within the reaction center. ❷ The energized electron is ejected from the chlorophyll a molecule. ❸ The energized ejected electron is captured by a primary electron acceptor in the reaction center (purple rectangle). ❹ The high-energy electron is passed through electron transport chain II. ❺ As electron transport chain II transfers the electron along, some of the released energy is used to generate ATP. The energy-depleted electron then enters the reaction center of photosystem I, replacing an ejected electron there. ❻ Light strikes photosystem I, and the energy is passed to the electron in the reaction center chlorophyll molecules. ❼ The energized electron is ejected from the reaction center and is captured by the primary electron acceptor. ❽ The electron moves down electron transport chain I. ❾ NADPH is formed when $NADP^+$ in the stroma picks up two energized electrons, along with one H^+.

▲ FIGURE 7-7 **Events of the light reactions occur in and near the thylakoid membrane** Trace the formation of ATP and NADPH as light is captured and an energized electron travels through molecules within the thylakoid membrane. ❶ Energy released as the electron passes through electron transport chain II is harnessed to pump H^+ across the thylakoid membrane and into the thylakoid space. ❷ A high concentration gradient of H^+ is generated as energy from electrons liberated during their passage through electron transport chain II is used to pump H^+ across the membrane into the thylakoid space. ❸ During chemiosmosis, H^+ flows down its concentration gradient through ATP synthase channels, which uses energy from the gradient to generate ATP. About one ATP molecule is synthesized for every three hydrogen ions that pass through the channel.

The Hydrogen Ion Gradient Generates ATP by Chemiosmosis

Figure 7-7 shows how electrons move through the thylakoid membrane and how their energy is used to create an H^+ gradient that drives ATP synthesis through a process called **chemiosmosis.** As an energized electron travels along electron transport chain II, some of the energy the electron liberates is used to pump H^+ into the thylakoid space (**Fig. 7-7 ❶**), creating a high concentration of H^+ inside the space (**Fig. 7-7 ❷**) and a low concentration in the surrounding stroma. During chemiosmosis, H^+ flows back down its concentration gradient through a special type of channel that spans the thylakoid membrane. This channel, called **ATP synthase,** generates

ATP from ADP and phosphate dissolved in the stroma as the H^+ flows through the channel (**Fig. 7-7 ❸**).

How is a gradient of H^+ used to synthesize ATP? Compare the H^+ gradient to water stored behind a dam at a hydroelectric plant (**Fig. 7-8**). The water behind the dam flows downward over turbines, rotating them. The turbines convert the energy of moving water into electrical energy. Like water stored behind a dam, hydrogen ions in the thylakoid space can move down their gradient. Just as the water flowing over a hydroelectric dam is channeled through turbines, the hydrogen ions can flow into the stroma only through ATP synthase channels. Like turbines generating electricity, ATP synthase captures the energy liberated by the flow of H^+ and uses it to drive ATP synthesis from ADP plus phosphate dissolved in the stroma.

① Energy is released as water flows downhill

② Energy is harnessed to rotate a turbine

③ The energy of the rotating turbine is used to generate electricity

▲ FIGURE 7-8 A dam allows a "water gradient" to be used to generate electricity

SUMMING UP Light Reactions

- Chlorophyll and carotenoid pigments of photosystem II absorb light that energizes and ejects an electron from a reaction center chlorophyll *a* molecule. The energized electron is captured by the primary electron acceptor molecule.
- The electron is passed from the primary electron acceptor to the adjacent electron transport chain II, where it moves from molecule to molecule, releasing energy. Some of the energy is used to create a hydrogen ion gradient across the thylakoid membrane. This gradient is used to drive ATP synthesis by chemiosmosis.
- Enzymes associated with photosystem II split water, releasing electrons that replace those ejected from the reaction center chlorophylls, and supplying H^+ that enhances the H^+ gradient for ATP production, and generating oxygen.
- Chlorophyll and carotenoid pigments in photosystem I absorb light that energizes and ejects an electron from a reaction center chlorophyll *a* molecule. The electron is replaced by an energy-depleted electron from electron transport chain II.
- The energized electron passes from the primary electron acceptor into electron transport chain I, where it moves from molecule to molecule, releasing energy.
- For every two energized electrons that exit electron transport chain I, one molecule of the energy carrier NADPH is formed from $NADP^+$ and H^+.
- The overall products of the light reactions are the energy carriers NADPH and ATP; O_2 is released as a by-product.

CHECK YOUR LEARNING

Can you list the light-capturing molecules in chloroplasts and describe their functions? Can you diagram and describe the molecules within the thylakoid membranes and explain how they capture and transfer light energy? Can you describe the products of the light reactions and the roles of these products? Can you explain how ATP is generated?

CASE STUDY continued

Did the Dinosaurs Die from Lack of Sunlight?

Scientists have calculated that the force of the asteroid impact blasted some debris so far into outer space that it took days to rain back down to Earth. Earth's rotation while the debris was aloft meant that much of the material fell on regions far from the point of impact. The plummeting chunks of rock would have made a flaming re-entry through Earth's atmosphere, setting huge fires on nearly every continent. Oxygen levels were high in the Cretaceous atmosphere, intensifying the conflagrations. A large portion of Earth's vegetation was likely consumed by fire, and many of the plants that managed to survive the fires must have succumbed during the cold, dark "global winter" that began as the planet was encompassed by soot and dust. Plant-eating animals that survived the initial blast would have soon starved, especially enormous ones like the 12-ton *Triceratops*, which needed to consume hundreds of pounds of vegetation daily. Predators such as *Tyrannosaurus*, which relied on plant-eaters for food, would have died soon afterward. During the Cretaceous, as now, interrupting the vital flow of solar energy captured by photosynthetic organisms would be catastrophic.

7.3 THE CALVIN CYCLE: HOW IS CHEMICAL ENERGY STORED IN SUGAR MOLECULES?

Our cells produce carbon dioxide as we burn sugar for energy (described in Chapter 8), but they can't form organic molecules by capturing (or *fixing*) the carbon atoms in CO_2. Although this feat can be accomplished by a few types of *chemosynthetic* bacteria that fix carbon using energy gained by breaking down inorganic molecules, nearly all carbon fixation is performed by photosynthetic organisms. The carbon is captured from atmospheric CO_2 during the Calvin cycle using energy from sunlight harnessed during the light reactions. The details of the Calvin cycle were discovered during the 1950s by chemists Melvin Calvin, Andrew Benson, and James Bassham. Using radioactive isotopes of carbon (see Chapter 2), the researchers were able to follow carbon atoms as they moved from CO_2 through the various compounds of the cycle and, finally, into sugar molecules.

The Calvin Cycle Captures Carbon Dioxide

The ATP and NADPH synthesized during the light reactions are dissolved in the fluid stroma that surrounds the thylakoids. There, these energy carriers power the synthesis of the three-carbon sugar glyceraldehyde-3-phosphate (G3P) from CO_2 during the Calvin cycle. This metabolic pathway is described as a "cycle" because it begins and ends with the same five-carbon molecule, ribulose bisphosphate (RuBP).

Keeping this in mind, for simplicity we will illustrate the cycle starting and ending with three molecules of RuBP. Each "turn" will then capture three molecules of CO_2 and produce one molecule of the simple sugar end product: G3P. The Calvin cycle is best understood if we divide it into three parts: (1) carbon fixation, (2) the synthesis of G3P, and (3) the regeneration of RuBP that allows the cycle to continue (Fig. 7-9).

During **carbon fixation,** carbon from CO_2 is incorporated into larger organic molecules. The enzyme **rubisco**

combines three CO_2 molecules with three RuBP molecules to produce three unstable six-carbon molecules that immediately split in half, forming six molecules of phosphoglyceric acid (PGA, a three-carbon molecule) (Fig. 7-9 ❶). Because carbon fixation generates this three-carbon PGA molecule, the Calvin cycle is often referred to as the **C_3 pathway.**

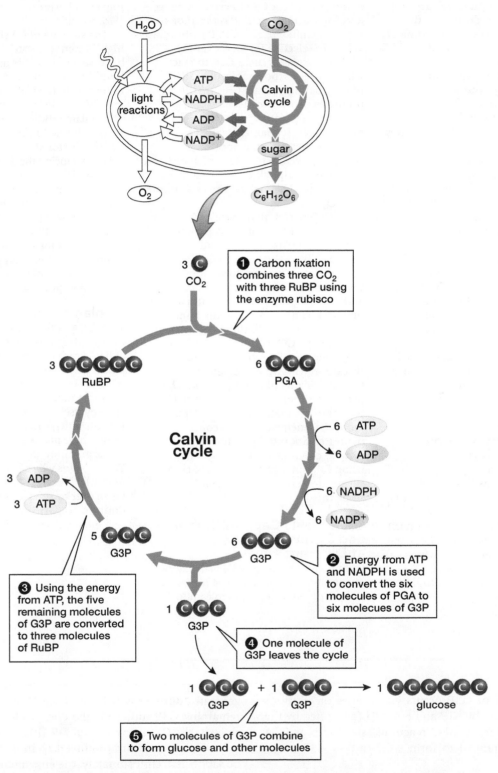

▲ FIGURE 7-9 **The Calvin cycle fixes carbon from CO_2 and produces the simple sugar G3P**

IN GREATER DEPTH Alternate Pathways Increase the Efficiency of Carbon Fixation

In hot, dry conditions, stomata remain closed much of the time to prevent water from evaporating. But this also prevents the exchange of gases, so as photosynthesis occurs, the concentration of CO_2 drops and the concentration of O_2 rises. Unfortunately O_2 as well as CO_2 can bind to the active site of the enzyme rubisco (an example of competitive inhibition; see Fig. 6-13b) and combine with RuBP, causing photorespiration. Plants, particularly fragile seedlings, may die under these circumstances because they are unable to capture enough energy to meet their metabolic needs.

Rubisco is the most abundant enzyme on Earth, and arguably one of the most important. It catalyzes the reaction by which carbon enters the biosphere, and all life is based on carbon. Why, then, is rubisco so nonselective? Apparently the necessary mutations to prevent competitive inhibition by oxygen have never occurred. Instead, over evolutionary time, flowering plants have evolved two different but related mechanisms to circumvent photorespiration: the C_4 pathway and CAM. Each involves several additional reactions and consumes more ATP than does the Calvin cycle alone, but they confer an important advantage under hot, dry conditions.

C_4 Plants Capture Carbon and Synthesize Sugar in Different Cells

In typical plants, known as C_3 plants (because they use the C_3 cycle, or Calvin cycle), the chloroplasts in which the Calvin cycle occurs are located primarily in mesophyll cells. No chloroplasts are found in bundle sheath cells (which surround the leaf's veins; see Fig. 7-1). In contrast, C_4 plants have chloroplasts in both mesophyll and bundle sheath cells. Such plants use an initial series of reactions, called the C_4 pathway, to selectively capture carbon in their mesophyll chloroplasts. The mesophyll chloroplasts lack Calvin cycle enzymes and use the enzyme PEP carboxylase to fix CO_2. Unlike rubisco, PEP carboxylase is highly selective for CO_2 over O_2. PEP carboxylase causes CO_2 to react with a three-carbon molecule called phosphoenolpyruvate (PEP). This produces the four-carbon molecule oxaloacetate, from which the C_4 pathway gets its name. Oxaloacetate is rapidly converted into another four-carbon molecule, malate, which diffuses from the mesophyll cells into bundle sheath cells. The malate acts as a shuttle for CO_2.

In C_4 plants, Calvin cycle enzymes (including rubisco) are only present in the chloroplasts of the bundle sheath cells. In the bundle sheath cells, malate is broken down, forming the three-carbon molecule pyruvate and releasing CO_2. This generates a high CO_2 concentration in the bundle sheath cells (up to 10 times higher than atmospheric CO_2). The resulting high CO_2 concentration allows rubisco to fix carbon with little competition from O_2, minimizing photorespiration. The pyruvate is then actively transported back into the mesophyll cells. Here, more ATP energy is used to convert pyruvate back into PEP, allowing the cycle to continue (Fig. E7-1a). Plants using C_4 photosynthesis include corn, sugarcane, sorghum, some grasses, and some thistles.

CAM Plants Capture Carbon and Synthesize Sugar at Different Times

CAM plants also use the C_4 pathway, but in contrast to C_4 plants, CAM plants do not use different cell types to capture carbon and to synthesize sugar. Instead, they perform both activities in the same mesophyll cells, but at different times; carbon fixation occurs at night, and sugar synthesis occurs during the day (Fig. E7-1b).

The stomata of CAM plants open at night, when less water will evaporate because temperatures are cooler and humidity is higher. Carbon dioxide diffuses into the leaf and is captured in mesophyll cells using the C_4 pathway. The malate produced by the C_4 pathway is then shuttled into the central vacuole where it is stored as malic acid until daytime. During the day, when stomata are closed to conserve water, the malic acid leaves the vacuole and re-enters the cytoplasm as malate. The malate is broken down, forming pyruvate (which will be converted to PEP) and releasing CO_2, which enters the Calvin cycle (via rubisco) to produce sugar. CAM plants include cacti, most succulents (such as the jade plant), and pineapples.

C_4 plants and CAM Pathways Are Specialized Adaptations

Because they are so much more efficient at fixing carbon, why haven't C_4 and CAM plants taken over the world by now? The trade-off is that both of these pathways consume more energy than does the Calvin cycle by itself; hence, they waste some of the solar energy that they capture. As a result, these plants only have an advantage in warm, sunny, dry environments. This explains why a lush spring lawn of Kentucky bluegrass (a C_3 plant) may be taken over by spiky crabgrass (a C_4 plant) during a hot, dry summer.

The synthesis of G3P occurs via a series of reactions using energy donated by ATP and NADPH (generated by the light reactions). During these reactions, six 3-carbon PGA molecules are rearranged to form six 3-carbon G3P molecules (Fig. 7-9 ❷).

Three molecules of RuBP are regenerated from five of the six G3P molecules; this regeneration is powered by ATP generated during the light reactions (Fig. 7-9 ❸). The single remaining G3P molecule, the end product of photosynthesis, exits the Calvin cycle (Fig. 7-9 ❹).

Carbon fixation, the first step in the Calvin cycle, can be sabotaged. Unfortunately, the enzyme rubisco that allows carbon fixation is not very selective, and will cause either CO_2 or O_2 to combine with RuBP. If O_2 is fixed, the result

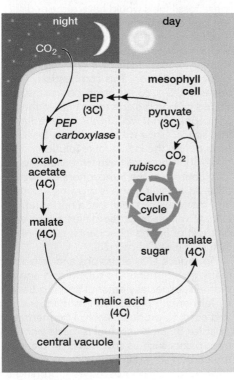

▶ FIGURE E7-1 **The C₄ pathway and the CAM pathway** Some of the reactions illustrated here occur in the cytoplasm, whereas others, including all those of the Calvin cycle, occur in chloroplasts. Both include the C₄ pathway. **(a)** The C₄ pathway occurs in plant groups including corn. **(b)** The CAM pathway occurs in plant groups including pineapples. By creating a high level of CO_2 in **(a)** the bundle sheath cells of C₄ plants and **(b)** the mesophyll cells of CAM plants (during the day, when stomata are closed), each of these pathways minimizes photorespiration.

QUESTION Why do C₃ (Calvin cycle) plants have an advantage over C₄ plants under conditions that are not hot and dry?

(a) **C₄ plants**

(b) **CAM plants**

is a wasteful process called **photorespiration.** Photorespiration prevents the Calvin cycle from synthesizing sugar, effectively derailing photosynthesis. If photorespiration could be avoided, plants could capture solar energy much more efficiently. Many researchers are working to genetically modify the enzyme rubisco to make it more selective for CO_2, with the hope of increasing the yields of crops such as wheat.

A small percentage of Earth's terrestrial plants have evolved biochemical pathways that consume a bit more energy but increase the efficiency of carbon fixation in hot, dry environments. These pathways—the **C₄ pathway** and the **crassulacean acid metabolism (CAM)** pathway—are explored in "In Greater Depth: Alternate Pathways Increase the Efficiency of Carbon Fixation."

Carbon Fixed During the Calvin Cycle Is Used to Synthesize Glucose

In reactions that occur outside of the Calvin cycle, two G3P molecules can be combined to form one six-carbon glucose molecule (Fig. 7-9 ❺). Glucose can then be used to synthesize sucrose (table sugar), a disaccharide storage molecule consisting of a glucose linked to a fructose. Glucose molecules are also linked together in long chains to form starch (another storage molecule) or cellulose (a major component of plant cell walls). Some glucose molecules are also broken down during cellular respiration to provide energy for the plant's cells.

Earth|Watch

Biofuels—Are Their Benefits Bogus?

When you drive your car, turn up the thermostat, or flick on your desk lamp, you are actually unleashing the energy of prehistoric sunlight trapped by prehistoric photosynthetic organisms. This is because over hundreds of millions of years, heat and pressure converted the bodies of these organisms—with their stored solar energy and carbon captured from ancient atmospheric CO_2—into coal, oil, and natural gas. Without human intervention, these fossil fuels would have remained trapped deep underground.

Global climate change is big news, and a major contributor to it is increased burning of fossil fuels by a growing human population. This combustion releases CO_2 into the atmosphere; the added carbon dioxide traps heat in the atmosphere that would otherwise radiate into space. Since we began using fossil fuels during the industrial revolution in the mid-1800s, humans have increased the CO_2 content of the atmosphere by about 38%. As a result, Earth is growing warmer, and many experts fear that a hotter future climate will place extraordinary stresses on most of Earth's inhabitants, ourselves included (see Chapter 28).

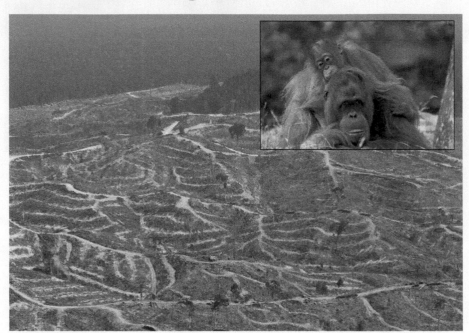

▲ FIGURE E7-2 **Cleared tropical forest** This aerial view shows the aftermath of clearing lush tropical forest, the former home of rare Sumatran tigers, elephants, leopards, orangutans, and a wealth of bird species. This will become a palm oil plantation for biofuels. (Inset) Endangered orangutans such as these are increasingly rendered homeless by deforestation, and are often killed as they are forced closer to human settlements.

To reduce CO_2 emissions and reliance on imported oil, many governments are subsidizing and promoting the use of biofuels, especially ethanol and biodiesel. Ethanol is produced by fermenting plants rich in sugars, such as sugarcane and corn, to produce alcohol (fermentation is described in Chapter 8). Biodiesel fuel is made primarily from oil derived from plants such as soybeans, canola, or palms. Because the carbon stored in biofuels was removed from the modern atmosphere by photosynthesis, burning them seems to simply restore CO_2 that was recently present in the atmosphere. Is this a solution to global climate change?

The environmental and social benefits of burning fuels derived from food crops in our gas tanks are hotly debated. Roughly 40% of the U.S. corn crop is now feeding vehicles rather than animals and people. One concern is that this added demand for such crops will drive up food prices as cars compete with animal and human consumers. Another concern is that growing corn and converting it into ethanol uses up large quantities of fossil fuel, making ethanol's "carbon footprint" little, if any, better than burning gasoline. The environmental costs of using food crops as an alternative fuel source are also enormous.

For example, Indonesia's luxurious tropical rain forests—home to orangutans, Sumatran tigers, and clouded leopards—are being destroyed to make room for oil palm plantations for biofuels (Fig. E7-2). In Brazil, soybean plantations for biofuels have replaced large expanses of rain forest. Ironically, clearing these forests for agriculture increases atmospheric CO_2 because rain forests trap far more carbon than the crops that replace them.

Biofuels would have far less environmental and social impact if they were not produced from food crops or by destroying Earth's dwindling rain forests. Algae show great promise as an alternative. These photosynthesizers can double their mass in a day or less. Some algae produce starch that can be fermented into ethanol; others produce oil that can become biodiesel. Researchers are also attempting to cleave cellulose into its component sugars, which would allow ethanol to be generated from corn stalks, wood chips, or grasses. This concept is being tested at several small cellulose biorefineries in the United States. Although the benefits of most biofuels in wide use today may not justify their environmental costs, there is hope that this will change as we develop better technologies to harness the energy captured by photosynthesis.

The storage products of photosynthesis are being eyed by Earth's growing and energy-hungry human population as a substitute for fossil fuels. These "biofuels" have the potential advantage of not adding additional carbon dioxide (a "greenhouse gas" that contributes to global climate change) to the atmosphere, but do they live up to their promise? We explore this question in "Earth Watch: Biofuels—Are Their Benefits Bogus?"

SUMMING UP The Calvin Cycle

The Calvin cycle can be divided into three stages:

- **Carbon fixation:** Three RuBP capture three CO_2, forming six PGA.
- **G3P synthesis:** A series of reactions, driven by energy from ATP and NADPH (from the light reactions), produces six G3P, one of which leaves the cycle and is available to form glucose.
- **RuBP regeneration:** ATP energy is used to regenerate three RuBP molecules from the remaining five G3P molecules, allowing the cycle to continue.

In a separate process outside the chloroplast, two G3P molecules produced by the Calvin cycle combine to form glucose.

CHECK YOUR LEARNING

Can you describe the function of the Calvin cycle and where it occurs? Can you list the three stages of the Calvin cycle, including the molecules that enter the cycle and those that are formed at each stage? Can you describe the fate of the simple sugar generated by the Calvin cycle?

CASE STUDY revisited

Did the Dinosaurs Die from Lack of Sunlight?

Did an asteroid end the reign of dinosaurs? The Alvarez hypothesis was initially met with skepticism. If such a cataclysmic event had occurred, where was the crater?

In 1991, scientists finally located it centered near the coastal town of Chicxulub on Mexico's Yucatán Peninsula. The crater, estimated at over 150 miles (200 to 300 km) in diameter and 10 miles (16 km) deep, was filled by debris and sedimentary rock laid down during the 65.5 million years since the impact. Ocean and dense vegetation hid most remaining traces from satellite images. The final identification of the Chicxulub crater was based on rock core samples, unusual gravitational patterns, and faint surface features. Convincing geological evidence shows that the crater was formed at the end of the Cretaceous period, the same time at which the K-T boundary layer was deposited.

Some paleontologists argue that the impact may have exacerbated more gradual changes in climate, to which the dinosaurs (with the exception of those ancestral to modern-day birds) could not adapt. Such changes might have been caused by prolonged intense volcanic activity, such as occurred at a site in India at about the time of the K-T extinction. Volcanoes spew out soot and ash, and iridium is found in higher levels in lava from Earth's molten mantle than in its crust. So furious volcanism could significantly reduce the amount of sunlight for plant growth, spew climate-changing gases into the air, and also contribute to the iridium-rich K-T boundary layer.

In 2010, alternative hypotheses to the asteroid impact were dealt a blow when an expert group of 41 researchers published a review article in the prestigious journal *Science*. This publication analyzed the previous 20 years of research by paleontologists, geochemists, geophysicists, climatologists, and sedimentation experts dealing with the K-T extinction event. The conclusion: Land and ocean ecosystems were destroyed extremely rapidly, and evidence overwhelmingly supports the asteroid impact hypothesis first proposed by the Alvarez group 30 years earlier.

Consider This

Has the publication described above changed the asteroid impact hypothesis into a scientific theory that is "set in stone"? Can the cause of the K-T extinction ever be proven? Should scientists who believed that the evidence pointed to alternative causes for the extinction now abandon their hypotheses based on this article? Does debate among scientists weaken or strengthen the role of science in society?

CHAPTER REVIEW

Summary of Key Concepts

7.1 What Is Photosynthesis?
Photosynthesis captures the energy of sunlight and uses it to convert the inorganic molecules of carbon dioxide and water into a high-energy sugar molecule, releasing oxygen as a byproduct. In plants, photosynthesis takes place in the chloroplasts, using two major reaction sequences: the light reactions and the Calvin cycle.

7.2 The Light Reactions: How Is Light Energy Converted to Chemical Energy?
The light reactions occur in the thylakoids of chloroplasts. Light energizes electrons in chlorophyll molecules located in photosystems II and I. Energetic electrons jump to a primary electron acceptor, then move into adjacent electron transport chains. Energy lost as the electrons travel through electron transport chain II is used to pump hydrogen ions into the thylakoid space, creating an H^+ gradient across the thylakoid membrane.

Hydrogen ions flow down this concentration gradient through ATP synthase channels in the membrane, driving ATP synthesis. For every two energized electrons that pass through electron transport chain I, one molecule of the energy carrier NADPH is formed from $NADP^+$ and H^+. Electrons lost from photosystem II are replaced by electrons liberated by splitting water, which also generates H^+ and O_2.

7.3 The Calvin Cycle: How Is Chemical Energy Stored in Sugar Molecules?

The Calvin cycle, which occurs in the stroma of chloroplasts, uses energy from the ATP and NADPH generated during the light reactions to drive the synthesis of G3P. Two molecules of G3P may then combine to form glucose. The Calvin cycle has three parts: (1) *Carbon fixation:* Carbon dioxide combines with ribulose bisphosphate (RuBP) to form phosphoglyceric acid (PGA). (2) *Synthesis of G3P:* PGA is converted to glyceraldehyde-3-phosphate (G3P), using energy from ATP and NADPH. (3) *Regeneration of RuBP:* Five molecules of G3P are used to regenerate three molecules of RuBP, using ATP energy. One molecule of G3P exits the cycle; this G3P may be used to synthesize glucose and other molecules.

Key Terms

accessory pigment   *112*
ATP synthase   *115*
bundle sheath cells   *109*
C_3 pathway   *117*
C_4 pathway   *119*
Calvin cycle   *110*
carbon fixation   *117*
carotenoid   *112*
chemiosmosis   *115*
chlorophyll *a*   *112*
chloroplast   *109*
crassulacean acid metabolism
    (CAM)   *119*
cuticle   *109*
electromagnetic
    spectrum   *112*

electron transport
    chain   *113*
epidermis   *109*
light reactions   *110*
mesophyll   *109*
photon   *112*
photorespiration   *119*
photosynthesis   *109*
photosystem   *112*
reaction center   *113*
rubisco   *117*
stoma (plural, stomata)   *109*
stroma   *109*
thylakoid   *109*

Learning Outcomes

In this chapter, you have learned to . . .

LO1 Explain the process of photosynthesis and discuss why photosynthesis is crucial to most forms of life.

LO2 Describe the structures of plant leaves and chloroplasts and explain how these structures support the process of photosynthesis.

LO3 Identify the source of energy for photosynthesis and describe how this energy

is captured and transferred during the light reactions.

LO4 Describe the inputs and products of the light reactions.

LO5 Explain how the products of the light reactions are used during the Calvin cycle and discuss how plants use the products of the Calvin cycle.

Thinking Through the Concepts

Fill-in-the-Blank

1. Plant leaves contain pores called _____ that allow the plant to release _____ and take in _____. In hot dry weather, these pores are closed to prevent _____. Photosynthesis occurs in organelles called _____ that are concentrated within the _____ cells of most plant leaves. **LO2**

2. Chlorophyll *a* captures wavelengths of light that correspond to the three colors _____, _____, and _____. What color does chlorophyll reflect? _____ Accessory pigments that reflect yellow and orange are called _____. These pigments are located in clusters called _____ in the _____ membrane of the chloroplast. **LO2 LO3**

3. During the first stage of photosynthesis, light is captured and funneled into _____ chlorophyll *a* molecules. The energized electron is then passed into a _____. From here, it is transferred through a series of molecules called the _____. Energy lost during these transfers is used to create a gradient of _____. The process that uses this gradient to generate ATP is called _____. **LO3 LO4**

4. The oxygen produced as a by-product of photosynthesis is derived from _____, and the carbons used to make glucose are derived from _____. The biochemical pathway that captures atmospheric carbon is called the _____. The process of capturing carbon is called _____. **LO3 LO4 LO5**

5. In plants, the enzyme that catalyzes carbon capture is _____, which is quite nonselective and binds _____ as well as CO_2. When it binds the "wrong" molecule, this enzyme causes _____ to occur. Two pathways that reduce this process are called the _____ and the_____. **LO5**

6. Light reactions generate the energy-carrier molecules _____ and _____, which are then used in the _____ cycle. Carbon fixation combines carbon dioxide with the five-carbon molecule _____. Two molecules of _____ can be combined to produce the six-carbon sugar _____. **LO3 LO4 LO5**

Review Questions

1. Explain what would happen to life if photosynthesis ceased. Why would this occur? **LO1**

2. Write and then explain the equation for photosynthesis. **LO1**

3. Draw a simplified diagram of a leaf cross-section and label it. Explain how a leaf's structure supports photosynthesis. **LO2**

4. Draw a simplified diagram of a chloroplast, and label it. Explain how the individual parts of the chloroplast support photosynthesis. **LO2**

5. Explain photorespiration and why it occurs. Describe the two mechanisms that some groups of plants have evolved to reduce photorespiration. LO5

6. Trace the flow of energy in chloroplasts from sunlight to ATP, including an explanation of chemiosmosis. LO3

7. Summarize the events of the Calvin cycle. Where does it occur? What molecule is fixed? What is the product of the cycle? Where does the energy come from to drive the cycle? What molecule is regenerated? LO5

Applying the Concepts

1. Suppose an experiment is performed in which plant I is supplied with normal carbon dioxide but with water that contains radioactive oxygen atoms. Plant II is supplied with normal water but with carbon dioxide that contains radioactive oxygen atoms. Each plant is allowed to perform photosynthesis, and the oxygen gas and sugars produced are tested for radioactivity. Which plant would you expect to produce radioactive sugars, and which plant would you expect to produce radioactive oxygen gas? Explain why.

2. You continuously monitor the photosynthetic oxygen production from the leaf of a plant illuminated by white light. Explain how oxygen production will change—and why—if you place filters in front of the light source that transmit (a) only red, (b) only blue, and (c) only green light onto the leaf.

3. If you were to measure the pH in the space surrounded by the thylakoid membrane in an actively photosynthesizing plant, would you expect it to be acidic, basic, or neutral? Explain your answer.

4. Assume you want to add an accessory pigment to the photosystems of a plant chloroplast to help it photosynthesize more efficiently. What wavelengths of light would the new pigment absorb? Describe the color of your new pigment. Would this be a useful project for genetic engineers? Explain.

Answers to Figure Caption questions and Fill-in-the-Blank questions can be found in the Answers section at the back of the book.

(MB) *Go to MasteringBiology for practice quizzes, activities, eText, videos, current events, and more.*

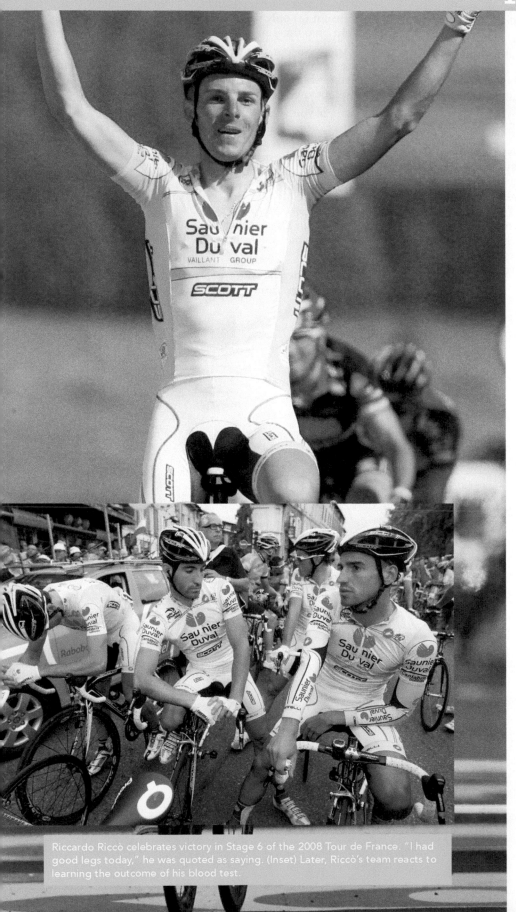

CASE STUDY

When Athletes Boost Their Blood Counts: Do Cheaters Prosper?

AN HOUR BEFORE THE START of the 12th stage of the 2008 Tour de France, the Saunier-Duval team was in high spirits. Their star cyclist, Riccardo Riccò, had led the pack in two stages, including the grueling Stage 9, which crested two mountains over a 139-mile (224-km) course. But the team's optimism turned to consternation as they watched their top rider escorted away by police. Minutes later, the entire team withdrew from the race. Riccò's offense? Blood doping.

Blood doping packs more oxygen-carrying red blood cells into the bloodstream with the goal of enhancing athletic performance. Riccò injected the drug CERA (continuous erythropoietin receptor activator), a synthetic version of erythropoietin. The natural hormone erythropoietin (EPO) stimulates bone marrow to produce red blood cells. A healthy body produces just enough EPO to ensure that red blood cells are replaced as they age and die. If a person moves to a higher altitude where each lungful of air provides less oxygen, the body naturally compensates by increasing EPO and producing just enough more red blood cells. An injection of synthetic EPO, however, can stimulate the production of a huge number of extra red blood cells, increasing the oxygen-carrying capacity of the blood beyond normal levels and enhancing performance in sports that require endurance, such as cycling. Why is endurance improved by extra oxygen in the blood? How did this extra oxygen contribute to Riccò's "good legs"? Think about these questions as we examine the role of oxygen in the metabolic pathway that supplies energy to cells.

Riccardo Riccò celebrates victory in Stage 6 of the 2008 Tour de France. "I had good legs today," he was quoted as saying. (Inset) Later, Riccò's team reacts to learning the outcome of his blood test.

AT A GLANCE

8.1 How Do Cells Obtain Energy?
8.2 What Happens During
       Glycolysis?

8.3 What Happens During Cellular
       Respiration?

8.4 What Happens During
       Fermentation?

LEARNING GOALS

LG1 Using their overall chemical equations, explain how photosynthesis and glucose breakdown are interdependent processes.

LG2 Summarize and describe the relationship between the two stages of glucose breakdown when oxygen is available.

LG3 Explain the energy investment and energy harvesting phases of glycolysis, including their substrate and product molecules.

LG4 Summarize the relationship between glycolysis and cellular respiration and describe how the structure of the mitochondrion supports cellular respiration.

LG5 Summarize the three stages of cellular respiration, including the input and output molecules at each stage.

LG6 Explain how ATP is generated by chemiosmosis, including the role of the electron transport chain.

LG7 Describe the role of oxygen in cellular respiration.

LG8 Describe the molecules used to capture and transport energy during glycolysis and cellular respiration.

LG9 Compare the amounts of ATP generated and the mechanisms by which the ATP is produced during fermentation, glycolysis, and cellular respiration.

LG10 Explain the function of fermentation, the substrates and products of fermentation, and some ways that people put fermentation to use.

8.1 HOW DO CELLS OBTAIN ENERGY?

Cells require a continuous supply of energy to power the multitude of metabolic reactions that are essential just to stay alive. In this chapter, we describe the cellular reactions that transfer energy from energy-storage molecules, particularly glucose, to energy-carrier molecules, such as ATP.

The second law of thermodynamics tells us that every time a spontaneous reaction occurs, the amount of useful energy in a system decreases and heat is produced (see Chapter 6). Cells are relatively efficient at capturing chemical energy during glucose breakdown when oxygen is available, storing about 40% of the chemical energy from glucose in ATP molecules, and releasing the rest as heat. (If 60% waste heat sounds high, compare this to the 80% of chemical energy released as heat by conventional engines burning gasoline.)

Photosynthesis Is the Ultimate Source of Cellular Energy

The energy utilized by life on Earth comes almost entirely from sunlight, captured during photosynthesis by plants and other photosynthetic organisms, and stored in the chemical bonds of sugars and other organic molecules (see Chapter 7). Almost all organisms, including those that photosynthesize, use glycolysis and cellular respiration to break down these sugars and other organic molecules and capture some of the energy as ATP. **Figure 8-1** illustrates the interrelationship between photosynthesis and the breakdown of glucose (by glycolysis and cellular respiration). Glucose ($C_6H_{12}O_6$) breakdown begins with glycolysis in the cell cytosol, liberating small quantities of ATP. Then, the end product of glycolysis is further broken down during cellular respiration in mitochondria, supplying far greater amounts of energy in ATP. In forming ATP during cellular respiration, cells use oxygen (originally released by photosynthetic organisms) and liberate both water and carbon dioxide—the raw materials for photosynthesis.

If you examine their equations on the next page, you will see that the chemical equation describing complete glucose breakdown (by glycolysis and cellular respiration) is the reverse of glucose formation by photosynthesis. The only difference is in the forms of energy involved. The light energy stored

▲ FIGURE 8-1 **Photosynthesis provides the energy released during glycolysis and cellular respiration** The products of photosynthesis are used in glycolysis and cellular respiration, the products of which are, in turn, used in photosynthesis. Photosynthesis captures sunlight energy in glucose. In photosynthetic eukaryotic cells, photosynthesis occurs in chloroplasts. Then glycolysis (in the cytosol) and cellular respiration (in the mitochondria of eukaryotic cells) liberate the chemical energy stored in glucose.

in glucose during photosynthesis is released during glucose breakdown and used to generate ATP, with some lost as heat.

Photosynthesis

$$6\ CO_2 + 6\ H_2O + \text{light energy} \rightarrow C_6H_{12}O_6 + 6\ O_2$$

Complete Glucose Breakdown

$$C_6H_{12}O_6 + 6\ O_2 \rightarrow 6\ CO_2 + 6\ H_2O + \text{ATP energy} + \text{heat energy}$$

Glucose Is a Key Energy-Storage Molecule

Few organisms store glucose in its simple form. Plants convert glucose to sucrose or starch for storage. Humans and many other animals store energy in molecules such as glycogen (a long chain of glucose molecules) and fat (see Chapter 3). Although most cells can use a variety of organic molecules to produce ATP, in this chapter, we focus on the breakdown of glucose, which all cells can use as an energy source. Glucose breakdown occurs in stages, starting with glycolysis and proceeding to fermentation in the absence of oxygen, and to cellular respiration if oxygen is available. Energy is captured in ATP during both glycolysis and cellular respiration, as summarized in **Figure 8-2**.

CHECK YOUR LEARNING

Can you explain how photosynthesis and glucose breakdown are related to one another using their overall chemical equations? Can you summarize glucose breakdown in the presence and absence of oxygen, explaining which reactions generate the most ATP?

8.2 WHAT HAPPENS DURING GLYCOLYSIS?

Glycolysis (from the Greek, "glyco," meaning "sweet," and "lysis," meaning "to split apart") splits the six-carbon glucose molecule into two molecules of pyruvate. Glycolysis has an *energy investment stage* and an *energy harvesting stage*, each with several steps (**Fig. 8-3**). To extract energy from glucose first requires an investment of energy from ATP. During a series of reactions, each of two ATP molecules donates a phosphate group and energy to glucose, forming an "energized" molecule of fructose bisphosphate. Fructose is a sugar very similar to glucose; "bisphosphate" ("bis" means "two") refers to the two phosphate groups acquired from the ATP molecules. Fructose bisphosphate is much more easily broken down than glucose because of the extra energy it has acquired from ATP.

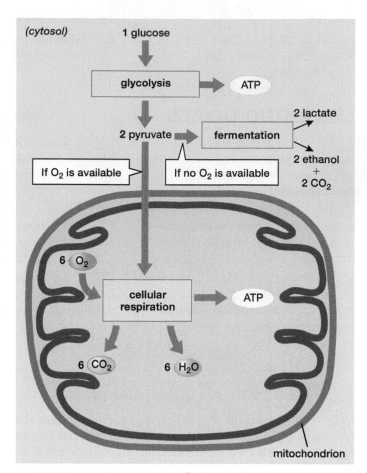

▲ FIGURE 8-2 **A summary of glucose breakdown**

Next, during the energy harvesting stage, fructose bisphosphate is converted into two 3-carbon molecules of glyceraldehyde-3-phosphate, or G3P. Each G3P molecule, which retains one phosphate and some energy from ATP, then undergoes a series of reactions that convert the G3P to pyruvate. During these reactions, two ATP are generated from each G3P, for a total of four ATP per glucose molecule. Because two ATP were used up to form fructose bisphosphate, there is a net gain of only two ATP per glucose molecule during glycolysis. Additional energy is stored when two high-energy electrons and a hydrogen ion (H^+) are added to the electron-carrier **nicotinamide adenine dinucleotide (NAD^+)** to produce **NADH.** Two molecules of NADH are produced for every glucose molecule broken down. For the details of glycolysis, see "In Greater Depth: Glycolysis."

▲ FIGURE 8-3 **The essentials of glycolysis** *Energy investment stage:* The energy of two ATP molecules is used to convert glucose into the fructose bisphosphate, which then breaks down into two molecules of G3P. *Energy harvesting stage:* The two G3P molecules undergo a series of reactions that capture energy in four ATP and two NADH molecules.

QUESTION What is the net energy yield in ATP and NADH produced?

IN GREATER DEPTH Glycolysis

Glycolysis is a series of enzyme-catalyzed reactions that break down a single molecule of glucose into two molecules of pyruvate. To help you follow the reactions in Figure E8-1, we show only the carbon skeletons of glucose and other molecules produced during glycolysis. Each blue arrow represents one (or occasionally more) reactions. Each reaction is catalyzed by an enzyme.

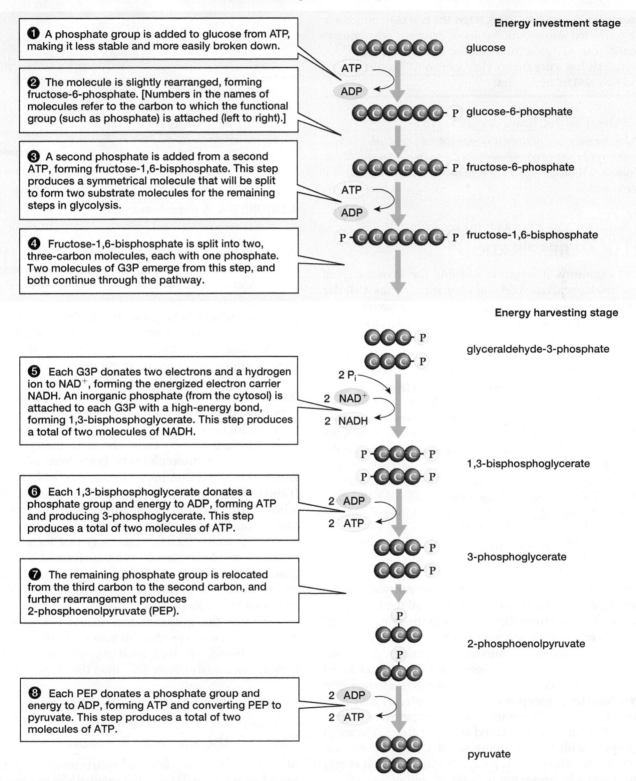

Energy investment stage

❶ A phosphate group is added to glucose from ATP, making it less stable and more easily broken down.

glucose

ATP
ADP

❷ The molecule is slightly rearranged, forming fructose-6-phosphate. [Numbers in the names of molecules refer to the carbon to which the functional group (such as phosphate) is attached (left to right).]

glucose-6-phosphate

❸ A second phosphate is added from a second ATP, forming fructose-1,6-bisphosphate. This step produces a symmetrical molecule that will be split to form two substrate molecules for the remaining steps in glycolysis.

fructose-6-phosphate

ATP
ADP

❹ Fructose-1,6-bisphosphate is split into two, three-carbon molecules, each with one phosphate. Two molecules of G3P emerge from this step, and both continue through the pathway.

fructose-1,6-bisphosphate

Energy harvesting stage

glyceraldehyde-3-phosphate

❺ Each G3P donates two electrons and a hydrogen ion to NAD$^+$, forming the energized electron carrier NADH. An inorganic phosphate (from the cytosol) is attached to each G3P with a high-energy bond, forming 1,3-bisphosphoglycerate. This step produces a total of two molecules of NADH.

2 P$_i$
2 NAD$^+$
2 NADH

1,3-bisphosphoglycerate

❻ Each 1,3-bisphosphoglycerate donates a phosphate group and energy to ADP, forming ATP and producing 3-phosphoglycerate. This step produces a total of two molecules of ATP.

2 ADP
2 ATP

3-phosphoglycerate

❼ The remaining phosphate group is relocated from the third carbon to the second carbon, and further rearrangement produces 2-phosphoenolpyruvate (PEP).

2-phosphoenolpyruvate

❽ Each PEP donates a phosphate group and energy to ADP, forming ATP and converting PEP to pyruvate. This step produces a total of two molecules of ATP.

2 ADP
2 ATP

pyruvate

▲ FIGURE E8-1 **Glycolysis**

SUMMING UP Glycolysis

- During the energy investment stage, phosphate groups and energy from each of two ATP are added to glucose to produce fructose bisphosphate.
- Fructose bisphosphate is broken down into two G3P molecules.
- During the energy harvesting stage, the two G3P molecules are converted into two molecules of pyruvate, generating a total of four ATP molecules and two NADH molecules.
- Glycolysis has a net energy yield of two ATP molecules and two NADH molecules.

CHECK YOUR LEARNING

Can you explain the energy investment and energy harvesting phases of glycolysis? Can you describe the two types of high-energy molecule produced by glucose breakdown?

8.3 WHAT HAPPENS DURING CELLULAR RESPIRATION?

In most organisms, if oxygen is available, the second stage of glucose breakdown, called cellular respiration, occurs. **Cellular respiration** breaks down the two pyruvate molecules (produced by glycolysis) into six carbon dioxide molecules and six water molecules. During this process, the chemical energy from the two pyruvate molecules is used to produce 32 ATP.

In eukaryotic cells, cellular respiration occurs within **mitochondria,** organelles that are sometimes called the "powerhouses of the cell." A mitochondrion has two membranes. The inner membrane encloses a central compartment containing the fluid **matrix,** and the outer membrane surrounds the organelle, producing an **intermembrane space** between the two membranes (**Fig. 8-4**). In the following sections, we discuss the three stages of cellular respiration: the breakdown of pyruvate, the transfer of electrons along the electron transport chain, and the generation of ATP by chemiosmosis.

During the First Stage of Cellular Respiration, Pyruvate Is Broken Down

Pyruvate, the end product of glycolysis, is synthesized in the cytosol. Before cellular respiration can occur, the pyruvate is actively transported from the cytosol into the mitochondrial matrix, where cellular respiration begins.

The reactions of the mitochondrial matrix, illustrated in **Figure 8-5**, occur in two stages: the formation of acetyl CoA and the Krebs cycle. Acetyl CoA consists of a two-carbon (acetyl) functional group attached to a molecule called coenzyme A (CoA). To generate acetyl CoA, pyruvate is split, releasing CO_2 and leaving behind an acetyl group. The acetyl group reacts with CoA, forming acetyl CoA. This reaction liberates energy and stores it by transferring two high-energy electrons and a hydrogen ion to NAD^+, forming NADH.

The next set of mitochondrial matrix reactions is known as the **Krebs cycle** named after its discoverer, Hans

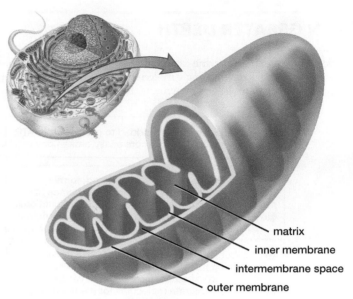

▲ FIGURE 8-4 **A mitochondrion**

matrix
inner membrane
intermembrane space
outer membrane

Krebs, who won a Nobel Prize for this work in 1953. The Krebs cycle is also called the *citric acid cycle* because citrate (the dissolved, ionized form of citric acid) is the first molecule produced in the cycle.

The Krebs cycle begins by combining acetyl CoA with a four-carbon molecule, forming a six-carbon citrate molecule and releasing CoA. CoA is not permanently altered during these reactions and is reused many times. As the Krebs cycle proceeds, enzymes within the mitochondrial matrix break down the acetyl group, releasing two CO_2 (whose carbons come from the acetyl group) and regenerating the four-carbon molecule for use in future cycles.

During the Krebs cycle, chemical energy is captured in energy-carrier molecules. The breakdown of each acetyl group from acetyl CoA produces one ATP and three NADH. It also produces one **flavin adenine dinucleotide ($FADH_2$),** a high-energy electron carrier similar to NADH. During the Krebs cycle, FAD picks up two energetic electrons along with two H^+, forming $FADH_2$. Remember that for each glucose molecule, two pyruvate molecules are formed, so the energy generated per glucose molecule is twice that generated for one pyruvate (for details see "In Greater Depth: The Mitochondrial Matrix Reactions".)

During the mitochondrial matrix reactions, CO_2 is generated as a waste product. In your body, this CO_2 diffuses into your blood, which carries it to your lungs, so the air you breathe out contains more CO_2 than the air you breathe in.

During the Second Stage of Cellular Respiration, High-Energy Electrons Travel Through the Electron Transport Chain

At the end of the mitochondrial matrix reactions, the cell has gained only four ATP from the original glucose molecule (a net of two during glycolysis and two during the Krebs cycle). During glycolysis and the mitochondrial matrix reactions,

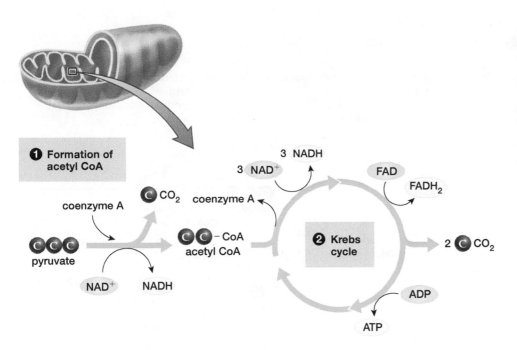

◀FIGURE 8-5 Reactions in the mitochondrial matrix ❶ Pyruvate reacts with CoA, forming acetyl CoA and releasing CO_2. During this reaction, two high-energy electrons and a hydrogen ion are added to NAD^+, forming NADH. ❷ When acetyl CoA enters the Krebs cycle, CoA is released for reuse. The Krebs cycle produces one ATP, three NADH, one $FADH_2$, and two CO_2 from each acetyl CoA.

however, the cell has captured many high-energy electrons in a total of 10 NADH and two $FADH_2$ for each glucose molecule. In the next stage of cellular respiration, these carriers each release two high-energy electrons into an **electron transport chain (ETC),** a series of electron transporting molecules, many copies of which are embedded in the inner mitochondrial membrane (**Fig. 8-6**). The depleted carriers are then available for recharging by glycolysis and the Krebs cycle.

The ETCs in the mitochondrial membrane serve the same function as the ETCs embedded in the thylakoid membrane of chloroplasts (see Chapter 7). High-energy electrons jump from molecule to molecule along the ETC, releasing small amounts of energy at each step. Although some energy is lost as heat, some is harnessed to pump H^+ across the inner membrane, from the matrix into the intermembrane space. This ion pumping produces a concentration gradient of H^+, which is then used to generate ATP by chemiosmosis, discussed next.

Finally, at the end of the electron transport chain, the energy-depleted electrons are transferred to oxygen, which acts as an electron acceptor. This step clears out the ETC, allowing it to accept more electrons. The energy-depleted electrons, oxygen, and hydrogen ions combine, forming water. One water molecule is produced for every two electrons that traverse the ETC.

◀FIGURE 8-6 The electron transport chain Many copies of the electron transport chain are embedded in the inner mitochondrial membrane. ❶ NADH and $FADH_2$ donate their energetic electrons and hydrogen ions to the electron transport chain. As the electrons pass along the chain (thick gray arrows), some of their energy is used to pump hydrogen ions from the matrix into the intermembrane space (red arrows). ❷ This creates a hydrogen ion gradient that is used to drive ATP synthesis. ❸ At the end of the electron transport chain, the energy-depleted electrons combine with oxygen and hydrogen ions in the mitochondrial matrix, forming water. ❹ The hydrogen ions flow down their concentration gradient from the intermembrane space and into the matrix through ATP synthase channels, generating ATP from ADP and phosphate.

QUESTION How would the rate of ATP production be affected by the absence of oxygen?

IN GREATER DEPTH The Mitochondrial Matrix Reactions

Mitochondrial matrix reactions occur in two stages: (1) the breakdown of pyruvate and formation of acetyl CoA and (2) the Krebs cycle (Fig. E8-2). Here we show only the carbon skeletons of the molecules. The blue arrows represent enzyme-catalyzed reactions.

First Stage: Formation of Acetyl Coenzyme A

Pyruvate is split to form CO_2 and an acetyl group. The acetyl group attaches to CoA to form acetyl CoA. Simultaneously, NAD^+ receives two high-energy electrons and a hydrogen ion to make NADH. Acetyl CoA enters the Krebs cycle.

Second Stage: The Krebs Cycle

❶ Acetyl CoA donates its acetyl group to the four-carbon molecule oxaloacetate, forming citrate. CoA is released. Water is split, donating hydrogen to CoA and oxygen to citrate.

❷ Citrate is rearranged to form isocitrate.

❸ Isocitrate forms α-ketoglutarate by releasing CO_2. Two energetic electrons and an H^+ are captured by NAD^+ to form NADH.

❹ Alpha-ketoglutarate forms succinate by releasing CO_2. Two energetic electrons and an H^+ are captured by NAD^+ to form NADH, and additional energy is captured in a molecule of ATP.

❺ Succinate is converted to fumarate. Two energetic electrons and two H^+ are captured by FAD, forming $FADH_2$.

❻ Fumarate combines with water to form malate.

❼ Malate is converted to oxaloacetate. Two energetic electrons and an H^+ ion are captured by NAD^+ to form NADH.

For each acetyl CoA, the Krebs cycle produces two CO_2, one ATP, three NADH, and one $FADH_2$. The formation of each acetyl CoA prior to the Krebs cycle also generates one CO_2 and one NADH. So for each pyruvate molecule supplied by glycolysis, the mitochondrial matrix reactions produce three CO_2, one ATP, four NADH, and one $FADH_2$. Because each glucose molecule produces two pyruvates, the number of high-energy products and CO_2 per glucose molecule will be double that from a single pyruvate. The electron-carrier molecules NADH and $FADH_2$ will deliver their high-energy electrons to the electron transport chain, where their energy will be used to synthesize additional ATP by chemiosmosis.

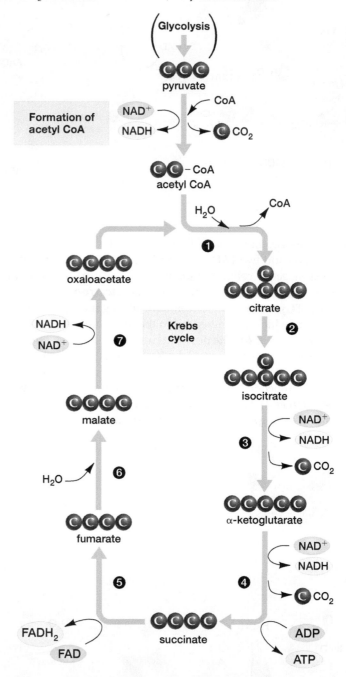

▲ FIGURE E8-2 The mitochondrial matrix reactions

Without oxygen to accept electrons, the electrons would be unable to move through the ETC, and H^+ would not be pumped across the inner membrane. The H^+ gradient would rapidly dissipate, and ATP synthesis by chemiosmosis would stop. Most eukaryotic cells would die within minutes without a steady supply of oxygen.

During the Third Stage of Cellular Respiration, Chemiosmosis Generates ATP

Chemiosmosis is the process by which energy is used to generate a concentration gradient of H^+ (see Chapter 7), and then some of that energy is captured in ATP as H^+ flows

When Athletes Boost Their Blood Counts: Do Cheaters Prosper?

When people and other animals exercise vigorously, they are unable to get enough air into their lungs, enough oxygen into their blood, and enough blood circulating to their muscles to allow cellular respiration to meet all their energy needs. As oxygen demand exceeds oxygen supply, muscles must rely on glycolysis (which yields far less ATP than does cellular respiration) for periods of intense exercise. This explains why some athletes, desperate for a competitive edge, may turn to illegal blood doping to increase the ability of their blood to carry oxygen.

down its gradient. As the ETC pumps H^+ across the inner membrane, it produces a high concentration of H^+ in the intermembrane space and a low concentration in the matrix (see Fig. 8-6). Expending energy to produce this nonuniform distribution of H^+ is similar to charging a battery. This energy is released as hydrogen ions flow down their concentration gradient, a process somewhat like using the energy stored in a battery to light a bulb.

How is the released energy captured in ATP? As in the thylakoid membranes of chloroplasts, the inner membranes of mitochondria are permeable to H^+ only at ATP synthase channels. As hydrogen ions flow from the intermembrane space into the matrix through these ATP-synthesizing enzymes, the flow of ions generates ATP from ADP and inorganic phosphate dissolved in the matrix.

How does ATP escape from the mitochondrion? A carrier protein in the inner membrane uses the energy of the H^+ gradient to transport ATP out of the matrix into the intermembrane space, and simultaneously to transport ADP from the intermembrane space into the matrix. From the intermembrane space, ATP molecules diffuse through large pores in the outer mitochondrial membrane and enter the surrounding cytosol, where they provide the energy needed by the cell. The ADP released by energy-requiring activities in the cell continuously diffuses back through the mitochondrial membrane into the intermembrane space, allowing more ATP synthesis. Without this continuous recycling, life would cease. A person produces, uses, and then regenerates the equivalent of roughly his or her body weight of ATP daily.

You now know why glycolysis followed by cellular respiration generates far more ATP than glycolysis alone. **Figure 8-7** summarizes the breakdown of one glucose molecule in a eukaryotic cell with oxygen present, showing the energy produced during each stage and the general locations where the pathways occur. Chemiosmosis generates 32 ATP from high-energy electron-carrier molecules produced during glycolysis and cellular respiration.

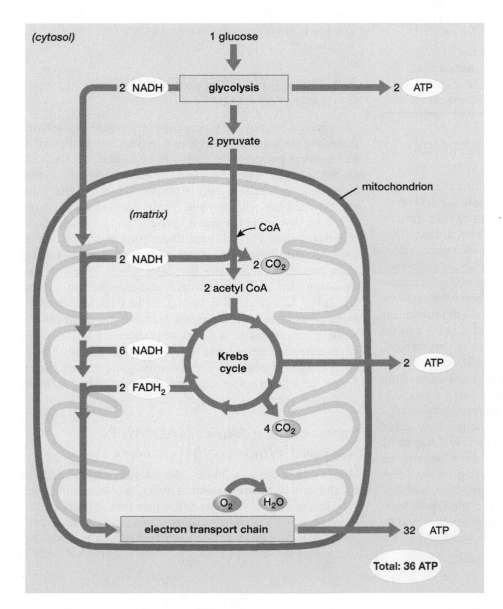

◀ FIGURE 8-7 The energy sources and ATP harvest from glycolysis and cellular respiration Here we follow the energy captured from one glucose molecule. Notice that most of the ATP derived from glucose breakdown comes as a result of high-energy electrons donated by NADH and FADH$_2$ moving through the electron transport chain, which allows chemiosmosis to occur.

SUMMING UP Cellular Respiration

- In the mitochondrial matrix, each pyruvate molecule is converted into acetyl CoA, producing one NADH per pyruvate molecule and releasing one CO_2.
- As each acetyl CoA passes through the Krebs cycle, its energy is captured in one ATP, three NADH, and one $FADH_2$. The carbons of acetyl CoA are released in two CO_2 molecules.
- During the matrix reactions, the two pyruvate molecules produced from glucose during glycolysis are completely broken down, yielding two ATP and 10 high-energy electron carriers: eight NADH and two $FADH_2$. The carbon atoms from the pyruvates are released in six molecules of CO_2.
- The NADH and $FADH_2$ molecules donate their energetic electrons to the ETC embedded in the inner mitochondrial membrane.
- As they pass through the ETC, high-energy electrons release energy that is harnessed to pump H^+ into the intermembrane space.
- As they leave the ETC, the energy-depleted electrons combine with the electron acceptor oxygen and hydrogen ions to form water.
- During chemiosmosis, hydrogen ions in the intermembrane space flow down their concentration gradient through ATP synthase channels. The complete breakdown of glucose yields 32 ATP via chemiosmosis.

Cellular Respiration Can Extract Energy from a Variety of Molecules

Glucose often enters the body as starch (a long chain of glucose molecules) or sucrose (table sugar; glucose linked to fructose), but the typical human diet also provides considerable energy in the form of fat, and some from protein. This is possible because various intermediate molecules of cellular respiration can be formed by other metabolic pathways. These molecules can enter cellular respiration at appropriate stages of this metabolic pathway, and are then broken down to produce ATP. For example, the amino acids of protein can serve as an energy source. The amino acid alanine can be converted into pyruvate, which enters the very first stage of cellular respiration. Various other amino acids can be converted to intermediate molecules of the Krebs cycle, thus contributing to the ATP output of the cycle. Fats are an excellent source of energy, and serve as the major energy-storage molecule in animals. To release this energy, fatty acids (which make up most of each fat molecule; see Chapter 3) are combined with CoA and then broken down to produce acetyl CoA molecules, which enter the first stage of the Krebs cycle. This will happen if you limit your food intake and rely on stored fat for energy. But if you overeat, the fats in your meal are stored, and excess sugar and starch are also used to synthesize body fat, as described in "Health Watch: Why Can You Get Fat by Eating Sugar?"

? HAVE **YOU** EVER WONDERED ...

Why Is Cyanide So Deadly?

Cyanide is a common weapon in old murder mysteries, where the hapless victims of the poison die almost instantly. Cyanide exerts its lethal effects by blocking the last protein in the ETC; this protein is an enzyme that combines electrons with oxygen. If these energy-depleted electrons are not carried away by oxygen, the electrons act like a plug in a pipeline. More high-energy electrons cannot travel through the ETC, so no more hydrogen can be pumped across the membrane, and ATP production by chemiosmosis comes to a screeching halt. Blocking cellular respiration with cyanide can kill a person within a few minutes.

CHECK YOUR LEARNING

Can you summarize the three stages of cellular respiration? Can you explain how ATP is generated by chemiosmosis? Are you able to describe the role of oxygen in cellular respiration?

8.4 WHAT HAPPENS DURING FERMENTATION?

Glycolysis is employed by virtually every organism on Earth, providing evidence that this is one of the most ancient of all biochemical pathways. Scientists hypothesize that the earliest forms of life appeared under the **anaerobic** (no oxygen) conditions that existed before photosynthesis evolved and enriched the air with oxygen. These pioneering life-forms relied on glycolysis for energy production, breaking down the organic molecules formed under the conditions that existed on Earth before life appeared (see Chapter 17). Many microorganisms still thrive in places where oxygen is rare or absent, such as in the stomach and intestines of animals (including humans), deep in soil, or in bogs and marshes. Most of these rely on glycolysis followed by fermentation. Some microorganisms are opportunists, using fermentation when oxygen is absent, but switching to cellular respiration when oxygen is available. Some microorganisms lack the enzymes for cellular respiration and are completely dependent on fermentation.

Fermentation Allows NAD⁺ to Be Recycled When Oxygen Is Absent

Under anaerobic conditions, the second stage of glucose breakdown is **fermentation.** During fermentation, pyruvate in the cytosol is converted either into lactate, or into ethanol and CO_2. Fermentation does not produce additional ATP, so why is it necessary? Fermentation is required to convert the NADH produced during glycolysis back to

Health|Watch

Why Can You Get Fat by Eating Sugar?

From an evolutionary perspective, feeling hungry even when we are overweight and overeating when food is abundant are highly adaptive behaviors. During times of famine, common during early human history, heavier people were more likely to survive, while lean individuals starved. It is only recently (from an evolutionary vantage point) that many people have had continuous access to high-calorie food. Craving foods laden with sugar and fat is another adaptation that helped our prehistoric ancestors survive. But today, the evolutionary drive to eat and the adaptation of storing excess food as fat lead to obesity, a growing health problem in the United States, Mexico, and many other countries throughout the world.

We don't use ATP for long-term energy storage because the large amount of energy stored in its bonds makes ATP too unstable and likely to break down. Fats, however, are stable and also store twice as much energy for their weight as do carbohydrates. Storing energy with minimum weight was important to our prehistoric ancestors who needed to move quickly to catch prey or to avoid becoming prey themselves.

Gaining fat by eating sugar or other carbohydrates is common among animals. For example, a ruby-throated hummingbird begins the summer weighing about 3 to 4 grams (a nickel weighs 5 grams). During late summer, a hummingbird feeds voraciously on the sugary nectar of flowers (Fig. E8-3),

▲ FIGURE E8-3 **A ruby-throated hummingbird feeds on nectar**

storing enough fat to almost double its weight. The energy in this fat allows it to make its long migration from the eastern United States, across the Gulf of Mexico and into Mexico or Central America for the winter. If the hummingbird stored sugar instead of fat, it would be too heavy to fly.

Because fat storage is so important for survival, cells have metabolic pathways that can chemically transform a variety of foods into fat. In addition to breaking down glucose, the biochemical pathways described in this chapter also participate in producing fat (a fat molecule consists of three fatty acids attached to a glycerol backbone; see Fig. 3-12). When you eat a candy bar loaded with sucrose, for example, this disaccharide is broken down into glucose and fructose. Through slightly different pathways (fructose is only metabolized in the liver), both are converted into G3P. If cells have plenty of ATP, some of this G3P is diverted from cellular respiration and used to make the glycerol backbone of fat. As the sugars continue to be broken down, acetyl CoA is formed (see Fig. 8-5). Excess acetyl CoA molecules are used as raw materials to synthesize the fatty acids that will be linked to the glycerol to form a fat molecule. Starches, such as those in potatoes or bread, are actually long chains of glucose molecules, so you can see how eating excess starch can also cause you to store fat.

NAD^+, which needs to be continuously available for glycolysis to continue.

Under **aerobic** (with oxygen) conditions, most organisms use cellular respiration, regenerating NAD^+ by donating the energetic electrons from NADH to the electron transport chain. But under anaerobic conditions, with no oxygen to allow the ETC to function, the cell must regenerate the NAD^+ using fermentation. During fermentation, the electrons from NADH (along with some hydrogen ions) are donated to pyruvate, changing the pyruvate chemically. Fermentation seems to waste the energy in NADH, because this energy is not used to generate ATP. But if the supply of NAD^+ were to be exhausted—which would happen quickly without fermentation—glycolysis would stop, energy production would cease, and the organism would soon die.

Organisms use one of two types of fermentation to regenerate NAD^+: lactic acid fermentation, which produces lactic acid from pyruvate, or alcoholic fermentation, which

generates alcohol and CO_2 from pyruvate. Because glycolysis followed by fermentation produces far less ATP than does cellular respiration, organisms that rely on fermentation must consume relatively large quantities of energy-rich molecules to meet their ATP requirements.

Some Cells Ferment Pyruvate to Form Lactate

Fermentation of pyruvate to lactate is called **lactic acid fermentation** (in the watery cytosol, lactic acid is dissolved and becomes ionized, forming lactate). When deprived of adequate oxygen, muscles do not immediately stop working. This makes sense from an evolutionary standpoint, because animals exercise most vigorously when fighting, fleeing, or pursuing prey. During such activities, the ability to continue just a little bit longer can make the difference between life and death. When muscles are sufficiently low on oxygen,

▲ FIGURE 8-8 **Glycolysis followed by lactic acid fermentation**

QUESTION When fermentation follows glycolysis, what is the net energy yield in molecules of ATP and NADH?

they rely on glycolysis to supply its meager two ATP per glucose molecule, which may provide the energy needed for a final, brief burst of speed. Muscle cells then ferment the resulting pyruvate molecules to lactate, using electrons from NADH and hydrogen ions (**Fig. 8-8**).

For example, if you're breathing hard after sprinting to arrive at class on time, your muscles have been relying on glycolysis for part of their energy, and your lungs are working to restore the oxygen needed for cellular respiration (**Fig. 8-9a**). As oxygen is replenished, lactate is converted back into pyruvate in muscle cells, where it will be used

for cellular respiration, and also in the liver, where the pyruvate is converted back into glucose. This glucose may then be stored as glycogen or released back into the bloodstream and distributed to cells throughout the body. The burning sensation you feel as you exert your muscles to their limit is caused by the production of lactic acid, and the burn subsides as adequate oxygen becomes available to restore pyruvate.

A variety of microorganisms use lactic acid fermentation, including the bacteria that convert milk into yogurt, sour cream, and cheese. Acids, including lactic acid, taste sour and contribute to the distinctive tastes of these foods. Lactic acid also denatures milk protein, altering its three-dimensional structure. This causes the milk to thicken, giving sour cream and yogurt their semisolid textures.

CASE STUDY c o n t i n u e d

When Athletes Boost Their Blood Counts: Do Cheaters Prosper?

Why is the average speed of the 5,000-meter run in the Olympics slower than that of the 100-meter dash? During the dash, runners' leg muscles use more ATP than cellular respiration can supply. But anaerobic fermentation can only provide ATP for a short dash. Longer runs must be aerobic, and thus slower, to prevent lactic acid buildup from causing extreme fatigue, muscle pain, and cramps.

▶▶ **LINKS** TO EVERYDAY LIFE

A Jug of Wine, a Loaf of Bread, and a Nice Bowl of Sauerkraut

Persian poet Omar Khayyam (1048–1122) described his vision of paradise on Earth as "A Jug of Wine, a Loaf of Bread—and Thou Beside Me" (**Fig. E8-4**). Historical evidence suggests that wine and beer were commercially produced at least 5,000 years ago. Yeasts are opportunists; they engage in efficient cellular respiration if oxygen is available, but switch to alcoholic fermentation if they run out of oxygen. To make champagne, fermentation is allowed to continue after the bottle is sealed, trapping carbon dioxide, which produces the tiny bubbles for which this drink is famous.

Fermentation also gives bread its airy texture. Bread contains yeast, flour, and water. After dry yeast cells are awakened from their dormant state by water, their enzymes break the starch in flour into its component glucose molecules. As the yeast cells rapidly grow and divide, they release CO_2, first during cellular respiration, and later during alcoholic fermentation when the O_2 is used up. The dough, made stretchy and resilient by kneading, traps the CO_2 gas, which expands in the heat of the oven, giving the bread its porous texture.

For thousands of years, people have relied on bacteria that utilize lactic acid fermentation to convert milk into sour cream, yogurt, and a wide variety of cheeses. In addition, lactate fermentation by salt-loving bacteria converts the sugars in cucumbers and cabbage to lactic acid. The result: pickles and sauerkraut.

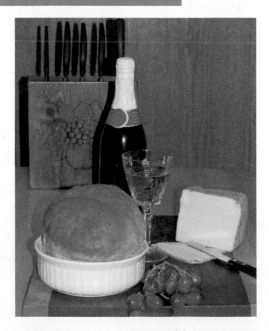

▲ FIGURE E8-4 **Some products of fermentation**

(a)   (b)

◀FIGURE 8-9 **Fermentation in action** (a) Sprinters rely on lactic acid fermentation in their leg muscle cells for their final burst of speed. (b) Bread dough rises because of the millions of tiny CO_2 bubbles released by both cellular respiration and alcoholic fermentation in yeast cells.

QUESTION Some species of bacteria use aerobic respiration and other species use fermentation. In an oxygen-rich environment, would either type be at a competitive advantage? What about in an oxygen-poor environment?

Some Cells Ferment Pyruvate to Form Alcohol and Carbon Dioxide

Many microorganisms, such as yeast (single-celled fungi), engage in **alcoholic fermentation** under anaerobic conditions. During alcoholic fermentation, pyruvate is converted into ethanol and CO_2 (rather than lactate). This releases NAD^+, which is then available to accept more high-energy electrons during glycolysis (**Fig. 8-10**). If you've ever been sufficiently bored to watch bread rise, you've seen the effects of fermentation in action (Fig. 8-9b). For more about how people use fermentation, see "Links to Everyday Life: A Jug of Wine, a Loaf of Bread, and a Nice Bowl of Sauerkraut."

◀FIGURE 8-10 **Glycolysis followed by alcoholic fermentation**

CASE STUDY revisited

When Athletes Boost Their Blood Counts: Do Cheaters Prosper?

Although runners who do the 100-meter dash rely heavily on lactic acid fermentation to supply ATP, long-distance athletes, including cyclists, marathon runners, and cross-country skiers, must pace themselves. They must rely on aerobic cellular respiration for most of the race, saving the anaerobic sprint for the finish. Training for distance events focuses on increasing the capacity of the athletes' respiratory and circulatory systems to deliver enough oxygen to their muscles. Blood doping most often occurs among distance athletes seeking to increase the oxygen-carrying capacity of their blood so that cellular respiration can generate the maximum amount of ATP from glucose.

The EPO-mimicking drug CERA—that the disgraced cyclist Riccò now admits having taken—helped keep his muscles supplied with ATP by stimulating overproduction of oxygen-carrying red blood cells. In the particularly demanding mountain stages of the Tour de France, which Riccò won, his clean competitors were at a disadvantage because their leg muscles became painfully laden with lactate from fermentation sooner than Riccò's did.

Because EPO is produced naturally in the human body, its abuse is hard to detect. CERA, developed for use by people with anemia (who have too few red blood cells), was new on the market at the time of the 2008 Tour de France, and Riccò may have assumed it would be undetectable. But CERA's manufacturer, the pharmaceutical firm Hoffman-La Roche, had provided samples of the drug to the World Anti-Doping Agency before it was marketed, allowing researchers to develop urine tests to identify users. This led to Riccò's exposure and disgrace, and his team's devastating disappointment.

Consider This

BioEthics Some athletes move to high-altitude locations to train for races run at lower altitudes, because the low oxygen levels at high altitudes stimulate increased production of red blood cells. Is this cheating? Explain your reasoning. Advances in gene therapy may one day make it possible to modify athletes' cells so that they have extra copies of the gene that produces EPO. Would this be cheating?

CHAPTER REVIEW

Summary of Key Concepts

8.1 How Do Cells Obtain Energy?
The ultimate source of energy for nearly all life is sunlight, captured during photosynthesis and stored in molecules such as glucose. Cells produce chemical energy by breaking down glucose into smaller molecules and capturing some of the released energy as ATP. During glycolysis, glucose is broken down in the cytosol, forming pyruvate and generating a small quantity of ATP and the high-energy electron-carrier NADH. If oxygen is available, the NADH from glycolysis is captured in ATP, and pyruvate is broken down through cellular respiration in the mitochondria, generating many more molecules of ATP.

8.2 What Happens During Glycolysis?
During the energy investment stage of glycolysis, glucose is energized by adding a phosphate group and some energy from each of two ATP molecules, forming fructose bisphosphate. Then, during the energy harvesting stage, a series of reactions breaks down the fructose bisphosphate into two molecules of pyruvate. This produces a net energy yield of two ATP molecules and two NADH molecules.

8.3 What Happens During Cellular Respiration?
Cellular respiration requires oxygen. Pyruvate is transported into the matrix of the mitochondria, where it reacts with coenzyme A, forming acetyl CoA, generating NADH, and releasing CO_2. The acetyl CoA enters the Krebs cycle, which releases the remaining two carbons as CO_2. One ATP, three NADH, and one $FADH_2$ are also formed for each acetyl group that goes through the cycle. In the mitochondrial matrix, each molecule of glucose that originally entered glycolysis produces a total of two ATP, eight NADH, and two $FADH_2$ (see Fig. 8-7).

The NADH and $FADH_2$ deliver their high-energy electrons to the electron transport chain (ETC) embedded in the inner mitochondrial membrane. As they pass along the ETC, energy released by the electrons is used to pump hydrogen ions across the inner membrane from the matrix to the intermembrane space, creating a hydrogen ion gradient. At the end of the ETC, the depleted electrons combine with oxygen (acting as an electron acceptor) and hydrogen ions to form water; this is the oxygen-requiring step of cellular respiration. During chemiosmosis, the energy stored in the hydrogen ion gradient is used to produce ATP as the hydrogen ions diffuse back across the inner membrane through ATP synthase channels. Chemiosmosis yields 32 ATP from the complete breakdown of a glucose molecule. These ATPs are generated by energy supplied by the two NADH formed during glycolysis, and the additional eight NADH and two $FADH_2$ produced during cellular respiration. In addition, a net of 2 ATP is formed directly during glycolysis, and two more ATPs are formed directly during the Krebs cycle. So altogether, a single molecule of glucose provides a net yield of 36 ATP when it is broken down by glycolysis followed by cellular respiration.

8.4 What Happens During Fermentation?
Glycolysis uses up NAD^+ to produce NADH as glucose is broken down into pyruvate. For these reactions to continue, NAD^+ must be continuously recycled. Under anaerobic conditions, NADH cannot release its high-energy electrons to the electron transport chain because there is no oxygen to accept them. Fermentation regenerates NAD^+ from NADH by converting pyruvate to lactate (via lactic acid fermentation) or to ethanol and CO_2 (via alcoholic fermentation), allowing glycolysis to continue.

Key Terms

aerobic *133*
alcoholic fermentation *135*
anaerobic *132*
cellular respiration *128*
chemiosmosis *130*
electron transport chain (ETC) *129*
fermentation *132*
flavin adenine dinucleotide (FAD or $FADH_2$) *128*
glycolysis *126*
intermembrane space *128*
Krebs cycle *128*
lactic acid fermentation *133*
matrix *128*
mitochondrion (plural, mitochondria) *128*
nicotinamide adenine dinucleotide (NAD^+ or NADH) *126*

Learning Outcomes

In this chapter, you have learned to . . .

LO1 Using their overall chemical equations, explain how photosynthesis and glucose breakdown are interdependent processes.

LO2 Summarize and describe the relationship between the two stages of glucose breakdown when oxygen is available.

LO3 Explain the energy investment and energy harvesting phases of glycolysis, including their substrate and product molecules.

LO4 Summarize the relationship between glycolysis and cellular respiration and describe how the structure of the mitochondrion supports cellular respiration.

LO5 Summarize the three stages of cellular respiration, including the input and output molecules at each stage.

LO6 Explain how ATP is generated by chemiosmosis, including the role of the electron transport chain.

LO7 Describe the role of oxygen in cellular respiration.

LO8 Describe the molecules used to capture and transport energy during glycolysis and cellular respiration.

LO9 Compare the amounts of ATP generated and the mechanisms by which the ATP is produced during fermentation, glycolysis, and cellular respiration.

LO10 Explain the function of fermentation, the substrates and products of fermentation, and some ways that people put fermentation to use.

Thinking Through the Concepts

Fill-in-the-Blank

1. The complete breakdown of glucose in the presence of oxygen occurs in two stages: _____ and _____. The first of these stages occurs in the

_____ of the cell, and the second stage occurs in organelles called _____. Which stage generates the most ATP? _____. LO2 LO4 LO9

2. Conditions in which oxygen is absent are described as _____. In the absence of oxygen, some microorganisms break down glucose using _____, which generates only _____ molecules of ATP. This process is followed by _____, in which no more ATP is produced, but the electron-carrier molecule _____ is regenerated so it can be used in further glucose breakdown. LO3 LO5 LO8 LO9 LO10

3. Yeasts in bread dough and alcoholic beverages use a type of fermentation that generates _____ and _____. Muscles pushed to their limit use _____ fermentation. Which form of fermentation is used by microorganisms that produce yogurt, sour cream, and sauerkraut? _____ LO10

4. The hormone _____ causes production of extra _____ cells, which increase the ability of the blood to carry _____. This gives athletes a competitive edge because their muscle cells can engage in _____ for energy production for a longer time during vigorous exercise. LO7

5. During cellular respiration, the electron transport chain pumps H^+ out of the mitochondrial _____ into the _____, producing a large _____ of H^+. The ATP produced by cellular respiration is generated by a process called _____. ATP is generated as H^+ travels through membrane channels linked to _____. LO4 LO6

6. The cyclic portion of cellular respiration is called the _____ cycle. The molecule that enters this cycle is _____. How many ATP molecules are generated by the cycle per molecule of glucose? _____ What two types of high-energy electron-carrier molecules are generated during the cycle? _____ and _____ LO5 LO8 LO9

Review Questions

1. Starting with glucose ($C_6H_{12}O_6$), write the overall equation for glucose breakdown in the presence of oxygen, compare this to the overall equation for photosynthesis, and explain how the energy components of the equations differ. LO1

2. Draw and label a mitochondrion, and explain how its structure relates to its function. LO4

3. What role do the following play in breaking down and harvesting energy from glucose: glycolysis, cellular respiration, chemiosmosis, fermentation, and NADH? LO2 LO3 LO5 LO6 LO8

4. Outline the two major stages of glycolysis. How many ATP molecules (overall) are generated per glucose molecule during glycolysis? Where in the cell does glycolysis occur? LO3 LO8 LO9

5. Under what conditions does fermentation occur? What are its possible products? What is its function? LO9 LO10

6. What three-carbon molecule is the end product of glycolysis? How are the carbons of this molecule used in the mitochondrial matrix reactions? In what form is most of the energy from the Krebs cycle captured? LO3 LO5 LO9

7. Describe the electron transport chain and the process of chemiosmosis. LO6

8. Why is oxygen necessary for cellular respiration to occur? LO7

9. Compare the structure of chloroplasts (described in Chapter 7) to that of mitochondria, and describe how the similarities in structure relate to similarities in function. LO4 LO6

Applying the Concepts

1. Some years ago a freight train overturned, spilling a load of grain. Because the grain was unusable, it was buried in the railroad embankment. Although there is no shortage of other food, the local bear population has become a nuisance by continually uncovering the grain. Yeasts are common in the soil. What do you think has happened to the grain to make the bears keep digging it up, and how is their behavior related to human cultural evolution?

2. Why can't a victim of cyanide poisoning survive by using anaerobic respiration?

3. Some species of bacteria that live at the surface of sediment on the bottom of lakes are capable of using either glycolysis plus fermentation or cellular respiration to generate ATP. There is very little circulation of water in lakes during the summer. Predict and explain what will happen to the bottommost water of lakes as the summer progresses, and describe how this situation will affect energy production by bacteria.

4. Dumping large amounts of raw sewage into rivers or lakes typically leads to massive fish kills, even if the sewage itself is not toxic to fish. What kills the fish? How might you reduce fish mortality after raw sewage is accidentally released into a small pond?

5. Why is it advantageous for different types of cells to undergo cellular respiration at different rates? How could you predict the relative rates of cellular respiration of different tissues by examining cells through a microscope?

6. Imagine a hypothetical situation in which a starving cell reaches the stage where every bit of its ATP has been depleted and converted to ADP plus phosphate. If at this point you place the cell in a solution containing glucose, will it recover and survive? Explain your answer based on what you know about glucose breakdown.

Answers to Figure Caption questions and Fill-in-the-Blank questions can be found in the Answers section at the back of the book.

(MB) *Go to MasteringBiology for practice quizzes, activities, eText, videos, current events, and more.*

UNIT 2
Inheritance

The capacity to blunder slightly is the real marvel of DNA. Without this special attribute, we would still be anaerobic bacteria and there would be no music.

"A structure of astounding elegance, a ladder delicately twisting into a double helix, packing into one, efficient strand all the information to create a living being."

G.Santis, Cyprus

CHAPTER 9

The Continuity of Life: Cellular Reproduction

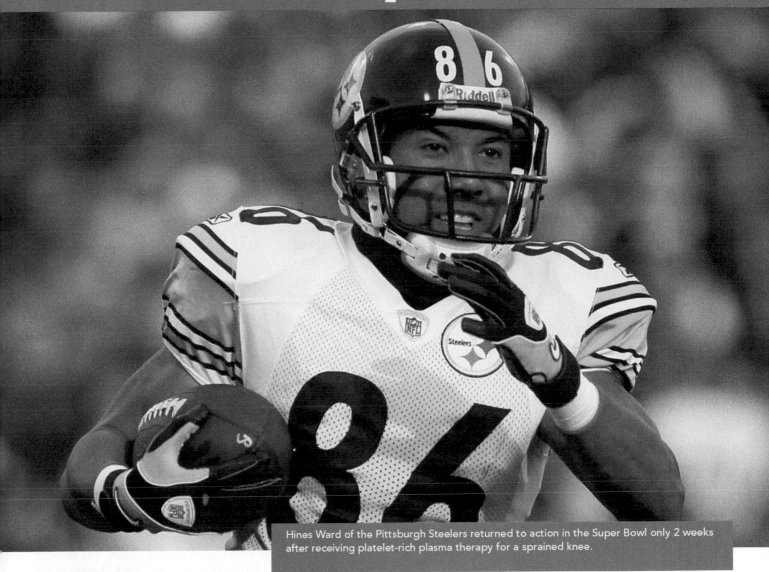

Hines Ward of the Pittsburgh Steelers returned to action in the Super Bowl only 2 weeks after receiving platelet-rich plasma therapy for a sprained knee.

CASE STUDY

Body, Heal Thyself

ON JANUARY 18, 2009, in the first quarter of a National Football League playoff game, the Pittsburgh Steelers' star wide receiver Hines Ward sprained a ligament in his right knee. In Ward's words, "[It] was a severe injury, maybe a four- or six-week injury." But only 2 weeks later, he played in the Super Bowl, catching two passes during the Steelers victory over the Arizona Cardinals.

Healing injured ligaments is a complicated process. Ligaments consist mostly of specialized proteins, including collagen and elastin, organized in a precise, orderly arrangement that provides both strength and flexibility. A relatively small number of cells, which originally produced these proteins, are scattered throughout the ligament. When a ligament is sprained,

broken blood vessels leak blood into the site of injury. Platelets, a type of blood cell, help to form clots, preventing further bleeding, and release a number of different proteins, collectively called growth factors, into the injured ligament. The growth factors attract various types of cells to the site of injury, and stimulate cell division in both these new cells and the existing cells in the ligament. These cells produce new ligament proteins. Ideally, the injured ligament gradually develops the correct protein composition and arrangement, returning to its original size, strength, and flexibility. Unfortunately, this process is slow. To make things worse, it isn't always completely successful.

So how could Hines Ward play football in just 2 weeks? Of course, he had the best treatment that money could buy. Part of that treatment was platelet-rich plasma (PRP) therapy. In PRP therapy, blood is

taken from a patient, centrifuged, and a portion rich in platelets is injected directly into the wound site. Because the patient's own cells are used, there is no risk of rejection or introducing disease organisms from a donor's blood. Although PRP therapy for sports injuries is still considered experimental, studies in mice, rats, rabbits, horses, and humans have found that it stimulates faster and more complete healing for a wide range of damaged tissues, including bone, skin, tendons, ligaments, and muscle.

As you read this chapter, consider the following questions: How do growth factors cause cells to divide? Why don't cells in undamaged tissues divide rapidly all the time? Why are the dividing cells genetically identical to the cells they came from and, in fact, genetically identical to most of the rest of the cells of the body?

AT A GLANCE

LEARNING GOALS

LG1 Describe the fundamental components of inheritance, including chromosomes, DNA, nucleotides, and genes.

LG2 Compare and contrast the categories of cells, as distinguished by their ability to divide and differentiate.

LG3 Compare and contrast sexual reproduction and asexual reproduction.

LG4 Describe the prokaryotic cell cycle, including the mechanisms of prokaryotic fission.

LG5 Describe the structure of a eukaryotic chromosome.

LG6 Define homologous chromosome, autosome, and sex chromosome.

LG7 Distinguish between diploid and haploid cells.

LG8 Describe the eukaryotic cell cycle, including the steps and outcome of mitotic cell division.

LG9 Describe how the eukaryotic cell cycle is regulated.

LG10 Describe the steps and outcome of meiotic cell division.

LG11 Compare and contrast the three main types of eukaryotic life cycles.

LG12 Explain how meiosis and sexual reproduction produce genetic variability in populations.

9.1 WHY DO CELLS DIVIDE?

"All cells come from cells." This insight, first stated by the German physician Rudolf Virchow in the mid-1800s, captures the critical importance of cellular reproduction for all living organisms. Cells reproduce by **cell division,** in which a parent cell usually produces two **daughter cells.** In typical cell division, each daughter cell receives a complete set of hereditary information, identical to the hereditary information of the parent cell, and about half the parent cell's cytoplasm.

Cell Division Transmits Hereditary Information to Each Daughter Cell

The hereditary information of all living cells is contained in **deoxyribonucleic acid (DNA).** DNA is a polymer composed of subunits called **nucleotides** (**Fig. 9-1a;** see also Chapter 3). Each nucleotide consists of a phosphate, a sugar (deoxyribose), and one of four bases—adenine (A), thymine (T), guanine (G), or cytosine (C). A **chromosome** consists of DNA, together with proteins that organize its three-dimensional structure and regulate its use. The DNA in a chromosome consists of two long strands of nucleotides wound around each other, as a ladder would look if it were twisted into a corkscrew shape. This structure is called a double helix (**Fig. 9-1b**).

The units of inheritance, called **genes,** are segments of DNA ranging from a few hundred to many thousands of nucleotides in length. Like the letters of an alphabet, in a language with very long sentences, the specific sequences of nucleotides in genes spell out the instructions for making the proteins of a cell. (We will see in Chapters 11 and 12 how DNA encodes genetic information and how a cell regulates which genes it uses at any given time.)

For a cell to survive, it must have a complete set of genetic instructions. Therefore, when a cell divides, it cannot simply split its set of genes in half and give each daughter cell half a set. Rather, the cell must first duplicate its DNA to make two identical copies, much like making a photocopy of an instruction manual. Each daughter cell then receives a complete "DNA manual" containing all the genes.

Cell Division Is Required for Growth and Development

The familiar form of cell division in eukaryotic cells, in which each daughter cell is genetically identical to the parent cell, is called mitotic cell division (see Sections 9.4 and 9.5). Since your conception as a single fertilized egg, mitotic cell division has produced all the cells in your body, and continues every day in many organs. After cell division, the daughter cells may grow and divide again, or they may **differentiate,** becoming specialized for specific functions, such as contraction (muscle cells), fighting infections (white blood cells), or producing digestive enzymes (cells of the pancreas, stomach, and intestine). This repeating pattern of divide, grow, and (possibly) differentiate, then divide again, is called the **cell cycle** (see Sections 9.2 and 9.4).

nucleotide
- phosphate
- base
- sugar

(a) A single strand of DNA

(b) The double helix

◄FIGURE 9-1 **The structure of DNA**
(a) A nucleotide consists of a phosphate, a sugar, and one of four bases—adenine (A), thymine (T), guanine (G), or cytosine (C). A single strand of DNA consists of a long chain of nucleotides held together by bonds between the phosphate of one nucleotide and the sugar of the next. **(b)** Two DNA strands twist around one another to form a double helix.

Most multicellular organisms have three categories of cells, based on their abilities to divide and differentiate:

- **Stem Cells** Most of the cells formed by the first few cell divisions of a fertilized egg, and a few cells in adults, including cells in the heart, skin, intestines, fat, brain, and bone marrow, are **stem cells.** Stem cells have two important characteristics: self-renewal and the ability to differentiate into a variety of cell types. Self-renewal means that stem cells retain the capacity to divide, perhaps for the entire life of the organism. Usually, when a stem cell divides, one of its daughters remains a stem cell, maintaining the population of stem cells. The other daughter cell often undergoes several rounds of cell division, but the resulting cells eventually differentiate into specialized cell types. Some stem cells in early embryos can produce any of the specialized cell types of the entire body.
- **Other Cells Capable of Dividing** Many cells of the bodies of embryos, juveniles, and adults can also divide, but each type of cell can typically differentiate into only one or two different cell types. Dividing cells in your liver, for example, can only become more liver cells.
- **Permanently Differentiated Cells** Some cells differentiate and never divide again. For example, most of the cells in your heart and brain cannot divide.

Cell Division Is Required for Sexual and Asexual Reproduction

Organisms reproduce by either or both of two fundamentally different processes: sexual reproduction or asexual reproduction. **Sexual reproduction** in eukaryotic organisms occurs when offspring are produced by the fusion of **gametes** (sperm and eggs) generated in the gonads of adults. Cells in the adult's reproductive system undergo a specialized

type of cell division called meiotic cell division, which we will describe in Section 9.8. Meiotic cell division produces daughter cells with exactly half of the genetic information of their parent cells. In animals, these daughter cells become sperm or eggs. When a sperm fertilizes an egg, the resulting offspring once again contains the full complement of genetic information.

Reproduction in which offspring are formed from a single parent, without having a sperm fertilize an egg, is called **asexual reproduction.** Asexual reproduction produces offspring that are genetically identical to the parent and to each other—they are **clones.** Bacteria (**Fig. 9-2a**) and many single-celled eukaryotic organisms, such as *Paramecium* (**Fig. 9-2b**), reproduce asexually by cell division, in which two new cells arise from each preexisting cell. Some multicellular organisms can also reproduce by asexual reproduction. For example, a *Hydra* reproduces by budding. First it grows a small replica of itself, called a bud, on its body (**Fig. 9-2c**). Eventually, the bud is able to live independently and separates from its parent, forming a new *Hydra*. Many plants and fungi can reproduce both asexually and sexually. The beautiful aspen groves of Colorado, Utah, and New Mexico, for example, develop asexually from shoots growing up from the root system of a single parent tree (**Fig. 9-2d**). Although a grove looks like a cluster of separate trees, it is often a single individual whose multiple trunks are interconnected by a common root system. Aspen can also reproduce by seeds, which result from sexual reproduction.

CHECK YOUR LEARNING

Can you describe the types of cells found in a multicellular organism, distinguished by their ability to divide and differentiate? What are the similarities and differences between sexual reproduction and asexual reproduction?

(a) Dividing bacteria

(b) Cell division in *Paramecium*

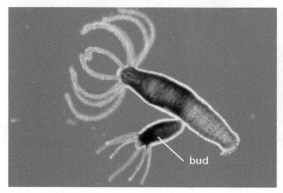

bud

(c) *Hydra* reproduces asexually by budding

The trees in this grove have already lost their leaves

The trees in this grove have begun to change color

The trees in this grove are still green

(d) A grove of aspens often consists of genetically identical trees produced by asexual reproduction

▲ **FIGURE 9-2 Cell division enables asexual reproduction (a)** Bacteria reproduce asexually by dividing in two. **(b)** In single-celled eukaryotic microorganisms, such as the protist *Paramecium* that is commonly found in ponds, cell division produces two new, independent organisms. **(c)** *Hydra*, a freshwater relative of the sea anemone, grows a miniature replica of itself (a bud) on its side. When fully developed, the bud breaks off and assumes independent life. **(d)** Trees in an aspen grove are often genetically identical. Each tree grows up from the roots of a single ancestral tree. This photo shows three separate groves near Aspen, Colorado. In fall, the timing of the changing color of their leaves shows the genetic identity within a grove and the genetic difference between groves.

9.2 WHAT OCCURS DURING THE PROKARYOTIC CELL CYCLE?

The DNA of a prokaryotic cell is contained in a single, circular chromosome about a millimeter or two in circumference. Unlike eukaryotic chromosomes, prokaryotic chromosomes are not contained in a membrane-bound nucleus (see Chapter 4).

The prokaryotic cell cycle consists of a relatively long period of growth—during which the cell replicates its DNA—followed by a type of cell division called **prokaryotic fission** (Fig. 9-3a). (Prokaryotic fission is often called "binary fission." However, many biologists use the term binary fission to describe cell division in both prokaryotes and single-celled eukaryotes. To avoid confusion, we will use the term prokaryotic fission to describe cell division in prokaryotic cells.) The prokaryotic chromosome is

usually attached at one point to the inside of the plasma membrane of the cell (Fig. 9-3b ❶). During the growth phase of the prokaryotic cell cycle, the DNA is replicated, producing two identical chromosomes that become attached to the plasma membrane at nearby, but separate, sites (Fig. 9-3b ❷). As the cell grows, new plasma membrane is added between the attachment sites of the chromosomes, pushing them apart (Fig. 9-3b ❸). When the cell has approximately doubled in size, the plasma membrane around the middle of the cell grows inward between the two attachment sites (Fig. 9-3b ❹). The plasma membrane then fuses along the equator of the cell, producing two daughter cells, each containing one of the chromosomes (Fig. 9-3b ❺). Because DNA replication produces two identical DNA molecules, the two daughter cells are genetically identical to one another and to the parent cell.

(a) The prokaryotic cell cycle

attachment site of chromosome

cell wall

plasma membrane

chromosome

❶ The prokaryotic chromosome, a circular DNA double helix, is attached to the plasma membrane at one point.

❷ The DNA replicates and the resulting two chromosomes attach to the plasma membrane at nearby points.

❸ New plasma membrane is added between the attachment points, pushing the two chromosomes farther apart.

❹ The plasma membrane grows inward at the middle of the cell.

❺ The parent cell divides into two daughter cells.

(b) Prokaryotic fission

Under ideal conditions, the prokaryotic cell cycle proceeds rapidly. For example, the common intestinal bacterium *Escherichia coli* (usually called simply *E. coli*) can grow, replicate its DNA, and divide in about 20 minutes. Luckily, the environment in our intestines isn't ideal for bacterial growth; otherwise, the bacteria would soon outweigh the rest of our bodies!

CHECK YOUR LEARNING

Can you describe the prokaryotic cell cycle and the major events of prokaryotic fission?

9.3 HOW IS THE DNA IN EUKARYOTIC CHROMOSOMES ORGANIZED?

Eukaryotic chromosomes differ from prokaryotic chromosomes in that they are separated from the cytoplasm in a membrane-bound nucleus. Further, eukaryotic cells always have multiple chromosomes—the smallest number, 2, is found in the cells of females of a species of ant, but most animals have dozens and some ferns have more than 1,200! Finally, eukaryotic chromosomes usually contain far more DNA than do prokaryotic chromosomes. Human chromosomes, for example, contain 10 to 50 times more DNA than the typical prokaryotic chromosome. The complex events of eukaryotic cell division are largely an evolutionary solution to the problem of sorting out a large number of long chromosomes. Therefore, we will begin by taking a closer look at the structure of the eukaryotic chromosome.

The Eukaryotic Chromosome Consists of a Linear DNA Double Helix Bound to Proteins

Each human chromosome contains a single DNA double helix; depending on the chromosome, the length ranges from about 50 million to 250 million nucleotides. If their DNA were completely relaxed and extended, human chromosomes would each be about 0.6 to 3.0 inches long (15 to 75 millimeters), and a single human cell would contain about 6 feet (1.8 meters) of DNA.

Fitting this huge amount of DNA into a nucleus only a few ten-thousandths of an inch in diameter is no trivial task. For most of a cell's life, the DNA in each chromosome is wrapped around proteins called histones (**Fig. 9-4** ❶ and ❷). The DNA/histone beads further coil up like a spring or Slinky toy (**Fig. 9-4** ❸), and then these coils are bent by attaching them to "scaffolds" made of additional proteins. All of this wrapping and coiling condenses the DNA to about 1/1,000th of its original length (**Fig. 9-4** ❹). However, even this enormous degree of compaction still leaves the chromosomes much too long to be sorted out and moved into the daughter nuclei during cell division. Just as thread is easier

◀FIGURE 9-3 **The prokaryotic cell cycle** (a) The prokaryotic cell cycle consists of growth and DNA replication, followed by prokaryotic fission. (b) The process of prokaryotic fission.

① **DNA double helix**

histone proteins

② **DNA wound around histone proteins**

③ **Coiled DNA/histone beads**

④ **Loops attached to a protein scaffold; this stage of partial condensation typically occurs in a nondividing cell**

protein scaffold

⑤ **Folded chromosome, fully condensed in a dividing cell**

▲ **FIGURE 9-4 Chromosome structure ①** A eukaryotic chromosome contains a single DNA double helix. **②** The DNA is wound around proteins called histones, reducing the length by about a factor of 6. **③** Other proteins coil up the DNA/histone beads, much like a Slinky toy, reducing the length by another factor of 6 or 7. **④** These coils are attached in loops to protein "scaffolding" to complete the chromosome as it occurs during most of the life of a cell. The wrapping, coiling, and looping make the chromosome roughly 1,000 times shorter than the DNA molecule it contains. **⑤** During cell division, still other proteins fold up the chromosome, yielding about another 10-fold condensation. (Inset) The fuzzy edges visible in the electron micrograph are loops of folded chromosome.

to organize when it is wound onto spools, sorting and transporting chromosomes is easier when they are condensed and shortened. During cell division, additional proteins fold up the DNA of each chromosome into compact structures that are less than 2 ten-thousandths of an inch long (about 4 micrometers), which is 10 times shorter than they are during the rest of the cell cycle (**Fig. 9-4 ⑤**).

Genes Are Segments of the DNA of a Chromosome

Genes are sequences of DNA ranging from hundreds to thousands of nucleotides long. Each gene occupies a specific place, or **locus** (plural, loci), on a chromosome (**Fig. 9-5a**). Chromosomes vary in the number of genes they contain. Although the exact numbers remain uncertain, human chromosomes may contain as few as 70 genes (the lowest estimate for the Y chromosome) to over 3,000 genes (in chromosome 1, the largest chromosome).

In addition to genes, every chromosome has specialized regions that are crucial to its structure and function: two telomeres and one centromere (see Fig. 9-5a). **Telomeres** ("end body" in Greek) are protective caps at each end of a chromosome. Without telomeres, genes located at the ends

gene loci

centromere

telomeres

(a) A eukaryotic chromosome (one DNA double helix) before DNA replication

sister chromatids

duplicated chromosome (two DNA double helices)

centromere

(b) A eukaryotic chromosome after DNA replication

independent daughter chromosomes, each with one identical DNA double helix

(c) Separated sister chromatids become independent chromosomes

▲ **FIGURE 9-5 The principal features of a eukaryotic chromosome during cell division (a)** Before DNA replication, each chromosome consists of a single DNA double helix. Genes are segments of the DNA, usually hundreds to thousands of nucleotides in length. The ends of the chromosome are protected by telomeres. **(b)** The two sister chromatids of a duplicated chromosome are held together by the centromere. **(c)** The sister chromatids separate during cell division to become two independent, genetically identical, chromosomes.

of the chromosomes would be lost during DNA replication. Telomeres also keep chromosomes from fusing with one another and forming long, unwieldy structures that probably could not be distributed properly to the daughter cells during cell division. The second specialized region of the chromosome is the **centromere.** As we will see, the centromere has two principal functions: (1) It temporarily holds two daughter DNA double helices together after DNA replication, and (2) it is the attachment site for microtubules that move the chromosomes during cell division.

Duplicated Chromosomes Separate During Cell Division

Prior to cell division, the DNA in each chromosome is replicated (see Chapter 11). At the end of DNA replication, a **duplicated chromosome** consists of two identical DNA double helices, now called sister **chromatids,** which are attached to each other at the centromere (**Fig. 9-5b**). During mitotic cell division, the two sister chromatids separate, each becoming an independent chromosome that is delivered to one of the two daughter cells (**Fig. 9-5c**).

Eukaryotic Chromosomes Usually Occur in Pairs Containing Similar Genetic Information

The chromosomes of each eukaryotic species have characteristic sizes, shapes, and patterns of bands when stained by dyes used in light microscopy. The entire set of chromosomes from a single cell is called its **karyotype** (**Fig. 9-6**). For most eukaryotic organisms, including humans, a karyotype consists of pairs of chromosomes. The two chromosomes that make up a pair are called **homologous chromosomes,** or **homologues,** from Greek words that mean "to say the same thing." Cells with pairs of homologous chromosomes are **diploid,** meaning "double." As the karyotype in Figure 9-6 shows, a typical human cell is diploid, with 23 pairs of chromosomes, for a total of 46.

Homologous chromosomes are the same length and have the same staining pattern, because both chromosomes in the pair contain the same genes arranged in the same order. These chromosomes of similar appearance and similar DNA sequences, called **autosomes,** are paired in diploid cells of both sexes. People have 22 pairs of autosomes.

In addition to autosomes, humans and most other mammals have two **sex chromosomes:** either two X chromosomes (in females) or an X and a Y chromosome (in males). Although X and Y chromosomes are quite different in size (see Fig. 9-6) and in genetic composition, a small portion of the X and Y chromosomes are homologous to each other.

Homologous Chromosomes Are Usually Not Identical

Despite their name, the two homologues in a pair don't say exactly the "same thing." Why not? A cell might make a mistake when it copies the DNA of one homologue but not the other (see Chapter 11). Or a ray of ultraviolet light from the sun might zap the DNA of one homologue but not the other. The resulting changes in the sequence of nucleotides in DNA are called **mutations.** Mutations make some

▶FIGURE 9-6 **The karyotype of a human male** Staining and photographing the entire set of duplicated chromosomes from a single cell produces a karyotype. Pictures of the individual chromosomes are cut out and arranged in descending order of size. The chromosome pairs (homologues) are similar in size and have similar genetic material. Chromosomes 1 through 22 are the autosomes; the X and Y chromosomes are the sex chromosomes. Note that the Y chromosome is much smaller than the X chromosome. If this were a female karyotype, it would have two X chromosomes and no Y chromosomes.

▲ FIGURE 9-7 **Homologous chromosomes may have the same or different alleles of individual genes** The two homologues have the same genes at the same locations (loci). The homologues may have the same allele of a gene at certain loci (left) and different alleles of a gene at other loci (right).

genes on one homologue slightly different from the same genes on the other homologue. A given mutation might have happened yesterday, or it may have occurred in a sperm or egg 10,000 years ago and been inherited ever since. Such enduring mutations, inherited generation after generation, are called **alleles**—alternate forms of a given gene that may produce differences in structure or function, such as black, brown, or blond hair in humans, or different songs in birds. Thus, although homologous chromosomes have the same genes, a pair of homologues may have the same alleles of some genes and different alleles of other genes (**Fig. 9-7**). (We'll explore the consequences of having paired genes, and more than one allele of each gene, in Chapter 10.)

If we think of DNA as an instruction manual for building a cell or an organism, then mutations are like misspelled words in the manual. Although some misspellings might not matter much, others can have serious consequences. For example, single-letter misspellings in crucial genes are the alleles that can cause inherited diseases such as sickle-cell anemia and cystic fibrosis. Occasionally, however, a mutation may actually improve the DNA manual and spread throughout a species, if the organisms carrying the mutation are more likely to survive and reproduce than members of the species that lack the mutation (see Chapters 14 and 15).

Not All Cells Have Paired Chromosomes

Most cells in our bodies are diploid. However, during sexual reproduction, cells in the ovaries or testes undergo meiotic cell division (described in Section 9.8) to produce gametes (sperm or eggs). Each gamete contains only one member of each pair of autosomes and one of the two sex chromosomes. Cells that contain only one of each type of chromosome are called **haploid** (meaning "single"). In humans, a haploid cell contains one of each of the 22 autosomes, plus either an X or Y sex chromosome, for a total of 23 chromosomes.

When a sperm fertilizes an egg, fusion of the two haploid cells produces a diploid cell that once again contains pairs of homologous chromosomes. Because one homologue of each pair is inherited from the mother (in her egg), it is called a maternal chromosome. Each homologue inherited from the father (in his sperm) is called a paternal chromosome.

In biological shorthand, the number of different types of chromosomes in a species is called the haploid number and is designated n. For humans, $n = 23$ because we have 23 different types of chromosomes (22 autosomes plus one sex chromosome). Diploid cells contain $2n$ chromosomes. Thus, the body cells of humans have 46 (2×23) chromosomes.

Not all eukaryotic organisms are diploid. The bread mold *Neurospora*, for example, has haploid cells for most of its life cycle. Many plants, on the other hand, have more than two copies of each type of chromosome, with $4n$ (tetraploid), $6n$ (hexaploid), or even more chromosomes per cell. Many common flowers, including some daylilies, orchids, lilies, and phlox, are tetraploid; most wheat is either tetraploid or hexaploid.

CHECK YOUR LEARNING

Can you describe the structure of a eukaryotic chromosome? Can you define the terms *homologous chromosome, autosome,* and *sex chromosome*? What is the difference between a diploid and a haploid cell?

9.4 WHAT OCCURS DURING THE EUKARYOTIC CELL CYCLE?

In the eukaryotic cell cycle, newly formed cells usually acquire nutrients from their environment, synthesize more cytoplasm and organelles, and grow larger. After a variable amount of time—depending on the organism, the type of cell, and the nutrients available—the cell may divide. Each daughter cell may then enter another cell cycle, producing more cells. Many cells, however, divide only if they receive signals, such as hormone-like molecules called growth factors, that cause them to enter another cell cycle (see Section 9.6). Other cells may differentiate and never divide again.

The Eukaryotic Cell Cycle Consists of Interphase and Mitotic Cell Division

The eukaryotic cell cycle is divided into two major phases: interphase and mitotic cell division (**Fig. 9-8**).

During Interphase, a Cell Grows in Size, Replicates Its DNA, and Often Differentiates

Most eukaryotic cells spend the majority of their time in **interphase,** the period between cell divisions. For example, some cells in human skin spend roughly 22 hours in interphase and only a couple of hours dividing. Interphase itself contains three subphases: G_1 (the first *g*rowth phase and the first *g*ap in DNA synthesis), S (DNA *s*ynthesis), and G_2 (the second *g*rowth phase and the second *g*ap in DNA synthesis).

A newly formed daughter cell enters the G_1 portion of interphase. During G_1, a cell carries out one or more of three activities. First, it almost always grows in size. Second, it often differentiates, developing the structures and biochemical pathways that allow it to perform a specialized function. For example, most nerve cells grow long strands, called axons, that allow them to connect with other cells, whereas liver cells produce bile, proteins that aid blood clotting, and enzymes that detoxify many poisonous materials. Third, the cell is sensitive to internal and external signals that determine whether or not it will divide. If the cell is stimulated to divide, it enters the S phase, when DNA synthesis

▲ FIGURE 9-8 **The eukaryotic cell cycle** The eukaryotic cell cycle consists of interphase and mitotic cell division.

(replication) occurs. The cell then proceeds to the G_2 phase, during which it may grow some more and then synthesize the proteins needed for cell division.

Many differentiated cells, such as liver cells, can be recalled from the differentiated state back into the dividing state, whereas others, such as most heart muscle and nerve cells, remain in interphase and never divide again. That is

CASE STUDY continued

Body, Heal Thyself

Like platelet-rich plasma therapy, stem cell injection is a potential treatment for wounds. For horses with many types of leg injuries, a veterinarian can take a small sample of a horse's own fat and send it to a company called Vet-Stem, which isolates stem cells from the fat. Vet-Stem sends the stem cells back to the vet, who injects them into the horse's injured leg. The stem cells divide and differentiate, producing specialized cells that repair the damaged structures.

In 2010, professional baseball pitcher Bartolo Colon received similar stem-cell therapy for a shoulder injury that never fully healed after rotator cuff surgery. In 2011, he was back pitching for the New York Yankees, with a 90+ mph fastball. Effective stem cell therapy? Or just more time to heal? No one knows for sure, but Major League Baseball seems to believe that the therapy works, and has launched an investigation into whether stem cell therapy might produce superhuman powers, and hence should be banned as a performance-enhancing drug.

one reason why heart attacks and strokes are so devastating: The dead cells usually cannot be replaced. However, the heart and brain contain a few stem cells that *can* divide. Biomedical researchers hope that, one day, these stem cells can be coaxed into dividing rapidly and repairing damaged organs.

We will investigate how the cell cycle is controlled in Section 9.6.

Mitotic Cell Division Consists of Nuclear Division and Cytoplasmic Division

Mitotic cell division, the division of one parental cell into two daughter cells, consists of two processes: mitosis and cytokinesis. **Mitosis** is the division of the nucleus. The word "mitosis" is derived from a Greek word meaning "thread," because, in its early stages, the chromosomes condense and shorten, becoming visible in a light microscope as thread-like structures. Mitosis produces two daughter nuclei, each containing one copy of each of the chromosomes that were present in the parent nucleus. **Cytokinesis** (from Greek words meaning "cell movement") is the division of the cytoplasm. Cytokinesis places about half the cytoplasm, half the organelles (such as mitochondria, ribosomes, and Golgi apparatus), and one of the newly formed nuclei into each of two daughter cells. Thus, mitotic cell division typically produces daughter cells that are physically similar and genetically identical to each other and to the parent cell.

Mitotic cell division takes place in all eukaryotic organisms. It is the mechanism of asexual reproduction in eukaryotic cells, including single-celled organisms such as yeast, amoebas, and *Paramecium*, and multicellular organisms such as *Hydra* and aspens. Mitotic cell division followed by differentiation of the daughter cells allows a fertilized egg to grow into an adult with perhaps trillions of specialized cells. Mitotic cell division also allows an organism to maintain its tissues, many of which require frequent replacement; to repair damaged parts of the body, for example, after an injury; and sometimes even to regenerate body parts. Mitotic cell division is also the mechanism by which stem cells reproduce.

CHECK YOUR LEARNING

Can you describe the events of the eukaryotic cell cycle? What is the difference between mitotic cell division and mitosis?

9.5 HOW DOES MITOTIC CELL DIVISION PRODUCE GENETICALLY IDENTICAL DAUGHTER CELLS?

Remember that the chromosomes have already been duplicated during the S phase of interphase. Therefore, when mitosis begins, each chromosome consists of two sister chromatids attached at the centromere (see Fig. 9-5b).

For convenience, biologists divide mitosis into four phases, based on the appearance and behavior of the chromosomes: prophase, metaphase, anaphase, and telophase (**Fig. 9-9**). However, these phases are not really discrete

INTERPHASE

MITOSIS

(a) Late Interphase: nuclear envelope, chromatin, nucleolus, centriole pairs

(b) Early Prophase: condensing chromosomes, beginning of spindle formation

(c) Late Prophase: spindle pole, spindle microtubules, kinetochore, spindle pole

(d) Metaphase: kinetochore microtubules

(a) Late Interphase
Duplicated chromosomes are in the relaxed uncondensed state; duplicated centrioles remain clustered.

(b) Early Prophase
Chromosomes condense and shorten; spindle microtubules begin to form between separating centriole pairs.

(c) Late Prophase (also called Prometaphase)
The nucleolus disappears; the nuclear envelope breaks down; some spindle microtubules attach to the kinetochore (blue) located at the centromere of each sister chromatid.

(d) Metaphase
Kinetochore microtubules line up the chromosomes at the cell's equator.

▲ FIGURE 9-9 **Mitotic cell division in an animal cell**

QUESTION What would the consequences be if one set of sister chromatids failed to separate at anaphase?

events; they instead form a continuum, with each phase merging into the next.

During Prophase, the Chromosomes Condense, the Spindle Microtubules Form, the Nuclear Envelope Breaks Down, and the Chromosomes Are Captured by the Spindle Microtubules

The first phase of mitosis is called **prophase** (meaning "the stage before" in Greek). During prophase, four major events occur: (1) The duplicated chromosomes condense (see Fig. 9-4), (2) the spindle microtubules form, (3) the nuclear envelope breaks down, and (4) the chromosomes are captured by the spindle microtubules (**Figs. 9-9b, c**). Chromosome condensation also causes the nucleolus to disappear. The nucleolus

consists of partially assembled ribosomes and the genes, located on several different chromosomes, that code for the RNA of the ribosomes (see Chapter 4). As the chromosomes condense, they separate from one another and ribosome synthesis ceases, so the nucleolus gradually fades away.

After the duplicated chromosomes condense, the **spindle microtubules** begin to assemble. In all eukaryotic cells, the movement of chromosomes during mitosis depends on spindle microtubules. In animal cells, the spindle microtubules originate from a region that contains a pair of microtubule-containing structures called **centrioles.** Although the cells of plants, fungi, many algae, and even some mutant fruit flies do not contain centrioles, they nevertheless form functional spindles during mitotic cell division, showing that centrioles are not required for spindle formation.

INTERPHASE

polar
microtubules

chromosomes
extending

nuclear envelope
re-forming

microfilaments

nucleolus
reappearing

(e) Anaphase
Sister chromatids separate
and move to opposite poles
of the cell; polar microtubules
push the poles apart.

(f) Telophase
One set of chromosomes
reaches each pole and begins
to decondense; nuclear
envelopes start to form;
nucleoli begin to reappear;
spindle microtubules begin to
disappear; microfilaments form
rings around the equator.

(g) Cytokinesis
The ring of microfilaments
contracts, dividing the cell
in two; each daughter cell
receives one nucleus and
about half of the cytoplasm.

**(h) Interphase of daughter
cells**
Spindles disappear,
intact nuclear envelopes
form, and the chromosomes
extend completely.

In animal cells, a new pair of centrioles forms during interphase near the previously existing pair. During prophase, the two centriole pairs migrate to opposite sides of the nucleus (see Fig. 9-9b). When the cell divides, each daughter cell will receive a pair of centrioles. Each centriole pair serves as a central point from which the spindle microtubules radiate, both inward toward the nucleus and outward toward the plasma membrane (see Fig. 9-9c). These points are called spindle poles. (Picture the cell as a globe of Earth. The spindle poles are roughly where the north and south poles would be, and the spindle microtubules correspond to the lines of longitude. As on a globe, the equator of the cell cuts across the middle, halfway between the poles.)

As the spindle microtubules form into a complete basket around the nucleus, the nuclear envelope disintegrates, releasing the duplicated chromosomes. Each sister chromatid in a duplicated chromosome has a protein-containing structure, called a **kinetochore,** located at its centromere. The kinetochores of the two sister chromatids are arranged back-to-back, facing away from one another. The kinetochore of one sister chromatid binds to the ends of spindle microtubules leading to one pole of the cell, while the kinetochore of the other sister chromatid binds to spindle microtubules leading to the opposite pole of the cell (see Fig. 9-9c). The microtubules that bind to kinetochores are called kinetochore microtubules, to distinguish them from microtubules that do not bind to a kinetochore (discussed in the next paragraph). When the sister chromatids separate later in mitosis, the newly independent chromosomes will move along the kinetochore microtubules to opposite poles.

Other spindle microtubules, called polar microtubules, do not attach to kinetochores or to any other part of the chromosomes; rather, they have free ends that overlap along the cell's equator. As we will see, the polar microtubules will push the two spindle poles apart later in mitosis.

During Metaphase, the Chromosomes Line Up Along the Equator of the Cell

At the end of prophase, the two kinetochores of each duplicated chromosome are connected to spindle microtubules leading to opposite poles of the cell. As a result, each duplicated chromosome is connected to both spindle poles. During **metaphase** (the "middle stage"), the two kinetochores on a duplicated chromosome pull toward opposite poles of the cell. During this process, the microtubules lengthen or shorten, until each chromosome lines up along the equator of the cell, with one kinetochore facing each pole (**Fig. 9-9d**).

During Anaphase, Sister Chromatids Separate and Are Pulled to Opposite Poles of the Cell

At the beginning of **anaphase** (**Fig. 9-9e**), the sister chromatids separate, becoming independent daughter chromosomes. This separation allows each kinetochore to move its chromosome poleward, while simultaneously nibbling off the end of the attached microtubule, thereby shortening it (a mechanism appropriately called "Pac-Man" movement). One of the two daughter chromosomes derived from each parental chromosome moves to each pole of the cell. Because the daughter chromosomes are identical copies of the parental chromosomes, each cluster of chromosomes that forms at opposite poles of the cell contains one copy of every chromosome that was in the parent cell.

At about the same time, polar microtubules radiating from each pole grab one another where they overlap at the equator. These polar microtubules then simultaneously lengthen and push on one another, forcing the poles of the cell apart (see Fig. 9-9e).

During Telophase, a Nuclear Envelope Forms Around Each Group of Chromosomes

When the chromosomes reach the poles, **telophase** (the "end stage") begins (**Fig. 9-9f**). The spindle microtubules disintegrate and a nuclear envelope forms around each group of chromosomes. The chromosomes revert to their extended state, and nucleoli begin to re-form. In most cells, cytokinesis occurs during telophase, isolating each daughter nucleus in its own daughter cell (**Fig. 9-9g**). However, mitosis sometimes occurs without cytokinesis, producing cells with multiple nuclei.

During Cytokinesis, the Cytoplasm Is Divided Between Two Daughter Cells

Cytokinesis differs considerably between animal cells and plant cells. In animal cells, microfilaments attached to the plasma membrane assemble into a ring around the equator of the cell, usually late in anaphase or early in telophase (see Fig. 9-9f). The ring contracts and constricts the cell's equator, much like pulling the drawstring on a pair of sweatpants tightens the waist (see Fig. 9-9g). Eventually the "waist" of the parent cell constricts completely, dividing the cytoplasm into two new daughter cells (**Fig. 9-9h**).

Cytokinesis in plant cells is quite different, perhaps because their stiff cell walls make it impossible to divide one cell into two by pinching at the waist. Instead, carbohydrate-filled sacs called vesicles bud off the Golgi apparatus and line up along the equator of the cell between the two nuclei (**Fig. 9-10**). The vesicles fuse, producing a structure called the **cell plate,** which is shaped like a flattened sac, surrounded by membrane and filled with sticky carbohydrates. When enough vesicles have fused, the edges of the cell plate merge with the plasma membrane around the circumference of the cell. The two sides of the cell plate membrane become new plasma membranes between the two daughter cells. The carbohydrates formerly contained in the vesicles remain between the plasma membranes as the beginning of the new cell wall.

cell plate forming
a new cell wall

Golgi
apparatus

cell wall

plasma
membrane

carbohydrate-
filled vesicles

❶ Carbohydrate-filled vesicles bud off the Golgi apparatus and move to the equator of the cell.

❷ The vesicles fuse to form a new cell wall (red) and plasma membrane (yellow) between the daughter cells.

❸ Complete separation of the daughter cells.

◀FIGURE 9-10 **Cytokinesis in a plant cell**

CASE STUDY continued

Body, Heal Thyself

The precision of mitotic cell division is essential for wound repair, because it ensures that the daughter cells are genetically identical to their parent cells. Imagine what might happen if DNA synthesis during interphase did not copy all of the genes accurately, or if mitotic cell division sent random numbers and types of chromosomes into the daughter cells. Some of the daughter cells might not contain all the genes needed to form the various cell types that are required to repair damaged tissues. Worse yet, some daughter cells might have genetic changes that would cause cancer, in which cells divide uncontrollably.

CHECK YOUR LEARNING

Can you describe the steps of mitotic cell division? What is the usual outcome of mitotic cell division? How does cytokinesis differ in plant and animal cells?

9.6 HOW IS THE CELL CYCLE CONTROLLED?

Cell division is regulated by a bewildering array of molecules, not all of which have been identified and studied. Nevertheless, some general principles apply to cell cycle control in most eukaryotic cells.

The Activities of Specific Proteins Drive the Cell Cycle

Normal cell cycle control works like this: During development, after an injury, or to compensate for normal wear and tear, a variety of cells in the body release hormone-like molecules called **growth factors.** Most growth factors stimulate cell division by controlling the synthesis of proteins inside the cell called cyclins, which in turn regulate the actions of enzymes called cyclin-dependent kinases. The name "cyclin" was chosen because these proteins help to govern the cell cycle. Cyclin-dependent kinases (Cdks) get their name from two features: A "kinase" is an enzyme that adds a phosphate group to another protein, stimulating or inhibiting the activity of the target protein. "Cyclin dependent" means that the kinase is active only when it binds cyclin.

Let's see how growth factors, cyclins, and Cdks stimulate cell division, for example, if you cut your skin (Fig. 9-11). Platelets (blood cells that are involved in clotting) accumulate at the wound site and release several growth factors, including platelet-derived growth factor and epidermal growth factor. These growth factors bind to receptors on the surfaces of cells in damaged areas of the skin (Fig. 9-11 ❶), stimulating the cells to synthesize cyclin proteins (Fig. 9-11 ❷). Cyclins bind to specific Cdks (Fig. 9-11 ❸), forming cyclin–Cdk complexes that promote the manufacture and activity of the proteins required for DNA synthesis (Fig. 9-11 ❹). The cells enter the S phase and replicate their DNA. After DNA replication is complete, other Cdks become activated during G_2 and mitosis, causing chromosome condensation, breakdown of the nuclear envelope, formation of the spindle, and attachment of the chromosomes to the spindle microtubules. Finally, still other Cdks stimulate processes that allow the sister chromatids to separate into individual chromosomes and move to opposite poles during anaphase.

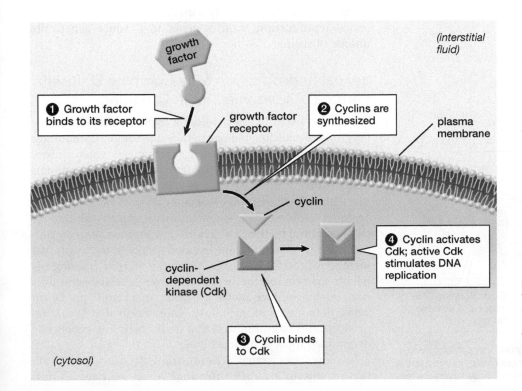

◀FIGURE 9-11 **Growth factors stimulate cell division** Progress through the cell cycle is under the overall control of cyclin and cyclin-dependent kinases (Cdks). In most cases, growth factors stimulate synthesis of cyclin proteins, which activate Cdks, starting a cascade of events that lead to DNA replication and cell division.

?HAVE **YOU** EVER WONDERED …

Why Dogs Lick Their Wounds? The saliva of dogs, like the saliva of most mammals (including humans), contains enzymes, antibacterial compounds, epidermal growth factor (EGF), and a variety of other growth factors. When a dog licks a wound, it not only cleans out some of the dirt that may have entered, but also leaves EGF and other growth factors behind. The growth factors speed up the synthesis of cyclins, thereby stimulating the division of cells that regenerate the skin, helping to heal the wound more rapidly.

Checkpoints Regulate Progress Through the Cell Cycle

Unregulated cell division can be dangerous. If a cell contains mutations in its DNA or if daughter cells receive too many or too few chromosomes, the daughter cells may die. If they survive, they may become cancerous. To prevent this, the eukaryotic cell cycle has three major **checkpoints** (**Fig. 9-12**). At each checkpoint, proteins in the cell determine whether the cell has successfully completed a specific phase of the cycle:

- **G_1 to S** Is the cell's DNA intact and suitable for replication?
- **G_2 to Mitosis** Has the DNA been completely and accurately replicated?

▲ **FIGURE 9-12 Control of the cell cycle** Three major checkpoints regulate a cell's transitions from one phase of the cell cycle to the next: (1) G_1 to S, (2) G_2 to mitosis (M), and (3) metaphase to anaphase.

- **Metaphase to Anaphase** Are all the chromosomes attached to the spindle and aligned properly at the equator of the cell?

The checkpoint proteins usually regulate the production of cyclins or the activity of Cdks, or both, thereby regulating progression from one phase of the cell cycle to the next. Defective checkpoint control is a primary cause of cancer, as we explore in the "Health Watch: Cancer—Running Through the Stop Signs at the Cell Cycle Checkpoints."

CHECK YOUR LEARNING

Can you describe the interactions among growth factors, cyclins, and cyclin-dependent kinases that control the eukaryotic cell cycle? How does a cell protect against producing defective daughter cells?

9.7 WHY DO SO MANY ORGANISMS REPRODUCE SEXUALLY?

Some very successful organisms routinely reproduce asexually. For example, some species of the molds *Penicillium* (which synthesizes penicillin) and *Aspergillus* (used in the manufacture of vitamin C) reproduce by "mitospores"—clouds of tiny cells produced by mitosis—and in fact have never been observed to reproduce sexually. Many of the grasses and weeds in your lawn can reproduce by sprouting whole new plants from their stems or roots. Some, like Kentucky bluegrass and dandelions, even bear flowers that can produce seeds without being fertilized! Clearly, asexual reproduction must work pretty well.

Why, then, do nearly all eukaryotic organisms reproduce sexually (even bluegrass and dandelions reproduce sexually some of the time)? As we have seen, asexual reproduction produces genetically identical offspring. In contrast, sexual reproduction shuffles genes to produce genetically unique offspring.

Sexual Reproduction May Combine Different Parental Alleles in a Single Offspring

Why is this useful? Let's consider a hypothetical situation: a prey animal avoiding being eaten by a predator. Camouflage colors can help the prey to keep from being eaten only if it stays still when it sees a predator. Camouflaged animals that constantly jump around and brightly colored animals that "freeze" when a predator appears will both probably be eaten. How might a single animal combine camouflage coloration and freezing behavior? Let's suppose that one animal has better-than-average camouflage color, while another member of the same species has more effective freezing behavior. Combining the two traits through sexual reproduction might produce some offspring that avoid predation better than either parent could. One reason that sexual reproduction is so common is that it allows useful, genetically determined traits to be combined.

How does sexual reproduction combine traits from two parents in a single offspring? As we will see shortly, meiotic cell division produces haploid cells, each containing only one homologue of each pair of chromosomes. In animals, these haploid cells usually become gametes. Consider again our hypothetical prey animals. A haploid sperm from animal A might contain alleles contributing to camouflage coloration, and a haploid egg from animal B might contain alleles that favor freezing in place at the first sign of a predator. Fusion of these gametes may combine the alleles in a single animal that has both camouflage coloration and becomes motionless when a predator approaches.

Although mutations create new alleles, and are therefore the ultimate source of the genetic variability upon which evolution is based, the rate of mutations is very low. Combining useful alleles through sexual reproduction allows for much more rapid evolution, as new combinations of alleles better adapt organisms to changing environments.

CHECK YOUR LEARNING

Can you describe an important advantage of sexual reproduction over asexual reproduction?

9.8 HOW DOES MEIOTIC CELL DIVISION PRODUCE HAPLOID CELLS?

The key to sexual reproduction in eukaryotes is **meiotic cell division,** in which a diploid cell with paired chromosomes gives rise to haploid daughter cells with unpaired chromosomes. Meiotic cell division consists of **meiosis** (the specialized nuclear division that produces haploid nuclei) followed by cytokinesis. Each daughter cell receives one homologue of each pair of chromosomes. For

example, each diploid cell in your body contains 23 *pairs* of chromosomes, 46 chromosomes in all; meiotic cell division produces sperm or eggs with 23 chromosomes, one from each pair. (Fittingly, "meiosis" comes from a Greek word meaning "to diminish.")

Many of the structures and events of meiotic cell division are similar to those of mitotic cell division. However, meiotic cell division differs from mitotic cell division in several important ways. A crucial difference involves DNA replication: In mitotic cell division, the parent cell undergoes one round of DNA replication followed by one nuclear division. In meiotic cell division, the parent cell undergoes a single round of DNA replication followed by *two* nuclear divisions (**Fig. 9-13**). Thus, in meiosis, the DNA is replicated before the first division (**Fig. 9-13a**), but it is *not replicated again* between the first and second divisions.

The first division of meiosis (called *meiosis I*) separates the pairs of homologous chromosomes and sends one homologue into each of two daughter nuclei, producing two haploid nuclei. Each chromosome, however, still consists of two chromatids (**Fig. 9-13b**). The second division (called *meiosis II*) separates the chromatids into independent chromosomes and parcels one into each of two daughter nuclei. Therefore, at the end of meiosis, there are four haploid daughter nuclei, each with one copy of each homologous chromosome. Because each nucleus is usually enclosed in a different cell, meiotic cell division normally produces four haploid cells from a single diploid parent cell (**Fig. 9-13c**). Then, when a haploid sperm fuses with a haploid egg, the resulting offspring are diploid once again (**Fig. 9-14**). We'll explore the stages of meiosis in more detail in the following sections.

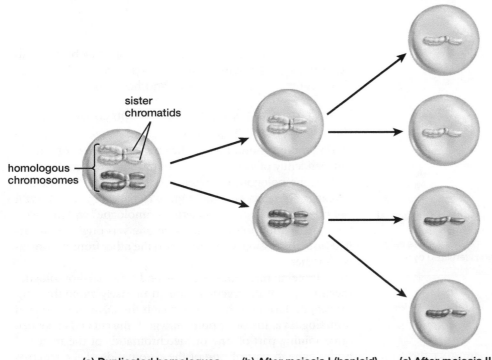

(a) Duplicated homologues prior to meiosis (diploid)   (b) After meiosis I (haploid)   (c) After meiosis II (haploid)

◀FIGURE 9-13 **Meiosis halves the number of chromosomes** (a) Both members of a pair of homologous chromosomes are duplicated prior to meiosis. (b) During meiosis I, each daughter cell receives one member of each pair of homologues. (c) During meiosis II, sister chromatids separate into independent chromosomes, and each daughter cell receives one of these chromosomes.

Health|Watch

Cancer—Running Through the Stop Signs at the Cell Cycle Checkpoints

The ultimate causes of most cancers are mutations—damage to DNA resulting from a variety of possible causes, including mistakes during replication, infection by certain viruses, exposure to ultraviolet radiation in sunlight or tanning beds, or chemicals in the environment (including pesticides, a variety of industrial products, and chemicals naturally produced by plants or fungi). In most cases, a mutation is quickly fixed by enzymes that repair DNA, or the defective cell is killed by one of the body's defenses, such as the immune system. Occasionally, however, a renegade cell survives. A single mutated cell isn't very dangerous, but if it divides repeatedly, it may form a multicellular, life-threatening tumor.

Progression through the cell cycle, including cell division, is regulated primarily by two interacting processes: (1) responses to growth factors that start or speed up the cell cycle and (2) checkpoints that stop the cell cycle if problems such as mutations in DNA or misalignment of chromosomes have occurred. Cancers develop when cells evade these controls.

Responses to Growth Factors

Most normal cells divide only when stimulated by growth factors. When a growth factor binds to its receptor on the surface of a cell, a cascade of biochemical changes results in cyclin synthesis, activation of Cdks, and progression through the cell cycle (see Fig. 9-11). Many cancerous cells have mutations, collectively called *oncogenes* (literally, "to cause cancer"), that promote uncontrolled cell division. Some oncogenes produce growth factor receptors that are permanently activated, even in the absence of growth factors (**Fig. E9-1**). Mutations in cyclin genes may cause cyclins to be synthesized at a high rate, again independently

of growth factors. Still other oncogenes cause changes that activate molecules "downstream" of growth factor receptors. The result: an abnormally large supply of activated Cdks and other molecules that stimulate cell division. When growth factors are present, cell division is stimulated even more. Like a driver who hits the accelerator instead of the brake while approaching a stop sign, a cell with these mutations is likely to barge right through the checkpoints and multiply without control.

Evading the Checkpoint Stop Signs

Cells, however, have ways of enforcing the checkpoint stop signs. All cells contain a variety of proteins collectively called *tumor suppressors*. These proteins prevent uncontrolled cell division and block the production of daughter cells that have mutated DNA. For example, the tumor suppressor protein called p53 (which means simply "a **p**rotein with a molecular mass of **53**,000") monitors the integrity of the cell's DNA. Healthy cells, with intact DNA, contain little p53. However, p53 levels rapidly increase in cells with damaged DNA. The p53 protein activates reactions in the cell that inhibit Cdks and block DNA synthesis, halting the cell cycle at the checkpoint between the G_1 and S phases. Therefore, the cell does not produce daughter cells with damaged DNA. The p53 protein also stimulates the synthesis of DNA repair enzymes. After the DNA has been repaired, p53 levels decline, Cdks become active, and the cell enters the S phase. If the DNA cannot be repaired, p53 triggers a special form of cell death called apoptosis, in which the cell cuts up its DNA and effectively commits suicide. Thus, p53 acts as a checkpoint enforcer, much

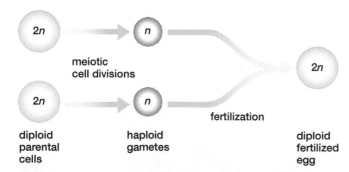

▲ FIGURE 9-14 **Meiotic cell division is essential for sexual reproduction** In sexual reproduction, specialized reproductive cells undergo meiosis to produce haploid cells. In animals, these cells become gametes (sperm or eggs). When an egg is fertilized by a sperm, the resulting fertilized egg, or zygote, is diploid.

Meiosis I Separates Homologous Chromosomes into Two Haploid Daughter Nuclei

The phases of meiosis have the same names as the similar phases in mitosis, followed by I or II to distinguish the two nuclear divisions that occur in meiosis (**Fig. 9-15**). When

meiosis I begins, the chromosomes have already been duplicated during interphase, and the sister chromatids of each chromosome are attached to one another at the centromere.

During Prophase I, Homologous Chromosomes Pair Up and Exchange DNA

During mitosis, homologous chromosomes move completely independently of each other. In contrast, during prophase I of meiosis, homologous chromosomes line up side by side and exchange segments of DNA (**Fig. 9-15a** and **Fig. 9-16**). We'll call one homologue the "maternal homologue" and the other the "paternal homologue," because one was originally inherited from the organism's mother and the other from the organism's father.

Proteins bind the maternal and paternal homologues together so that their gene loci align precisely along their entire length. Enzymes then cut through the DNA of the paired homologues at the same point and graft the cut ends together, often joining part of one of the chromatids of the maternal homologue to part of one of the chromatids of the paternal homologue, and vice versa. The binding proteins and enzymes then depart, leaving crosses, or **chiasmata** (singular, chiasma),

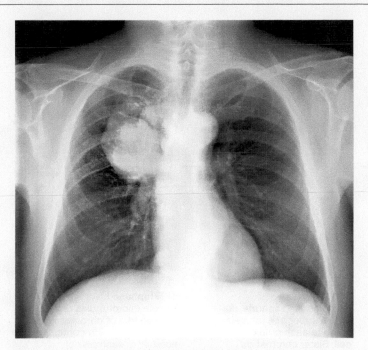

▲ **FIGURE E9-1 A CT scan of advanced lung cancer**
In women and in people who have never smoked, about 40% to
50% of lung cancer seems to be caused by too many receptors for
epidermal growth factor or by mutated receptors that are active
even in the absence of EGF.

like the tire-spiking strips that police sometimes use to prevent
criminals from racing through roadblocks. Chances are the
cell cannot plow through the G₁ to S checkpoint, so it will not
continue through the cell cycle.

But what if mutation strikes the gene encoding the
p53 protein? The result will often be inactive p53. Then, even
if the cell's DNA is damaged, the cell skips through the G_1
to S checkpoint. Not surprisingly, about half of all cancers—
including tumors of the breast, lung, brain, pancreas, bladder,
stomach, and colon—have mutations in the p53 gene.

Cancer Treatments

Why is medical science, which has conquered smallpox,
measles, and a host of other diseases, having such a difficult
time curing cancer? One reason is that both normal and
cancerous cells use the same machinery for cell division. Most
treatments that slow down the multiplication of cancer cells
do so by reducing growth factor responses, by inhibiting
DNA replication, or by reinforcing the checkpoints in the cell
cycle. Unfortunately, these treatments also inhibit the division
of normal cells. Essential body parts, such as the stomach,
intestine, and blood cells, require continual cell division
to replace worn-out or damaged cells. The side effects of
traditional chemotherapy are only too well known: hair loss,
nausea, and skin disorders.

Effective and selective treatments for cancer must target
cell division only, or at least mostly, in cancerous cells.
There are a few treatments, some available to patients and
some in clinical trials, that block growth factor actions only
in cells that usually don't divide very often in adults, such
as breast cells. Others inhibit certain Cdks that are not
very active in adults or that are active only in certain cell
types (which at least reduces the side effects). Still others
target mutations that are found only in specific cancer cells
and not in normal cells. Unfortunately, each of these less
toxic treatments is effective only on a subset of cancers. A
nontoxic, universal cure for all cancers is far off, and may
not even be possible.

where the maternal and paternal chromosomes have exchanged parts (see Fig. 9-16). In human cells, each pair of
homologues usually forms two or three chiasmata during prophase I. The mutual exchange of DNA between maternal and
paternal chromosomes at chiasmata is called **crossing over.**
If the chromosomes have different alleles, then crossing over
creates genetic **recombination:** the formation of new combinations of alleles on a chromosome. Even after the exchange
of DNA, the arms of the homologues remain temporarily en-
tangled at the chiasmata. This keeps the two homologues together until they are pulled apart during anaphase I.

As in mitosis, the spindle microtubules begin to assemble outside the nucleus during prophase I. Near the end
of prophase I, the nuclear envelope breaks down and spindle
microtubules invade the nuclear region, capturing the chromosomes by attaching to their kinetochores.

During Metaphase I, Paired Homologous Chromosomes Line Up at the Equator of the Cell

During metaphase I, interactions between the kinetochores
and the spindle microtubules move the paired homologues

to the equator of the cell (**Fig. 9-15b**). Unlike in metaphase
of mitosis, in which *individual* duplicated chromosomes
line up along the equator, in metaphase I of meiosis, *homologous pairs* of duplicated chromosomes, held together by
chiasmata, line up along the equator. Which member of a
pair of homologous chromosomes faces which pole of the
cell is random—the maternal homologue may face "north"
for some pairs and "south" for other pairs. This randomness
(also called *independent assortment*), together with genetic recombination caused by crossing over, is responsible for the
genetic diversity of the haploid cells produced by meiosis.

During Anaphase I, Homologous Chromosomes Separate

Anaphase in meiosis I differs considerably from anaphase in
mitosis. In anaphase of mitosis, the *sister chromatids separate*
and move to opposite poles. In contrast, in anaphase I of
meiosis, the sister chromatids of each duplicated homologue
remain attached to each other and move to the same pole.
However, the chiasmata joining the two homologues untan-
gle, allowing the *homologues to separate* and move to opposite
poles (**Fig. 9-15c**).

MEIOSIS I

(a) Prophase I
Duplicated chromosomes condense. Homologous chromosomes pair up and chiasmata occur as chromatids of homologues exchange parts by crossing over. The nuclear envelope disintegrates, and spindle microtubules form.

(b) Metaphase I
Paired homologous chromosomes line up along the equator of the cell. One homologue of each pair faces each pole of the cell and attaches to the spindle microtubules via the kinetochore (blue).

(c) Anaphase I
Homologues separate, one member of each pair going to each pole of the cell. Sister chromatids do not separate.

(d) Telophase I
Spindle microtubules disappear. Two clusters of chromosomes have formed, each containing one member of each pair of homologues. The daughter nuclei are therefore haploid. Cytokinesis commonly occurs at this stage. There is little or no interphase between meiosis I and meiosis II.

▲ FIGURE 9-15 **Meiotic cell division** In meiotic cell division, the homologous chromosomes of a diploid cell are separated, producing four haploid daughter cells. Two pairs of homologous chromosomes are shown. Yellow chromosomes are from one parent and violet chromosomes are from the other parent.

QUESTION What would be the consequences for the resulting gametes if one pair of homologues failed to separate at anaphase I?

▲ FIGURE 9-16 **Crossing over** Nonsister chromatids of different members of a homologous pair of chromosomes exchange DNA at chiasmata.

MEIOSIS II

(e) Prophase II
Spindle microtubules
re-form and attach to
the sister chromatids.

(f) Metaphase II
The chromosomes line
up along the equator,
with sister chromatids
of each chromosome
attached to kinetochore
microtubules that lead
to opposite poles.

(g) Anaphase II
The chromatids
separate into
independent daughter
chromosomes,
one former chromatid
moving toward each
pole.

(h) Telophase II
The chromosomes
finish moving to
opposite poles.
Nuclear envelopes
re-form, and the
chromosomes
decondense
again (not shown here).

(i) Four haploid cells
Cytokinesis results in
four haploid cells,
each containing one
member of each pair
of homologous
chromosomes (shown
here in the
condensed state).

During Telophase I, Two Haploid Clusters of Duplicated Chromosomes Form

At the end of anaphase I, the cluster of chromosomes at each pole contains one member of each pair of homologous chromosomes. Therefore, each cluster contains the haploid number of chromosomes. In telophase I, the spindle microtubules disappear. Cytokinesis commonly occurs during telophase I (**Fig. 9-15d**). In many, but not all, organisms, nuclear envelopes re-form. Telophase I is usually followed immediately by meiosis II, with little or no intervening interphase. The chromosomes do not replicate between meiosis I and meiosis II.

Meiosis II Separates Sister Chromatids into Four Daughter Nuclei

During meiosis II, the sister chromatids of each duplicated chromosome separate in a process that is virtually identical to mitosis, though it takes place in haploid cells. During

prophase II, the spindle microtubules re-form (**Fig. 9-15e**). As in mitosis, the kinetochores of the sister chromatids of each duplicated chromosome attach to spindle microtubules extending to opposite poles of the cell. During metaphase II, the duplicated chromosomes line up at the cell's equator (**Fig. 9-15f**). During anaphase II, the sister chromatids separate and move to opposite poles (**Fig. 9-15g**). Telophase II and cytokinesis conclude meiosis II as nuclear envelopes re-form, the chromosomes decondense into their extended state, and the cytoplasm divides (**Fig. 9-15h**). Both daughter cells produced in meiosis I usually undergo meiosis II, producing a total of four haploid cells from the original parental diploid cell (**Fig. 9-15i**).

Now that we have covered all of the processes in detail, examine **Table 9-1** to review and compare mitotic and meiotic cell division.

CHECK YOUR LEARNING

Can you describe the steps and outcome of meiotic cell division? What are the functions of crossing over?

TABLE 9-1 A Comparison of Mitotic and Meiotic Cell Division in Animal Cells

Feature	Mitotic Cell Division	Meiotic Cell Division
Cells in which it occurs	Body cells	Gamete-producing cells
Final chromosome number	Diploid—2n; two copies of each type of chromosome (homologous pairs)	Haploid—1n; one member of each homologous pair
Number of daughter cells	Two, identical to the parent cell and to each other	Four, containing recombined chromosomes due to crossing over
Number of cell divisions per DNA replication	One	Two
Function in animals	Development, growth, repair, and maintenance of tissues; asexual reproduction	Gamete production for sexual reproduction

MITOSIS

no stages comparable to meiosis I

interphase   prophase   metaphase   anaphase   telophase   two diploid cells

MEIOSIS

Recombination occurs   Homologues pair   Sister chromatids remain attached

interphase   prophase   metaphase   anaphase   telophase   prophase   metaphase   anaphase   telophase   four haploid cells

MEIOSIS I   MEIOSIS II

In these diagrams, comparable phases are aligned. In both mitosis and meiosis, chromosomes are duplicated during interphase. Meiosis I, with the pairing of homologous chromosomes, formation of chiasmata, exchange of chromosome parts, and separation of homologues to form haploid daughter nuclei, has no counterpart in mitosis. Meiosis II, however, is virtually identical to mitosis in a haploid cell.

9.9 WHEN DO MITOTIC AND MEIOTIC CELL DIVISION OCCUR IN THE LIFE CYCLES OF EUKARYOTES?

The life cycles of almost all eukaryotic organisms share a common overall pattern. First, two haploid cells fuse during the process of fertilization, bringing together genes from different parental organisms and endowing the resulting diploid cell with new gene combinations. Second, at some point in the life cycle, meiotic cell division occurs, re-creating haploid cells. Third, at some time in the life cycle, mitotic cell division of either haploid or diploid cells, or both, results in the growth of multicellular bodies or in asexual reproduction.

The seemingly vast differences between the life cycles of, say, ferns and humans are caused by variations in three aspects: (1) the interval between meiotic cell division and

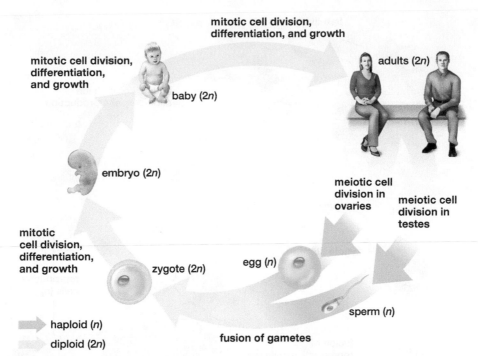

mitotic cell division, differentiation, and growth

mitotic cell division, differentiation, and growth

baby (2n)

adults (2n)

embryo (2n)

meiotic cell division in ovaries

meiotic cell division in testes

mitotic cell division, differentiation, and growth

zygote (2n)

egg (n)

sperm (n)

haploid (n)

diploid (2n)

fusion of gametes

▲ **FIGURE 9-17 The human life cycle** Through meiotic cell division, the two sexes produce gametes—sperm in males and eggs in females—that fuse to form a diploid zygote. Mitotic cell division and differentiation of the daughter cells produce an embryo, child, and ultimately a sexually mature adult. The haploid stages last only a few hours to a few days; the diploid stages may survive for a century.

the fusion of haploid cells, (2) the points in the life cycle at which mitotic and meiotic cell division occur, and (3) the relative proportions of the life cycle spent in the diploid and haploid states. We can conveniently label life cycles according to the relative dominance of diploid and haploid stages.

In Diploid Life Cycles, the Majority of the Cycle Is Spent as Diploid Cells

In most animals, virtually the entire life cycle is spent in the diploid state (**Fig. 9-17**). Diploid adults produce short-lived haploid gametes (sperm in males, eggs in females) by meiotic cell division. These fuse to form a diploid fertilized egg, called a zygote. Growth and development of the zygote to the adult organism result from mitotic cell division and differentiation of diploid cells.

In Haploid Life Cycles, the Majority of the Cycle Is Spent as Haploid Cells

Some eukaryotes, such as many fungi and single-celled algae, spend most of their life cycles in the haploid state, in which each cell contains a single copy of each type of chromosome (**Fig. 9-18**). Asexual reproduction by mitotic cell division produces a population of identical, haploid cells. Under certain environmental conditions, specialized haploid reproductive cells are produced. Two of these reproductive cells fuse, forming a short-lived diploid zygote. The zygote immediately undergoes meiotic cell division, producing haploid

cells again. In organisms with haploid life cycles, mitotic cell division never occurs in diploid cells.

In Alternation of Generations Life Cycles, There Are Both Diploid and Haploid Multicellular Stages

The life cycle of plants is called *alternation of generations*, because it alternates between multicellular diploid and multicellular haploid forms. In the typical pattern (**Fig. 9-19**), specialized cells of a multicellular diploid adult stage (the "diploid generation") undergo meiotic cell division, producing haploid cells called spores. The spores undergo many rounds of mitotic cell division and their daughter cells differentiate, producing a multicellular haploid adult stage (the "haploid generation"). At some point, certain haploid cells differentiate into haploid gametes. Two gametes then fuse to form a diploid zygote. The zygote grows by mitotic cell division into another multicellular diploid adult stage.

In some plants, such as ferns, both the haploid and diploid stages are free-living, independent plants. Flowering plants, however, have reduced haploid stages, represented only by the pollen grain and a small cluster of cells in the ovary of the flower (see Chapters 21 and 44).

CHECK YOUR LEARNING

Can you compare and contrast the three main types of eukaryotic life cycles, and give examples of organisms that exhibit each type?

▲ FIGURE 9-18 **The life cycle of the single-celled alga *Chlamydomonas***
Chlamydomonas reproduces asexually by mitotic cell division of haploid cells. When nutrients are scarce, specialized haploid reproductive cells (usually from genetically different populations) fuse to form a diploid cell. Meiotic cell division then immediately produces four haploid cells, usually with different genetic compositions than either of the parental strains.

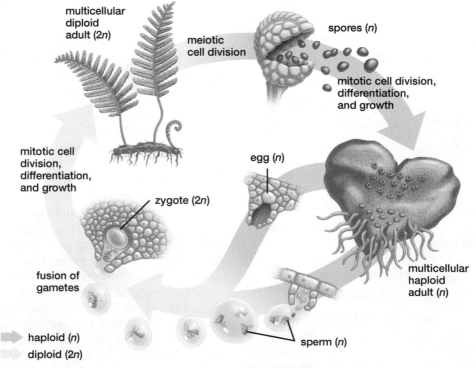

▲ FIGURE 9-19 **Alternation of generations** In plants, such as this fern, specialized cells in the multicellular diploid adult stage undergo meiotic cell division to produce haploid spores. The spores undergo mitotic cell division and differentiation of the daughter cells to produce a multicellular haploid adult stage. Sometime later, perhaps many weeks later, some of these haploid cells differentiate into sperm and eggs. These fuse to form a diploid zygote. Mitotic cell division and differentiation once again give rise to a multicellular diploid adult stage.

9.10 HOW DO MEIOSIS AND SEXUAL REPRODUCTION PRODUCE GENETIC VARIABILITY?

The individual members of most species are genetically different from one another. Further, the offspring of a single pair of parents are usually genetically different from each other and from their parents. Where do these genetic differences come from? Mutations occurring randomly over millions of years provide the original sources of genetic variability. However, mutations are rare events. Therefore, the genetic variability that occurs from one generation to the next results almost entirely from meiosis and sexual reproduction.

Shuffling of Homologues Creates Novel Combinations of Chromosomes

How does meiosis produce genetic diversity? One mechanism is the random distribution of maternal and paternal homologues to the daughter nuclei during meiosis I. Remember, at metaphase I the paired homologues line up at the cell's equator. In each pair of homologues, the maternal chromosome faces one pole and the paternal chromosome faces the opposite pole, but which homologue faces which pole is random, and is not affected by the distribution of the homologues of other chromosome pairs.

Let's consider meiosis in mosquitoes, which have three pairs of homologous chromosomes ($n = 3$, $2n = 6$). At metaphase I, the chromosomes can align in four possible configurations (**Fig. 9-20a**). Therefore, anaphase I can produce eight possible sets of chromosomes ($2^3 = 8$; **Fig. 9-20b**). A single mosquito, with three pairs of homologous chromosomes, can thus produce gametes with eight different sets of chromosomes. In people, meiosis randomly shuffles 23 pairs of homologous chromosomes, and can theoretically produce more than 8 million (2^{23}) different combinations of maternal and paternal chromosomes in their gametes.

(a) The four possible chromosome arrangements at metaphase of meiosis I

(b) The eight possible sets of chromosomes after meiosis I

▲ FIGURE 9-20 **Random separation of homologous pairs of chromosomes produces genetic variability** For clarity, the chromosomes are depicted as large, medium, and small. The paternal chromosomes are colored yellow and the maternal chromosomes are colored violet.

Crossing Over Creates Chromosomes with Novel Combinations of Genes

Crossing over during meiosis produces chromosomes with combinations of alleles that differ from those of either parent. In fact, some of these new combinations may never have existed before, because homologous chromosomes cross over in new and different places at each meiotic division. In humans, 1 in 8 million gametes could have the same combination of maternal and paternal chromosomes. However, crossing over ensures that none of those chromosomes will be purely maternal or purely paternal. Even though a man produces about 100 million sperm each day, he may never produce two that carry exactly the same combinations of alleles. In all probability, every sperm and every egg is genetically unique.

Fusion of Gametes Adds Further Genetic Variability to the Offspring

At fertilization, two gametes, each containing a unique combination of alleles, fuse to form a diploid offspring. Even if we ignore crossing over, every human can theoretically produce about 8 million different gametes based solely on the random separation of the homologues. Therefore, fusion of gametes from just two people could produce 8 million × 8 million, or 64 trillion, genetically different children, which is far more people than have ever existed on Earth. Put another way, the chances that your parents could produce another child who is genetically the same as you are about $^1/_{8,000,000} \times {}^1/_{8,000,000}$, or about 1 in 64 trillion! When we factor in the almost endless variability produced by crossing over, we can confidently say that (except for identical twins) there never has been, and never will be, anyone just like you.

CHECK YOUR LEARNING

Can you explain how meiosis and sexual reproduction generate genetic variability in populations?

CASE STUDY revisited

Body, Heal Thyself

When Hines Ward sprained the ligaments in his knee, the normal healing process started immediately. Platelets from damaged blood vessels accumulated in the injured ligament and secreted growth factors, stimulating cell division. The cells produced new ligament proteins, replacing those that were torn during the injury. Why, then, should platelet-rich plasma therapy assist healing—shouldn't platelets already present in the blood and leaking into the wound be able to do the job?

In most cases, that's exactly what happens. Nevertheless, PRP therapy can be valuable for two major reasons. First, some tissues, particularly tendons, ligaments, and some bones, have a rather sparse blood supply, so torn ligaments or tendons receive only a low dose of growth factors. As a result, cell division occurs slowly, and the injured structures often never regain their original strength. Incompletely healed tendons and ligaments may be chronically painful, especially during and after exercise, and are prone to re-injury. Injection of platelet-rich plasma can provide a larger dose of growth factors, which stimulates faster cell division and more complete healing. In a study with horses, PRP treatment resulted in better healing of tendon injuries, including more and better-organized collagen protein, and greater strength. Even tissues with a good blood supply, such as skin, may benefit from an extra dose of growth factors; some cosmetic surgeons use PRP therapy after facial surgery to improve healing.

Hines Ward's experience is an example of a second potential benefit of PRP therapy: Faster cell division may promote more rapid healing. No one, not even a weekend warrior or a couch potato, wants to be out of action longer than necessary. The extra growth factors supplied by PRP may speed up healing, even if the body would eventually have done a perfectly good job without the extra help. However, in most real-life cases, including Ward's, no one

knows for sure if healing was really faster or better because PRP therapy stimulated cell division in the injured ligament—there was, of course, no "control Ward," who was not receiving PRP for comparison.

Consider This

BioEthics   Is PRP therapy a wonder treatment that should be routinely used for most injuries? Maybe not. First, PRP apparently isn't always helpful; for example, a few studies have found little or no benefit of PRP for injuries to the Achilles tendon. Second, injecting PRP directly into a wound is quite painful. Third, PRP costs around $500 to $1,000, and is generally not covered by health insurance. In the United States and many other countries, controlling medical costs has become a major political and economic issue. Should PRP be reserved for major injuries? Or only for the wealthy? Would you want PRP for a sprained knee?

CHAPTER REVIEW

Summary of Key Concepts

9.1 Why Do Cells Divide?
Growth of multicellular eukaryotic organisms and replacement of cells that die during an organism's life occur through cell division and differentiation of the daughter cells. Asexual reproduction also occurs through cell division. A specialized type of cell division, called meiotic cell division, is required for sexual reproduction in eukaryotes.

9.2 What Occurs During the Prokaryotic Cell Cycle?
A prokaryotic cell contains a single, circular chromosome. The prokaryotic cell cycle consists of growth, replication of the DNA, and division of the cell by prokaryotic fission. The two resulting daughter cells are genetically identical to one another and to the parent cell.

9.3 How Is the DNA in Eukaryotic Chromosomes Organized?
Each chromosome in a eukaryotic cell consists of a single DNA double helix and proteins that organize the DNA. Genes are segments of DNA found at specific locations on a chromosome. During cell growth, the chromosomes are extended and accessible for use by enzymes that read their genetic instructions. During cell division, the chromosomes are duplicated and condense into short, thick structures. Eukaryotic cells typically contain pairs of chromosomes, called homologues, that carry the same genes with similar, although usually not identical, nucleotide sequences. Cells with pairs of homologous chromosomes are diploid. Cells with only one member of each chromosome pair are haploid.

9.4 What Occurs During the Eukaryotic Cell Cycle?
The eukaryotic cell cycle consists of interphase and mitotic cell division. During interphase, the cell grows and duplicates its chromosomes. Interphase is divided into G_1 (growth phase 1), S (DNA synthesis), and G_2 (growth phase 2). During G_1, many cells differentiate to perform a specific function. Some differentiated cells can reenter the dividing state; other cells remain differentiated for the life of the organism and never divide again. Eukaryotic cells divide by mitotic cell division, which produces two daughter cells that are genetically identical to their parent cell.

9.5 How Does Mitotic Cell Division Produce Genetically Identical Daughter Cells?
The chromosomes are duplicated during interphase, prior to mitotic cell division. A duplicated chromosome consists of two identical sister chromatids that remain attached to one another at the centromere during the early stages of mitotic cell division. Mitosis (nuclear division) consists of four phases, usually accompanied by cytokinesis (cytoplasmic division) during the last phase (see Fig. 9-9):

- **Prophase** The chromosomes condense and their kinetochores attach to spindle microtubules, called kinetochore microtubules, that form at this time.
- **Metaphase** Kinetochore microtubules move the chromosomes to the equator of the cell.
- **Anaphase** The two chromatids of each duplicated chromosome separate and become independent chromosomes. The kinetochore microtubules move the chromosomes to opposite poles of the cell. Meanwhile, polar microtubules force the cell to elongate.
- **Telophase** The chromosomes decondense, and nuclear envelopes re-form around each new daughter nucleus.
- **Cytokinesis** Cytokinesis normally occurs at the end of telophase and divides the cytoplasm into approximately equal halves, each containing a nucleus. In animal cells, a ring of microfilaments pinches the plasma membrane in along the equator. In plant cells, new plasma membrane forms along the equator by the fusion of vesicles produced by the Golgi apparatus.

9.6 How Is the Cell Cycle Controlled?
Complex interactions among many proteins, particularly cyclins and cyclin-dependent protein kinases, drive the cell cycle. There are three major checkpoints where progress through the cell cycle

is regulated: between G$_1$ and S, between G$_2$ and mitosis, and between metaphase and anaphase. These checkpoints ensure that the DNA is intact and replicated accurately and that the chromosomes are properly arranged for mitosis before the cell divides.

9.7 Why Do So Many Organisms Reproduce Sexually?

Genetic differences among organisms originate as mutations, which, when preserved within a species, produce alternate forms of genes, called alleles. Alleles in different individuals of a species may be combined in their offspring through sexual reproduction, creating variation among the offspring and potentially improving their likelihood of surviving and reproducing.

9.8 How Does Meiotic Cell Division Produce Haploid Cells?

Meiosis separates homologous chromosomes and produces haploid cells with only one homologue from each pair. During interphase before meiosis, chromosomes are duplicated. The cell then undergoes two specialized divisions—meiosis I and meiosis II—to produce four haploid daughter cells (see Fig. 9-15).

Meiosis I

During prophase I, homologous duplicated chromosomes, each consisting of two chromatids, pair up and exchange parts by crossing over. During metaphase I, homologues move together as pairs to the cell's equator, one member of each pair facing opposite poles of the cell. Homologous chromosomes separate during anaphase I, and two nuclei form during telophase I. Cytokinesis also usually occurs during telophase I. Each daughter nucleus receives only one member of each pair of homologues and, therefore, is haploid. The sister chromatids remain attached to each other throughout meiosis I.

Meiosis II

Meiosis II resembles mitosis in a haploid cell. The duplicated chromosomes move to the cell's equator during metaphase II. The two chromatids of each chromosome separate and move to opposite poles of the cell during anaphase II. This second division produces four haploid nuclei. Cytokinesis normally occurs during or shortly after telophase II, producing four haploid cells.

9.9 When Do Mitotic and Meiotic Cell Division Occur in the Life Cycles of Eukaryotes?

Most eukaryotic life cycles have three parts: (1) Sexual reproduction combines haploid gametes to form a diploid cell. (2) At some point in the life cycle, diploid cells undergo meiotic cell division to produce haploid cells. (3) At some point in the life cycle, mitosis of either a haploid cell, or a diploid cell, or both, results in the growth of multicellular bodies. When these stages occur, and what proportion of the life cycle is occupied by each stage, varies greatly among different species.

9.10 How Do Meiosis and Sexual Reproduction Produce Genetic Variability?

The random shuffling of homologous maternal and paternal chromosomes during meiosis I creates new chromosome combinations. Crossing over creates chromosomes with allele combinations that may never have occurred before on single chromosomes. Because of the separation of homologues and crossing over, a parent probably never produces any gametes that are completely identical. The fusion of two genetically unique gametes adds further genetic variability to the offspring.

Key Terms

allele 146	growth factor 151
anaphase 150	haploid 146
asexual reproduction 141	homologous
autosome 145	chromosome 145
cell cycle 140	homologue 145
cell division 140	interphase 146
cell plate 150	karyotype 145
centriole 148	kinetochore 149
centromere 145	locus (plural, loci) 144
checkpoint 152	meiosis 153
chiasma (plural,	meiotic cell division 153
chiasmata) 154	metaphase 150
chromatid 145	mitosis 147
chromosome 140	mitotic cell division 147
clone 141	mutation 145
crossing over 155	nucleotide 140
cytokinesis 147	prokaryotic fission 142
daughter cell 140	prophase 148
deoxyribonucleic acid	recombination 155
(DNA) 140	sex chromosome 145
differentiate 140	sexual reproduction 141
diploid 145	spindle microtubule 148
duplicated chromosome 145	stem cell 141
gamete 141	telomere 144
gene 140	telophase 150

Learning Outcomes

In this chapter, you have learned to . . .

LO1 Describe the fundamental components of inheritance, including chromosomes, DNA, nucleotides, and genes.

LO2 Compare and contrast the categories of cells, as distinguished by their ability to divide and differentiate.

LO3 Compare and contrast sexual reproduction and asexual reproduction.

LO4 Describe the prokaryotic cell cycle, including the mechanisms of prokaryotic fission.

LO5 Describe the structure of a eukaryotic chromosome.

LO6 Define homologous chromosome, autosome, and sex chromosome.

LO7 Distinguish between diploid and haploid cells.

LO8 Describe the eukaryotic cell cycle, including the steps and outcome of mitotic cell division.

LO9 Describe how the eukaryotic cell cycle is regulated.

LO10 Describe the steps and outcome of meiotic cell division.

LO11 Compare and contrast the three main types of eukaryotic life cycles.

LO12 Explain how meiosis and sexual reproduction generate genetic variability in populations.

Thinking Through the Concepts

Fill-in-the-Blank

1. The genetic material of all living organisms is _____, which is contained in chromosomes. A gene is a part of a chromosome found at a specific place, or _____ . Alternate forms of a gene are called _____. **LO1 LO5**

2. Genetically identical offspring are produced during _____ reproduction; genetically variable offspring are produced during _____ reproduction. _____ cell division is required for sexual reproduction. LO3 LO12

3. Prokaryotic cells divide by a process called _____. LO4

4. Growth and development of eukaryotic organisms occur through _____ cell division and _____ of the resulting daughter cells. _____ cells in multicellular eukaryotes remain capable of dividing throughout the life of the organism, and can differentiate into a variety of cell types. LO2 LO8

5. Most plants and animals have pairs of chromosomes that have similar appearance and genetic composition. These pairs are called _____. Pairs of chromosomes that are the same in both males and females are called _____. Pairs that are different in males and females are called _____. LO6

6. The four phases of mitosis are _____, _____, _____, and _____. Division of the cytoplasm into two cells, called _____, usually occurs during which phase? _____ LO8

7. Chromosomes attach to spindle microtubules at structures called _____. Some spindle microtubules, called _____ microtubules, do not bind to chromosomes, but have free ends that overlap along the equator of the cell. These microtubules push the poles of the cell apart. LO8

8. Meiotic cell division produces _____ haploid daughter cells from each diploid parental cell. The first haploid nuclei are produced at the end of _____. In animals, the haploid daughter cells produced by meiotic cell division are called _____. LO7 LO10

9. During _____ of meiosis I, homologous chromosomes intertwine, forming structures called _____. These structures are the sites of what event? _____ LO10

10. Three processes that promote genetic variability of offspring during sexual reproduction are _____, _____, and _____. LO12

Review Questions

1. Compare sexual and asexual reproduction. What type(s) of cell division are involved in each? LO2

2. Diagram and describe the eukaryotic cell cycle. Name the phases, and briefly describe the events that occur during each. LO8

3. Define *mitosis* and *cytokinesis*. What changes in cell structure would result if cytokinesis did not occur after mitosis? LO8

4. Diagram the stages of mitosis. How does mitosis ensure that each daughter nucleus receives a full set of chromosomes? LO8

5. Define the following terms: *homologous chromosome (homologue), centromere, kinetochore, chromatid, diploid,* and *haploid.* LO6 LO8

6. Describe and compare the process of cytokinesis in animal cells and in plant cells. LO8

7. How is the cell cycle controlled? Why is it important to regulate progression through the cell cycle? LO9

8. Diagram the events of meiosis. At which stage do homologous chromosomes separate? LO10

9. Describe crossing over. At which stage of meiosis does it occur? Name two functions of chiasmata. LO10

10. In what ways are mitosis and meiosis similar? In what ways are they different? LO8 LO10

11. Describe or diagram the three main types of eukaryotic life cycles. When do meiotic cell division and mitotic cell division occur in each? LO11

12. Describe how meiosis provides for genetic variability. If an animal had a haploid number of two (no sex chromosomes), how many genetically different gametes could it produce? (Assume no crossing over.) If it had a haploid number of five? LO12

Applying the Concepts

1. Most nerve cells in the adult human central nervous system, as well as heart muscle cells, do not divide. In contrast, cells lining the inside of the small intestine divide frequently. Discuss this difference in terms of why damage to the nervous system and heart muscle cells (for example, caused by a stroke or heart attack) is so dangerous. What do you think might happen to tissues such as the intestinal lining if a disorder blocked mitotic cell division in all cells of the body?

2. Cancer cells divide out of control. Side effects of chemotherapy and radiation therapy that fight cancers include loss of hair and of the intestinal lining, the latter producing severe nausea. What can you infer about the mechanisms of these treatments? What would you look for in an improved cancer therapy?

3. Some animal species can reproduce either asexually or sexually, depending on the state of the environment. Which form of reproduction do you think would have the greatest advantage in a rapidly changing environment? Which form would be most successful in a stable environment? Explain your reasoning in each case.

Answers to Figure Caption questions and Fill-in-the-Blank questions can be found in the Answers section at the back of the book.

(MB) °*Go to MasteringBiology for practice quizzes, activities, eText, videos, current events, and more.*

CASE STUDY
Sudden Death on the Court

FLO HYMAN, 6 feet, 5 inches tall, graceful and athletic, was probably the best woman volleyball player of her time. Captain of the American women's volleyball team that won a silver medal in the 1984 Olympics, Hyman later joined a professional Japanese squad. In 1986, at the age of 31, she was taken out of a game for a short breather, and died while sitting quietly on the bench. How could this happen to someone so young and fit?

Hyman had a genetic disorder called Marfan syndrome, which affects about 1 in 5,000 to 10,000 people, probably including classical musicians and composers Sergei Rachmaninoff and Nicolo Paganini, and possibly American president Abraham Lincoln. People with Marfan syndrome are typically tall and slender, with long, flexible limbs and large hands and feet. For some people with Marfan syndrome, these characteristics lead to fame and fortune. Unfortunately, Marfan syndrome can also be deadly.

Hyman died from a ruptured aorta, the massive artery that carries blood from the heart to most of the body. Why did Hyman's aorta burst? What does a weak aorta have in common with tallness and large hands? Marfan syndrome is caused by a mutation in the gene that encodes a protein called fibrillin, an essential component of connective tissue. Many parts of your body contain connective tissue, including the tendons that attach muscles to bones, the ligaments that fasten bones to other bones in joints, and the walls of arteries. Fibrillin forms long fibers that give strength and elasticity to connective tissue. Normal fibrillin also traps certain growth factors, preventing them from stimulating excessive cell division in, for example, bone-forming cells. Defective fibrillin cannot trap these growth factors, with the result that the arms, legs, hands, and feet of people with Marfan syndrome tend to become unusually long. The combination of defective fibrillin and high concentrations of growth factors also weakens bone, cartilage, and artery walls.

Diploid organisms, including people, generally have two copies of each gene, one on each homologous chromosome. One defective copy of the fibrillin gene is enough to cause Marfan syndrome. What does this tell us about the inheritance of Marfan syndrome? Are all inherited diseases caused by a single defective copy of a gene? To find out, we must go back in time to a monastery in Moravia and visit the garden of Gregor Mendel.

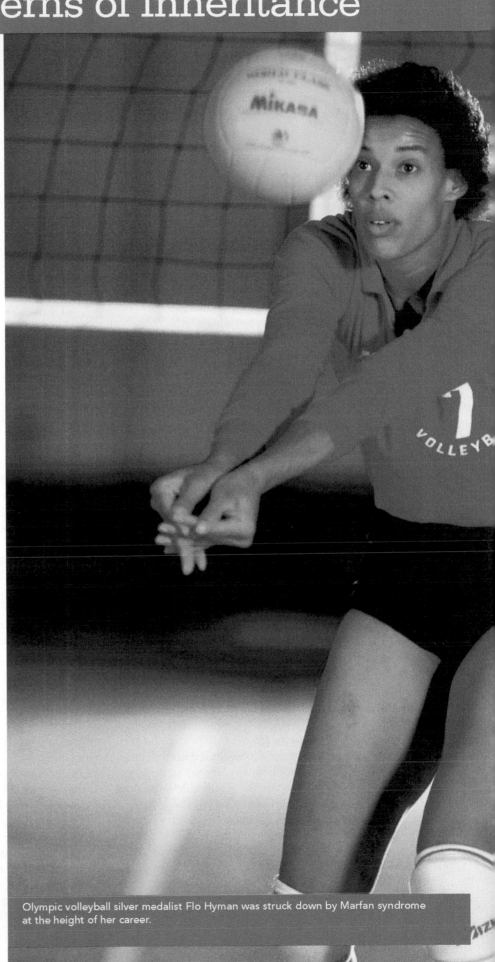

Olympic volleyball silver medalist Flo Hyman was struck down by Marfan syndrome at the height of her career.

AT A GLANCE

LEARNING GOALS

LG1   Describe the relationships among chromosomes, DNA, genes, mutations, and alleles, and explain their function in inheritance.

LG2   Summarize Mendel's conclusions about the inheritance of single and multiple traits and explain how the results of his experiments support those conclusions.

LG3   Determine the genotypes and phenotypes of offspring that result from mating organisms with traits that follow simple patterns of Mendelian inheritance.

LG4   Describe the inheritance of traits characterized by incomplete dominance, codominance, polygenic inheritance, and pleiotropy.

LG5   Explain how the physical locations of genes and the events that occur during meiosis affect inheritance.

LG6   Explain the chromosomal basis of sex determination and how it influences the inheritance of sex-linked traits.

LG7   Interpret pedigrees for dominant and recessive traits.

LG8   Describe the causes and symptoms of inherited human disorders produced by defective alleles of individual genes and by abnormal numbers of chromosomes.

10.1   WHAT IS THE PHYSICAL BASIS OF INHERITANCE?

Inheritance is the process by which the traits of organisms are passed to their offspring. We will begin our exploration of inheritance with a brief overview of the structures that form its physical basis. In this chapter, we will confine our discussion to diploid organisms, including most plants and animals, that reproduce sexually by the fusion of haploid gametes.

Genes Are Sequences of Nucleotides at Specific Locations on Chromosomes

A chromosome consists of a single double helix of DNA, packaged with a variety of proteins (see Figs. 9-1 and 9-4). Segments of DNA ranging from a few hundred to many thousands of nucleotides in length are the units of inheritance—the **genes**—that encode the information needed to produce proteins, cells, and entire organisms. Therefore, genes are parts of chromosomes (**Fig. 10-1**). A gene's physical location on a chromosome is called its **locus** (plural, loci). The chromosomes of diploid organisms occur in pairs called homologues. Both members of a pair of homologues carry the same genes, located at the same loci. However, the nucleotide sequences of a given gene may differ in different members of a species, or even on the two homologues of a single individual. These different versions of a gene at a given locus are called **alleles** (see Fig. 10-1). To understand the relationship between genes and alleles, it may be helpful to think of genes as very long sentences, written in an alphabet of nucleotides instead of letters. The alleles of a gene are like slightly different spellings of words in different versions of the same nucleotide sentence.

Mutations Are the Source of Alleles

The different alleles that you have on your chromosomes were almost all inherited from your parents. But where did these alleles come from in the first place? All alleles originally arose as **mutations**—changes in the sequence of nucleotides in the DNA of a gene. If a mutation occurs in a cell that becomes a sperm or egg, it can be passed on from parent to offspring. Most of the alleles in an organism's DNA first appeared as mutations in the reproductive cells of the organism's ancestors, perhaps hundreds or even millions of years ago, and have been inherited, generation after generation, ever since. A few alleles, which we will call "new mutations," may have occurred in the reproductive cells of the organism's own parents, but this is quite rare.

An Organism's Two Alleles May Be the Same or Different

Because a diploid organism has pairs of homologous chromosomes, and both members of a pair contain the same gene loci, the organism has two copies of each gene. If both homologues have the same allele at a given gene locus, the organism is said to be **homozygous** at that locus. ("Homozygous" comes from Greek words meaning "same pair.") The chromosomes shown in Figure 10-1 are homozygous at two loci. If two homologous chromosomes have different alleles at a locus, the organism is **heterozygous** ("different pair") at that locus. The chromosomes in Figure 10-1 are heterozygous at one locus. Organisms that are heterozygous at a specific locus are often called hybrids.

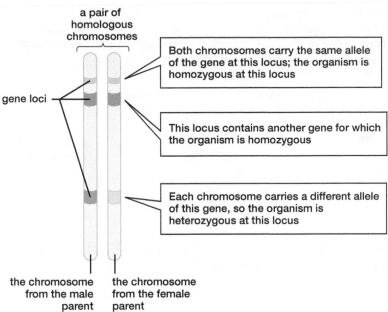

a pair of
homologous
chromosomes

gene loci

Both chromosomes carry the same allele
of the gene at this locus; the organism is
homozygous at this locus

This locus contains another gene for which
the organism is homozygous

Each chromosome carries a different allele
of this gene, so the organism is
heterozygous at this locus

the chromosome
from the male
parent

the chromosome
from the female
parent

◀ FIGURE 10-1 **The relationships among genes, alleles, and chromosomes** Each homologous chromosome carries the same set of genes. Each gene is located at the same position, or locus, on its chromosome. Differences in nucleotide sequences at the same gene locus produce different alleles of the gene. Diploid organisms have two alleles of each gene, one on each homologue. The alleles on the two homologues may be the same or different.

or meiosis had been discovered, his research revealed many essential facts about genes, alleles, and the distribution of alleles in gametes and zygotes during sexual reproduction. Because his experiments are succinct, elegant examples of science in action, let's follow Mendel's paths of discovery.

Doing It Right: The Secrets of Mendel's Success

There are three key steps to any successful experiment in biology: choosing the right organism with which to work, designing and performing the experiment correctly, and analyzing the data properly. Mendel was the first geneticist to complete all three steps.

Mendel chose the edible pea as the subject for his experiments on inheritance (**Fig. 10-3**). The male reproductive structures of a flower, called stamens, produce pollen. Each pollen grain contains sperm. Pollination allows a sperm to fertilize an egg, which is located within the ovary of the flower's female reproductive structure, called the carpel. In pea flowers, the petals enclose all of the reproductive structures, preventing another flower's pollen from entering. Therefore, the eggs in a pea flower must be fertilized by sperm from the pollen of the same flower. When an organism's sperm fertilize its own eggs, the process is called **self-fertilization.**

Mendel, however, often wanted to mate two different pea plants to see what characteristics their offspring would inherit. To do this, he opened a pea flower and removed its stamens,

CHECK YOUR LEARNING

Can you describe the relationships among chromosomes, DNA, genes, mutations, and alleles? Do you understand what it means for an organism to be heterozygous or homozygous for a gene?

10.2 HOW WERE THE PRINCIPLES OF INHERITANCE DISCOVERED?

The common patterns of inheritance were discovered in the mid-1800s by an Austrian monk, Gregor Mendel (**Fig. 10-2**). Although Mendel worked long before DNA, chromosomes,

▲ FIGURE 10-2 **Gregor Mendel**

intact pea flower

flower dissected to show
its reproductive structures

Carpel (female,
produces eggs)

Stamens (male, produce pollen
grains that contain sperm)

▲ FIGURE 10-3 **Flowers of the edible pea** In the intact pea flower (left), the lower petals form a container enclosing the reproductive structures—the stamens (male) and carpel (female). Pollen normally cannot enter the flower from outside, so peas usually self-pollinate and, hence, self-fertilize. If the flower is opened (right), it can be cross-pollinated by hand.

preventing self-fertilization. Then, he dusted the sticky tip of the carpel with pollen from the flower of another plant. When sperm from one organism fertilize eggs from a different organism, the process is called **cross-fertilization.**

Mendel's experimental design was simple, but brilliant. Earlier researchers had generally tried to study inheritance by simultaneously considering all of the features of entire organisms, including traits that differed only slightly among organisms. Not surprisingly, the investigators were often confused rather than enlightened. Mendel, however, chose to study traits with unmistakably different forms, such as white versus purple flowers. He also began by studying only one trait at a time.

Mendel followed the inheritance of these traits for several generations, counting the numbers of offspring with each type of trait. By analyzing these numbers, the basic patterns of inheritance became clear. Today, quantifying experimental results and applying statistical analysis are essential tools in virtually every field of biology, but in Mendel's time, numerical analysis was an innovation.

CHECK YOUR LEARNING

Can you distinguish between self-fertilization and cross-fertilization? Can you explain how Mendel used these processes in his studies of inheritance?

10.3 HOW ARE SINGLE TRAITS INHERITED?

True-breeding organisms possess a trait, such as purple flowers, that is always inherited unchanged by all offspring produced by self-fertilization. In his first set of experiments, Mendel cross-fertilized pea plants that were true-breeding for different forms of a single trait. He saved the resulting seeds and grew them the following year to determine the traits of the offspring.

In one of these experiments, Mendel cross-fertilized true-breeding, white-flowered plants with true-breeding, purple-flowered plants. This was the parental generation, denoted by the letter P. When he grew the resulting seeds, he found that all the first-generation offspring (the "first filial," or F_1 generation) produced purple flowers (**Fig. 10-4**). What had happened to the white color? The flowers of the F_1 hybrids were just as purple as their true-breeding purple parent. The white color of their true-breeding white parent seemed to have disappeared.

Mendel then allowed the F_1 flowers to self-fertilize, collected the seeds, and planted them the next spring. In the second (F_2) generation, Mendel counted 705 plants with purple flowers and 224 plants with white flowers. These numbers are approximately three-fourths purple flowers and one-fourth white flowers, or a ratio of about 3 purple to 1 white (**Fig. 10-5**). This result showed that the capacity to produce white flowers had not disappeared in the F_1 plants, but had only been hidden.

Mendel allowed the F_2 plants to self-fertilize and produce a third (F_3) generation. He found that all the white-flowered F_2 plants produced white-flowered offspring; that is, they were true-breeding. For as many generations as he

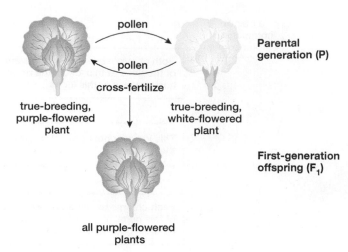

▲ FIGURE 10-4 **Cross of pea plants true-breeding for white or purple flowers** All of the offspring bear purple flowers.

had time and patience to raise, white-flowered plants always gave rise only to white-flowered offspring. In contrast, when purple-flowered F_2 plants self-fertilized, their offspring were of two types. About one-third were true-breeding for purple, but the other two-thirds were hybrids that produced both purple- and white-flowered offspring, again in the ratio of 3 purple to 1 white. Therefore, the F_2 generation included one-quarter true-breeding purple plants, one-half hybrid purple, and one-quarter true-breeding white.

The Inheritance of Dominant and Recessive Alleles on Homologous Chromosomes Can Explain the Results of Mendel's Crosses

Mendel's results, supplemented by modern knowledge of genes and chromosomes, allow us to develop a five-part hypothesis to explain the inheritance of single traits:

- Each trait is determined by pairs of discrete physical units called genes. Each organism has two alleles for each gene, one on each homologous chromosome. True-breeding, white-flowered peas have different alleles of the flower-color gene than true-breeding, purple-flowered peas do.

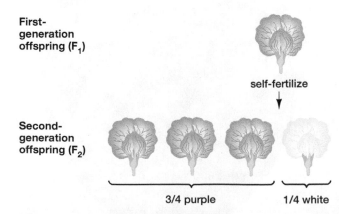

▲ FIGURE 10-5 **Self-fertilization of F_1 pea plants with purple flowers** Three-quarters of the offspring bear purple flowers and one-quarter bear white flowers.

- When two different alleles are present in an organism, one—the **dominant** allele—may mask the expression of the other—the **recessive** allele. The recessive allele, however, is still present. In the edible pea, the allele for purple flowers is dominant, and the allele for white flowers is recessive.

- Homologous chromosomes separate, or segregate, from each other during meiosis, thus separating the alleles they carry. This is known as Mendel's **law of segregation:** Each gamete receives only one allele of each pair of genes. When a sperm fertilizes an egg, the resulting offspring receives one allele from the father (in his sperm) and one from the mother (in her egg).

- Because homologous chromosomes separate randomly during meiosis, the distribution of alleles into the gametes is also random.

- True-breeding organisms have two copies of the same allele for a given gene, and are therefore homozygous for that gene. All of the gametes from a homozygous individual receive the same allele for that gene (Fig. 10-6a). Hybrid organisms have two different alleles for a given gene and so are heterozygous for that gene. Half of a heterozygote's gametes will contain one allele for that gene and half will contain the other allele (Fig. 10-6b).

Let's see how this hypothesis explains the results of Mendel's experiments with flower color (Fig. 10-7). We will use letters to represent the different alleles, assigning the uppercase letter P to the dominant allele for purple flower color and the lowercase letter p to the recessive allele for white flower color. A homozygous purple-flowered plant has two alleles for purple flower color (PP), whereas a homozygous white-flowered plant has two alleles for white flower color

(pp). Therefore, all the sperm and eggs produced by a PP plant carry the P allele, and all the sperm and eggs of a pp plant carry the p allele (Fig. 10-7a).

The F_1 offspring were produced when P sperm fertilized p eggs or when p sperm fertilized P eggs. In both cases, the F_1 offspring were Pp. Because P is dominant over p, all of the offspring were purple (Fig. 10-7b).

For the F_2 generation, Mendel allowed the heterozygous F_1 plants to self-fertilize. A heterozygous plant produces equal numbers of P and p sperm and equal numbers of P and p eggs. When a Pp plant self-fertilizes, each type of sperm has an equal chance of fertilizing each type of egg (Fig. 10-7c). Therefore, the F_2 generation contained three types of offspring: PP, Pp, and pp. The three types occurred in the approximate proportions of one-quarter PP (homozygous purple), one-half Pp (heterozygous purple), and one-quarter pp (homozygous white).

? HAVE **YOU** EVER WONDERED …

Why Dogs Vary So Much in Size?

All dogs evolved from wolves. Although all wolves are about the same size, dogs vary in size more than any other mammal—from huge Great Danes and Irish wolfhounds to minuscule toy breeds such as Chihuahuas and Pomeranians. Toy breeds are usually homozygous for a "small" allele of the gene that encodes insulin-like growth factor (IGF), a protein that helps to regulate body size in many mammals. Great Danes and Irish wolfhounds are usually homozygous or heterozygous for the "large" allele. The "small" allele probably arose as a mutation in dogs, because it does not exist in wolves—just imagine the fate of a Chihuahua-sized wolf in the wild!

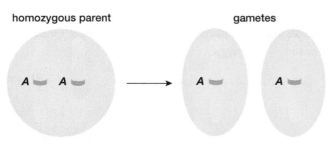

(a) Gametes produced by a homozygous parent

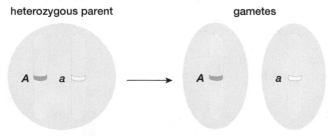

(b) Gametes produced by a heterozygous parent

▲ FIGURE 10-6 **The distribution of alleles in gametes**
(a) All of the gametes produced by homozygous organisms contain the same allele. **(b)** Half of the gametes produced by heterozygous organisms contain one allele, and half of the gametes contain the other allele.

Two organisms that look alike may actually have different combinations of alleles. The combination of alleles carried by an organism (for example, *PP* or *Pp*) is its **genotype.** The organism's traits, including its outward appearance, behavior, digestive enzymes, blood type, or any other observable or measurable feature, make up its **phenotype.** As we have seen, plants with either the *PP* or the *Pp* genotype have the phenotype of purple flowers. Therefore, the F_2 generation of Mendel's peas consisted of three genotypes (one-quarter *PP*, one-half *Pp*, and one-quarter *pp*), but only two phenotypes (three-quarters purple and one-quarter white).

Simple "Genetic Bookkeeping" Can Predict Genotypes and Phenotypes of Offspring

The **Punnett square method,** named after R. C. Punnett, a famous geneticist of the early 1900s, is a convenient way to predict the genotypes and phenotypes of offspring. **Figure 10-8a** shows how to use a Punnett square to determine the expected proportions of offspring that arise from the self-fertilization of a flower that is heterozygous for color (or the proportions of offspring produced by breeding any two organisms that are heterozygous for a single trait). **Figure 10-8b** shows how to calculate the proportions of offspring using the probabilities that each type of sperm will fertilize each type of egg.

As you use these genetic bookkeeping techniques, keep in mind that in a real experiment, the actual offspring will not occur in exactly the predicted proportions. Why not? Let's consider a familiar example. Each time a baby is conceived, it has a 50:50 chance of being a boy or a girl. However, many families with two children do not have one girl and one boy. The 50:50 ratio of girls to boys occurs only if we average the genders of the children in many families.

Mendel's Hypothesis Can Be Used to Predict the Outcome of New Types of Single-Trait Crosses

You have probably recognized that Mendel used the scientific method: He made an observation and used it to formulate a hypothesis. But does Mendel's hypothesis accurately predict the results of further experiments? Based on the hypothesis that heterozygous F_1 plants have one allele for purple flowers and one for white (that is, they have the *Pp* genotype), Mendel predicted the outcome of cross-fertilizing *Pp* plants with homozygous recessive white plants (*pp*): There should

▶ FIGURE 10-7 **Segregation of alleles and fusion of gametes predict the distribution of alleles and traits in the inheritance of flower color in peas (a)** The parental generation: All of the gametes of homozygous *PP* parents contain the *P* allele; all of the gametes of homozygous *pp* parents contain the *p* allele. **(b)** The F_1 generation: Fusion of gametes containing the *P* allele with gametes containing the *p* allele produces only *Pp* offspring. (Note that *Pp* is the same genotype as *pP*.) **(c)** The F_2 generation: Half of the gametes of heterozygous *Pp* parents contain the *P* allele and half contain the *p* allele. Fusion of these gametes produces *PP*, *Pp*, and *pp* offspring.

(a) **Gametes produced by homozygous parents**

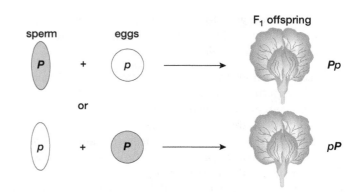

(b) **Fusion of gametes produces F₁ offspring**

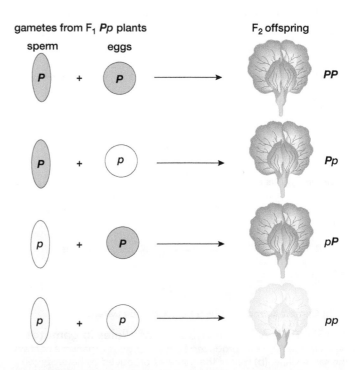

(c) **Fusion of gametes from the F₁ generation produces F₂ offspring** be equal numbers of *Pp* (purple) and *pp* (white) offspring. This is indeed what he found.

This type of experiment also has practical uses. Cross-fertilization of an organism with a dominant phenotype (in this case, a purple flower) but an unknown genotype with a homozygous recessive organism (a white flower) tests whether the organism with the dominant phenotype is homozygous or heterozygous. Logically, this is called a **test cross** (Fig. 10-9). When crossed with a homozygous recessive (*pp*), a homozygous dominant (*PP*) produces all phenotypically dominant offspring, whereas a heterozygous dominant (*Pp*) yields offspring with both dominant and recessive phenotypes in a 1:1 ratio.

CHECK YOUR LEARNING

Can you describe the pattern of inheritance of a trait controlled by a single gene with two alleles, one dominant and one recessive? Can you calculate the proportions of offspring with each genotype and phenotype that would be produced by mating parents with various combinations of the two alleles?

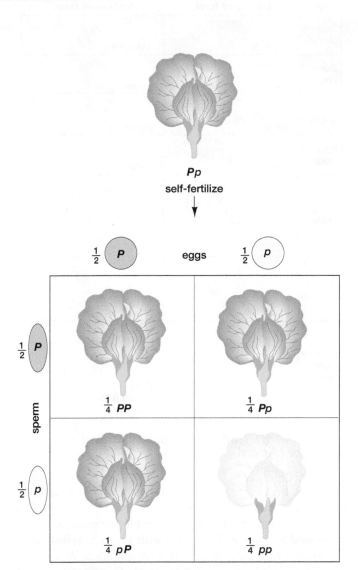

(a) Punnett square of a single-trait cross

sperm	eggs	offspring genotypes	genotypic ratio (1:2:1)	phenotypic ratio (3:1)
½ P × ½ P	= ¼ PP	¼ PP	
½ P × ½ p	= ¼ Pp	½ Pp	¾ purple
½ p × ½ P	= ¼ pP		
½ p × ½ p	= ¼ pp	¼ pp	¼ white

(b) Using probabilities to determine the offspring of a single-trait cross

◄FIGURE 10-8 **Determining the outcome of a single-trait cross** **(a)** The Punnett square allows you to predict both genotypes and phenotypes of specific crosses; here we use it for a cross between pea plants that are heterozygous for a single trait—flower color.

(1) Assign letters to the different alleles; use uppercase for dominant alleles and lowercase for recessive alleles.

(2) Determine all the types of genetically different gametes that can be produced by the male and female parents.

(3) Draw the Punnett square, with the columns labeled with all possible genotypes of the eggs and the rows labeled with all possible genotypes of the sperm. (We also show the fractions of each genotype.)

(4) Fill in the genotype of the offspring in each box by combining the genotype of the sperm in its row with the genotype of the egg in its column. (Multiply the fraction of sperm of each type in the row headers by the fraction of eggs of each type in the column headers.)

(5) Count the number of offspring with each genotype. Note that *Pp* is the same genotype as *pP*.

(6) Convert the number of offspring of each genotype to a fraction of the total number of offspring. In this example, out of four fertilizations, only one is predicted to produce the *pp* genotype, so one-quarter of the total number of offspring produced by this cross is predicted to be white. To determine phenotypic fractions, add the fractions of genotypes that would produce a given phenotype. For example, purple flowers are produced by ¼ *PP* + ¼ *Pp* + ¼ *pP*, for a total of three-quarters of the offspring.

(b) Probabilities may also be used to predict the outcome of a single-trait cross. Determine the fractions of eggs and sperm of each genotype, and multiply these fractions together to calculate the fraction of offspring of each genotype. When two genotypes produce the same phenotype (e.g., *Pp* and *pP*), add the fractions of each genotype to determine the phenotypic fraction.

QUESTION If you crossed a heterozygous *Pp* plant with a homozygous recessive *pp* plant, what would be the expected ratio of offspring? How does this differ from the offspring of a *PP* × *pp* cross? Try working this out before you read further in the text.

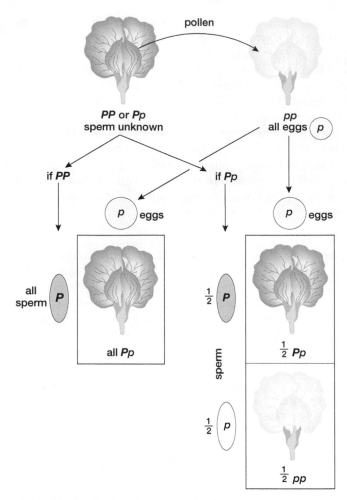

▲ FIGURE 10-9 Punnett square of a test cross An organism with a dominant phenotype may be either homozygous or heterozygous. Crossing such an organism with a homozygous recessive organism can determine whether the dominant organism is homozygous (left) or heterozygous (right).

Trait	Dominant form		Recessive form	
Seed shape	smooth		wrinkled	
Seed color	yellow		green	
Pod shape	inflated		constricted	
Pod color	green		yellow	
Flower color	purple		white	
Flower location	at leaf junctions		at tips of branches	
Plant size	tall (about 6 feet)		dwarf (about 8 to 16 inches)	

▲ FIGURE 10-10 Traits of pea plants studied by Gregor Mendel

10.4 HOW ARE MULTIPLE TRAITS INHERITED?

Having determined how single traits are inherited, Mendel then turned to the more complex question of the inheritance of multiple traits (**Fig. 10-10**). He began by crossbreeding plants that differed in two traits—for example, seed color (yellow or green) and seed shape (smooth or wrinkled). From other crosses of plants with these traits, Mendel already knew that the smooth allele of the seed shape gene (S) is dominant to the wrinkled allele (s), and that the yellow allele of the seed color gene (Y) is dominant to the green allele (y). He crossed a true-breeding plant with smooth, yellow seeds ($SSYY$) to a true-breeding plant with wrinkled, green seeds ($ssyy$). The $SSYY$ plant can produce only SY gametes, and the $ssyy$ plant can produce only sy gametes. Therefore, all the F_1 offspring were heterozygotes: genotypically $SsYy$ with the phenotype of smooth, yellow seeds.

Mendel allowed these heterozygous F_1 plants to self-fertilize. The F_2 generation consisted of 315 plants with smooth, yellow seeds; 101 with wrinkled, yellow seeds; 108 with smooth, green seeds; and 32 with wrinkled, green seeds—a ratio of about 9:3:3:1. The offspring produced from other crosses of plants that were heterozygous for two traits also had phenotypic ratios of about 9:3:3:1.

Mendel Hypothesized That Traits Are Inherited Independently

Mendel realized that these results could be explained if the genes for seed color and seed shape were inherited independently of each other and did not influence each other during gamete formation. If this hypothesis is correct, then for each trait, three-quarters of the offspring should show the dominant phenotype and one-quarter should show the recessive phenotype. This result is just what Mendel

CASE STUDY continued

Sudden Death on the Court

When a person with Marfan syndrome has children with a person without the syndrome, those children have a 50% chance of inheriting the condition. Do you think that Marfan is inherited as a dominant or a recessive allele? Why? Check your reasoning in "Case Study Revisited: Sudden Death on the Court" at the end of the chapter.

observed. He found 423 plants with smooth seeds (of either color) and 133 with wrinkled seeds (of either color), a ratio of about 3:1; 416 plants produced yellow seeds (of either shape) and 140 produced green seeds (of either shape), also about a 3:1 ratio. **Figure 10-11** shows how a Punnett square or probability calculation can be used to estimate the proportions of genotypes and phenotypes of the offspring of a cross between organisms that are heterozygous for two traits.

The independent inheritance of two or more traits is called the **law of independent assortment.** Multiple traits are inherited independently if the alleles of the gene controlling any given trait are distributed to gametes independently of the alleles for the genes controlling all the other traits. Independent assortment will occur when the traits being studied are controlled by genes on different pairs of homologous chromosomes. Why? During meiosis, paired homologous chromosomes line up at metaphase I. Which homologue faces which pole of the cell is random, and the orientation of one homologous pair does not influence other pairs (see Chapter 9). Therefore, when the homologues separate during anaphase I, which homologue of pair 1 moves "north" does not affect which homologue of pair 2 moves "north." The result is that the alleles of genes on different chromosomes are distributed, or assorted, independently of one another (**Fig. 10-12**).

In an Unprepared World, Genius May Go Unrecognized

In 1865, Gregor Mendel presented his results to the Brünn Society for the Study of Natural Science, and they were published the following year. His paper did not mark the beginning of genetics. In fact, it didn't make any impression at all on the study of biology during his lifetime. Apparently, very few biologists read his paper, and those who did failed to recognize its significance.

It was not until 1900 that three biologists—Carl Correns, Hugo de Vries, and Erich von Tschermak—working independently of one another and knowing nothing of Mendel's work, rediscovered the principles of inheritance. No doubt to their intense disappointment, when they searched the scientific literature before publishing their results, they found that Mendel had scooped them more than 30 years earlier. To their credit, they graciously acknowledged the important work of the Austrian monk, who had died in 1884.

CHECK YOUR LEARNING

Can you describe the pattern of inheritance of two traits, if each of the traits is controlled by a separate gene with only two alleles, one dominant and one recessive? Are you able to calculate the frequencies of the genotypes and phenotypes of the offspring that would be produced by mating organisms with various combinations of the two alleles of each gene, assuming independent assortment of the two genes?

(a) Punnett square of a two-trait cross

seed shape		seed color		phenotypic ratio (9:3:3:1)
$\frac{3}{4}$ smooth	×	$\frac{3}{4}$ yellow	=	$\frac{9}{16}$ smooth yellow
$\frac{3}{4}$ smooth	×	$\frac{1}{4}$ green	=	$\frac{3}{16}$ smooth green
$\frac{1}{4}$ wrinkled	×	$\frac{3}{4}$ yellow	=	$\frac{3}{16}$ wrinkled yellow
$\frac{1}{4}$ wrinkled	×	$\frac{1}{4}$ green	=	$\frac{1}{16}$ wrinkled green

(b) Using probabilities to determine the offspring of a two-trait cross

▲ **FIGURE 10-11 Predicting genotypes and phenotypes for a cross between parents that are heterozygous for two traits** In pea seeds, yellow color (*Y*) is dominant to green (*y*), and smooth shape (*S*) is dominant to wrinkled (*s*). **(a)** Punnett square analysis. In this cross, an individual heterozygous for both traits self-fertilizes. In a cross involving two independent genes, there will be equal numbers of gametes with all of the possible combinations of alleles of the two genes—*S* with *Y*, *S* with *y*, *s* with *Y*, and *s* with *y*. Place these gamete combinations as the labels for the rows and columns in the Punnett square, and then calculate the offspring as explained in Figure 10-8. Note that the Punnett square predicts both the frequencies of combinations of traits ($\frac{9}{16}$ smooth yellow, $\frac{3}{16}$ smooth green, $\frac{3}{16}$ wrinkled yellow, and $\frac{1}{16}$ wrinkled green) and the frequencies of individual traits ($\frac{3}{4}$ yellow, $\frac{1}{4}$ green, $\frac{3}{4}$ smooth, and $\frac{1}{4}$ wrinkled). **(b)** In probability theory, the probability of two independent events is the product (multiplication) of their independent probabilities. For example, to find the probability of tossing two coins and having both come up heads, multiply the independent probabilities of each coin coming up heads ($\frac{1}{2} \times \frac{1}{2} = \frac{1}{4}$). Seed shape is independent of seed color. Therefore, multiplying the independent probabilities of the genotypes or phenotypes for each trait produces the predicted frequencies for the combined genotypes or phenotypes of the offspring. These frequencies are identical to those generated by the Punnett square.

QUESTION Can the genotype of a plant bearing smooth yellow seeds be revealed by a test cross with a plant bearing wrinkled green seeds?

▶FIGURE 10-12 **Independent assortment of alleles** Chromosome movements during meiosis produce independent assortment of alleles, shown here for two genes. Each combination of alleles is equally likely to occur, producing gametes in the predicted proportions one-quarter *SY*, one-quarter *sy*, one-quarter *Sy*, and one-quarter *sY*.

QUESTION If the genes for seed color and seed shape were on the same chromosome rather than on different chromosomes, would their alleles assort independently? Why or why not?

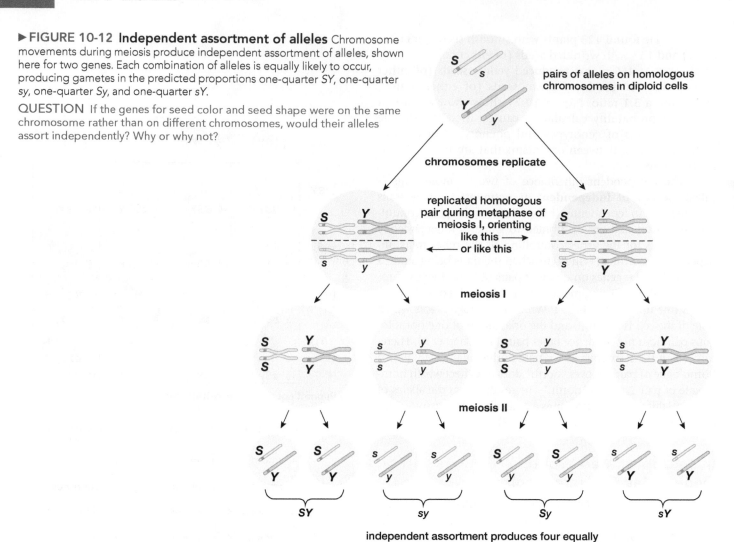

pairs of alleles on homologous chromosomes in diploid cells

chromosomes replicate

replicated homologous pair during metaphase of meiosis I, orienting like this ⟶ ⟵ or like this

meiosis I

meiosis II

SY   sy   Sy   sY

independent assortment produces four equally likely allele combinations during meiosis

10.5 DO THE MENDELIAN RULES OF INHERITANCE APPLY TO ALL TRAITS?

In our discussion thus far, we have made some major simplifying assumptions: Each trait is completely controlled by a single gene, there are only two possible alleles of each gene, and one allele is completely dominant to the other, recessive, allele. Most traits, however, are influenced in more varied and subtle ways.

In Incomplete Dominance, the Phenotype of Heterozygotes Is Intermediate Between the Phenotypes of the Homozygotes

When one allele is completely dominant over a second allele, heterozygotes with one dominant allele have the same phenotype as homozygotes with two dominant alleles (see Figs. 10-8 and 10-9). However, in some cases the heterozygous phenotype is intermediate between the two homozygous phenotypes, a pattern of inheritance called **incomplete dominance.** In humans, hair texture is influenced by a gene with two incompletely dominant alleles, which we will call H_1 and H_2 (**Fig. 10-13**). A person with two copies of the H_1 allele

has curly hair; two copies of the H_2 allele produce straight hair. Heterozygotes, with the H_1H_2 genotype, have wavy hair. Two wavy-haired people might have children with any of the three hair types, with probabilities of one-quarter curly (H_1H_1), one-half wavy (H_1H_2), and one-quarter straight (H_2H_2).

A Single Gene May Have Multiple Alleles

Recall that all alleles originated as mutations (see Section 10.1), which may then be inherited from generation to generation. A gene may suffer many different mutations over thousands or millions of years of evolution, with the result that there are multiple alleles of many genes. Although an *individual* can have at most two different alleles (one on each of two homologous chromosomes), if we examined the genes of all the members of a *species*, we would find that many genes have dozens, even hundreds, of different alleles. Which of these alleles an offspring inherits, of course, depends on which alleles were present in its parents. There are multiple alleles for many human genetic disorders, including Marfan syndrome, Duchenne muscular dystrophy (see the "Health Watch: Muscular Dystrophy" on p. **185**), and cystic fibrosis (see the case study in Chapter 12).

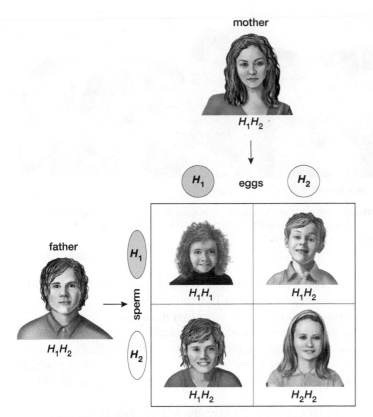

mother

H_1H_2

eggs

H_1 H_2

father

sperm

H_1H_2

H_1

H_2

H_1H_1	H_1H_2
H_1H_2	H_2H_2

▲ FIGURE 10-13 **Incomplete dominance** The inheritance of hair texture in humans is an example of incomplete dominance. In such cases, we use capital letters for both alleles, here H_1 and H_2. Homozygotes may have curly hair (H_1H_1) or straight hair (H_2H_2). Heterozygotes (H_1H_2) have wavy hair. The children of a man and a woman, both with wavy hair, may have curly, straight, or wavy hair, in the approximate ratio of $\frac{1}{4}$ curly: $\frac{1}{2}$ wavy: $\frac{1}{4}$ straight.

Human blood types are an example of multiple alleles of a single gene. The blood types A, B, AB, and O arise as a result of three different alleles of a single gene (we will designate the alleles *A*, *B*, and *o*). This gene codes for an enzyme that adds sugar molecules to the ends of glycoproteins that protrude from the surfaces of red blood cells. Alleles *A* and *B* code for enzymes that add different sugars to the glycoproteins (we'll call the resulting molecules glycoproteins A and B, respectively). Allele *o* codes for a nonfunctional enzyme that doesn't add any sugar molecules.

A person may have one of six genotypes: *AA, BB, AB, Ao, Bo,* or *oo* (Table 10-1). Alleles *A* and *B* are dominant to *o*. Therefore, people with genotypes *AA* or *Ao* make only type A glycoproteins and have type A blood. Those with genotypes *BB* or *Bo* synthesize only type B glycoproteins and have type B blood. Homozygous recessive *oo* individuals lack both types of glycoproteins and have type O blood. In people with type AB blood, both enzymes are present, so their red blood cells have both A and B glycoproteins. When a heterozygote expresses the phenotypes of both of the homozygotes (in this case, both A and B glycoproteins), the pattern of inheritance is called **codominance,** and the alleles are said to be codominant to one another.

As you probably know, the fact that people may have different blood types is medically important. The human immune system produces proteins called antibodies, which bind to complex molecules that are not produced by a person's own body (if they did bind to "self" molecules, your immune system would destroy the cells of your own body). In their usual role in defending against disease, antibodies bind to molecules on the surfaces of invading bacteria or viruses, and help to destroy the invaders (see Chapter 36).

TABLE 10-1	Human Blood Group Characteristics					
Blood Type	Genotype	Red Blood Cells	Has Plasma Antibodies to:	Can Receive Blood from:	Can Donate Blood to:	Frequency in U.S.
A	*AA* or *Ao*	A glycoprotein	B glycoprotein	A or O (no blood with B glycoprotein)	A or AB	42%
B	*BB* or *Bo*	B glycoprotein	A glycoprotein	B or O (no blood with A glycoprotein)	B or AB	10%
AB	*AB*	Both A and B glycoproteins	Neither A nor B glycoprotein	AB, A, B, O (universal recipient)	AB	4%
O	*oo*	Neither A nor B glycoprotein	Both A and B glycoproteins	O (no blood with A or B glycoprotein)	O, AB, A, B (universal donor)	44%

Humans show a wide range of skin tones, from almost white to very dark brown

▲ FIGURE 10-14 **Polygenic inheritance of skin color in humans** At least three separate genes, each with two incompletely dominant alleles, determine human skin color (the inheritance is actually more complex than this). The combination of complex polygenic inheritance and exposure to sunlight produces an almost continuous gradation of skin colors.

However, antibodies also complicate blood transfusions. Most antibodies are secreted by cells of the immune system and then circulate in the blood. The immune system makes antibodies that can bind to glycoproteins on red blood cells, if those glycoproteins include sugars that are different from the sugars on a person's own red blood cells. The antibodies cause red blood cells with foreign glycoproteins to clump together and rupture. The resulting clumps and fragments can clog small blood vessels and damage vital organs such as the brain, heart, lungs, or kidneys. This means that blood type must be carefully matched before a blood transfusion.

Table 10-1 summarizes human blood types and safe transfusions. Obviously, a person can donate blood to anyone with the same blood type. In addition, type O blood, lacking any sugars, can be safely transfused to all other blood types, because type O red blood cells are not attacked by antibodies in A, B, or AB blood. (The antibodies present in the transfused blood become too diluted by the much larger volume of the recipient's blood to cause problems.) People with type O blood are called "universal donors." But O blood carries antibodies to both A and B glycoproteins, so type O individuals can receive transfusions of only type O blood. Type AB blood doesn't contain antibodies against any type of red blood cells, so a person with type AB blood can receive blood from people with any other blood type; thus, they are called "universal recipients."

Many Traits Are Influenced by Several Genes

Your class probably contains people of varied heights, skin colors, and body builds—variation that cannot be divided into convenient, easily defined phenotypes. Traits such as these are influenced by interactions among two or more genes, a process called **polygenic inheritance.** As you might imagine, the more genes that contribute to a single trait, the greater the number of possible phenotypes and the smaller the differences among them. Traits that are affected by polygenic inheritance are often also strongly affected by the environment, further blurring the differences among phenotypes.

For example, recent research suggests that at least 180 genes contribute to human height. Add in the effects of nutrition, and it's no wonder that there aren't discrete steps in height. Human skin color is probably controlled by at least three different genes, each with pairs of incompletely dominant alleles. Exposure to sunlight further affects skin color, resulting in virtually continuous variation in phenotype (**Fig. 10-14**).

Single Genes Typically Have Multiple Effects on Phenotype

We have just seen that a single phenotype may result from the interaction of several genes. The reverse is also true: Single genes often have multiple phenotypic effects, a phenomenon called **pleiotropy.** For example, a mutation in a single gene in a lab mouse in 1962 produced a nude mouse (**Fig. 10-15**). Researchers rapidly discovered that nude mice are not only hairless; they lack a thymus gland, have virtually no immune response, and females do not develop functional mammary glands, so they can't nurse their pups.

▲ FIGURE 10-15 **Nude mice**

CASE STUDY continued

Sudden Death on the Court

In Marfan syndrome, a single defective fibrillin allele causes increased height, long limbs, large hands and feet, weak walls in the aorta, and often dislocated lenses in one or both eyes—a striking example of pleiotropy in humans.

The Environment Influences the Expression of Genes

An organism is not just the sum of its genes. In addition to its genotype, the environment in which an organism lives profoundly affects its phenotype. Fur color in Siamese cats vividly illustrates environmental effects on gene action. All Siamese cats are born with pale fur, but within the first few weeks, the ears, nose, paws, and tail turn dark (**Fig. 10-16**). A Siamese cat actually has the genotype for dark fur everywhere on its body. However, the enzyme that produces the dark pigment is inactive at temperatures above about 93°F (34°C). While inside their mother's uterus, unborn kittens are warm all over, so newborn Siamese kittens have pale fur on their entire bodies. After they are born, the ears, nose, paws, and tail become cooler than the rest of the body, so dark pigment is produced in those areas.

Most environmental influences are more complicated and subtle than this. Complex environmental influences are particularly common in human characteristics. We have already seen that skin color is modified by sun exposure and height is influenced by nutrition.

CHECK YOUR LEARNING

Can you describe the patterns of inheritance of traits showing incomplete dominance, codominance, and multiple alleles? Are you able to explain how polygenic inheritance and environmental influences combine to produce nearly continuous variation in many phenotypes?

▲ FIGURE 10-16 **Environmental influence on phenotype** The distribution of dark fur in the Siamese cat is an interaction between genotype and environment, producing a particular phenotype. Newborn Siamese kittens have pale fur everywhere on their bodies. In an adult Siamese, the allele for dark fur is expressed only in the cooler areas (nose, ears, paws, and tail).

10.6 HOW ARE GENES LOCATED ON THE SAME CHROMOSOME INHERITED?

Gregor Mendel knew nothing about the physical nature of genes or chromosomes. We now know that genes are parts of chromosomes, and that each chromosome contains many genes, up to several thousand in a really large chromosome. These facts have important implications for inheritance.

Genes on the Same Chromosome Tend to Be Inherited Together

Chromosomes, not individual genes, assort independently during meiosis I. Therefore, genes located on *different chromosomes* assort independently into gametes. In contrast, genes on the *same chromosome* tend to be inherited together, a phenomenon called **gene linkage.** One of the first pairs of linked genes to be discovered was found in the sweet pea, a different species from Mendel's edible pea. In sweet peas, the gene for flower color (purple vs. red) and the gene for pollen grain shape (round vs. long) are carried on the same chromosome. Thus, the alleles for these genes normally assort together into gametes during meiosis and are inherited together.

Consider a heterozygous sweet pea plant with purple flowers and long pollen (**Fig. 10-17**). The dominant purple allele of the flower-color gene and the dominant long allele of the pollen-shape gene are located on one homologous chromosome (Fig. 10-17, top). The recessive red allele of the flower-color gene and the recessive round allele of the pollen-shape gene are located on the other homologue (Fig. 10-17, bottom). Therefore, the gametes produced by this plant are likely to have either purple and long alleles or red and round alleles. This pattern of inheritance does not conform to the law of independent assortment, because the alleles for flower color and pollen shape do not segregate independently of one another, but tend to stay together during meiosis.

Crossing Over Creates New Combinations of Linked Alleles

Although they *tend* to be inherited together, genes on the same chromosome do not *always* stay together. If you cross-fertilized two sweet peas with the chromosomes shown in Figure 10-17, you might expect that all of the offspring would have either purple flowers with long pollen grains, or

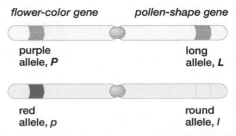

▲ FIGURE 10-17 **Linked genes on homologous chromosomes in the sweet pea** The genes for flower color and pollen shape are on the same chromosome, so they tend to be inherited together.

red flowers with round pollen grains. (Try working this out with a Punnett square.) In reality, you would usually find a few offspring with purple flowers and round pollen, and a few with red flowers and long pollen, as if, sometimes, the genes for flower color and pollen shape became unlinked. How can this happen?

During prophase I of meiosis, homologous chromosomes sometimes exchange parts, a process called crossing over (see Chapter 9, Fig. 9-16). In most chromosomes, at least one exchange between each homologous pair occurs during each meiotic cell division. The exchange of corresponding segments of DNA during crossing over produces new allele combinations on both homologous chromosomes. Then, when homologues separate at anaphase I, the chromosomes that the haploid daughter cells receive will have different sets of alleles than the chromosomes of the parent cell had.

Crossing over during meiosis explains **genetic recombination:** new combinations of alleles of genes that are located on the same chromosome. Let's look at the sweet pea chromosomes during meiosis. During prophase I, the duplicated, homologous chromosomes pair up (**Fig. 10-18a**). Each homologue will have one or more regions where crossing over occurs. Imagine that crossing over exchanges the alleles for flower color between nonsister chromatids of the two homologues (**Fig. 10-18b**). At anaphase I, the separated homologues will each now have one chromatid bearing a piece of DNA from a chromatid of the other homologue (**Fig. 10-18c**). During meiosis II, four types of chromosomes will be distributed to the four daughter cells: two unchanged chromosomes and two recombined chromosomes (**Fig. 10-18d**).

Therefore, some gametes will be produced with each of four configurations: *PL* and *pl* (on the original parental chromosomes) and *Pl* and *pL* (on the recombined chromosomes). If a sperm with a *Pl* chromosome fertilizes an egg with a *pl* chromosome, the offspring plant will have purple flowers (*Pp*) and round pollen (*ll*). If a sperm with a *pL* chromosome fertilizes an egg with a *pl* chromosome, then the offspring will have red flowers (*pp*) and long pollen (*Ll*).

Not surprisingly, the farther apart the genes are on a chromosome, the more likely it is that crossing over will occur between them. Two genes close together on a chromosome are strongly linked and will rarely be separated by a crossover. However, if two genes are very far apart, crossing over between the genes occurs so often that they seem to be independently assorted, just as if they were on different chromosomes. When Gregor Mendel discovered independent assortment, he was not only clever and careful, he was also lucky. The seven traits that he studied were controlled by genes on only four different chromosomes. He observed independent assortment because the genes that were on the same chromosomes were far apart.

CHECK YOUR LEARNING

Can you describe how the patterns of inheritance differ between traits controlled by genes on a single chromosome and traits controlled by genes on different chromosomes?

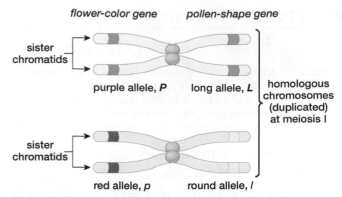

(a) Duplicated chromosomes in prophase of meiosis I

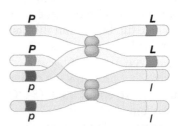

(b) Crossing over during prophase I

(c) Homologous chromosomes separate at anaphase I

(d) Unchanged and recombined chromosomes after meiosis II

▲ FIGURE 10-18 **Crossing over recombines alleles on homologous chromosomes** (a) During prophase of meiosis I, duplicated homologous chromosomes pair up. (b) Nonsister chromatids of the two homologues exchange parts by crossing over. (c) When the homologous chromosomes separate during anaphase of meiosis I, one chromatid of each of the homologues now contains a piece of DNA from a chromatid of the other homologue. (d) After meiosis II, two of the haploid daughter cells receive unchanged chromosomes, and two receive recombined chromosomes. The recombined chromosomes contain allele arrangements that did not occur in the original parental chromosomes.

10.7 HOW ARE SEX AND SEX-LINKED TRAITS INHERITED?

In many animals, an individual's sex is determined by its **sex chromosomes.** In mammals, females have two identical sex chromosomes, called **X chromosomes,** whereas males have one X chromosome and one **Y chromosome** (Fig. 10-19). Although the Y chromosome is much smaller than the X chromosome, a small part of both sex chromosomes is homologous. As a result, the X and Y chromosomes pair up during prophase of meiosis I and separate during anaphase I. The other chromosomes, which occur in pairs that have identical appearance in both males and females, are called **autosomes.**

In Mammals, the Sex of an Offspring Is Determined by the Sex Chromosome in the Sperm

During sperm formation, the sex chromosomes segregate, and each sperm receives either the X or the Y chromosome (plus one member of each pair of autosomes). The sex chromosomes also segregate during egg formation, but because females have two X chromosomes, every egg receives one X chromosome (and one member of each pair of autosomes). Thus, a male offspring is produced if an egg is fertilized by a Y-bearing sperm, and a female offspring is produced if an egg is fertilized by an X-bearing sperm (Fig. 10-20).

Sex-Linked Genes Are Found Only on the X or Only on the Y Chromosome

Genes that are located only on sex chromosomes are referred to as **sex-linked.** In many animal species, the Y chromosome carries only a few genes. In humans, the Y chromosome

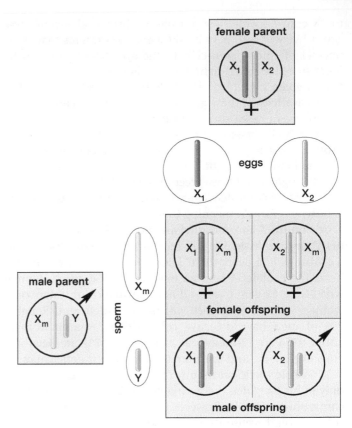

▲ FIGURE 10-20 **Sex determination in mammals** Male offspring receive their Y chromosome from their father; female offspring receive the father's X chromosome (labeled X_m). Both male and female offspring receive an X chromosome (either X_1 or X_2) from their mother.

▲ FIGURE 10-19 **Human sex chromosomes** The Y chromosome (right), which carries relatively few genes, is much smaller than the X chromosome (left). Image courtesy of Indigo® Instruments: http://www.indigo.com.

contains a few dozen genes (probably less than 100), many of which play a role in male reproduction. The most well-known Y-linked gene is the sex-determining gene, called *SRY.* During embryonic life, the action of *SRY* sets in motion the entire male developmental pathway. Under normal conditions, *SRY* causes the male gender to be 100% linked to the Y chromosome.

In contrast to the small Y chromosome, the human X chromosome contains more than 1,000 genes, most of which have no counterpart on the Y chromosome. Few X chromosome genes have a specific role in reproduction. Most of the genes on the X chromosome determine traits that are important in both sexes, such as color vision, blood clotting, and certain structural proteins in muscles.

How does linkage of genes on the X chromosome affect inheritance? Because females have two X chromosomes, they can be either homozygous or heterozygous for genes on the X chromosome, and dominant versus recessive relationships among alleles will be expressed. Males, in contrast, fully express all the alleles they have on their single X chromosome, regardless of whether those alleles would be dominant or recessive in females.

Let's look at a familiar example: red-green color deficiency, more commonly—though usually incorrectly—called color blindness (Fig. 10-21). Color deficiency is caused by recessive alleles of either of two genes located on the X chromosome. The normal, dominant alleles of these genes (we will call them both *C*) encode proteins that allow one set of color-vision cells in the eye, called cones, to be most sensitive to red light and another set to be most sensitive to green light (**Fig. 10-21a**). There are several defective recessive alleles of these genes (we will call them all *c*). In the most extreme cases, one of the genes will actually be missing from an X chromosome, or the defective alleles will encode proteins that make both sets of cones equally sensitive to both red and green light. Therefore, the affected person cannot distinguish red from green (**Fig. 10-21b**).

How is color deficiency inherited? A man can have the genotype *CY* or *cY*, meaning that he has a color-vision allele *C* or *c* on his X chromosome and no corresponding gene on his Y chromosome. He will have normal color vision if his X chromosome bears the *C* allele, or be color-deficient if it bears the *c* allele. A woman may be *CC, Cc,* or *cc*. Women with *CC* or *Cc* genotypes will have normal color vision; only women with *cc* genotypes will be color-deficient. Roughly 7% of men have defective color vision. Among women, about 93% are homozygous normal *CC*, 7% are heterozygous normal *Cc*, and less than 0.5% are color-deficient *cc*.

A color-deficient man (*cY*) will pass his defective allele only to his daughters, because only his daughters inherit his X chromosome. Usually, however, the daughters will have normal color vision, because they will also inherit a normal *C* allele from their mother, who is very likely homozygous normal *CC*.

A heterozygous woman (*Cc*), although she has normal color vision, has a 50% chance of passing her defective allele to her sons (**Fig. 10-21c**). Sons who receive the defective allele will be color-deficient (*cY*), whereas sons who inherit the functional allele will have normal color vision (*CY*).

CHECK YOUR LEARNING

Do you understand why sperm determine the gender of offspring in mammals? Are you able to explain why most sex-linked traits are controlled by genes on the X chromosome? Can you describe the pattern of inheritance of sex-linked traits?

10.8 HOW ARE HUMAN GENETIC DISORDERS INHERITED?

Many human diseases are influenced by genetics to a greater or lesser degree. Because experimental crosses with people are out of the question, human geneticists search medical, historical, and family records to study past crosses. Records

(a) Normal color vision

(b) Red-green color blindness

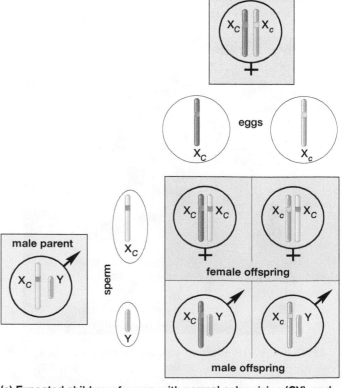

(c) Expected children of a man with normal color vision (CY), and a heterozygous woman (Cc)

▶ FIGURE 10-21 **Sex-linked inheritance of red-green color deficiency** Color grids can help people with normal color vision imagine the world as seen by someone with red-green color deficiency. **(a)** Normal color vision. **(b)** To a person who is really red-green "color-blind," both grids look exactly the same. Usually, an affected person isn't completely color-blind—he sees most of the colors that normal people see, but not as well. Therefore, the grids would look very similar, but not identical. **(c)** A Punnett square showing the inheritance of color deficiency from a heterozygous woman (*Cc*) to her sons.

(a) A pedigree for a dominant trait

(b) A pedigree for a recessive trait

How to read pedigrees

I, II, III = generations

☐ = male   ○ = female

☐—○ = parents

☐ ○ ○ = offspring

■ or ● = shows trait

☐ or ○ = does not show trait

◨ or ◑ = known carrier (heterozygote) for recessive trait

? or ⦵ = cannot determine the genotype from this pedigree

▲ **FIGURE 10-22 Family pedigrees (a)** A pedigree for a dominant trait. Note that any offspring showing a dominant trait must have at least one parent with the trait (see Figs. 10-8, 10-9, and 10-11). **(b)** A pedigree for a recessive trait. Any individual showing a recessive trait must be homozygous recessive. If that person's parents did not show the trait, then both parents must be heterozygotes (carriers). Note that the genotype cannot be determined for some offspring, who may be either carriers or homozygous dominants.

extending across several generations can be arranged in the form of family **pedigrees,** diagrams that show the genetic relationships among a set of related individuals (**Fig. 10-22**).

Careful analysis of pedigrees can reveal whether a particular trait is inherited in a dominant, recessive, or sex-linked pattern. Since the mid-1960s, analysis of human pedigrees, combined with molecular genetic technology, has produced great strides in understanding human genetic diseases. For instance, geneticists now know the genes responsible for dozens of inherited diseases, including

sickle-cell anemia, hemophilia, muscular dystrophy, Marfan syndrome, and cystic fibrosis. Research in molecular genetics has increased our ability to predict genetic diseases and perhaps even to cure them (a topic we explore further in Chapter 13).

Some Human Genetic Disorders Are Controlled by Single Genes

Some common human traits, such as freckles, cleft chin, and dimples, are inherited in a simple Mendelian fashion; that is, each trait appears to be controlled by a single gene with a recessive and a dominant allele. Some human genetic disorders are also caused by defective alleles of a single gene.

Some Human Genetic Disorders Are Caused by Recessive Alleles

The human body depends on the actions of thousands of enzymes and other proteins. A mutation in an allele of the gene coding for one of these proteins can impair or destroy its function. However, the presence of one normal allele may generate enough functional protein to enable heterozygotes to be phenotypically indistinguishable from homozygotes with two normal alleles. Therefore, for many genes, a normal allele that encodes a functional protein is dominant to a mutant allele that encodes a nonfunctional protein. Put another way, a mutant allele of these genes is recessive to a normal allele. Thus, an abnormal phenotype occurs only in people who inherit two copies of the mutant allele.

A **carrier** for a genetic disorder is a person who is heterozygous, with one normal, dominant allele and one defective, recessive allele: That person is phenotypically healthy but can pass on his or her defective allele to offspring. Geneticists estimate that each of us carries recessive alleles of 5 to 15 genes that would cause serious genetic defects in homozygotes. Every time we have a child, there is a 50:50 chance that we will pass on the defective allele. This is usually harmless, because an unrelated man and woman are unlikely to possess a defective allele of the same gene, so they are unlikely to produce a child who is homozygous for a recessive genetic disease. Related couples, however (especially first cousins or closer), have inherited some of their genes from recent common ancestors, and so are more likely to carry a defective allele of the same gene. If a man and woman are both heterozygous for the same defective recessive allele, they have a 1 in 4 chance of having a child with the genetic disorder (see Fig. 10-22).

Albinism Results from a Defect in Melanin Production

An enzyme called tyrosinase is needed to produce melanin—the dark pigment in skin, hair, and the iris of the eye. Normal melanin production will occur if a person has either one or two functional tyrosinase alleles. However, if a person is homozygous for an allele that encodes defective tyrosinase, **albinism** occurs (**Fig. 10-23**). Albinism in humans and other mammals results in very pale skin and hair.

(a) Human   (b) Wallaby

▲ FIGURE 10-23 **Albinism** (a) Albinism occurs in most vertebrates, including people. This boy's irises are extremely pale, so his eyes are very sensitive to bright light. (b) The albino wallaby in the foreground is safe in a zoo, but in the wild, its bright white fur would make it very conspicuous to predators.

Sickle-Cell Anemia Is Caused by a Defective Allele for Hemoglobin Synthesis Red blood cells are packed with hemoglobin proteins, which transport oxygen and give the cells their red color. Anemia is a generic term given to a number of diseases, all characterized by a low red blood cell count or below-normal hemoglobin in the blood. **Sickle-cell anemia** is an inherited form of anemia that results from a mutation in the hemoglobin gene. A change in a single nucleotide results in an incorrect amino acid at a crucial position in the hemoglobin protein (see Section 12.4 in Chapter 12). When people with sickle-cell anemia exercise or move to high altitude, oxygen concentrations in their blood drop, and the sickle-cell hemoglobin proteins inside their red blood cells stick together. The resulting clumps of hemoglobin force red blood cells out of their usual flexible, disk shapes (**Fig. 10-24a**) into long, stiff, sickle shapes (**Fig. 10-24b**). The sickled cells are fragile and easily damaged. Anemia occurs because the sickled red blood cells are destroyed before their usual life span is completed.

The sickle shape also causes other complications. Sickle cells jam up in capillaries, causing blood clots. Tissues downstream of the clot do not receive enough oxygen. Paralyzing strokes can result if blocks occur in blood vessels in the brain.

People homozygous for the sickle-cell allele synthesize only defective hemoglobin. Consequently, many of their red blood cells become sickled, and they suffer

▶ FIGURE 10-24 **Sickle-cell anemia** (a) Normal red blood cells are disk shaped with indented centers. (b) When blood oxygen is low, the red blood cells in a person with sickle-cell anemia become long, slender and curved, resembling a sickle.

from sickle-cell anemia. Although heterozygotes produce about half normal and half abnormal hemoglobin, they have very few sickled red blood cells and seldom show any symptoms. Because only people who are homozygous for the sickle-cell allele usually show symptoms, sickle-cell anemia is considered to be a recessive disorder. However, during exceptionally strenuous exercise, some heterozygotes may experience life-threatening complications, as we explore in "Links to Everyday Life: The Sickle-Cell Allele and Athletics."

About 5% to 25% of sub-Saharan Africans and 8% of African Americans are heterozygous for sickle-cell anemia, but the allele is very rare in Caucasians. Why the difference? Shouldn't natural selection work to eliminate the sickle-cell allele in both African and Caucasian populations? The difference arises because heterozygotes have some resistance to the parasite that causes malaria, which is common in Africa and other places with warm

(a) Normal red blood cells

(b) Sickled red blood cells

climates, but not in colder regions such as most of Europe. This "heterozygote advantage" explains the prevalence of the sickle-cell allele in people of African origin.

Some Human Genetic Disorders Are Caused by Dominant Alleles

Some serious genetic disorders, such as Huntington disease, are caused by dominant alleles. Just as a pea plant needs only one dominant allele for purple color to bear purple flowers (see Figs. 10-7 and 10-8), so too a person needs to have only one defective dominant allele in order to suffer from these disorders. Therefore, everyone who inherits a dominant genetic disorder must have at least one parent with the disease (see Fig. 10-22a), which means that some people with dominant diseases must remain healthy enough to grow up and have children. In rare cases, a dominant allele that causes a genetic disorder may result not from an inherited allele but from a mutation in the egg or sperm of a parent who is otherwise unaffected. In this case, neither parent would have the disease.

How can a defective allele be dominant to the normal, functional allele? Some dominant alleles encode an abnormal protein that interferes with the function of the normal one. Other dominant alleles may encode proteins that carry out new, toxic reactions. Finally, dominant alleles may encode a protein that is overactive, performing its function at inappropriate times and places in the body.

Huntington Disease Is Caused by a Defective Protein That Kills Cells in Specific Brain Regions **Huntington disease** is a dominant disorder that causes a slow, progressive deterioration of parts of the brain, resulting in a loss of coordination, flailing movements, personality disturbances, and eventual death. The symptoms of Huntington disease typically do not appear until 30 to 50 years of age. Therefore, before they experience their first symptoms, many Huntington victims pass the allele to their children. Geneticists isolated the Huntington gene in 1993, and a few years later, identified the gene's product, a protein they named "huntingtin." The function of normal huntingtin

---

⟫⟫ **LINKS** TO EVERYDAY LIFE

The Sickle-Cell Allele and Athletics

Sickle-cell anemia is considered to be a recessive trait, because only homozygous recessive people usually show any symptoms. At the molecular level, though, half the hemoglobin proteins in a heterozygote are defective. Does this really have no effect at all?

For the vast majority of heterozygotes (often described as having "sickle-cell trait"), there indeed are no health effects. However, a very small number of heterozygotes may experience serious medical problems if they participate in extreme exercise. Consider Devard and Devaughn Darling, identical twin brothers, who shared all their genes, including one copy of the sickle-cell allele (**Fig. E10-1**).

The Darling brothers starred in multiple sports in high school. Both were probable starters for the Florida State University football team when the unthinkable happened during practice on February 26, 2001: Devaughn collapsed and died. No one could prove that Devaughn's death was caused by the combination of strenuous workouts and the sickle-cell trait, but suspicions ran high. The university decided that it didn't want to risk Devard suffering the same fate, and barred Devard from playing football. Devard, however, transferred to Washington State University and played football for the Cougars for 2 years. He then played for five seasons in the National Football League.

The Darling brothers epitomize the rare, but real, dilemmas facing athletes with sickle-cell trait. Devard's football career and the accomplishments of many other heterozygotes show that having sickle-cell trait does not preclude strenuous athletics. The National Collegiate Athletic Association agrees: "Student-athletes with sickle-cell trait should not be excluded from athletics participation." However, Devaughn's tragic death underscores the need to take appropriate precautions.

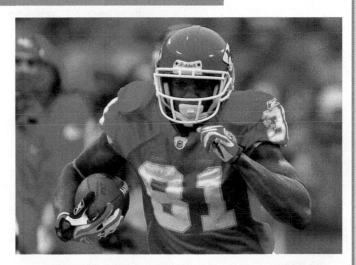

▲ FIGURE E10-1 **Devard Darling runs to daylight for the Kansas City Chiefs** Devard's identical twin Devaughn died during football practice in college, probably from complications of sickle-cell trait.

Dehydration during extreme exercise, especially in hot weather, is probably the most important risk to heterozygotes, so the NCAA recommends that athletes "stay well hydrated at all times." These and other simple precautions have helped the U.S. Army to eliminate excess deaths caused by sickle-cell trait during basic training. In fact, the Army no longer even screens for sickle-cell trait. Medically appropriate and humane training procedures—realizing, for example, that failing to "tough it out" in the face of serious physical distress is not a sign of mental weakness—help all athletes, not only those with sickle-cell trait.

remains unknown. Mutant huntingtin seems to be cut up into toxic fragments inside brain cells, ultimately killing them.

Some Human Genetic Disorders Are Sex-Linked

As we described earlier, the X chromosome contains many genes that have no counterpart on the Y chromosome. Because males have only one X chromosome, they have only one allele for each of these genes. Therefore, males will show the phenotypes produced by these single alleles, even if the alleles are recessive and could be masked by dominant alleles in females.

A son receives his X chromosome from his mother and passes it only to his daughters. Thus, X-linked disorders caused by recessive alleles have a unique pattern of inheritance. Such disorders appear far more frequently in males and typically skip generations: An affected male passes the

trait to a phenotypically normal, carrier daughter, who in turn bears some affected sons. The most familiar genetic defects due to recessive alleles of X-chromosome genes are red-green color deficiency (see Fig. 10-21), muscular dystrophy, and hemophilia.

Hemophilia is caused by a recessive allele on the X chromosome that results in a deficiency in one of the proteins needed for blood clotting. People with hemophilia bruise easily and may bleed extensively from minor injuries. They often have anemia due to blood loss. Nevertheless, even before modern treatment with clotting factors, some hemophiliac males survived to pass on their defective allele to their daughters, who in turn could pass it to their sons (**Fig. 10-25**). Muscular dystrophy, a fatal degeneration of the muscles in young boys, is another recessive sex-linked disorder that we describe in "Health Watch: Muscular Dystrophy" on p. **185**.

▲ **FIGURE 10-25 Hemophilia among the royal families of Europe** A famous genetic pedigree shows the transmission of sex-linked hemophilia from Queen Victoria of England (seated center front, with cane, in 1885) to her offspring and eventually to virtually every royal house in Europe, because of the extensive intermarriage of her children to the royalty of other European nations. Because Victoria's ancestors were free of hemophilia, the hemophilia allele must have arisen as a mutation either in Victoria herself or in one of her parents (or as a result of marital infidelity).

QUESTION Why is it not possible that a mutation in Victoria's husband, Albert, was the original source of hemophilia in this family pedigree?

Health|Watch
Muscular Dystrophy

When Olympic weightlifter Matthias Steiner of Germany won the gold medal in 2008 with a "clean and jerk" lift of almost 569 pounds (258 kilograms), he exerted tremendous forces on his body (Fig. E10-2). How could his muscles withstand these stresses?

Muscle cells are firmly tied together by a very long protein called dystrophin. The almost 3,700 amino acids of dystrophin form a supple yet strong rod that connects the cytoskeleton inside a muscle cell to proteins in its plasma membrane, which in turn attach to supporting proteins that surround each muscle. When a muscle contracts, the muscle cells remain intact because the forces are evenly distributed throughout each cell and to the extracellular support proteins.

Unfortunately, about 1 in 3,500 boys synthesizes seriously defective dystrophin proteins and suffers from **muscular dystrophy,** which literally means "degeneration of the muscles." The most severe form of the disease is named Duchenne muscular dystrophy; a less severe form is called Becker muscular dystrophy. Both forms are named after the physicians who first described the disorders. Muscular dystrophy is caused by a defective allele of the dystrophin gene (usually called the *DMD* gene because of its involvement in **D**uchenne **M**uscular **D**ystrophy). As boys with muscular dystrophy use their muscles, the lack of functioning dystrophin means that ordinary muscle contraction tears the muscle cells. The cells die and are replaced by fat and connective tissue. By the age of 7 or 8, boys with Duchenne muscular dystrophy can no longer walk. Death usually occurs in the early 20s from heart and respiratory problems.

Girls almost never have Duchenne muscular dystrophy. Why not? Because the dystrophin gene is on the X chromosome, and muscular dystrophy alleles are recessive. Therefore, a boy will suffer muscular dystrophy if he has a defective dystrophin allele on his single X chromosome, but a girl, with two X chromosomes, would need two defective copies to suffer the disorder. This virtually never happens, because a girl would have to receive one defective dystrophin allele from her mother, on one of her X chromosomes, and one from her father, on his X chromosome. Because they suffer early disability and death, boys with Duchenne muscular dystrophy almost never have children.

This scenario makes genetic sense, but it may seem to defy the concept of evolution by natural selection. Shouldn't natural selection have almost completely eradicated defective dystrophin alleles? Actually, natural selection does rapidly eliminate defective dystrophin alleles. However, the dystrophin gene is enormous—about 2.2 *million* nucleotides long, compared to about 27 *thousand* nucleotides for the average human gene. In fact, the dystrophin gene occupies about 2% of the entire X chromosome.

Why does this matter? Remember, alleles arise as mutations in DNA. The longer the gene, the greater the chances for a mistake during DNA replication, so the mutation rate for the dystrophin gene is almost a hundred times greater than for the average gene. In fact, it is a tribute to the astounding accuracy of DNA copying that we don't all suffer from muscular dystrophy. About one-third of the boys with muscular dystrophy receive a new mutation that occurred in an X chromosome of a reproductive cell of their mother, and two-thirds inherit a preexisting allele in one of their mother's X chromosomes. The new mutations counterbalance natural selection, resulting in the steady incidence of about 1 in 3,500 boys.

Can anything be done for boys with muscular dystrophy? Right now, there are no cures, although treatments are available that slow muscle degeneration, prolong life, and make the affected boys more comfortable. However, in 2011, clinical trials showed that a novel molecular technique can trick the muscles of boys with muscular dystrophy into making partially functional dystrophin from a faulty *DMD* allele. Several research labs are trying to devise ways to colonize dystrophic muscles with stem cells that carry a completely functional copy of the *DMD* gene. If this works, the decades-old dream of curing muscular dystrophy may finally be realized.

▲ FIGURE E10-2 Matthias Steiner wins the gold with a lift of almost 569 pounds.

Some Human Genetic Disorders Are Caused by Abnormal Numbers of Chromosomes

Usually, the intricate mechanisms of meiotic cell division ensure that each sperm and egg receives only one chromosome from each homologous pair (see Chapter 9). However, this elaborate dance of the chromosomes occasionally misses a step, resulting in gametes that have too many or too few chromosomes. Such errors in meiosis, called **nondisjunction,** can affect the number of sex chromosomes or autosomes in a gamete (Fig. 10-26). Most embryos that arise from the fusion of gametes with abnormal chromosome numbers spontaneously abort, accounting for 20% to 50% of all miscarriages, but some embryos with abnormal numbers of chromosomes survive to birth or beyond.

Some Genetic Disorders Are Caused by Abnormal Numbers of Sex Chromosomes

Sperm usually carry either an X or a Y chromosome (see Fig. 10-20). Nondisjunction of sex chromosomes in males produces sperm with either no sex chromosome (often called

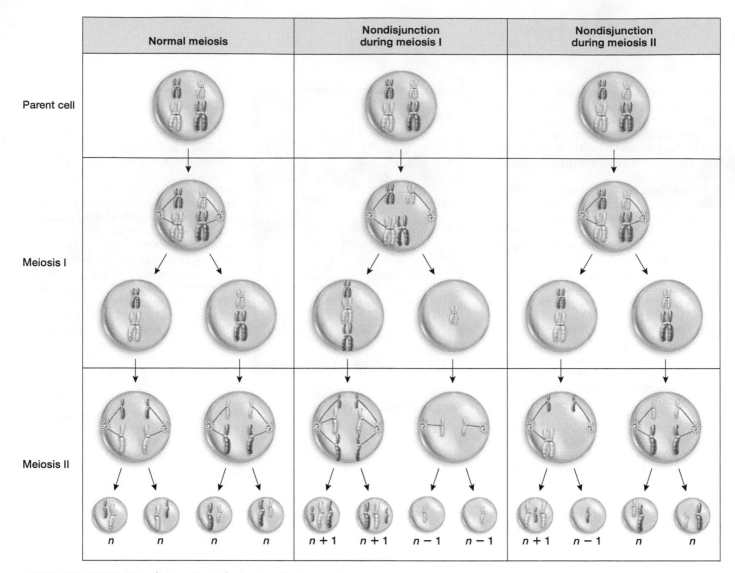

	Normal meiosis	Nondisjunction during meiosis I	Nondisjunction during meiosis II

▲ FIGURE 10-26 Nondisjunction during meiosis Nondisjunction may occur either during meiosis I or meiosis II, resulting in gametes with too many ($n + 1$) or too few ($n - 1$) chromosomes.

"O" sperm), or two sex chromosomes (XX, YY, or XY, depending on whether the nondisjunction occurred in meiosis I or II). Nondisjunction of the sex chromosomes in females produces O or XX eggs instead of eggs with one X chromosome. When normal gametes fuse with these defective sperm or eggs, the zygotes have normal numbers of autosomes but abnormal numbers of sex chromosomes (Table 10-2). The most common abnormalities are XO, XXX, XXY, and XYY. (Genes on the X chromosome are essential to survival, so any embryo without at least one X chromosome spontaneously aborts very early in development.)

Turner Syndrome (XO) About 1 in every 3,000 female babies has only one X chromosome, a condition known as **Turner syndrome** (also called monosomy X, meaning "having one X chromosome"). At puberty, hormone deficiencies prevent XO females from menstruating or developing secondary sexual characteristics, such as enlarged breasts.

Treatment with estrogen promotes physical development. However, because most women with Turner syndrome lack mature eggs, hormone treatment does not make it possible for them to bear children. Other common characteristics of women with Turner syndrome include short stature, folds of skin around the neck, and increased risk of cardiovascular disease, kidney defects, and hearing loss. Because women with Turner syndrome have only one X chromosome, they display X-linked recessive disorders, such as hemophilia and color deficiency, much more frequently than XX women do.

Trisomy X (XXX) About 1 in every 1,000 women has three X chromosomes, a condition known as **trisomy X,** or triple X. Most such women have no detectable differences from XX women, except for a tendency to be taller and to have a higher incidence of learning disabilities. Unlike women with Turner syndrome, most trisomy X women are fertile and, interestingly enough, almost always bear normal XX and XY children. Some

TABLE 10-2   Effects of Nondisjunction of the Sex Chromosomes During Meiosis

	Nondisjunction in Father		
Sex Chromosomes of Defective Sperm	Sex Chromosomes of Normal Egg	Sex Chromosomes of Offspring	Phenotype
O (none)	X	XO	Female—Turner syndrome
XX	X	XXX	Female—Trisomy X
XY	X	XXY	Male—Klinefelter syndrome
YY	X	XYY	Male—Jacob syndrome
	Nondisjunction in Mother		
Sex Chromosomes of Normal Sperm	Sex Chromosomes of Defective Egg	Sex Chromosomes of Offspring	Phenotype
X	O (none)	XO	Female—Turner syndrome
Y	O (none)	YO	Dies as embryo
X	XX	XXX	Female—Trisomy X
Y	XX	XXY	Male—Klinefelter syndrome

unknown mechanism must operate during meiosis to prevent an extra X chromosome from being included in their eggs.

Klinefelter Syndrome (XXY) About 1 male in every 1,000 is born with two X chromosomes and one Y chromosome. Most of these men go through life never realizing that they have an extra X chromosome. However, at puberty, some show mixed secondary sexual characteristics, including partial breast development, broadening of the hips, and small testes. These symptoms are known as **Klinefelter syndrome.** XXY men may be infertile because of low sperm count but are not impotent. They are usually diagnosed when an XXY man and his partner seek medical help because they are unable to have children.

Jacob Syndrome (XYY) **Jacob syndrome** (XYY) occurs in about 1 male in every 1,000. You might expect that an extra Y chromosome, which has few active genes, would not make very much difference, and this seems to be true in most cases. The most common effect is that XYY males tend to be taller than average. There may also be a slightly increased likelihood of learning disabilities.

Some Genetic Disorders Are Caused by Abnormal Numbers of Autosomes

Nondisjunction of the autosomes produces eggs or sperm that are missing an autosome or that have two copies of an autosome. Fusion with a normal gamete (bearing one copy of each autosome) leads to an embryo with either one or three copies of the affected autosome. Embryos that have only one copy of any of the autosomes abort so early in development that the woman never knows she was pregnant. Embryos with three copies of an autosome (trisomy) also usually spontaneously abort. However, a small fraction of embryos with three copies of chromosomes 13, 18, or 21 survive to birth. In the case of trisomy 21, the child may live into adulthood.

Trisomy 21 (Down Syndrome) An extra copy of chromosome 21, a condition called **trisomy 21,** or **Down syndrome,** occurs in about 1 of every 800 births, although this rate varies tremendously with the age of the parents (see below). Children with Down syndrome have several distinctive physical characteristics, including weak muscle tone, a small mouth held partially open because it cannot accommodate the tongue, and distinctively shaped eyelids (**Fig. 10-27**). More serious problems include heart malformations, low resistance to infectious diseases, and varying degrees of mental retardation.

The frequency of nondisjunction increases with the age of the parents, especially the mother. Only about 0.05% of children born to 20-year-old women, but more than 3% of children born to women over 45 years of age, have Down syndrome. Nondisjunction in sperm accounts for about 10% of the cases of Down syndrome, and there is only a small increase in defective sperm with increasing age of the father. Since the 1970s, it has become more common for couples to delay having children, increasing the probability of trisomy 21. Trisomy 21 can be diagnosed before birth by examining the chromosomes of fetal cells and, with less certainty, by biochemical tests and ultrasound examination of the fetus (see "Health Watch: Prenatal Genetic Screening" in Chapter 13).

CHECK YOUR LEARNING

Can you use pedigrees to determine the pattern of inheritance of a trait? Can you describe why some genetic disorders might be dominant while others are recessive, and give examples of each? Are you able to explain how nondisjunction causes offspring to have too many or too few chromosomes? Can you describe some of the human genetic disorders that are caused by nondisjunction?

(a) Karyotype showing three copies of chromosome 21   **(b) Girl with Down syndrome**

▲ FIGURE 10-27 **Trisomy 21, or Down syndrome (a)** This karyotype of a Down syndrome child reveals three copies of chromosome 21 (arrow). **(b)** The younger of these two sisters shows the facial features common in people with Down syndrome.

CASE STUDY revisited

Sudden Death on the Court

Medical examinations revealed that Flo Hyman's father and sister have Marfan syndrome, but her mother and brother do not. A single defective fibrillin allele is enough to cause Marfan syndrome. What can we conclude about the inheritance of Marfan syndrome from these data?

First, if even one defective fibrillin allele produces Marfan syndrome, then Hyman's mother must carry two normal alleles, because she does not have Marfan syndrome. Second, because Hyman's father has Marfan syndrome, it is very likely that Hyman inherited a defective fibrillin allele from him. The fact that her sister also has Marfan syndrome makes this virtually certain. Third, is Marfan syndrome inherited as a dominant or a recessive condition? If one defective allele is enough to cause Marfan syndrome, then this allele must be dominant and the normal allele must be recessive. Fourth, there seems to be no gender effect in Hyman's family. Marfan syndrome is not sex-linked, because the fibrillin gene is on an autosome.

Finally, if Hyman had borne children, could they have inherited Marfan syndrome from her? For a dominant disorder, any children who inherited her defective allele would develop Marfan syndrome. Therefore, her children would have had a 50% chance of inheriting Marfan syndrome. (Try working this out with a Punnett square.)

At the beginning of this chapter, we suggested that Rachmaninoff, Paganini, and Lincoln may have had Marfan syndrome. You may wonder how anyone can be sure that they actually had the disorder. Well, you're right—nobody really knows. The "diagnosis" is based on photographs and descriptions. There is considerable dispute about whether Lincoln had Marfan syndrome or some other condition. There is less controversy about Rachmaninoff, who was 6′6″ tall—extremely tall for a man born in 1873—and whose hands could span 13 white keys on a piano (try it yourself!). Most modern pianists cannot play some of Rachmaninoff's music as he originally wrote it, because the notes in some of the chords are so far apart on the keyboard.

Consider This

BioEthics   If a parent has been diagnosed with Marfan syndrome, then in some instances the defective gene can be detected in an embryo. Some other genetic disorders, such as cystic fibrosis and sickle-cell anemia, can easily be detected, in adults, children, and embryos. In these recessive diseases, if two heterozygotes have children together, each of their children has a 25% chance of having the disorder. Although there is no cure for these diseases, there will probably be better treatments within a few years. If you and your spouse were both heterozygotes for a genetic disorder, would you seek prenatal diagnosis of an embryo? What would you do if your embryo were destined to be born with Marfan syndrome?

CHAPTER REVIEW

Summary of Key Concepts

10.1 What Is the Physical Basis of Inheritance?
The units of inheritance are genes, which are segments of DNA found at specific locations (loci) on chromosomes. Genes may exist in two or more slightly different, alternative forms, called alleles. When both homologous chromosomes carry the same allele at a given locus, the organism is homozygous for that particular gene. When the two homologous chromosomes have different alleles at a given locus, the organism is heterozygous for that gene.

10.2 How Were the Principles of Inheritance Discovered?
Gregor Mendel deduced many principles of inheritance in the mid-1800s, before the discovery of DNA, genes, chromosomes, or meiosis. He did this by choosing an appropriate experimental subject, designing his experiments carefully, following progeny for several generations, and analyzing his data statistically.

10.3 How Are Single Traits Inherited?
A trait is an observable or measurable feature of an organism's phenotype, such as hair texture or blood type. Traits are inherited in particular patterns that depend on the alleles that parents pass on to their offspring. Each parent provides its offspring with one allele of every gene, so the offspring inherits a pair of alleles for every gene. The combination of alleles in the offspring determines whether it displays a particular phenotype. Dominant alleles mask the expression of recessive alleles. The masking of recessive alleles can result in organisms with the same phenotype but different genotypes. Organisms with two dominant alleles (homozygous dominant) have the same phenotype as do organisms with one dominant and one recessive allele (heterozygous). Because each allele segregates randomly during meiosis, we can predict the relative proportions of offspring with a particular trait, using Punnett squares or probability.

10.4 How Are Multiple Traits Inherited?
If the genes for two traits are located on separate chromosomes, their alleles assort independently of one another into the egg or sperm; that is, the distribution of alleles of one gene into the gametes does not affect the distribution of the alleles of the other gene. Thus, breeding two organisms that are heterozygous at two loci on separate chromosomes produces offspring with nine different genotypes. For typical dominant and recessive alleles, the offspring will display only four different phenotypes (see Fig. 10-11).

10.5 Do the Mendelian Rules of Inheritance Apply to All Traits?
Not all inheritance follows the simple dominant-recessive pattern:

- In incomplete dominance, heterozygotes have a phenotype that is intermediate between the two homozygous phenotypes.

- If we examine the genes of many members of a given species, we find that many genes have more than two alleles; that is, there are multiple alleles of the gene.
- Codominance is a relationship among the alleles of a single gene in which two alleles independently contribute to the observed phenotype.
- Many traits are determined by several different genes that all contribute to the phenotype, a phenomenon called polygenic inheritance.
- Pleiotropy occurs when a single gene has multiple effects on an organism's phenotype.
- The environment influences the phenotypic expression of all traits.

10.6 How Are Genes Located on the Same Chromosome Inherited?
Genes on the same chromosome (encoded on the same DNA double helix) are linked to one another and therefore tend to be inherited together. However, crossing over will result in some recombination of alleles on each chromosome. Crossing over will occur more often the farther apart on a chromosome the genes lie.

10.7 How Are Sex and Sex-Linked Traits Inherited?
In many animals, sex is determined by sex chromosomes, often designated X and Y. In mammals, females have two X chromosomes, whereas males have one X and one Y chromosome. The rest of the chromosomes, identical in the two sexes, are called autosomes. Males include either an X or a Y chromosome in their sperm, whereas females always include an X chromosome in their eggs. Therefore, gender is determined by the sex chromosome in the sperm that fertilizes an egg.

Sex-linked genes are found on the X or Y chromosome. In mammals, the Y chromosome has many fewer genes than the X chromosome, so most sex-linked genes are found on the X chromosome. Because males have only one copy of X chromosome genes, recessive traits on the X chromosome are more likely to be phenotypically expressed in males.

10.8 How Are Human Genetic Disorders Inherited?
The genetics of humans is similar to the genetics of other animals, but is more difficult to study because experimental crosses are not feasible. Analysis of family pedigrees and, more recently, molecular genetic techniques are used to determine the mode of inheritance of human traits.

Some genetic disorders are inherited as recessive traits; therefore, only homozygous recessive persons show symptoms of the disease. Heterozygotes are called carriers; they carry the recessive allele but do not express the trait. Some other diseases are inherited as simple dominant traits. In such cases, only one copy of the dominant allele is needed to cause disease symptoms. Some human genetic disorders are sex-linked.

Errors in meiosis can result in gametes with abnormal numbers of sex chromosomes or autosomes. Many people with abnormal numbers of sex chromosomes have distinguishing physical characteristics. Abnormal numbers of autosomes typically lead to spontaneous abortion early in pregnancy. In rare instances, the fetus may survive to birth, but mental and physical deficiencies always occur, as is the case with Down syndrome (trisomy 21). The likelihood of abnormal numbers of chromosomes increases with increasing age of the mother and, to a lesser extent, the father.

Key Terms

albinism *181*	law of segregation *169*
allele *166*	locus (plural, loci) *166*
autosome *179*	muscular dystrophy *185*
carrier *181*	mutation *166*
codominance *175*	nondisjunction *185*
cross-fertilization *168*	pedigree *181*
dominant *169*	phenotype *170*
Down syndrome *187*	pleiotropy *176*
gene *166*	polygenic inheritance *176*
gene linkage *177*	Punnett square method *170*
genetic recombination *178*	recessive *169*
genotype *170*	self-fertilization *167*
hemophilia *184*	sex chromosome *179*
heterozygous *166*	sex-linked *179*
homozygous *166*	sickle-cell anemia *182*
Huntington disease *183*	test cross *171*
incomplete dominance *174*	trisomy 21 *187*
inheritance *166*	trisomy X *186*
Jacob syndrome *187*	true-breeding *168*
Klinefelter syndrome *187*	Turner syndrome *186*
law of independent	X chromosome *179*
assortment *173*	Y chromosome *179*

Learning Outcomes

In this chapter, you have learned to . . .

LO1 Describe the relationships among chromosomes, DNA, genes, mutations, and alleles, and explain their function in inheritance.

LO2 Summarize Mendel's conclusions about the inheritance of single and multiple traits and explain how the results of his experiments support those conclusions.

LO3 Determine the genotypes and phenotypes of offspring that result from mating organisms with traits that follow simple patterns of Mendelian inheritance.

LO4 Describe the inheritance of traits characterized by incomplete dominance, codominance, polygenic inheritance, and pleiotropy.

LO5 Explain how the physical locations of genes and the events that occur during meiosis affect inheritance.

LO6 Explain the chromosomal basis of sex determination and how it influences the inheritance of sex-linked traits.

LO7 Interpret pedigrees for dominant and recessive traits.

LO8 Describe the causes and symptoms of inherited human disorders produced by defective alleles of individual genes and by abnormal numbers of chromosomes.

Thinking Through the Concepts

Fill-in-the-Blank

1. The physical position of a gene on a chromosome is called its _____. Alternative forms of a gene are called _____. These alternative forms of genes arise as _____, which are changes in the nucleotide sequence of a gene. **LO1**

2. An organism is described as *Rr*: red. *Rr* is the organism's _____, while red color is its _____. This organism would be (homozygous/heterozygous) for this color gene. **LO2 LO3**

3. The inheritance of multiple traits depends on the locations of the genes that control the traits. If the genes are on different chromosomes, then the traits are inherited (as a group/independently). If the genes are located close together on a single chromosome, then the traits tend to be inherited (as a group/independently). Genes on the same chromosome are said to be _____. **LO3 LO5**

4. Many organisms, including mammals, have both autosomes and sex chromosomes. In mammals, males have _____ sex chromosomes and females have _____ chromosomes. The sex of offspring depends on which chromosome is present in the (sperm/egg). **LO6**

5. Genes that are present on one sex chromosome but not the other are called _____. **LO6**

6. If the phenotype of heterozygotes is intermediate between the phenotypes of the two homozygotes, this pattern of inheritance is called _____. If heterozygotes express phenotypes of both homozygotes (not intermediate, but showing both traits), this is called _____. In _____, many genes, usually with similar effects on phenotype, control the inheritance of a trait. **LO4**

Review Questions

1. Define the following terms: *gene, allele, dominant, recessive, true-breeding, homozygous, heterozygous, cross-fertilization,* and *self-fertilization.* **LO1 LO2 LO3**

2. Explain why genes located on the same chromosome are said to be linked. Why do alleles of linked genes sometimes separate during meiosis? **LO5**

3. Define *polygenic inheritance.* Why does polygenic inheritance sometimes allow parents to produce offspring that are notably different in skin color than either parent? **LO4**

4. What is sex linkage? In mammals, which sex would be most likely to show recessive sex-linked traits? **LO6**

5. What is the difference between a phenotype and a genotype? Does knowledge of an organism's phenotype always allow you to determine the genotype? What type of experiment would you perform to determine the genotype of a phenotypically dominant individual? **LO2 LO3**

6. In the pedigree of part (a) of Figure 10-22, do you think that the individuals showing the trait are homozygous or heterozygous? How can you tell from the pedigree? **LO7**

7. Define *nondisjunction,* and describe the common syndromes caused by nondisjunction of sex chromosomes and autosomes. **LO8**

Applying the Concepts

1. Sometimes the term *gene* is used rather casually. Compare the terms *allele* and *gene*.

2. In an alternate universe, all the genes in all species have only two alleles, one dominant and one recessive. Would every trait have only two phenotypes? Would all members of a species that are dominant for a given gene have exactly the same phenotype? Explain your reasoning.

3. Although American society has been described as a "melting pot," people often engage in "assortative mating," in which they marry others of similar height, socioeconomic status, race, and IQ. Discuss the consequences to society of assortative mating among humans. Would society be better off if people mated more randomly? Explain.

Genetics Problems

1. In certain cattle, hair color can be red (homozygous R_1R_1), white (homozygous R_2R_2), or roan (a mixture of red and white hairs, heterozygous R_1R_2).

   a. When a red bull is mated to a white cow, what genotypes and phenotypes of offspring could be obtained?

   b. If one of the offspring bulls in part (a) were mated to a white cow, what genotypes and phenotypes of offspring could be produced? In what proportion?

2. The palomino horse is golden in color. Unfortunately for horse fanciers, palominos do not breed true. In a series of matings between palominos, the following offspring were obtained:

   65 palominos
   32 cream-colored
   34 chestnut (reddish brown)

   What is the probable mode of inheritance of palomino coloration?

3. In the edible pea, tall (*T*) is dominant to short (*t*), and green pods (*G*) are dominant to yellow pods (*g*). List the types of gametes and offspring that would be produced in the following crosses:

   a. $TtGg \times TtGg$
   b. $TtGg \times TTGG$
   c. $TtGg \times Ttgg$

4. In tomatoes, round fruit (*R*) is dominant to long fruit (*r*), and smooth skin (*S*) is dominant to fuzzy skin (*s*). A true-breeding round, smooth tomato (*RRSS*) was crossbred with a true-breeding long, fuzzy tomato (*rrss*). All the F_1 offspring were round and smooth (*RrSs*). When these F_1 plants were bred, the following F_2 generation was obtained:

   Round, smooth: 43
   Long, fuzzy: 13

   Are the genes for skin texture and fruit shape likely to be on the same chromosome or on different chromosomes? Explain your answer.

5. In the tomatoes of Problem 4, an F_1 offspring (*RrSs*) was mated with a homozygous recessive (*rrss*). The following offspring were obtained:

   Round, smooth: 583   Long, fuzzy: 602
   Round, fuzzy: 21   Long, smooth: 16

   What is the most likely explanation for this distribution of phenotypes?

6. In humans, hair color is controlled by two interacting genes. The same pigment, melanin, is present in both brown-haired and blond-haired people, but brown hair has much more of it. Brown hair (*B*) is dominant to blond (*b*). Whether any melanin can be synthesized depends on another gene. The dominant form of this second gene (*M*) allows melanin synthesis; the recessive form (*m*) prevents melanin synthesis. Homozygous recessives (*mm*) are albino. What will be the expected proportions of phenotypes in the children of the following parents?

   a. *BBMM* × *BbMm*
   b. *BbMm* × *BbMm*
   c. *BbMm* × *bbmm*

7. In humans, one of the genes determining color vision is located on the X chromosome. The dominant form (*C*) produces normal color vision; red-green color deficiency (*c*) is recessive. If a man with normal color vision marries a color-deficient woman, what is the probability of them having a color-deficient son? A color-deficient daughter?

8. In the couple described in Problem 7, the woman gives birth to a color-deficient but otherwise normal daughter. The husband sues for a divorce on the grounds of adultery. Will his case stand up in court? Explain your answer.

Answers to Figure Caption questions and Fill-in-the-Blank questions can be found in the Answers section at the back of the book.

(MB) *Go to MasteringBiology for practice quizzes, activities, eText, videos, current events, and more.*

CHAPTER 11

DNA: The Molecule of Heredity

Ordinary bull or incredible hulk? A tiny change in DNA makes all the difference.

CASE STUDY

Muscles, Mutations, and Myostatin

NO, THE BULL in the top photo hasn't been pumping iron or taking steroids—he's a Belgian Blue, and they always have bulging muscles. What makes a Belgian Blue look like a bodybuilder, compared to an ordinary bull, such as the Hereford in the bottom photo?

When any mammal develops, its cells divide many times, enlarge, and become specialized for a specific function. The size, shape, and cell types in any organ are precisely regulated during development, so that you don't wind up with a head the size of a basketball, or have hair growing on your liver. Muscle development is no exception. When you were very young, cells destined to form

your muscles multiplied, fused together to form long, relatively thick cells with multiple nuclei, and synthesized specialized proteins that cause muscles to contract and thereby move your skeleton. A protein called myostatin, found in all mammals, puts the brakes on muscle development. "Myostatin" literally means "to make muscles stay the same," and that is exactly what it does. As muscles develop, myostatin slows down—and eventually stops—the multiplication of these pre-muscle cells. Myostatin also regulates the ultimate size of muscle cells and, therefore, their strength.

Belgian Blues have more, and larger, muscle cells than ordinary cattle do. Why? You may have already guessed—they don't produce normal myostatin. As you will learn in this

chapter, proteins are synthesized from the genetic instructions contained in **deoxyribonucleic acid (DNA).** The DNA of a Belgian Blue is very slightly different from the DNA of other cattle—the Belgian Blue has a change, or mutation, in the DNA of its myostatin gene. As a result, it produces defective myostatin. Belgian Blue pre-muscle cells multiply more than normal, and the cells become extra large as they differentiate, producing remarkably buff cattle.

How does DNA contain the instructions for traits such as muscle size, flower color, or gender? How are these instructions passed, usually unchanged, from generation to generation? And why do the instructions sometimes change? To answer these questions, we must learn more about the structure and function of DNA.

AT A GLANCE

LEARNING GOALS

LG1 Describe the key experimental evidence indicating that DNA is the molecule of heredity.

LG2 Describe the structure of DNA, including nucleotides, the sugar-phosphate backbone, the double helix, and the role of hydrogen bonds.

LG3 Explain how genetic information is encoded in DNA.

LG4 Summarize the steps of DNA replication, including identification and action of the enzymes involved in each step.

LG5 Define the term *mutation*, and name and describe the different types of mutations.

11.1 HOW DID SCIENTISTS DISCOVER THAT GENES ARE MADE OF DNA?

By the late 1800s, scientists had learned that genetic information exists in discrete units that they called genes. However, they didn't know what a gene is. They knew only that genes determine many inherited traits; for example, genes determine whether roses are red, pink, yellow, or white. By the early 1900s, studies of dividing cells provided strong evidence that genes are parts of chromosomes. Soon, biochemists found that eukaryotic chromosomes are composed only of protein and DNA, so one of these must be the molecule of heredity. But which one?

Transformed Bacteria Revealed the Link Between Genes and DNA

In the late 1920s, Frederick Griffith, a British researcher, was trying to make a vaccine to prevent bacterial pneumonia, a major cause of death at that time. Some antibacterial vaccines consist of a weakened strain of the bacteria, which can't cause illness. Injecting this weakened but living strain into an animal may stimulate immunity against the disease-causing strains. Other vaccines use disease-causing (virulent) bacteria that have been killed by exposure to heat or chemicals.

Griffith experimented with two strains of the bacterium *Streptococcus pneumoniae*. One strain, R, did not cause pneumonia when injected into mice (**Fig. 11-1a**). Injecting mice with the other strain, S, caused pneumonia, killing the mice in a day or two (**Fig. 11-1b**). As expected, when the S-strain was killed and injected into mice, it did not cause disease (**Fig. 11-1c**). Unfortunately, neither the live R-strain nor the killed S-strain provided immunity against live S-strain bacteria.

Griffith also tried injecting a mixture of living R-strain bacteria and heat-killed S-strain bacteria (**Fig. 11-1d**). Because neither caused pneumonia on its own, he expected the mice to remain healthy. To his surprise, the mice sickened and died. When he autopsied the mice, he recovered living S-strain bacteria from them. Griffith hypothesized that some substance in the heat-killed S-strain changed the living, harmless R-strain bacteria into the deadly S-strain, a process he called transformation. These transformed bacteria could cause pneumonia.

Griffith never discovered an effective pneumonia vaccine, so in that sense his experiments were a failure (in fact, an effective vaccine against *Streptococcus pneumoniae* was not developed until the late 1970s). However, Griffith's experiments marked a turning point in our understanding of genetics, because other researchers suspected that the substance that causes transformation might be the long-sought molecule of heredity.

The Transforming Molecule Is DNA

In 1944, Oswald Avery, Colin MacLeod, and Maclyn McCarty discovered that the transforming molecule is DNA. They isolated DNA from S-strain bacteria, mixed it with live R-strain bacteria, and produced live S-strain bacteria. They treated some samples with protein-destroying enzymes and other samples with DNA-destroying enzymes. The protein-destroying enzymes did not prevent transformation. However, treating samples with DNA-destroying enzymes did prevent transformation. Therefore, they concluded that transformation must be caused by DNA, and not by traces of protein contaminating the DNA.

This discovery helps us to interpret the results of Griffith's experiments. Heating S-strain cells killed them but did not completely destroy their DNA. When killed S-strain bacteria were mixed with living R-strain bacteria, fragments of DNA from the dead S-strain cells entered into some of the R-strain cells and became incorporated into the chromosome of the R-strain bacteria (**Fig. 11-2**). Some of these DNA fragments contained the genes needed to cause pneumonia, transforming an R-strain cell into an S-strain cell. Thus, Avery, MacLeod, and McCarty concluded that DNA is the molecule of heredity.

Over the next decade, evidence continued to accumulate that DNA is the genetic material in many, or perhaps

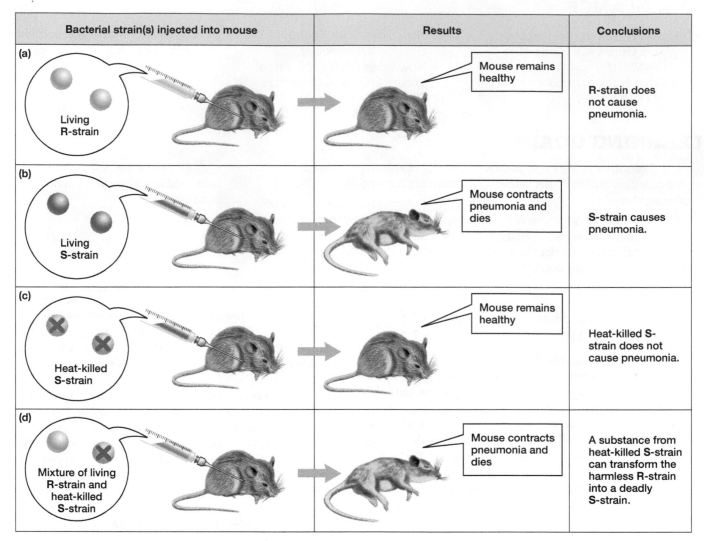

Bacterial strain(s) injected into mouse	Results	Conclusions
(a) Living R-strain	Mouse remains healthy	R-strain does not cause pneumonia.
(b) Living S-strain	Mouse contracts pneumonia and dies	S-strain causes pneumonia.
(c) Heat-killed S-strain	Mouse remains healthy	Heat-killed S-strain does not cause pneumonia.
(d) Mixture of living R-strain and heat-killed S-strain	Mouse contracts pneumonia and dies	A substance from heat-killed S-strain can transform the harmless R-strain into a deadly S-strain.

▲ FIGURE 11-1 **Transformation in bacteria** Griffith's discovery that bacteria can be transformed from harmless to deadly laid the groundwork for the discovery that genes are composed of DNA.

all, organisms. For example, before dividing, a eukaryotic cell duplicates its chromosomes (see Chapter 9) and exactly doubles its DNA content, but not its protein content—just what would be expected if genes are made of DNA. Virtually all of the remaining skeptics were convinced by a superb set of experiments performed in the early 1950s by Alfred Hershey and Martha Chase, which conclusively showed that DNA is the hereditary molecule of certain viruses (see "Science in Action: DNA Is the Hereditary Molecule of Bacteriophages" on pp. **196–197**).

CHECK YOUR LEARNING

Can you describe the experiments of Griffiths and those of Avery, MacLeod, and McCarty? Can you explain why these experiments showed that DNA is the hereditary molecule?

11.2 WHAT IS THE STRUCTURE OF DNA?

Knowing that genes are made of DNA does not answer critical questions about inheritance: How does DNA encode genetic information? How is DNA replicated so that a cell can pass its hereditary information to its daughter cells? The secrets of DNA function and replication are found in the three-dimensional structure of the DNA molecule.

DNA Is Composed of Four Nucleotides

DNA consists of long chains made of subunits called **nucleotides.** Each nucleotide consists of three parts: a phosphate group, a sugar called deoxyribose, and one of four nitrogen-containing **bases.** The bases found in DNA are **adenine (A), guanine (G), thymine (T),** and **cytosine (C)** (Fig. 11-3). Adenine and guanine both consist of fused five- and six-member rings of carbon and nitrogen atoms, with different functional groups attached to different positions on the six-member ring. Thymine and cytosine consist of a single six-member ring of carbon and nitrogen atoms, again with different functional groups attached to different positions on the ring.

In the 1940s, biochemist Erwin Chargaff of Columbia University analyzed the amounts of the four bases in DNA from organisms as diverse as bacteria, sea urchins, fish, and humans. He found a curious consistency: Although the

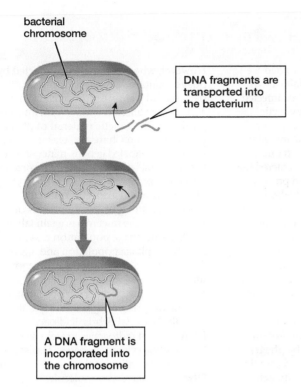

bacterial chromosome

DNA fragments are transported into the bacterium

A DNA fragment is incorporated into the chromosome

▲ FIGURE 11-2 **Molecular mechanism of transformation** Most bacteria have a single circular chromosome made of DNA. Transformation may occur when a living bacterium takes up pieces of DNA from its environment and incorporates those fragments into its chromosome.

proportions of each base differ from species to species, for a given species, there are always equal amounts of adenine and thymine, and equal amounts of guanine and cytosine. This consistency, often called "Chargaff's rule," certainly seemed significant, but it would be almost another decade before anyone figured out what it meant about DNA structure.

DNA Is a Double Helix of Two Nucleotide Strands

Determining the structure of large biological molecules isn't easy, even today. Nevertheless, in the late 1940s, several scientists began to investigate the structure of DNA. British scientists Maurice Wilkins and Rosalind Franklin used X-ray diffraction to study the DNA molecule. They bombarded crystals of purified DNA with X-rays and recorded how the X-rays bounced off the DNA molecules (**Fig. 11-4**). As you can see, the resulting pattern does not provide a direct picture of DNA structure. However, experts like Wilkins and Franklin could extract a lot of information about DNA from the pattern. First, a molecule of DNA is long and thin, with a uniform diameter of 2 nanometers (2 billionths of a meter). Second, DNA is helical, twisted like a corkscrew or a spiral staircase. Third, DNA is a double helix; that is, two DNA strands coil around one another. Fourth, DNA consists of repeating subunits. And fifth, the phosphates are probably on the outside of the helix.

Even with the X-ray diffraction data, it was no trivial task to work out the structure of DNA. However, by combining the

phosphate — sugar — base = adenine

phosphate — sugar — base = guanine

phosphate — sugar — base = thymine

phosphate — sugar — base = cytosine

▲ FIGURE 11-3 **DNA nucleotides**

diffraction data with a knowledge of how complex organic molecules bond together and an intuition that "important biological objects come in pairs," James Watson and Francis Crick deduced the structure of DNA (see "Science in Action: The Discovery of the Double Helix" on p. **199**).

Watson and Crick proposed that a single **strand** of DNA is a polymer consisting of many nucleotide subunits. The phosphate group of one nucleotide is bonded to the sugar of the next nucleotide in the strand, thus producing a **sugar-phosphate backbone** of alternating, covalently bonded sugars and phosphates (**Fig. 11-5**). The bases of the nucleotides stick out from this sugar-phosphate backbone.

All of the nucleotides in a single DNA strand are oriented in the same direction. Therefore, the two ends of a DNA strand differ; one end has a "free" or unbonded

SCIENCE IN ACTION DNA Is the Hereditary Molecule of Bacteriophages

Certain viruses infect only bacteria and are aptly called **bacteriophages,** meaning "bacteria eaters" (Fig. E11-1). A bacteriophage ("phage" for short) depends on a host bacterium for every aspect of its life cycle (Fig. E11-1b). When a phage encounters a bacterium, it attaches to the bacterial cell wall and injects its genetic material into the bacterium. The outer coat of the phage remains outside. The bacterium cannot distinguish phage genes from its own genes, so it "reads" the phage genes and uses that information to produce more phages. Finally, one of the phage genes directs the synthesis of an enzyme that ruptures the bacterium, freeing the newly manufactured phages.

Even though many bacteriophages have intricate structures (Fig. E11-1a), they are chemically very simple, containing only DNA and protein. Therefore, one of these two molecules must be the phage genetic material. Alfred Hershey and Martha Chase

used this chemical simplicity to deduce that the phage genetic material is DNA.

Hershey and Chase knew that infected bacteria should contain phage genetic material, so if they could "label" phage DNA and protein, and separate the infected bacteria from the phage coats left outside, they could see which molecule entered the bacteria (Fig. E11-2). DNA and protein both contain carbon, oxygen, hydrogen, and nitrogen (see Chapter 3). DNA also contains phosphorus but not sulfur, whereas proteins contain sulfur but not phosphorus.

Hershey and Chase forced one population of phages to synthesize DNA using radioactive phosphorus, thereby labeling the phage DNA. Another population of phages was forced to synthesize protein using radioactive sulfur, thus labeling the phage protein. When bacteria were infected by phages containing radioactively labeled protein, the bacteria did not become radioactive.

However, when bacteria were infected by phages containing radioactive DNA, the bacteria did become radioactive. Hershey and Chase concluded that DNA, and not protein, is the genetic material of phages.

Hershey and Chase also reasoned that some of the labeled genetic material from the "parental" phages might be incorporated into the genetic material of the "offspring" phages. (You will learn more about this in Section 11.4.) In a second set of experiments, the researchers again labeled DNA in one phage population and protein in another phage population and allowed the phages to infect bacteria. After enough time had passed so that the phages had reproduced, the bacteria were broken open, and the offspring phages were separated from the bacterial debris. Radioactive DNA, but not radioactive protein, was found in the offspring phages. This second experiment confirmed the results of the first: DNA is the hereditary molecule.

(a) Structure of a bacteriophage

❻ The bacterial wall is destroyed; phages are released

❶ The phage attaches to a bacterium

❷ The phage injects its DNA into the bacterium

❸ The phage DNA is replicated

❹ Phage parts are synthesized, using the bacterium's metabolism

❺ Complete phages are assembled

(b) Bacteriophage life cycle

▲ FIGURE E11-1 **Bacteriophages (a)** Many bacteriophages have complex structures, including a head containing genetic material, tail fibers that attach to the surface of a bacterium, and an elaborate apparatus for injecting their genetic material into the bacterium. **(b)** A bacteriophage uses the metabolism of a bacterium to produce more phages.

Observations:
1. Bacteriophage viruses consist of only DNA and protein.
2. Bacteriophages inject their genetic material into bacteria, forcing the bacteria to synthesize more phages.
3. The outer coat of bacteriophages stays outside of the bacteria.
4. DNA contains phosphorus but not sulfur.
   - DNA can be "labeled" with radioactive phosphorus.
5. Protein contains sulfur but not phosphorus.
   - Protein can be "labeled" with radioactive sulfur.

Question: Is DNA or protein the genetic material of bacteriophages?

Hypothesis: DNA is the genetic material.

Prediction:
1. If bacteria are infected with bacteriophages containing radioactively labeled DNA, the bacteria will be radioactive.
2. If bacteria are infected with bacteriophages containing radioactively labeled protein, the bacteria will not be radioactive.

Experiment:

Radioactive phosphorus (^{32}P)

Radioactive sulfur (^{35}S)

Radioactive DNA (blue)

Radioactive protein (gold)

❶ Label the phages with ^{32}P or ^{35}S.

❷ Infect the bacteria with the labeled phages; the phages inject their genetic material into the bacteria.

❸ Whirl in a blender to break off the phage coats from the bacteria.

❹ Centrifuge to separate the phage coats (low density: stay in the liquid) from the bacteria (high density: sink to the bottom as a "pellet")

❺ Measure the radioactivity of the phages and bacteria.

Results: Bacteria are radioactive; phages are not.

Results: Phages are radioactive; bacteria are not.

Conclusion: Infected bacteria contain radioactive phosphorus but not radioactive sulfur, supporting the hypothesis that the genetic material of bacteriophages is DNA, not protein.

▲ **FIGURE E11-2 The Hershey-Chase experiment** By radioactively labeling either the DNA or the protein of bacteriophages, Hershey and Chase tested whether the genetic material of phages is DNA (left side of the experiment) or protein (right side).

Diffraction pattern of DNA

▲ FIGURE 11-4 **X-ray diffraction image of DNA** The crossing pattern of dark spots is characteristic of helical molecules such as DNA. Measurements of various aspects of the pattern indicate the dimensions of the DNA helix; for example, the distance between the dark spots corresponds to the distance between turns of the helix.

sugar, and the other end has a "free" or unbonded phosphate (**Fig. 11-5a**). Picture a long line of cars stopped on a crowded one-way street at night; the cars' headlights (free phosphates) always point forward and their taillights (free sugars) always point backward. If the cars are jammed tightly together, a pedestrian standing in front of the line of cars will see only the headlights on the first car;

a pedestrian at the back of the line will see only the taillights of the last car.

Hydrogen Bonds Between Complementary Bases Hold Two DNA Strands Together in a Double Helix

Watson and Crick's crucial insight was that a complete DNA molecule in living organisms consists of two DNA strands, assembled like a twisted ladder. The sugar-phosphate backbones form the "uprights" of the DNA ladder. The "rungs" are composed of specific pairs of bases, with one member of each pair protruding from the sugar-phosphate backbone of each strand. A complete rung consists of a pair of bases held together by hydrogen bonds (see Fig. 11-5a). As the X-ray data showed, the DNA ladder isn't straight: The two strands are wound about each other to form a **double helix,** as if the ladder had been twisted lengthwise into the shape of a spiral staircase (**Fig. 11-5b**). Further, the two strands in a DNA double helix are antiparallel to one another; that is, they are oriented in opposite directions. In Figure 11-5a, note that the left-hand DNA strand has a free phosphate group at the top and a free sugar on the bottom; the ends are reversed on the right-hand DNA strand. Again imagine an evening traffic jam, this time on a crowded two-lane highway. A traffic helicopter pilot overhead would see only the headlights on cars in one lane, and only the taillights of cars in the other lane.

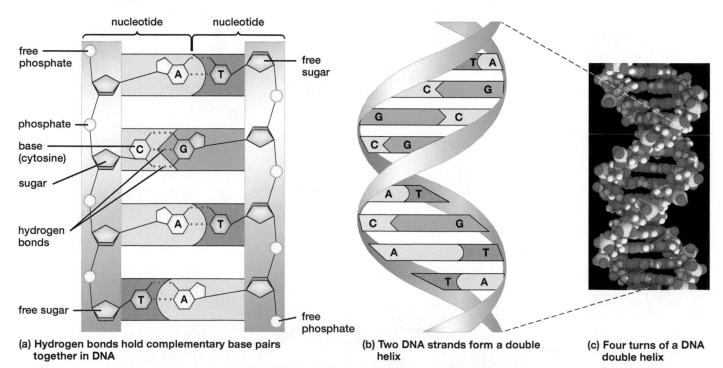

(a) Hydrogen bonds hold complementary base pairs together in DNA

(b) Two DNA strands form a double helix

(c) Four turns of a DNA double helix

▲ FIGURE 11-5 **The Watson-Crick model of DNA structure (a)** Hydrogen bonding between complementary base pairs holds the two strands of DNA together. Three hydrogen bonds hold guanine to cytosine, and two hydrogen bonds hold adenine to thymine. Note that each strand has a free phosphate on one end and a free sugar on the opposite end. Further, the two strands run in opposite directions. **(b)** Strands of DNA wind about each other in a double helix, like a twisted ladder, with the sugar-phosphate backbone forming the uprights and the complementary base pairs forming the rungs. **(c)** A space-filling model of DNA structure.

QUESTION Which do you think would be more difficult to break apart: an A–T base pair or a C–G base pair?

SCIENCE IN ACTION The Discovery of the Double Helix

In the early 1950s, many biologists realized that the key to understanding inheritance lay in the structure of DNA. They also knew that whoever deduced the correct structure of DNA would receive recognition, probably including a Nobel Prize. Linus Pauling of the California Institute of Technology was the leading contender. Pauling probably knew more about the chemistry of large organic molecules than any person alive. Like Rosalind Franklin and Maurice Wilkins, Pauling was an expert in X-ray diffraction techniques. In 1950, he used these techniques to show that many proteins were coiled into single-stranded helices (see Fig. 3-21b). Pauling, however, had two important handicaps. First, for years he had concentrated on protein research and, therefore, had little data about DNA. Second, he was active in the peace movement. At that time, some government officials considered such activity to be potentially subversive and a threat to national security. This latter handicap may have proved decisive.

The second most likely competitors were Wilkins and Franklin, the British scientists who had set out to determine the structure of DNA by using X-ray diffraction patterns. In fact, Franklin probably knew the most about the shape of the DNA molecule, based on her X-ray diffraction studies (see p. 195). However, the methodical approach used by Franklin and Wilkins was slow.

The door was open for the eventual discoverers of the double helix—James Watson and Francis Crick, two scientists with neither Pauling's tremendous understanding of chemical bonds nor Franklin and Wilkins' expertise in X-ray analysis. Watson and Crick did no experiments in the ordinary sense of the word. Instead, they spent their time trying to construct a model that made sense and fit the data. Because they were working in England and because Wilkins shared Franklin's data with them (probably without her knowledge), Watson and Crick were familiar with the X-ray information relating to DNA.

The X-ray data were just what Pauling lacked. Because of his presumed subversive tendencies, the U.S. State Department refused to issue Pauling a passport to leave the United States, so he could neither attend meetings at which Wilkins presented the X-ray data nor visit England to talk with Franklin and Wilkins directly. Watson and Crick knew that Pauling was working on DNA structure and were driven by the fear that he would beat them to it. In his book, *The Double Helix*, Watson recounts his belief that, if Pauling had seen the X-ray pictures, "in a week at most, Linus would have [had] the structure."

You might be thinking, "But wait just a minute! That's not fair. If the goal of science is to advance knowledge, then everyone should have access to all the data. If Pauling was the best, he should have discovered the double helix first." Perhaps. But after all, scientists are people, too. Although virtually all scientists want to see scientific progress and benefits for humanity, each individual also wants to be the one responsible for that progress and to receive the credit.

Soon after Watson and Crick proposed the double helix (Fig. E11-3), Watson described it in a letter to Max Delbrück, a friend and adviser at Caltech. When Delbrück told Pauling, Pauling graciously congratulated Watson and Crick on their brilliant solution. The race was over.

▲ **FIGURE E11-3 The discovery of DNA** James Watson and Francis Crick with a model of DNA structure.

Take a closer look at the pairs of bases that form each rung of the double helix ladder (see Figs. 11-5a, b). Adenine forms hydrogen bonds only with thymine, and guanine forms hydrogen bonds only with cytosine. These A–T and G–C pairs are called **complementary base pairs.** All of the bases of the two strands of a DNA double helix are complementary to each other. For example, if one strand reads A-T-T-C-C, then the other strand must read T-A-A-G-G.

Complementary base pairs explain "Chargaff's rule"—that the DNA of a given species contains equal amounts of adenine and thymine, and equal amounts of cytosine and guanine. Because an A in one DNA strand always pairs with a T in the other strand, the amount of A always equals the amount of T. Similarly, because a G in one strand always pairs with a C in the other DNA strand, the amount of G always equals the amount of C.

Finally, look at the sizes of the bases: Because adenine and guanine consist of two fused rings, they are large, whereas thymine and cytosine, composed of only a single ring, are small. Because the double helix has only A–T and G–C pairs, all the rungs of the DNA ladder are the same width. Therefore, the double helix has a constant diameter, just as the X-ray diffraction pattern indicated.

The structure of DNA was solved. On March 7, 1953, at the Eagle Pub in Cambridge, England, Francis Crick proclaimed to the lunchtime crowd, "We have discovered the secret of life." This claim was not far from the truth. Although further data would be needed to confirm the details, within just a few years, their DNA model revolutionized much of biology, including genetics, evolutionary biology, and medicine. The revolution continues today.

CHECK YOUR LEARNING

Can you describe the four nucleotides found in DNA, how individual DNA strands are constructed, and the three-dimensional structure of DNA?

11.3 HOW DOES DNA ENCODE GENETIC INFORMATION?

Look again at the structure of DNA shown in Figure 11-5. Can you see why many scientists had trouble believing that DNA could be the carrier of genetic information? Consider the many characteristics of just one organism. How can the color of a bird's feathers, the size and shape of its beak, its ability to make a nest, and its song all be determined by a molecule made with only four different nucleotides?

Genetic Information Is Encoded in the Sequence of Nucleotides

The answer is that it's not the *number* of different nucleotides but their *sequence* that's important. Within a DNA strand, the four nucleotides can be arranged in any order, and each unique sequence of nucleotides represents a unique set of genetic instructions. An analogy might help: You don't need a lot of different letters to make up a language. English has 26 letters, but Hawaiian has only 12, and the binary language of computers uses only two "letters" (0 and 1, or "off" and "on"). Nevertheless, all three languages can spell out thousands of different words. A stretch of DNA that is just 10 nucleotides long can form more than a million different sequences of the four nucleotides. Because an organism has millions (in bacteria) to billions (in plants or animals) of nucleotides, DNA molecules can encode a staggering amount of information.

Of course, to make sense, the letters of a language must be in the correct order. Similarly, a gene must have the right nucleotides in the right sequence. Just as "friend" and "fiend" mean different things, and "fliend" doesn't mean anything, different sequences of nucleotides in DNA may encode very different pieces of information or no information at all.

In the remainder of this chapter, we will examine how DNA is replicated during cell division to ensure accurate copying of its genetic information. (In Chapter 12, we will describe how the information in DNA is used to produce the structures of living cells.)

CHECK YOUR LEARNING

Can you explain how DNA encodes hereditary information?

CASE STUDY continued

Muscles, Mutations, and Myostatin

All "normal" mammals have a DNA sequence that encodes a functional myostatin protein, which limits their muscle growth. Belgian Blue cattle have a mutation that changes a "friendly" gene to a nonsensical "fliendly" one that no longer codes for a functional protein, so they have excessive muscle development.

11.4 HOW DOES DNA REPLICATION ENSURE GENETIC CONSTANCY DURING CELL DIVISION?

In the 1850s, Austrian pathologist Rudolf Virchow realized that "all cells come from [preexisting] cells." All the trillions of cells of your body are the offspring of other cells, going all the way back to when you were a fertilized egg. Moreover, almost every cell of your body contains identical genetic information—the same genetic information that was present in that fertilized egg. When cells reproduce by mitotic cell division, each daughter cell receives a nearly perfect copy of the parent cell's genetic information. Consequently, before cell division, the parent cell must synthesize two exact copies of its DNA. A process called **DNA replication** produces these two identical DNA double helices.

DNA Replication Produces Two DNA Double Helices, Each with One Original Strand and One New Strand

How does a cell accurately copy its DNA? In their paper describing DNA structure, Watson and Crick included one of the greatest understatements in all of science: "It has not escaped our notice that the specific [base] pairing we have postulated immediately suggests a possible copying mechanism for the genetic material." In fact, base pairing is the foundation of DNA replication. Remember, the rules for base pairing are that an adenine on one strand must pair with a thymine on the other strand, and a cytosine must pair with a guanine. Therefore, the base sequence of each strand contains all the information needed to replicate the other strand.

Conceptually, DNA replication is quite simple (**Fig. 11-6**). The essential ingredients are (1) the parental DNA strands (**Fig. 11-6 ❶**), (2) **free nucleotides** that were previously synthesized in the cytoplasm and imported into the nucleus, and (3) a variety of enzymes that unwind the parental DNA double helix and synthesize new DNA strands.

First, enzymes called **DNA helicases** (meaning "enzymes that break the double helix") pull apart the parental DNA double helix, so that the bases of the two DNA strands no longer form base pairs with one another (**Fig. 11-6 ❷**). Second, enzymes called **DNA polymerases** ("enzymes that synthesize a DNA polymer") move along each separated parental DNA strand, matching bases on the parental strands with complementary free nucleotides (**Fig. 11-6 ❸**). For

❶ Parental DNA double helix

❷ The parental DNA is unwound

❸ New DNA strands are synthesized with bases complementary to the parental strands

free nucleotides

❹ Each new double helix is composed of one parental strand (blue) and one new strand (red)

▲ FIGURE 11-6 **Basic features of DNA replication** During replication, the two strands of the parental DNA double helix separate. Free nucleotides that are complementary to those in each strand are joined to make new daughter strands. Each parental strand and its new daughter strand then form a new double helix.

example, DNA polymerase pairs an exposed adenine in the parental strand with a free thymine. DNA polymerase also connects these free nucleotides with one another to form two new DNA strands, each complementary to one of the parental DNA strands. Thus, if a parental DNA strand reads T–A–G, DNA polymerase will synthesize a new DNA strand with the complementary sequence A–T–C. For more information on how DNA is replicated, refer to "In Greater Depth: DNA Structure and Replication."

When replication is complete, each parental DNA strand and its newly synthesized, complementary daughter DNA strand wind together to form new double helixes (**Fig. 11-6 ❹**). Because DNA replication conserves one parental DNA strand and produces one newly synthesized strand, the process is called **semiconservative replication** (**Fig. 11-7**).

If no mistakes have been made, the base sequences of both new DNA double helixes are identical to the base sequence of the parental DNA double helix and, of course, to each other.

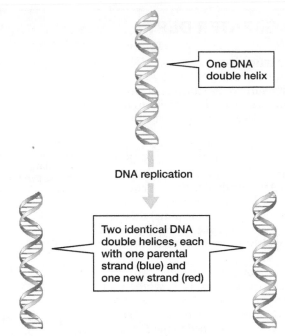

One DNA double helix

DNA replication

Two identical DNA double helices, each with one parental strand (blue) and one new strand (red)

▲ FIGURE 11-7 **Semiconservative replication of DNA**

CHECK YOUR LEARNING

Can you describe the process of DNA replication, including the enzymes involved and the actions that they perform? Can you explain why DNA replication is called "semiconservative"?

11.5 WHAT ARE MUTATIONS, AND HOW DO THEY OCCUR?

The nucleotide sequence of DNA is preserved, with great precision, from cell division to cell division, and from generation to generation. However, occasional changes in the nucleotide sequence, called **mutations,** do occur. Mutations are often harmful, much as randomly changing words in the middle of Shakespeare's *Hamlet* would probably interrupt the flow of the play. If they are really damaging, a cell or an organism inheriting such a mutation may quickly die. Some mutations, however, have no effect or, in very rare instances, are even beneficial. Mutations that are advantageous, at least in certain environments, may be favored by natural selection, and are the basis for the evolution of life on Earth (see Unit 3).

CASE STUDY c o n t i n u e d

Muscles, Mutations, and Myostatin

At the appropriate time during development, myostatin blocks the cell cycle in the G_1 phase, before DNA replication starts (see Fig. 9-8). Therefore when myostatin is present, pre-muscle cells do not enter the S phase, and do not replicate their DNA. The cells stop dividing, limiting the number of mature muscle cells. The mutated myostatin of Belgian Blue cattle does not block progression through the cell cycle. Pre-muscle cells replicate their DNA and continue to divide, producing many more muscle cells than in normal cattle.

IN GREATER DEPTH DNA Structure and Replication

DNA Structure

To fully understand DNA replication, we must return to the structure of DNA. Biochemists keep track of the atoms in a complex molecule by numbering them. In the case of a nucleotide (Fig. E11-4), the atoms that form the "corners" of the base are numbered 1 through 6 for the single rings of cytosine and thymine, or 1 through 9 for the double rings of adenine and guanine. The carbon atoms of the sugar are numbered 1' (1-prime) through 5' (5-prime). The prime symbol (') is used to distinguish atoms in the sugar from atoms in the base.

The sugar of a nucleotide has two "ends" that can be involved in synthesizing the sugar-phosphate backbone of a DNA strand: a 3' end, which has a free –OH (hydroxyl) group attached to the 3' carbon of the sugar, and a 5' end, which has a phosphate group attached to the 5' carbon. When a DNA strand is synthesized, the phosphate of one nucleotide bonds with the hydroxyl group on the sugar of the next nucleotide (Fig. E11-5).

This still leaves a free hydroxyl group on the 3' end of one nucleotide, and a free phosphate group on the 5' end of the other nucleotide. No matter how many nucleotides are joined, there is always a free hydroxyl on the 3' end of the strand and a free phosphate on the 5' end.

Because the sugar-phosphate backbones of the two strands of a double helix are antiparallel—they run in opposite directions—at one end of the double helix, one of the strands has a sugar with a free hydroxyl (the 3' end) and the other strand has a free phosphate (the 5' end). On the other end of the double helix, the free sugar and phosphate ends are reversed (Fig. E11-6).

DNA Replication

DNA replication involves three major actions (Fig. E11-7). First, the DNA double helix is unwound and the two strands are separated, allowing the nucleotide sequence to be read. Then, new DNA strands with nucleotide sequences complementary to the two original strands are synthesized. In eukaryotic cells, these new DNA strands are synthesized in short pieces, so the third step in DNA replication is to stitch the pieces together to form a continuous new strand of DNA. Each step is carried out by a distinct set of enzymes.

▲ FIGURE E11-4 Numbering of carbon atoms in a nucleotide

DNA Helicase Unwinds and Separates the Parental DNA Strands

Acting in concert with several other enzymes, DNA helicase breaks the hydrogen bonds between complementary base pairs that hold the two parental DNA strands together. This unwinds a segment of the parental double helix and separates the two strands, forming a replication bubble (Fig. E11-7 ❶ and ❷). Each replication bubble contains a replication fork at each end, where the two parental DNA strands are just beginning to be separated. Within the replication bubble, the bases of the parental DNA strands are no longer

attached to one another by hydrogen bonds.

DNA Polymerase Synthesizes New DNA Strands

Replication bubbles are essential because they allow a second enzyme, DNA polymerase, to attach to the separated DNA strands. At each replication fork, a complex of DNA polymerase and other proteins binds to each parental strand (Fig. E11-7 ❸). DNA polymerase recognizes an unpaired base in the parental strand and matches it up with a complementary base in a free nucleotide. Then, DNA polymerase bonds

▲ FIGURE E11-5 Numbering of carbon atoms in a dinucleotide

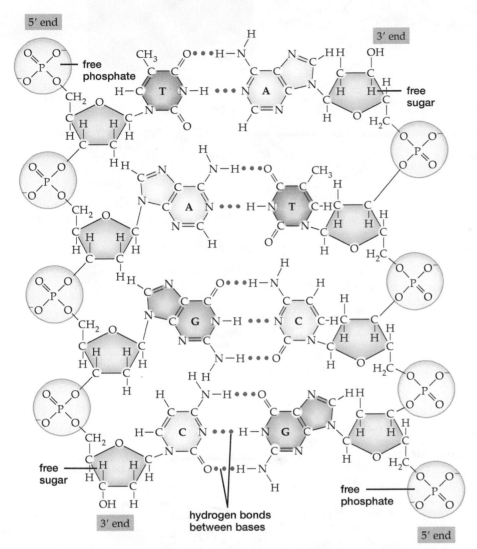

▲ FIGURE E11-6 The two strands of a DNA double helix are antiparallel

daughter strand. Because the two strands of the parental DNA double helix are oriented in opposite directions, the DNA polymerase molecules move in opposite directions on the two parental strands (see Fig. E11-7 ❸).

DNA helicase and DNA polymerase work together (Fig. E11-7 ❹). A DNA helicase binds to the double helix and moves along, unwinding the double helix and separating the strands. Because the two DNA strands run in opposite directions, as a DNA helicase enzyme moves toward the 5′ end of one parental strand, it is simultaneously moving toward the 3′ end of the other parental strand. Now visualize two DNA polymerases landing on the two separated strands of DNA. One DNA polymerase (call it polymerase #1) can follow behind the helicase toward the 5′ end of the parental strand and can synthesize a continuous daughter DNA strand, until it runs into another replication bubble. This continuous daughter DNA strand is called the leading strand. On the other parental strand, however, DNA polymerase #2 moves *away from* the helicase: in step ❸ of Figure E11-7, note that the helicase moves to the left, whereas DNA polymerase #2 moves to the right. Therefore, DNA synthesis on this strand will be discontinuous: DNA polymerase #2 will synthesize a short new DNA strand, called the lagging strand, but meanwhile, the helicase continues to move to the left, unwinding more of the double helix (see Fig. E11-7 ❹ and ❺). Additional DNA polymerases (#3, #4, and so on) must land on this strand and synthesize more short lagging strands.

DNA Ligase Joins Segments of DNA
Multiple DNA polymerases synthesize pieces of DNA of varying lengths. Each chromosome may form hundreds of replication bubbles. Within each bubble, there will be one leading strand and dozens to thousands of lagging strands. Therefore, a cell might synthesize millions of pieces of DNA while replicating a single chromosome. How are all of these pieces sewn together? This is the job of the third major enzyme, **DNA ligase** ("an enzyme that ties DNA together"; see Fig. E11-7 ❺). Many DNA ligase enzymes stitch the fragments of DNA together until each daughter strand consists of one long, continuous DNA polymer.

the phosphate of the incoming free nucleotide (the 5′ end) to the sugar of the most recently added nucleotide (the 3′ end) of the growing daughter strand. In this way, DNA polymerase synthesizes the sugar-phosphate backbone of the daughter strand.

Why make replication bubbles, rather than simply starting at one end of a double helix and letting a single DNA polymerase molecule copy the DNA in one continuous piece all the way to the other end? Recall that eukaryotic chromosomes are very long: Human chromosomes range from about 50 million nucleotides in the relatively tiny Y chromosome, to about 250 million nucleotides in chromosome 1. Eukaryotic DNA is copied at a rate of about

50 nucleotides per second, so it would take about 12 to 58 days to copy a human chromosome in one continuous piece. To replicate an entire chromosome in a reasonable time, many DNA helicase enzymes open up many replication bubbles simultaneously, allowing many DNA polymerase enzymes to copy the strands in fairly small pieces all at the same time. Each individual bubble enlarges as DNA replication progresses, and the bubbles merge when they contact one another.

DNA polymerase always moves away from the 3′ end of a parental DNA strand (the end with the free hydroxyl group of the sugar) toward the 5′ end (with a free phosphate group). New nucleotides are always added to the 3′ end of the

(continued) ▶

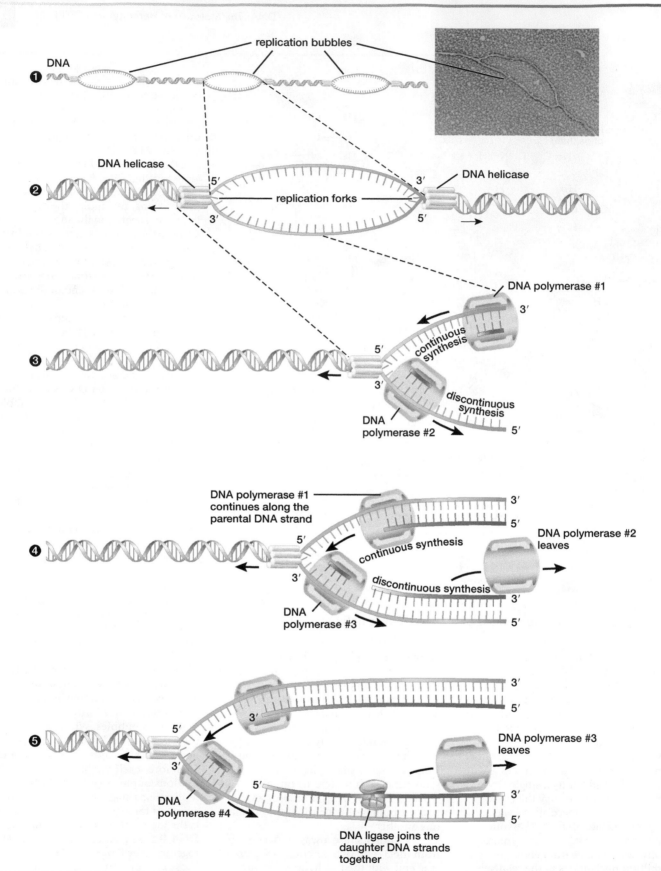

▲ FIGURE E11-7 **DNA replication** ❶ DNA helicase enzymes separate the parental strands of a chromosome to form replication bubbles. ❷ Each replication bubble consists of two replication forks, with unwound DNA strands between the forks. ❸ DNA polymerase enzymes synthesize new pieces of DNA. ❹ DNA helicase moves along the parental DNA double helix, unwinding it and enlarging the replication bubble. DNA polymerases in the replication bubble synthesize daughter DNA strands. ❺ DNA ligase joins the small DNA segments into a single daughter strand.

QUESTION During synthesis, why doesn't DNA polymerase move away from the replication fork on both strands?

| How Much Genes Influence Athletic Prowess? | Face it—you'll never run like Usain Bolt. But how much of his fantastic abilities are genetic? In some cases, genes clearly make a huge difference. Myostatin mutations, for example, can boost speed and strength, as we explain |

in the "Case Study Revisited." However, at least 240 genes contribute to athletic performance, and the effects of most individual genes are small. Do super-athletes have all the best "athletic alleles"? Right now, no one can tell.

Accurate Replication, Proofreading, and DNA Repair Produce Almost Error-Free DNA

The specificity of hydrogen bonding between complementary base pairs makes DNA replication highly accurate. DNA polymerase incorporates incorrect bases about once in every 1,000 to 100,000 base pairs. However, completed DNA strands contain only about one mistake in every 100 million to 1 billion base pairs (in humans, usually less than one per chromosome per replication). This phenomenally low error rate is the result of DNA repair enzymes that proofread each daughter strand during and after its synthesis. For example, some forms of DNA polymerase recognize a base pairing mistake as it is made. These types of DNA polymerase pause, fix the mistake, and then continue synthesizing more DNA. Other changes in the DNA base sequence that may occur during the life of a cell are also usually fixed by DNA repair enzymes.

Toxic Chemicals, Radiation, and Occasional Errors During DNA Replication Cause Mutations

Despite this amazing accuracy, neither humans nor any other organisms have error-free DNA. A few mutations creep into the genome from the rare, unrepaired mistakes made during normal DNA replication. DNA may also be harmed by toxic chemicals (such as free radicals formed during normal cellular metabolism, some components of cigarette smoke, and toxins produced by some molds) and some types of radiation (such as ultraviolet rays in sunlight). These chemicals and radiation increase the likelihood of base pairing errors during replication. Some even damage DNA between replications. Most, but not all, of these changes in DNA sequence are fixed by repair enzymes; the changes that remain are mutations.

Mutations Range from Changes in Single Nucleotide Pairs to Movements of Large Pieces of Chromosomes

If a pair of bases is mismatched during replication, repair enzymes usually recognize the mismatch, cut out the incorrect nucleotide, and replace it with a nucleotide containing the complementary base. Sometimes, however, the enzymes replace the parental nucleotide instead of the mismatched one. The resulting base pair is complementary, but incorrect. These **nucleotide substitutions** are also called **point mutations,** because individual nucleotides in the DNA sequence are changed (**Fig. 11-8a**). An **insertion mutation** occurs when one or more nucleotide pairs are inserted into the DNA double helix (**Fig. 11-8b**). A **deletion mutation** occurs when one or more nucleotide pairs are removed from the double helix (**Fig. 11-8c**).

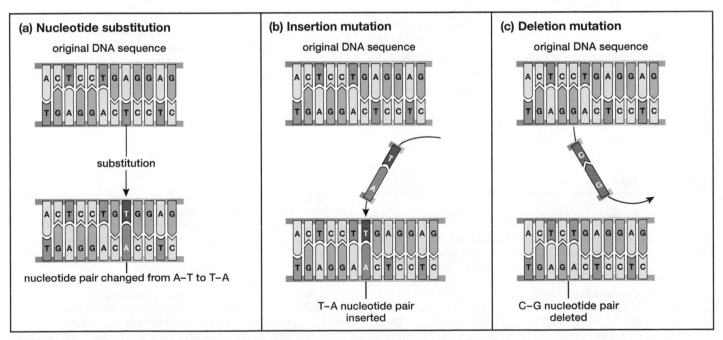

▲ FIGURE 11-8 **Mutations involving single pairs of nucleotides** (a) Nucleotide substitution. (b) Insertion mutation. (c) Deletion mutation. The original DNA bases are in pale colors with black letters; mutations are in deep colors with white letters.

▲ FIGURE 11-9 **Mutations that rearrange pieces of chromosomes** **(a)** Inversion mutation. **(b)** Translocation of pieces of DNA between two different chromosomes. In part (a), the original DNA bases are in pale colors with black letters; mutations are in deep colors with white letters. In part (b), the DNA bases of one chromosome are in pale colors with black letters, and the DNA bases of the second chromosome are in deep colors with white letters.

Pieces of chromosomes ranging in size from a single nucleotide pair to massive pieces of DNA are occasionally rearranged. An **inversion** occurs when a piece of DNA is cut out of a chromosome, turned around, and reinserted into the gap (**Fig. 11-9a**). Finally, a **translocation** results when a chunk of DNA, often very large, is removed from one chromosome and attached to a different one (**Fig. 11-9b**).

CHECK YOUR LEARNING

Can you explain what mutations are, and how they occur? Can you describe the different types of mutations? Do you know why mutations are rare and often harmful?

CASE STUDY revisited

Muscles, Mutations, and Myostatin

Belgian Blue cattle have a deletion mutation in their myostatin gene. The result is that their cells stop synthesizing the myostatin protein about halfway through. (In Chapter 12, we'll explain why some mutations cause short, or truncated, proteins to be synthesized.) Several breeds of "double-muscled" cattle have this same deletion mutation, but other double-muscled breeds have totally different mutations. Other animals, including several breeds of dogs, such as whippets (**Fig. 11-10**), may also have myostatin mutations. The mutations are generally different than those found in any of the breeds of cattle, but produce similar phenotypic effects.

All of these mutations result in nonfunctional myostatin proteins. This fact reveals an important feature of the language of DNA: The nucleotide words must be spelled just right, or at least really close, for the resulting proteins to function. In contrast, any one of an enormous number of possible mistakes will render the proteins useless.

Humans have myostatin, too; not surprisingly, mutations can occur in the human myostatin gene. A child inherits two copies of most genes, one from each parent. About a decade ago, a child was born in Germany who inherited a point mutation in his myostatin gene from both parents. This particular point mutation results in short, inactive, myostatin proteins. At 7 months, the boy already had well-developed calf, thigh, and buttock muscles. At 4 years, he could hold a

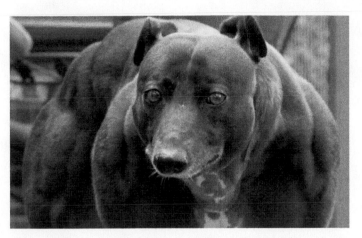

▲ FIGURE 11-10 **Myostatin mutation in a dog** Like Belgian Blue cattle, "bully" whippets have defective myostatin, resulting in enormous muscles.

7-pound (3.2-kilogram) dumbbell in each hand, with his arms fully extended horizontally out to his sides. (Try it—it's not that easy for many adults.)

Consider This

Mutations may be neutral, harmful, or beneficial. Into which category do myostatin mutations fall? Belgian Blue cattle are born so muscular and, consequently, so large, that they usually must be delivered by cesarean section. Myostatin-deficient mice have huge muscles, but small, brittle tendons. The result? Their oversize muscles are weakly attached to their bones. On the other hand, heterozygous whippets, with one normal and one defective myostatin allele, can run faster than ordinary whippets. Is it possible that myostatin mutations are harmful in homozygotes but beneficial in heterozygotes? How do you think that natural selection might operate in this situation?

CHAPTER REVIEW

Summary of Key Concepts

11.1 How Did Scientists Discover That Genes Are Made of DNA?

Studies by Griffith showed that genes can be transferred from one bacterial strain into another. This transfer could transform the bacterial strain from harmless to deadly. Avery, MacLeod, and McCarty showed that DNA was the molecule that could transform bacteria. Hershey and Chase found that DNA is also the hereditary material of bacteriophage viruses. Thus, genes must be made of DNA.

11.2 What Is the Structure of DNA?

DNA consists of nucleotides that are linked into long strands. Each nucleotide consists of a phosphate group, the five-carbon sugar deoxyribose, and a nitrogen-containing base. Four types of bases occur in DNA: adenine, guanine, thymine, and cytosine. The sugar of one nucleotide is linked to the phosphate of the next nucleotide, forming a sugar-phosphate backbone for each strand. The bases stick out from this backbone. Two nucleotide strands wind together to form a DNA double helix, which resembles a twisted ladder. The sugar-phosphate backbones form the sides of the ladder. The bases of each strand pair up in the middle of the helix, held together by hydrogen bonds, forming the rungs of the ladder. Only complementary base pairs can bond together in the helix: Adenine bonds with thymine, and guanine bonds with cytosine.

11.3 How Does DNA Encode Genetic Information?

Genetic information is encoded as the sequence of nucleotides in a DNA molecule. Just as a language can form thousands of words and complex sentences from a small number of letters by varying the sequence and number of letters in each word and sentence, so too DNA can encode large amounts of information with varying sequences and numbers of nucleotides in different genes. Because DNA molecules are usually millions of nucleotides long, DNA can encode huge amounts of information in its nucleotide sequence.

11.4 How Does DNA Replication Ensure Genetic Constancy During Cell Division?

When cells reproduce, they must replicate their DNA so that each daughter cell receives all the original genetic information. During DNA replication, enzymes unwind and separate part of the two parental DNA strands. Then DNA polymerase enzymes bind to each parental DNA strand. Free nucleotides form hydrogen bonds with complementary bases on the parental strands, and DNA polymerase links the free nucleotides to form new DNA strands. Therefore, the sequence of nucleotides in each newly formed strand is complementary to the sequence of a parental strand. Replication is semiconservative because both new DNA double helices consist of one parental DNA strand and one newly synthesized, complementary daughter strand. The two new DNA double helices are, therefore, duplicates of the parental DNA double helix.

11.5 What Are Mutations, and How Do They Occur?

Mutations are changes in the base sequence in DNA. DNA polymerase and other repair enzymes "proofread" the DNA, minimizing the number of mistakes during replication, but mistakes do occur. Other mutations occur as a result of radiation and damage from certain chemicals. Mutations include substitutions, insertions, deletions, inversions, and translocations. Most mutations are harmful or neutral, but a few are beneficial and may be favored by natural selection.

Key Terms

adenine (A) *194*
bacteriophage *196*
base *194*
complementary base pair *199*

cytosine (C) *194*
deletion mutation *205*
deoxyribonucleic acid
  (DNA) *192*

DNA helicase 200
DNA ligase 203
DNA polymerase 200
DNA replication 200
double helix 198
free nucleotide 200
guanine (G) 194
insertion mutation 205
inversion 206
mutation 201

nucleotide 194
nucleotide substitution 205
point mutation 205
semiconservative
   replication 201
strand 195
sugar-phosphate
   backbone 195
thymine (T) 194
translocation 206

Learning Outcomes

In this chapter, you have learned to . . .

LO1 Describe the key experimental evidence indicating that DNA is the molecule of heredity.

LO2 Describe the structure of DNA, including nucleotides, the sugar-phosphate backbone, the double helix, and the role of hydrogen bonds.

LO3 Explain how genetic information is encoded in DNA.

LO4 Summarize the steps of DNA replication, including identification and action of the enzymes involved in each step.

LO5 Define the term *mutation*, and name and describe the different types of mutations.

Thinking Through the Concepts

Fill-in-the-Blank

1. DNA consists of subunits called _____. Each subunit consists of three parts: _____, _____, and _____. LO2

2. The subunits of DNA are assembled by linking the _____ of one nucleotide to the _____ of the next. As it is found in chromosomes, two DNA polymers are wound together into a structure called a(n) _____. LO2

3. The "base pairing rule" in DNA is that adenine pairs with _____, and guanine pairs with _____. Bases that can form pairs in DNA are called _____. LO2

4. When DNA is replicated, two new DNA double helices are formed, each consisting of one parental strand and one new, daughter strand. For this reason, DNA replication is called _____. LO4

5. The DNA double helix is unwound by an enzyme called _____. Daughter DNA strands are synthesized by the enzyme _____. In eukaryotic cells, the daughter DNA strands are synthesized in pieces; these pieces are joined by the enzyme _____. LO4

6. Sometimes, mistakes are made during DNA replication. If uncorrected, these mistakes are called _____. When a single nucleotide is changed, this is called a(n) _____, or _____. LO5

Review Questions

1. Describe the experimental evidence that DNA is the hereditary material of bacteriophages. LO1

2. Draw the general structure of a nucleotide. Which parts are identical in all nucleotides, and which can vary? LO2

3. Name the four types of nitrogen-containing bases found in DNA. LO2

4. Describe the structure of DNA. Where are the bases, sugars, and phosphates in the structure? LO2

5. Which bases are complementary to one another? How are they held together in the double helix of DNA? LO2

6. How is information encoded in the DNA molecule? LO3

7. Describe the process of DNA replication. LO4

8. How do mutations occur? Describe the principal types of mutations. LO5

Applying the Concepts

1. In an alternate universe, DNA is constructed of six different nucleotides, not four as on Earth. Would you expect organisms in this universe to have more precise genetic instructions, or more different genes, than life on Earth? Would you expect the length of a typical gene to be the same, shorter, or longer than that of a typical gene on Earth?

2. Genetic information is encoded in the sequence of nucleotides in DNA. Let's suppose that the nucleotide sequence on one strand of a double helix encodes the information needed to synthesize a hemoglobin molecule. Do you think that the sequence of nucleotides on the other strand of the double helix also encodes useful information? Why? (An analogy might help. Suppose that English were a "complementary language," with letters at opposite ends of the alphabet complementary to one another; that is, A is complementary to Z, B to Y, C to X, and so on. Would a sentence composed of letters complementary to "To be or not to be?" make sense?) Finally, why do you think DNA is double-stranded?

3. BioEthics If you enter "myostatin blocker" into an Internet search engine, you will find sites selling substances that are claimed to block the action of myostatin, and thereby supposedly help to build larger muscles. Let's assume that they work (most probably don't). From what you have learned about myostatin in this chapter, would this be a safe, effective way to bulk up? If you were a member of the World Anti-Doping Agency, would you allow athletes to compete in the Olympics who have used myostatin blockers?

Answers to Figure Caption questions and Fill-in-the-Blank questions can be found in the Answers section at the back of the book.

MB Go to MasteringBiology for practice quizzes, activities, eText, videos, current events, and more.

CHAPTER 12

Gene Expression and Regulation

CASE STUDY
Cystic Fibrosis

IF ALL YOU knew was her music, you'd think Alice Martineau had it made—a young, pretty singer-songwriter under contract with a major recording label. However, like about 70,000 other people worldwide, Martineau had cystic fibrosis, a recessive genetic disorder caused by defective alleles of a gene that encodes a crucially important protein called CFTR (the CF in the name of the protein stands for "cystic fibrosis"). Cystic fibrosis occurs when a person is homozygous for these defective alleles. Before modern medical care, most people with cystic fibrosis died by age 4 or 5; even now, the average life span is only 35 to 40 years. Martineau died when she was 30.

The CFTR protein forms channels that allow chloride to move across plasma membranes down its concentration gradient. CFTR also helps sodium movement across plasma membranes. CFTR is found in many parts of the body, including the sweat glands, lungs, and intestines. In the sweat glands, CFTR helps to reclaim sodium chloride from the sweat and transport it back into the blood, so that the body doesn't lose too much salt. Probably the most crucial role of CFTR is in the cells lining the airways in the lungs. Normally, the airways are covered with a film of mucus, which traps bacteria and debris. The bacteria-laden mucus is then swept out of the lungs by cilia on the cells of the airways.

Normally, chloride moves through CFTR channels out of the airway cells into the mucus, and sodium follows. The resulting high concentration of sodium chloride causes water to move into the mucus by osmosis, resulting in a thin liquid that can be removed easily by the cilia. However, mutations in the *CFTR* gene produce defective chloride channel proteins. As a result, chloride and sodium do not move from the cells into the mucus, so water doesn't move into the mucus, either. The mucus becomes so thick that the cilia can't move it out of the lungs, leaving the airways partially clogged. Bacteria multiply in the mucus, causing chronic lung infections.

In this chapter, we examine the processes by which the instructions in genes are translated into proteins. As you will learn, changes in those instructions—mutations—alter the structure and function of proteins such as CFTR.

C is for contemplation

Alice Martineau, shown here in a portrait painted by her brother Luke, hoped that ". . . people will realize when they hear the music, I am a singer-songwriter who just happens to be ill."

AT A GLANCE

LEARNING GOALS

LG1 Describe the molecules and cellular structures that play central roles in the process by which information encoded in DNA is used to synthesize proteins.

LG2 Compare and contrast how information is encoded in DNA and in RNA.

LG3 Describe the functions of transcription and translation and identify the locations in the cell at which they occur.

LG4 Describe the main steps of transcription, including the molecules involved and how they interact.

LG5 Describe the main steps of translation, including the molecules involved and how they interact.

LG6 Describe the different types of mutations and explain their potential effects on protein synthesis.

LG7 Describe how gene expression is regulated.

12.1 HOW IS THE INFORMATION IN DNA USED IN A CELL?

Information itself doesn't do anything. For example, a blueprint may provide all the information needed to build a house, but unless that information is translated into action by construction workers, no house will be built. Likewise, although the base sequence of DNA, the molecular blueprint of every cell, contains an incredible amount of information, DNA cannot carry out any actions on its own. So how does DNA determine whether you have black, blond, or red hair or have normal lung function or cystic fibrosis?

Most Genes Contain the Information Needed to Synthesize a Protein

Long before scientists understood that genes are made of DNA, they tried to determine how genes affect the phenotype of individual cells and entire organisms. In the 1940s, biologists discovered that most genes contain the information needed to direct the synthesis of a protein (see "Science in Action: One Gene, One Protein"). Proteins, in turn, are the "molecular workers" of a cell, forming many cellular structures and the enzymes that catalyze chemical reactions within the cell. Therefore, information must flow from DNA to protein.

DNA Provides Instructions for Protein Synthesis via RNA Intermediaries

DNA cannot directly synthesize proteins. Instead, it directs protein synthesis through intermediary molecules of **ribonucleic acid,** or **RNA.** RNA is similar to DNA but differs structurally in three respects: (1) Instead of the deoxyribose sugar found in DNA, the backbone of RNA contains the sugar ribose (the "R" in RNA); (2) RNA is usually single-stranded instead of double-stranded; and (3) RNA has the base uracil instead of the base thymine (**Table 12-1**).

DNA codes for the synthesis of many types of RNA, three of which play specific roles in protein synthesis: messenger RNA, ribosomal RNA, and transfer RNA (**Fig. 12-1**). There are several other types of RNA, including RNA used as the genetic material in some viruses, such as HIV; enzymatic RNA molecules, called ribozymes, that catalyze certain chemical reactions; and "regulatory" RNA, which we will discuss later in this chapter. Here we will introduce the roles of messenger RNA, ribosomal RNA, and transfer RNA. Their interactions during protein synthesis will be explained in more detail in Section 12.3.

Messenger RNA Carries the Code for Protein Synthesis from DNA to Ribosomes

In eukaryotic cells, the DNA is located and remains stored in the nucleus, like a valuable document in a library, whereas **messenger RNA (mRNA),** like a molecular photocopy, carries the information to the cytoplasm to be used in protein synthesis (**Fig. 12-1a**). As we will see shortly, groups of three bases in mRNA, called **codons,** specify which amino acids will be incorporated into a protein.

Ribosomal RNA and Proteins Form Ribosomes

Ribosomes, the cellular structures that synthesize proteins from the instructions in mRNA, are composed of **ribosomal RNA (rRNA)** and dozens of proteins. Each ribosome consists of two subunits—one small and one large (**Fig. 12-1b**). The small subunit has binding sites for mRNA, a "start" transfer RNA, and several proteins that are essential for assembling the ribosome and starting protein synthesis. The large subunit has binding sites for two tRNA molecules and a site that catalyzes the formation of peptide bonds joining amino acids into proteins. During protein synthesis, the two subunits come together, clasping an mRNA molecule between them.

Transfer RNA Carries Amino Acids to the Ribosomes

Transfer RNA (tRNA) delivers amino acids to a ribosome, where they will be incorporated into a protein. Every cell synthesizes at least one unique type of tRNA for each amino acid. Twenty enzymes in the cytoplasm, one for each amino acid,

TABLE 12-1   A Comparison of DNA and RNA

	DNA	RNA	
Strands	Two	One	
Sugar	Deoxyribose	Ribose	
Types of bases	Adenine (A), thymine (T)	Adenine (A), uracil (U)	
	cytosine (C), guanine (G)	cytosine (C), guanine (G)	
Base pairs	DNA–DNA	RNA–DNA	RNA–RNA
	A–T	A–T	A–U
	T–A	U–A	U–A
	C–G	C–G	C–G
	G–C	G–C	G–C
Function	Contains genes; the sequence of bases in most genes determines the amino acid sequence of a protein	Messenger RNA (mRNA): carries the code for a protein-coding gene from DNA to ribosomes	
		Ribosomal RNA (rRNA): combines with proteins to form ribosomes, the structures that link amino acids to form a protein	
		Transfer RNA (tRNA): carries amino acids to the ribosomes	

recognize the different tRNA molecules and use the energy of ATP to attach the correct amino acid to one end of the tRNA molecule (Fig. 12-1c). These "loaded" tRNA molecules deliver their amino acids to a ribosome. A group of three bases, called an **anticodon,** protrudes from each tRNA. Complementary base pairing between codons of mRNA and anticodons of tRNA specifies which amino acids are used during protein synthesis.

codons

A U G U G C G A G U U A

The base sequence of mRNA carries the information for the amino acid sequence of a protein; groups of these bases, called codons, specify the amino acids

(a) Messenger RNA (mRNA)

catalytic site

large subunit

small subunit

tRNA/amino acid binding sites

rRNA combines with proteins to form ribosomes; the small subunit binds mRNA; the large subunit binds tRNA and catalyzes peptide bond formation between amino acids during protein synthesis

(b) Ribosome: contains ribosomal RNA (rRNA)

tyr

tRNA

attached amino acid

anticodon

Each tRNA carries a specific amino acid (in this example, tyrosine [tyr]) to a ribosome during protein synthesis; the anticodon of tRNA pairs with a codon of mRNA, ensuring that the correct amino acid is incorporated into the protein

(c) Transfer RNA (tRNA)

▲ FIGURE 12-1 **Cells synthesize three major types of RNA that are required for protein synthesis**

SCIENCE IN ACTION One Gene, One Protein

Ever since Gregor Mendel's work was rediscovered in the late 1800s, biologists have known that genes help to determine phenotypes as varied as hair texture, flower color, and inherited diseases such as sickle-cell anemia and cystic fibrosis. But how do individual cells and entire organisms convert their genotypes into phenotypes?

The first hint came from children born with defective metabolic pathways. Many metabolic pathways synthesize molecules in a series of steps, each catalyzed by a specific protein enzyme. The product produced by one enzyme becomes the substrate of the next enzyme, like a molecular assembly line (see Fig. 6-12). A defective pathway fails to produce its final product and may also cause intermediate molecules in the pathway to accumulate to dangerous levels.

For example, defects in the metabolism of two amino acids, phenylalanine and tyrosine, can cause albinism (no pigmentation in skin or hair; see Fig. 10-23) or several diseases with symptoms as varied as urine that turns brown when exposed to the air (alkaptonuria) or phenylalanine accumulation in the brain, leading to mental retardation (phenylketonuria). In the early 1900s, the English physician Archibald Garrod studied the inheritance of these inborn errors of metabolism. He hypothesized that (1) each inborn error

of metabolism is caused by a defective version of a specific enzyme; (2) each defective enzyme is caused by a defective allele of a single gene; and (3) therefore, at least some genes must encode the information needed for the synthesis of enzymes. In the early 1940s, geneticists George Beadle and Edward Tatum used the metabolic pathways of a common bread mold, *Neurospora crassa*, to show that Garrod's hypotheses were correct.

We usually encounter *Neurospora* growing on stale bread. However, it can survive on a much simpler diet, consisting of an energy source such as sugar, a few minerals, and vitamin B$_6$, because *Neurospora* can manufacture the enzymes needed to make virtually all of its own organic molecules, including amino acids. In contrast, we humans cannot synthesize many vitamins and 9 of the 20 common amino acids; we must obtain these from our food. Beadle and Tatum used *Neurospora* to test the hypothesis that many of an organism's genes encode the information needed to synthesize enzymes.

If this hypothesis was correct, a mutation in a specific gene might disrupt the synthesis of a specific enzyme, disabling one of the mold's metabolic pathways. Thus, a mutant mold wouldn't be able to synthesize some of the organic molecules, such as amino acids, that it needs to survive. The mutant *Neurospora*

could grow on a simple medium of sugar, minerals, and vitamin B$_6$ only if the missing organic molecules were provided.

Beadle and Tatum induced mutations by exposing *Neurospora* to X-rays, and then studied the inheritance of the metabolic pathway that synthesizes the amino acid arginine (Fig. E12-1). In normal molds, arginine is synthesized from citrulline, which in turn is synthesized from ornithine (Fig. E12-1a). Mutant A could grow only if supplemented with arginine, but not if supplemented with citrulline or ornithine (Fig. E12-1b). Therefore, this strain had a defect in the enzyme that converts citrulline to arginine. Mutant B could grow if supplemented with either arginine or citrulline, but not with ornithine (see Fig. E12-1b). This mutant had a defect in the enzyme that converts ornithine to citrulline. Because a mutation in a single gene affected only a single enzyme within a single metabolic pathway, Beadle and Tatum concluded that one gene encodes the information for one enzyme. Almost all enzymes are proteins, but many proteins are not enzymes (see Chapter 3). Thus, the "one gene, one enzyme" relationship was later clarified to "one gene, one protein." The importance of this observation was recognized in 1958 with a Nobel Prize, which Beadle and Tatum shared with Joshua Lederberg, one of Tatum's students.

Overview: Genetic Information Is Transcribed into RNA and Then Translated into Protein

Information in DNA is used to direct the synthesis of proteins in two steps, called *transcription* and *translation* (Fig. 12-2 and Table 12-2):

1. In **transcription** (Fig. 12-2a), the information contained in the DNA of a gene is copied into RNA. In eukaryotic cells, transcription occurs in the nucleus.
2. The base sequence of mRNA encodes the amino acid sequence of a protein. During protein synthesis, or **translation** (Fig. 12-2b), this mRNA base sequence is decoded. Transfer RNA molecules bring amino acids to a ribosome. Messenger RNA binds to a ribosome, where base pairing between mRNA and tRNA converts the base sequence of mRNA into the amino acid sequence of the protein. In eukaryotic cells, ribosomes are found in the cytoplasm, so translation occurs there as well.

It's easy to confuse the terms "transcription" and "translation." It may help to compare their common English meanings with their biological meanings. In English, to "transcribe" means to make a written copy of something, almost always in the same language. In an American courtroom, for example, verbal testimony is transcribed into a written copy, and both the testimony and the transcriptions are in English. In biology, transcription is the process of copying information from DNA to RNA using the common language of the bases found in their nucleotides. In contrast, the common English meaning of "translation" is to convert words from one language to another language. In biology, translation means to convert information from the "base language" of RNA to the "amino acid language" of proteins.

The Genetic Code Uses Three Bases to Specify an Amino Acid

Before we examine transcription and translation in detail, let's see how geneticists deciphered the **genetic code**—the

(a) The metabolic pathway for synthesizing the amino acid arginine

Genotype of *Neurospora*		Supplements Added to Medium				Conclusions
		none	ornithine	citrulline	arginine	
Normal *Neurospora*						Normal *Neurospora* can synthesize arginine, citrulline, and ornithine.
Mutants with single gene defect	A					Mutant A grows only if arginine is added. It cannot synthesize arginine because it has a defect in enzyme 2; gene *A* is needed for synthesis of arginine.
	B					Mutant B grows if either arginine or citrulline is added. It cannot synthesize arginine because it has a defect in enzyme 1. Gene *B* is needed for synthesis of citrulline.

(b) Growth of normal and mutant *Neurospora* on a simple medium with different supplements

▲ FIGURE E12-1 **Beadle and Tatum's experiments with *Neurospora* mutants** (a) Each step in the metabolic pathway for arginine synthesis is catalyzed by a different enzyme. (b) By analyzing which supplements allowed mutant molds to grow on simple nutrient medium, Beadle and Tatum concluded that a single gene codes for the synthesis of a single enzyme.

QUESTION What result would you expect for a mutant that lacks an enzyme needed to produce ornithine?

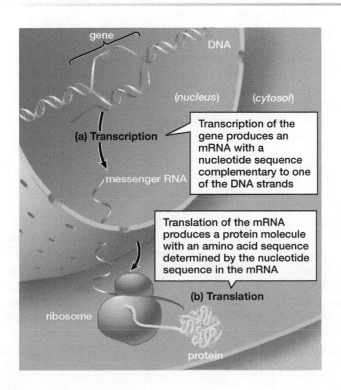

Transcription of the gene produces an mRNA with a nucleotide sequence complementary to one of the DNA strands

(a) Transcription

Translation of the mRNA produces a protein molecule with an amino acid sequence determined by the nucleotide sequence in the mRNA

(b) Translation

biological dictionary that spells out the rules for translating the base sequences in DNA and mRNA into the amino acid sequences in proteins. Both DNA and RNA contain four different bases: adenine (A); thymine (T; uracil [U] in RNA); guanine (G); and cytosine (C; see Table 12-1). However, proteins are made of 20 different amino acids, so one base cannot directly translate into one amino acid: there are not enough different bases. If a sequence of two bases codes for an amino acid, there would be 16 possible combinations (each of four possible first bases paired with each of four possible second bases, or $4 \times 4 = 16$). This still isn't enough to code for 20 amino acids. A three-base sequence

◀ FIGURE 12-2 **Genetic information flows from DNA to RNA to protein** (a) During transcription, the base sequence in a gene specifies the base sequence of a complementary RNA molecule. For protein-encoding genes, the product is an mRNA molecule that exits from the nucleus and enters the cytoplasm. (b) During translation, the base sequence in an mRNA molecule specifies the amino acid sequence of a protein.

TABLE 12-2   Transcription and Translation

Process	Information for the Process	Product	Major Enzyme or Structure Involved in the Process	Type of Base Pairing Required
Transcription (synthesis of RNA)	A segment of one DNA strand	One RNA molecule (e.g., mRNA, tRNA, or rRNA)	RNA polymerase	RNA with DNA: RNA bases pair with DNA bases as an RNA molecule is synthesized
Translation (synthesis of a protein)	mRNA	One protein molecule	Ribosome (also requires tRNA)	mRNA with tRNA: a codon in mRNA forms base pairs with an anticodon in tRNA

gives 64 possible combinations ($4 \times 4 \times 4 = 64$), which is more than enough. Using this reasoning, physicist George Gamow hypothesized in 1954 that sets of three bases in mRNA, called *codons*, specify each of the amino acids. In 1961, Francis Crick and three coworkers demonstrated that this hypothesis is correct.

For any language to be understood, its users must know what the words mean, where words start and stop, and where sentences begin and end. To decipher the codons, which are the "words" of the genetic code, Marshall Nirenberg and Heinrich Matthaei ground up bacteria and isolated the components needed to synthesize proteins. To this mixture, they added artificial mRNA, allowing them to control which codons were to be translated and to see which amino acids were incorporated into proteins. For example, an mRNA strand composed entirely of uracil (UUUUUUUU . . .) directed the mixture to synthesize a protein composed solely of the amino acid phenylalanine. Therefore, the triplet UUU must be the codon that translates into phenylalanine. Because the genetic code was deciphered by using these artificial mRNAs, it is usually written in terms of the base triplets in mRNA (rather than in DNA) that code for each amino acid (Table 12-3).

How does a cell recognize where codons start and stop, and where the code for an entire protein starts and stops? Translation always begins with the codon AUG, appropriately known as the **start codon.** Because AUG also codes for the amino acid methionine, all proteins originally begin with methionine, although it may be removed after the protein is synthesized. Three codons—UAG, UAA, and UGA—are **stop codons.** When the ribosome encounters any of these stop codons, it releases both the newly synthesized protein and the mRNA. Because all codons consist of three bases, and the beginning and end of a protein are specified, then "spaces" between codon "words" are unnecessary. Why? Consider what would happen if English used only three-letter words: a sentence such as THEDOGSAWTHECAT would be perfectly understandable, even without spaces between the words.

Because the genetic code has three stop codons, 61 triplets remain to specify only 20 amino acids. Therefore, several different codons may be translated into the same amino acid. For example, six codons—UUA, UUG, CUU, CUC, CUA, and CUG—all code for leucine (see Table 12-3). However, each codon specifies one, and only one, amino acid; UUA always specifies leucine, never isoleucine, glycine, or any other amino acid.

How are codons used to direct protein synthesis? Decoding the codons of mRNA is the job of tRNA and ribosomes. Remember that tRNA transports amino acids to the ribosome and that distinct tRNA molecules carry each different type of amino acid. Each of these unique tRNAs has three exposed bases, called an *anticodon*, which are complementary to the bases of a codon in mRNA. For example, the mRNA codon GUU forms base pairs with the anticodon CAA of a tRNA that has the amino acid valine attached to it. A ribosome can then incorporate valine into a growing protein chain (as we will see later).

CHECK YOUR LEARNING

Can you describe how information is encoded in DNA and RNA, and how this information flows from DNA to RNA to protein? Do you understand the difference between transcription and translation and how each process is used to convert information in DNA to the amino acid sequence of a protein?

12.2 HOW IS THE INFORMATION IN A GENE TRANSCRIBED INTO RNA?

Transcription (Fig. 12-3) consists of three steps: (1) initiation, (2) elongation, and (3) termination. These three steps correspond to the three major parts of most genes in both eukaryotes and prokaryotes: (1) a promoter region at the beginning of the gene, where transcription is started, or initiated; (2) the "body" of the gene, where elongation of the RNA strand occurs; and (3) a termination signal at the end of the gene, where RNA synthesis ceases, or terminates.

TABLE 12-3   The Genetic Code (Codons of mRNA)

		Second Base									
		U		**C**		**A**		**G**			
U	UUU	Phenylalanine (Phe)	UCU	Serine (Ser)	UAU	Tyrosine (Tyr)	UGU	Cysteine (Cys)	U		
	UUC	Phenylalanine	UCC	Serine	UAC	Tyrosine	UGC	Cysteine	C		
	UUA	Leucine (Leu)	UCA	Serine	UAA	Stop	UGA	Stop	A		
	UUG	Leucine	UCG	Serine	UAG	Stop	UGG	Tryptophan (Trp)	G		
C	CUU	Leucine	CCU	Proline (Pro)	CAU	Histidine (His)	CGU	Arginine (Arg)	U		
	CUC	Leucine	CCC	Proline	CAC	Histidine	CGC	Arginine	C		
	CUA	Leucine	CCA	Proline	CAA	Glutamine (Gln)	CGA	Arginine	A		
	CUG	Leucine	CCG	Proline	CAG	Glutamine	CGG	Arginine	G		
A	AUU	Isoleucine (Ile)	ACU	Threonine (Thr)	AAU	Asparagine (Asp)	AGU	Serine (Ser)	U		
	AUC	Isoleucine	ACC	Threonine	AAC	Asparagine	AGC	Serine	C		
	AUA	Isoleucine	ACA	Threonine	AAA	Lysine (Lys)	AGA	Arginine (Arg)	A		
	AUG	Methionine (Met) Start	ACG	Threonine	AAG	Lysine	AGG	Arginine	G		
G	GUU	Valine (Val)	GCU	Alanine (Ala)	GAU	Aspartic acid (Asp)	GGU	Glycine (Gly)	U		
	GUC	Valine	GCC	Alanine	GAC	Aspartic acid	GGC	Glycine	C		
	GUA	Valine	GCA	Alanine	GAA	Glutamic acid (Glu)	GGA	Glycine	A		
	GUG	Valine	GCG	Alanine	GAG	Glutamic acid	GGG	Glycine	G		

(First Base on left axis; Third Base on right axis)

Transcription Begins When RNA Polymerase Binds to the Promoter of a Gene

The enzyme **RNA polymerase** synthesizes RNA. Near the beginning of every gene is a DNA sequence called the **promoter.** In eukaryotic cells, a promoter consists of two main parts: (1) a short sequence of bases, often TATAAA, that binds RNA polymerase; and (2) one or more other sequences, often called *transcription factor binding sites*, or *response elements*. When RNA polymerase binds to the promoter of a gene, the DNA double helix at the beginning of the gene unwinds and transcription begins (**Fig. 12-3 ❶**). Proteins called transcription factors can attach to a transcription factor binding site, enhancing or suppressing binding of RNA polymerase to the promoter and, consequently, enhancing or suppressing transcription of the gene. We will return to the important topic of gene regulation in Section 12.5.

Elongation Generates a Growing Strand of RNA

After binding to the promoter, RNA polymerase travels down one of the DNA strands, called the **template strand,** synthesizing a single strand of RNA with bases complementary to those in the DNA (**Fig. 12-3 ❷**). Like DNA polymerase, RNA polymerase always travels along the DNA template strand starting at the 3′ end of a gene and moving toward the 5′ end. Base pairing between RNA and DNA is the same as between two strands of DNA, except that uracil in RNA pairs with adenine in DNA (see Table 12-1).

After about 10 nucleotides have been added to the growing RNA chain, the first nucleotides of the RNA separate from the DNA template strand. This separation allows the two DNA strands to rewind into a double helix (**Fig. 12-3 ❸**). As transcription continues to elongate the RNA molecule, one end of the RNA drifts away from the DNA, while RNA polymerase keeps the other end attached to the template strand of the DNA (see Fig. 12-3 ❸ and **Fig. 12-4**).

Transcription Stops When RNA Polymerase Reaches the Termination Signal

RNA polymerase continues along the template strand of the gene until it reaches a sequence of DNA bases known as the *termination signal*. At this point, RNA polymerase releases the completed RNA molecule and detaches from the DNA (**Fig. 12-3 ❸ and ❹**). The RNA polymerase is then available to bind to the promoter region of another gene and to synthesize another RNA molecule.

CHECK YOUR LEARNING

Can you describe the process of transcription? Do you understand how DNA, RNA, and RNA polymerase interact to produce a strand of RNA?

► FIGURE 12-3 **Transcription is the synthesis of RNA from instructions in DNA** A gene is a segment of a chromosome's DNA. One of the DNA strands that make up the double helix will serve as the template for the synthesis of an RNA molecule with bases complementary to the bases in the DNA strand.

QUESTION If the other DNA strand of this molecule were the template strand, in which direction would the RNA polymerase travel?

❶ **Initiation:** RNA polymerase binds to the promoter region of DNA near the beginning of a gene, separating the double helix near the promoter.

❷ **Elongation:** RNA polymerase travels along the DNA template strand (blue), unwinding the DNA double helix and synthesizing RNA by catalyzing the addition of ribose nucleotides into an RNA molecule (red). The nucleotides in the RNA are complementary to the template strand of the DNA.

❸ **Termination:** At the end of the gene, RNA polymerase encounters a DNA sequence called a termination signal. RNA polymerase detaches from the DNA and releases the RNA molecule.

❹ **Conclusion of transcription:** After termination, the DNA completely rewinds into a double helix. The RNA molecule is free to move from the nucleus to the cytoplasm for translation, and RNA polymerase may move to another gene and begin transcription once again.

12.3 HOW IS THE BASE SEQUENCE OF mRNA TRANSLATED INTO PROTEIN?

Prokaryotic and eukaryotic cells differ in the organization of their genes, how they produce a functional mRNA molecule from the instructions in their DNA, and the timing and location of translation.

Most prokaryotic genes are compact: All the nucleotides in a gene code for the amino acids in a protein. What's more, most or all of the genes for a complete metabolic pathway sit end to end on the chromosome (Fig. 12-5a). Therefore, prokaryotic cells usually transcribe a single, very long mRNA from a series of adjacent genes, each of which specifies a different protein in the pathway. Because prokaryotic cells do not have a nuclear membrane separating their DNA from the cytoplasm (see Fig. 4-19), transcription and translation are usually not separated, either in space or in time. In most cases, as an mRNA molecule begins to separate from the DNA during transcription, ribosomes immediately begin translating the mRNA into protein (Fig. 12-5b).

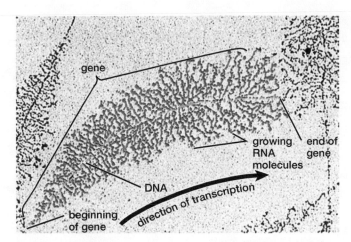

▲ **FIGURE 12-4 RNA transcription in action** This colorized electron micrograph shows the progress of RNA transcription in the egg of an African clawed toad. In each treelike structure, the central "trunk" is DNA and the "branches" are RNA molecules. A series of RNA polymerase molecules (too small to be seen in this micrograph) is traveling down the DNA, synthesizing RNA as they go. The beginning of the gene is on the left. The short RNA molecules on the left have just begun to be synthesized; the long RNA molecules on the right are almost finished.

QUESTION Why do you think so many mRNA molecules are being transcribed from the same gene?

In contrast, the DNA of eukaryotic cells is contained in the nucleus, whereas the ribosomes reside in the cytoplasm. Further, the genes that encode the proteins needed for a metabolic pathway in eukaryotes are not clustered together as they are in prokaryotes, but may be dispersed among several chromosomes. Finally, the RNA molecule formed during transcription is not a functional mRNA that can be immediately translated into protein.

In Eukaryotes, a Precursor RNA Is Processed to Form mRNA That Is Translated into Protein

Most eukaryotic genes consist of two or more segments of DNA with nucleotide sequences that code for a protein, interrupted by sequences that are not translated into protein. The coding segments are called **exons,** because they are *ex*pressed in protein, and the noncoding segments are called **introns,** because they are *intra*genic, meaning "within a gene" (Fig. 12-6a).

Transcription of a eukaryotic gene produces a very long RNA strand, often called a *precursor mRNA* or *pre-mRNA*, which starts before the first exon and ends after the last exon (Fig. 12-6b ❶). More nucleotides are added at the beginning and end of this pre-mRNA molecule, forming a "cap" and "tail" (Fig. 12-6b ❷). These nucleotides will help move the finished mRNA through pores in the nuclear envelope to the cytoplasm, bind the mRNA to a ribosome, and protect the mRNA molecule from degradation by cellular enzymes. To convert this pre-mRNA molecule into the finished mRNA, enzymes in the nucleus cut the pre-mRNA apart at the junctions between introns and exons, splice

(a) Gene organization on a prokaryotic chromosome

(b) Simultaneous transcription and translation in prokaryotes

▲ **FIGURE 12-5 Messenger RNA synthesis in prokaryotic cells (a)** In prokaryotes, many or all of the genes for a complete metabolic pathway lie side by side on the chromosome. **(b)** Transcription and translation are simultaneous in prokaryotes. In the electron micrograph, RNA polymerase (not visible at this magnification) travels from left to right on a strand of DNA. As it synthesizes an mRNA molecule, ribosomes bind to the mRNA and immediately begin synthesizing a protein (not visible). The diagram below the micrograph shows all of the key molecules involved.

together the protein-coding exons, and discard the introns (Fig. 12-6b ❸). The finished mRNA molecules leave the nucleus and enter the cytoplasm through pores in the nuclear envelope (Fig. 12-6b ❹). In the cytoplasm, the mRNA binds to ribosomes, which synthesize the protein specified by the mRNA base sequence.

Functions of Intron–Exon Gene Structure

Why do eukaryotic genes contain introns and exons? This gene structure appears to serve at least two functions. The first is to allow a cell to produce several different proteins from a single gene by splicing exons together in different ways. For example, a gene called *CT/CGRP* is transcribed in both the thyroid and the brain. In the thyroid, one splicing arrangement results in the synthesis of the hormone calcitonin,

exons

DNA

promoter   introns

(a) Eukaryotic gene structure

DNA

❶ Transcription

pre-mRNA

❷ An RNA cap and tail are added

cap   tail

❸ RNA splicing

finished mRNA

introns
are cut
out and
broken
down

❹ Finished mRNA is moved
to the cytoplasm for translation

(b) RNA synthesis and processing in eukaryotes

◀ **FIGURE 12-6 Messenger RNA synthesis in eukaryotic cells** **(a)** Eukaryotic genes consist of exons (medium blue), which code for the amino acid sequence of a protein, and introns (dark blue), which do not. **(b)** Messenger RNA synthesis in eukaryotes involves several steps: ❶ transcribing the gene into a long pre-mRNA molecule; ❷ adding additional RNA nucleotides to form the cap and tail; ❸ cutting out the introns and splicing the exons together into the finished mRNA; and ❹ moving the finished mRNA out of the nucleus into the cytoplasm for translation.

which helps regulate calcium concentrations in the blood. In the brain, a different splicing arrangement results in the synthesis of a protein used as a messenger for communication between nerve cells. Alternative splicing occurs in the RNA transcribed from most eukaryotic genes. Therefore, in eukaryotes, the "one gene, one protein" rule must be reworded as "one gene, one *or more* proteins."

In the second function, fragmented genes may provide a quick and efficient way for eukaryotes to evolve new proteins with new functions. Chromosomes sometimes break apart, and their parts may reattach to different chromosomes. If the breaks occur within the introns of genes, exons may be moved intact from one chromosome to another. Most such errors would be harmful. But sometimes, the exchange of exons between genes produces new genes that enhance the survival and reproduction of the organism that carries them.

During Translation, mRNA, tRNA, and Ribosomes Cooperate to Synthesize Proteins

Like transcription, translation has three steps: (1) initiation, (2) elongation of the protein chain, and (3) termination. We will describe translation only in eukaryotic cells (Fig. 12-7).

Initiation: Translation Begins When tRNA and mRNA Bind to a Ribosome

A "preinitiation complex"—composed of a small ribosomal subunit, a start (methionine) tRNA, and several other proteins

(Fig. 12-7 ❶)—binds to the beginning of an mRNA molecule. The preinitiation complex moves along the mRNA until it finds a start (AUG) codon, which forms base pairs with the UAC anticodon of the methionine tRNA (Fig. 12-7 ❷). A large ribosomal subunit then attaches to the small subunit, sandwiching the mRNA between the two subunits and holding the methionine tRNA in the first tRNA binding site (Fig. 12-7 ❸). The ribosome is now ready to begin translation.

Elongation: Amino Acids Are Added One at a Time to the Growing Protein Chain

A ribosome holds two mRNA codons aligned with the two tRNA binding sites of the large subunit. A second tRNA, with an anticodon complementary to the second codon of the mRNA, moves into the second tRNA binding site on the large subunit (Fig. 12-7 ❹). The catalytic site of the large subunit breaks the bond holding the first amino acid (methionine) to its tRNA and forms a peptide bond between this amino acid and the amino acid attached to the second tRNA (Fig. 12-7 ❺). Interestingly, rRNA, and not one of the proteins of the large subunit, catalyzes the formation of the peptide bond. Therefore, the catalytic site of a ribosome is a ribozyme.

After the peptide bond is formed, the first tRNA is "empty," and the second tRNA carries a two-amino-acid chain. The ribosome releases the empty tRNA and shifts to the next codon on the mRNA molecule (Fig. 12-7 ❻). The tRNA holding the chain of amino acids also shifts, moving from the second to the first binding site of the ribosome. A new tRNA,

① A tRNA with an attached methionine amino acid binds to a small ribosomal subunit, forming a preinitiation complex.

② The preinitiation complex binds to an mRNA molecule. The methionine (met) tRNA anticodon (UAC) base-pairs with the start codon (AUG) of the mRNA.

③ The large ribosomal subunit binds to the small subunit. The methionine tRNA binds to the first tRNA site on the large subunit.

④ The second codon of mRNA (GUU) base-pairs with the anticodon (CAA) of a second tRNA carrying the amino acid valine (val). This tRNA binds to the second tRNA site on the large subunit.

⑤ The catalytic site on the large subunit catalyzes the formation of a peptide bond linking the amino acids methionine and valine. The two amino acids are now attached to the tRNA in the second binding site.

⑥ The "empty" tRNA is released and the ribosome moves down the mRNA, one codon to the right. The tRNA that is attached to the two amino acids is now in the first tRNA binding site and the second tRNA binding site is empty.

ribosome moves one codon to the right

⑦ The third codon of mRNA (CAU) base-pairs with the anticodon (GUA) of a tRNA carrying the amino acid histidine (his). This tRNA enters the second tRNA binding site on the large subunit.

⑧ The catalytic site forms a peptide bond between valine and histidine, leaving the peptide attached to the tRNA in the second binding site. The tRNA in the first site leaves, and the ribosome moves one codon over on the mRNA.

⑨ This process repeats until a stop codon is reached; the mRNA and the completed peptide are released from the ribosome, and the subunits separate.

▲ FIGURE 12-7 **Translation is the process of protein synthesis** Translation decodes the base sequence of an mRNA into the amino acid sequence of a protein.

QUESTION Examine step 9. If mutations changed all of the guanine molecules visible in the mRNA sequence shown here to uracil, how would the translated peptide differ from the one shown?

with an anticodon complementary to the third codon of the mRNA, binds to the empty second site (**Fig. 12-7 ❼**). The catalytic site now joins the third amino acid to the growing protein chain (**Fig. 12-7 ❽**). The empty tRNA leaves the ribosome, the ribosome shifts to the next codon on the mRNA, and the process repeats, one codon at a time.

Termination: A Stop Codon Signals the End of Translation

When the ribosome reaches a stop codon in the mRNA, protein synthesis terminates. Stop codons do not bind to tRNA. Instead, the ribosome releases the finished protein chain and the mRNA (**Fig. 12-7 ❾**). The ribosome then disassembles into its large and small subunits.

SUMMING UP Decoding the Sequence of Bases in DNA into the Sequence of Amino Acids in Protein

Let's summarize how a cell decodes the genetic information of DNA and synthesizes a protein (**Fig. 12-8**):

a. With some exceptions, such as the genes for tRNA and rRNA, each gene codes for the amino acid sequence of a protein. The DNA of the gene consists of the template strand, which is transcribed into mRNA, and its complementary strand, which is not transcribed.

b. Transcription produces an mRNA molecule that is complementary to the template strand. Starting from the first AUG, each codon within the mRNA is a sequence of three bases that specifies an amino acid or a "stop."

c. Enzymes in the cytoplasm attach the appropriate amino acid to each tRNA, as determined by the tRNA's anticodon.

d. The mRNA moves out of the nucleus to a ribosome in the cytoplasm. Transfer RNAs carry their attached amino acids to the ribosome. There, the bases in tRNA anticodons bind to the complementary bases in mRNA codons. The ribosome catalyzes the formation of peptide bonds that join the amino acids to form a protein with the amino acid sequence specified by the sequence of bases in mRNA. When a stop codon is reached, the finished protein is released from the ribosome. This decoding chain, from DNA bases to mRNA codons to tRNA anticodons to amino acids, results in the synthesis of a protein with an amino acid sequence determined by the base sequence of a gene.

CHECK YOUR LEARNING

Can you describe the process of translation? Are you able to describe how the production of mRNA differs between prokaryotic and eukaryotic cells? Do you know how ribosomes, mRNA, and tRNA cooperate to produce a protein?

12.4 HOW DO MUTATIONS AFFECT PROTEIN STRUCTURE AND FUNCTION?

Mistakes during DNA replication, ultraviolet rays in sunlight, chemicals in cigarette smoke, and a host of other environmental factors may cause **mutations**—changes in the sequence of bases in DNA. The consequences for an organism's structure and function depend on how the mutation affects the protein encoded by the mutated gene.

CASE STUDY continued

Cystic Fibrosis

There are about 1,500 different defective alleles of the *CFTR* gene, all of which can cause cystic fibrosis. The most common defective allele is missing a single codon. The resulting lack of one crucial amino acid causes the CFTR protein to be misshapen. A normal CFTR protein is synthesized by ribosomes on rough endoplasmic reticulum (ER), enters the ER, and then is transported to the plasma membrane. The misshapen CFTR protein, however, is broken down within the ER and never reaches the plasma membrane. Four other common mutant *CFTR* alleles code for a stop codon in the middle of the protein, so translation terminates partway through. Still other mutant alleles produce proteins that are completely synthesized and inserted into the plasma membrane, but do not form functional chloride channels.

▲ **FIGURE 12-8 Complementary base pairing is required to decode genetic information** (a) The DNA of a gene contains two strands; only the template strand is used by RNA polymerase to synthesize an RNA molecule. (b) Bases in the template strand of DNA are transcribed into a complementary mRNA. Codons are sequences of three bases that specify an amino acid or a stop during protein synthesis. (c) Unless it is a stop codon, each mRNA codon forms base pairs with the anticodon of a tRNA molecule that carries a specific amino acid. (d) The amino acids borne by the tRNAs are joined to form a protein.

The Effects of Mutations Depend on How They Alter the Codons of mRNA

Mutations may be categorized as inversions, translocations, deletions, insertions, and substitutions. These different types of mutations differ greatly in how they affect DNA and, consequently, their likelihood of producing significant alterations in protein structure and function.

Inversions and Translocations

Inversions are mutations that occur when a piece of DNA is cut out of a chromosome, flipped around, and reinserted in a reversed orientation. **Translocations** are mutations that occur when a piece of DNA is removed from one chromosome and attached to another. Inversions and translocations may be relatively benign if entire genes, including their promoters, are merely moved from one place to another. In these cases, the mRNA transcribed from the gene will contain all of the original codons, and all will remain unchanged. However, if a gene is split in two, it will no longer code for a complete, functional protein. For example, almost half the cases of severe hemophilia are caused by an inversion in the gene that encodes a protein required for blood clotting.

Deletions and Insertions

In a **deletion mutation,** one or more pairs of nucleotides are removed from a gene. In an **insertion mutation,** one or more pairs of nucleotides are inserted into a gene. If one or two pairs of nucleotides are removed or added, protein function is usually completely ruined. Why? Think back to the genetic code: Three nucleotides encode a single amino acid. Therefore, deleting or inserting one or two nucleotides, or any number that isn't a multiple of three, alters all of the codons that follow the deletion or insertion. Why? Consider this sentence, composed of all three-letter words: THEDOGSAWTHECATSITANDTHEFOXRUN. Deleting or inserting a letter (deleting the first E, for example), changes all of the following words: THD OGS AWT HEC ATS ITA NDT HEF OXR UN. Most of the amino acids of a protein synthesized from an mRNA containing such a mutation will be incorrect, so the protein will be nonfunctional.

Deleting or inserting three pairs of nucleotides often has only minor effects on the protein, regardless of whether the three nucleotide pairs that were deleted or inserted make up a single codon or overlap into two codons. Returning to our model sentence, let's suppose that we delete OGS; the sentence reads: THE DAW THE CAT SIT AND THE FOX RUN, most of which still makes sense. If we add a new three-letter word, such as FAT, even in the middle of one of the original words, most of the sentence still makes sense, such as THE DOG SAF ATW THE CAT SIT AND THE FOX RUN.

Substitutions

In a **nucleotide substitution** (also called a **point mutation**), a single base pair in DNA is changed. A substitution within a protein-coding gene can produce one of four possible outcomes. To illustrate these outcomes, let's consider substitutions that occur in the gene encoding beta-globin, one of the subunits of hemoglobin, the oxygen-carrying protein in red blood cells (Table 12-4). The other type of subunit in hemoglobin is called alpha-globin; a normal hemoglobin molecule consists of two alpha and two beta subunits. In all but the last example, we will consider the results of mutations that occur in the sixth codon of the beta-globin gene (CTC in DNA, GAG in mRNA), which specifies glutamic acid—a charged, hydrophilic, water-soluble amino acid.

- **The amino acid sequence of the protein may be unchanged.** Recall that most amino acids can be encoded by several different codons. If a substitution mutation changes the beta-globin DNA base sequence from CTC to CTT, this sequence still codes for glutamic acid. Therefore, the protein synthesized from the mutated gene remains unchanged.
- **Protein function may be unchanged.** Many proteins have regions in which the exact amino acid sequence is relatively unimportant. In beta-globin, the amino acids on the outside of the protein must be hydrophilic to keep the protein dissolved in the cytoplasm of red blood cells. Exactly *which* hydrophilic amino acids are on the outside doesn't matter much. Substitutions in which the resulting amino acid is the same or functionally equivalent are

TABLE 12-4   Effects of Mutations in the Hemoglobin Gene

	DNA (Template Strand)	mRNA	Amino Acid	Properties of Amino Acid	Functional Effect on Protein	Disease
Original codon 6	CTC	GAG	Glutamic acid	Hydrophilic	Normal protein function	None
Mutation 1	CTT	GAA	Glutamic acid	Hydrophilic	Neutral; normal protein function	None
Mutation 2	GTC	CAG	Glutamine	Hydrophilic	Neutral; normal protein function	None
Mutation 3	CAC	GUG	Valine	Hydrophobic	Loses water solubility; compromises protein function	Sickle-cell anemia
Original codon 17	TTC	AAG	Lysine	Hydrophilic	Normal protein function	None
Mutation 4	ATC	UAG	Stop codon	Ends translation after amino acid 16	Synthesizes only part of the protein; eliminates protein function	Beta-thalassemia

called **neutral mutations** because they do not detectably change the function of the encoded protein.

- **Protein function may be changed by an altered amino acid sequence.** A mutation from CTC to CAC replaces glutamic acid (hydrophilic) with valine (hydrophobic). This substitution is the genetic defect that causes sickle-cell anemia (see Chapter 10). The hydrophobic valines on the outside of the hemoglobin molecules cause them to clump together, distorting the shape of the red blood cells and causing serious illness.

- **Protein function may be destroyed by a premature stop codon.** A particularly catastrophic mutation occasionally occurs in the 17th codon of the beta-globin gene (TTC in DNA, AAG in mRNA). This codon specifies the amino acid lysine. A mutation from TTC to ATC (UAG in mRNA) results in a stop codon, halting translation of beta-globin mRNA before the protein is completed. People who inherit this mutant allele from both parents do not synthesize any functional beta-globin protein; they manufacture hemoglobin consisting entirely of alpha-globin subunits. This "pure alpha" hemoglobin does not bind oxygen very well. People with this condition, called beta-thalassemia, require regular blood transfusions throughout life.

CHECK YOUR LEARNING

Can you describe the different types of mutations? Can you use your knowledge of the genetic code to explain why different mutations can have such different effects on protein function?

CASE STUDY continued

Cystic Fibrosis

Cystic fibrosis is the most common lethal genetic disease among people of European descent, about 4% of whom are carriers. Why hasn't natural selection eliminated defective *CFTR* alleles? One hypothesis is that mutated *CFTR* alleles protect against cholera and typhoid. Cholera toxin activates the normal CFTR protein, causing excessive movement of chloride and sodium from intestinal cells into the cavity of the intestine. Water follows by osmosis, causing massive diarrhea that kills by dehydration and loss of salts. Defective CFTR proteins cannot be activated by cholera toxin. The CFTR protein is also the site by which typhoid bacteria enter cells, but typhoid bacteria cannot enter via mutated CFTR proteins. Obviously, such protection cannot compensate for the fatal effects of cystic fibrosis in homozygotes. However, heterozygotes, with one normal and one mutated *CFTR* allele, have nearly normal CFTR function, and might be less severely affected by cholera and typhoid. This "heterozygote advantage" may explain the high frequency of mutated *CFTR* alleles, as it does for the sickle-cell anemia allele (see Chapter 10). However, hypotheses that are biologically reasonable may not be correct: So far, epidemiological studies have failed to convincingly demonstrate a selective advantage of mutated *CFTR* alleles in human populations.

12.5 HOW IS GENE EXPRESSION REGULATED?

The complete human genome contains 20,000 to 25,000 genes. All of these genes are present in almost every body cell, but any individual cell expresses (transcribes and, if the gene product is a protein, translates) only a small fraction of them. Some genes are expressed in all cells, because they encode proteins or RNA molecules that are essential for the life of any cell. For example, all cells need to synthesize proteins, so they all transcribe the genes for tRNA, rRNA, and ribosomal proteins. Other genes are expressed exclusively in certain types of cells, at certain times in an organism's life, or under specific environmental conditions. For example, even though every cell in your body contains the gene for the milk protein casein, that gene is expressed only in women, only in certain breast cells, and only when a woman is breast-feeding.

Regulation of gene expression may occur at the level of transcription (which genes are used to make mRNA in a given cell), translation (how much protein is made from a particular type of mRNA), or protein activity (how long the protein lasts in a cell and how rapidly protein enzymes catalyze specific reactions). Although these general principles apply to both prokaryotic and eukaryotic organisms, there are some differences as well.

In Prokaryotes, Gene Expression Is Primarily Regulated at the Level of Transcription

Bacterial DNA is often organized in packages called **operons,** in which the genes for related functions lie close to one another (**Fig. 12-9a**). An operon consists of four parts: (1) a **regulatory gene,** which controls the timing or rate of transcription of other genes; (2) a promoter, which RNA polymerase recognizes as the place to start transcribing; (3) an **operator,** which governs the access of RNA polymerase to the promoter or to the (4) **structural genes,** which actually encode the related enzymes or other proteins. Whole operons are regulated as units, so that proteins that work together to perform a specific function may be synthesized simultaneously when the need arises.

Prokaryotic operons may be regulated in a variety of ways. Some operons encode enzymes that are needed by the cell just about all the time, such as the enzymes that synthesize many amino acids. Such operons are usually transcribed continuously, unless the bacterium encounters a surplus of that particular amino acid. Other operons encode enzymes that are needed only occasionally, for instance, to digest a relatively rare food. They are transcribed only when the bacterium encounters that food.

Consider the common intestinal bacterium, *Escherichia coli (E. coli)*. This bacterium must live on whatever types of nutrients its host eats, and it can synthesize many different enzymes to metabolize a wide variety of foods.

regulatory gene: codes for repressor protein

operator: repressor protein binds here

promoter: RNA polymerase binds here

structural genes that code for enzymes of lactose metabolism

(a) Structure of the lactose operon

RNA polymerase

transcription blocked

a repressor protein bound to the operator site overlaps the promoter

free repressor proteins

(b) Lactose absent

RNA polymerase binds to the promoter and transcribes the structural genes

lactose bound to repressor proteins

lactose-metabolizing enzymes are synthesized

(c) Lactose present

▲ FIGURE 12-9 **Regulation of the lactose operon (a)** The lactose operon consists of a regulatory gene, a promoter, an operator, and three structural genes that code for enzymes necessary for lactose metabolism. **(b)** In the absence of lactose, repressor proteins bind to the operator of the lactose operon. RNA polymerase can bind to the promoter but cannot move past the repressor protein to transcribe the structural genes. **(c)** When lactose is present, it binds to the repressor proteins, making the repressor proteins unable to bind to the operator. RNA polymerase binds to the promoter, moves past the unoccupied operator, and transcribes the structural genes.

The genes that code for these enzymes are transcribed only when the enzymes are needed. The enzymes that metabolize lactose, the principal sugar in milk, are a case in point. The **lactose operon** contains three structural genes, each coding for an enzyme that aids in lactose metabolism (see Fig. 12-9a).

The lactose operon is shut off, or repressed, unless activated by the presence of lactose. The regulatory gene

of the lactose operon directs the synthesis of a **repressor protein** that binds to the operator site. RNA polymerase, although still able to bind to the promoter, cannot get past the repressor protein to transcribe the structural genes. Consequently, lactose-metabolizing enzymes are not synthesized (**Fig. 12-9b**).

When *E. coli* colonize the intestines of a newborn mammal, however, they find themselves bathed in lactose whenever their host nurses from its mother. Lactose molecules enter the bacteria and bind to the repressor proteins, changing their shape (**Fig. 12-9c**). The lactose–repressor complex cannot attach to the operator site. Therefore, when RNA polymerase binds to the promoter of the lactose operon, it transcribes the genes for lactose-metabolizing enzymes, allowing the bacteria to use lactose as an energy source. After the young mammal is weaned, it usually does not consume milk again. The intestinal bacteria no longer encounter lactose, the repressor proteins bind to the operator, and the genes for lactose metabolism are shut off.

In Eukaryotes, Gene Expression Is Regulated at Many Levels

In some respects, regulation of gene expression in eukaryotes is similar to regulation of expression in prokaryotes. In both, not all genes are transcribed and translated all the time. Further, controlling the rate of transcription is an important mechanism of gene regulation in both. However, eukaryotes sequester their DNA in a membrane-bound nucleus, have very different organization of both their genome and their individual genes, and cut and splice their RNA transcripts in complex ways. Further, multicellular eukaryotes have a variety of cell types, each performing distinct functions, in a single body. These differences require more sophisticated regulation of gene expression.

Gene expression in a eukaryotic cell is a multistep process, beginning with transcription of DNA and commonly ending with a protein that performs a particular function. Regulation of gene expression can occur at any of these steps, as shown in **Figure 12-10**:

❶ **Cells can control the frequency at which a gene is transcribed.** The rate of transcription of specific genes differs among organisms, among cell types in a given organism, within a given cell at different stages in the organism's life, and within a cell or organism depending on environmental conditions (see the following section).

❷ **The same gene may be used to produce different mRNAs and protein products.** The same gene may be used to produce several different protein products (as we described in Section 12.3), depending on how the pre-mRNA is spliced to form the finished mRNA that will be translated on the ribosomes.

❸ **Cells may control the stability and translation of mRNAs.** Some mRNAs are long lasting and are

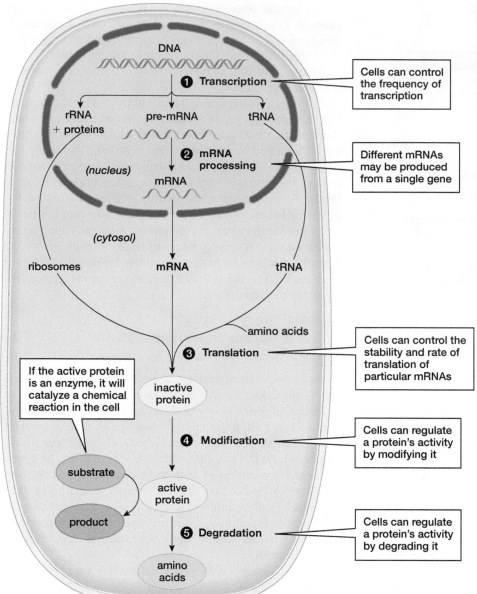

translated into protein many times. Others are translated only a few times before they are degraded. Recently, molecular biologists have discovered that certain small RNA molecules may block translation of some mRNAs or may target some mRNAs for destruction (see the following section).

❹ **Proteins may need to be modified before they can carry out their functions.** For instance, the protein-digesting enzymes produced by cells in your stomach wall and pancreas are initially synthesized in an inactive form, which prevents the enzymes from digesting the cells that produce them. After these inactive forms are secreted into the digestive tract, portions of the enzymes are snipped out to unveil the active site, allowing the enzymes to digest the proteins in food into smaller proteins or individual amino acids. Other modifications, such as adding or removing phosphate

groups, can temporarily activate or inactivate a protein, allowing second-to-second control of the protein's activity. Similar regulation of protein structure and function occurs in prokaryotic cells.

❺ **Cells can control the rate at which proteins are degraded.** By preventing or speeding up a protein's degradation, a cell can rapidly adjust the amount of a particular protein it contains. Protein degradation is also regulated in prokaryotic cells.

Let's examine some of these regulatory mechanisms in more detail.

Regulatory Proteins Binding to a Gene's Promoter Alter Its Rate of Transcription

The promoter regions of virtually all genes contain several different transcription factor binding sites, or response elements.

Health Watch

A Case of Mistaken Gender

Sometime between 7 and 14 years of age, a girl usually goes through puberty: Her breasts swell, her hips widen, and she begins to menstruate. In rare instances, however, a girl may develop all of the outward signs of womanhood, but without menstruation. How can that be? If her physician performs a chromosome test, in some cases the results seem to be impossible: The girl's sex chromosomes are XY. The reason she has not begun to menstruate is that she lacks ovaries and a uterus but instead has testes inside her abdominal cavity. She has about the same concentrations of androgens (male sex hormones, such as testosterone) circulating in her blood as would be found in a boy her age. In fact, androgens have been present since early in her development. However, her cells cannot respond to them—a condition called androgen insensitivity.

The affected gene codes for a protein known as an androgen receptor. In normal males, androgens bind to the receptor proteins, stimulating the transcription of genes that help to produce many male features, including the formation of a penis and the descent of the testes into sacs outside the body cavity. Androgen insensitivity is caused by defective androgen receptors. There are more than 200 mutant alleles of the androgen receptor gene. The most serious are mutations that create a premature stop codon. As you know, these mutations are likely to have catastrophic effects on protein structure and function.

Because the androgen receptor gene is on the X chromosome, a person who is genetically male (XY) inherits a single allele for the androgen receptor. If this allele is seriously defective, the person will not synthesize functional androgen receptor proteins. The person's cells will be unable to respond to testosterone, and male characteristics will not develop. In many respects, female development is the "default" option in humans, and without

functional androgen receptors, the affected person's body will develop female characteristics. Thus, a mutation that changes the nucleotide sequence of a single gene, causing a single type of defective protein to be produced, can cause a person who is genetically male to look like and perceive herself to be female (Fig. E12-2).

▲ FIGURE E12-2 **Androgen insensitivity leads to female features** This person has an X and a Y chromosome. She has testes that produce testosterone, but a mutation in her androgen receptor genes makes her cells unable to respond to testosterone, resulting in her female appearance.

Therefore, whether these genes are transcribed depends on which transcription factors are synthesized by the cell and whether those transcription factors are active. For example, when cells are exposed to free radicals (see Chapter 2), a transcription factor binds to antioxidant response elements in the promoters of several genes. As a result, the cell produces enzymes that break down free radicals to harmless substances.

Many transcription factors require activation before they can affect gene transcription. One of the best-known examples is the role that the sex hormone, estrogen, plays in controlling egg production in birds. The gene for albumin, the major protein in egg white, is not transcribed in winter when birds are not breeding and estrogen levels are low. During the breeding season, the ovaries of female birds release estrogen, which enters cells in the oviduct and binds to a transcription factor (usually called an estrogen receptor). The complex of estrogen and its receptor then attaches to an estrogen response element in the promoter of the

albumin gene, making it easier for RNA polymerase to bind to the promoter and start transcribing mRNA. The mRNA is translated into large amounts of albumin. Similar activation of gene transcription by steroid hormones occurs in other animals, including humans. The importance of hormonal regulation of transcription during development is illustrated by genetic defects in which receptors for sex hormones are nonfunctional (see "Health Watch: A Case of Mistaken Gender").

Epigenetic Controls Alter Gene Transcription and Translation

Epigenetics (which means "in addition to genetics") is the study of how cells and organisms change gene expression and function without changing the base sequence of their DNA. There is disagreement about what processes should be considered to be epigenetic. In general, however, epigenetic control works in three ways: (1) modification of DNA; (2) modification of chromosomal proteins; and (3) changing

Why Bruises Turn Colors?

Bruises typically progress from purple to green to yellow. This sequence is visual evidence of the control of gene expression. If you bang your shin on a chair, blood vessels break and release red blood cells, which burst and spill their hemoglobin. Hemoglobin and its iron-containing heme group are dark bluish-purple in the deoxygenated state, so fresh bruises are purple. Heme, which is toxic to the liver, kidneys, brain, and blood vessels, stimulates transcription of the heme oxygenase gene. Heme oxygenase is an enzyme that converts heme to biliverdin, which is green. A second enzyme, which is always present because its gene is always expressed, converts biliverdin to bilirubin, which is yellow. The bruise finally disappears as bilirubin moves to the liver, which secretes it into the bile. You can follow the detoxification of heme by watching your bruise change color.

transcription and translation through the actions of several types of RNA collectively called noncoding, or regulatory, RNA. Many types of epigenetic controls can be inherited from parent to daughter cell during mitotic cell division. Some may even be inherited from one generation to the next, as we explore in "Health Watch: The Strange World of Epigenetics."

Epigenetic Modification of DNA May Suppress Transcription Certain enzymes in a cell add methyl groups ($-CH_3$) to cytosine bases in specific locations in the cell's DNA, a process called *methylation*. If a gene or its promoter has lots of methyl groups, the gene usually will not be copied into mRNA, and so its instructions will not be used to make proteins. The number and location of methyl groups on DNA are important in normal development and in some diseases, such as cancer. In cancer cells, growth factor genes (see Chapter 9) often have too few methyl groups. This can cause the genes to be transcribed at a very high level, producing high concentrations of growth factors that inappropriately stimulate cell division. If tumor suppressor genes have too many methyl groups, shutting down their transcription, the body is robbed of one of its most effective weapons against cancer. Defective epigenetic control has also been implicated in disorders as varied as heart disease, obesity, infertility, and type 2 (adult-onset) diabetes.

Epigenetic Modification of Histones May Enhance Transcription In eukaryotic chromosomes, DNA is wound around "spools" made of proteins called *histones* (see Chapter 9). When the DNA is tightly wound, RNA polymerase can't get to the promoters of genes, so transcription occurs

slowly, if at all. However, when acetyl groups ($-COCH_3$) are added to histones, the DNA partially unwinds and RNA polymerase has better access to the promoters, making gene transcription easier.

Noncoding RNA May Alter Transcription or Translation

Protein-coding genes make up only a small percentage of human DNA. Does that mean that the rest of our DNA is pointless? Far from it. Recently, molecular biologists have found that some of this DNA is transcribed into *noncoding RNA*, which may exert major effects on gene expression.

MicroRNA and RNA Interference As you know, mRNA is transcribed from DNA and translated into protein, which then performs cellular functions such as catalyzing biochemical reactions. How much protein is synthesized depends both on how much mRNA is made and on how rapidly and for how long mRNA is translated. Enter RNA interference. The DNA of organisms as diverse as plants, roundworms, and people contains hundreds of genes that do not code for proteins, but that are nevertheless transcribed into RNA. In some cases, RNA polymerase transcribes a long piece of noncoding RNA. Cellular enzymes cut the RNA transcript into very short RNA strands appropriately named **microRNA.** Each microRNA is complementary to part of a specific mRNA. These microRNA molecules interfere with translation of the mRNA (hence, the name "RNA interference"). In some cases, these small RNA strands base-pair with the complementary mRNA, forming a little section of double-stranded RNA that cannot be translated. In other cases, the short RNA strands combine with enzymes to cut up complementary mRNA, which also prevents translation.

Why should a cell interfere with the translation of its own mRNA? RNA interference is important for the development of eukaryotic organisms. For example, in mammals microRNAs influence the development of the heart and brain, the secretion of insulin by the pancreas, and even learning and memory. Unfortunately, defects in microRNA production—either too much or too little of certain microRNAs—can lead to cancer or heart disease.

Some organisms use microRNA to defend against disease. Many plants produce microRNA that is complementary to the nucleic acids (usually RNA) of plant viruses. When the microRNA finds complementary viral RNA molecules, it directs enzymes to cut up the viral RNA, thereby preventing viral reproduction.

Altering Transcription with Noncoding RNA

Other types of noncoding RNA can affect gene transcription. Some noncoding RNAs inhibit the binding of RNA polymerase to specific gene promoters, thereby blocking transcription. Other noncoding RNAs stimulate or inhibit epigenetic changes to DNA or histones in specific locations on specific chromosomes. These noncoding RNAs may enhance

Health|Watch

The Strange World of Epigenetics

We have described many ways in which cells control gene expression. Most of these work for times ranging from a few seconds to a few days and then fade away. Epigenetic controls, however, often work for the life of an organism. Some may even be passed down from parent to offspring.

Epigenetic controls are important in ensuring proper control of gene transcription and translation. For example, adding methyl groups to the promoter of the insulin gene turns off transcription. All of the cells of early embryos have methylated, silenced insulin genes. Later in development, methyl groups on the insulin gene are selectively removed in cells destined to become insulin-secreting cells of the pancreas. Every other cell of the body has methylated, silenced insulin genes. Some cells, such as those in the intestinal lining, divide every day or two—thousands of divisions during a lifetime. Throughout all of these divisions, the insulin genes remain methylated. How? Recall that DNA replication is semiconservative (see Chapter 11). When an intestinal cell divides, both daughter cells inherit one parental DNA strand with methyls on the insulin gene and one new DNA strand without methyls on the gene. However, an enzyme in the daughter cells adds the parental methyl pattern to the daughter DNA strand. The result is that all intestinal cells have silenced insulin genes.

In the vast majority of cases, methyl patterns on DNA are erased during meiotic cell division or gamete development, so epigenetic changes do not pass from generation to generation. However, there are some exceptions. Methyl groups may be added to certain clusters of genes in either the sperm or the egg, resulting in genomic imprinting, in which a given gene will be expressed only if it is inherited from either the father or the mother, respectively. For example, the large, meaty buttocks of sheep called callipyge (Greek for "beautiful butt") develop only if the callipyge mutation is inherited from the father. In humans, Angelman syndrome, a rare genetic disease characterized by seizures, speech defects, and motor disabilities, is the result of a deletion mutation in chromosome 15. Angelman syndrome occurs only when the mutation has been inherited from the mother. The normal, functional genes on the father's chromosome are silenced by methyl groups, and cannot compensate for the mother's mutation.

Epigenetic changes that last for many generations have been documented in bacteria, protists, fungi, plants, and animals. This leads to a provocative question: In people, can epigenetic changes caused by parents' life experiences or environment become a long-lasting, even permanent, part of the inheritance of their offspring?

For now, the answer seems to be "Maybe." No one can perform controlled, multigenerational experiments on people, so good data are hard to obtain. Therefore, evidence for multigenerational epigenetic inheritance in humans will most likely be a "natural experiment" in which some major event affected a fairly large number of people. One such natural experiment has already occurred in a remote northern area of Sweden called Norrbotten. Until fairly recent times, Norrbotten was extremely isolated. Little food entered or left the region. If crop harvests were good, people stuffed themselves during the following winter; if harvests were bad, people starved. Researchers tracked birth and death records, and correlated those with harvests during the 1800s. They found that the grandsons of boys who lived during the years of abundant harvests, and therefore probably overate, lived remarkably shorter lives—from 6 to 32 years shorter, depending on how the data were analyzed—than the grandsons of boys who suffered through winters of near starvation. Similar effects were found in girls. The results are intriguing, but no one knows what genes were involved or whether epigenetic methyl groups on DNA caused the difference.

or reduce transcription, depending on the exact nature of the epigenetic controls that are affected.

Perhaps the best-known noncoding RNA silences transcription in mammalian X chromosomes. As you know, male mammals have an X and a Y chromosome (XY), and females have two X chromosomes (XX). As a consequence, females have the capacity to synthesize mRNA from genes on their two X chromosomes, whereas males, with only one X chromosome, may produce only half as much. In 1961, Mary Lyon, an English geneticist, hypothesized that one of the two X chromosomes in females is inactivated in some way, so that its genes are not expressed. Subsequent research showed that she was correct. In female mammals, one of the X chromosomes is inactivated, and about 85% of its genes are not transcribed. Early in embryonic development (about the 16th day in humans), one X chromosome in each of a female's cells begins to produce large amounts of a noncoding RNA molecule called Xist. Xist RNA coats most of the X chromosome, condenses it into a tight mass, and prevents transcription. The condensed X chromosome, called a **Barr body** after its discoverer, Murray Barr, appears as a discrete spot in the nuclei of the cells of female mammals (**Fig. 12-11**).

Usually, large clusters of cells (with each cluster descended from a single cell of the early embryo) have the same X chromosome inactivated. As a result, the bodies of female mammals are composed of patches of cells in which one of the X chromosomes is fully active and patches of cells in which the other X chromosome is active. The results of this phenomenon are easily observed in calico cats (**Fig. 12-12**). The X chromosome of a cat contains a gene encoding an enzyme that produces fur pigment. There are two common alleles of this gene: One produces orange fur

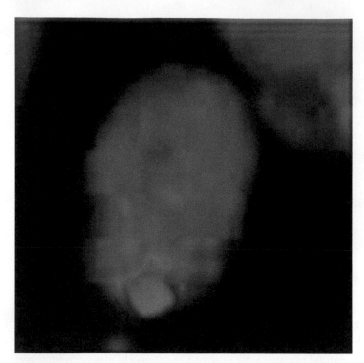

▲ FIGURE 12-11 **A Barr body** The red spot at the bottom of the nucleus is an inactivated X chromosome called a Barr body. In this fluorescence micrograph, the Barr body is stained with a dye that binds to the Xist RNA coating the inactivated X chromosome.

▲ FIGURE 12-12 **Inactivation of the X chromosome regulates gene expression** This female calico kitten carries a gene for orange fur on one X chromosome and a gene for black fur on her other X chromosome. Inactivation of different X chromosomes produces the black and orange patches. The white color is due to an entirely different gene that prevents pigment formation altogether.

and the other produces black fur. If one X chromosome in a female cat has the orange allele and the other X chromosome has the black allele, the cat will have patches of orange and black fur. These patches represent areas of skin that developed from cells in the early embryo in which different X chromosomes were inactivated. Calico coloring is almost exclusively found in female cats. Because male cats

normally have only one X chromosome, which is active in all of their cells, male cats usually have black fur or orange fur, but not both.

CHECK YOUR LEARNING

Can you describe the ways in which information flow from DNA to RNA to protein synthesis to protein function can be regulated? Do you understand which controls over gene expression are likely to be very brief, which may be long lasting, and why they differ?

CASE STUDY revisited

Cystic Fibrosis

All of the defective alleles of the *CFTR* gene are recessive to the functional *CFTR* allele. People who are heterozygous, with one normal *CFTR* allele and one copy of any of the defective alleles, produce enough functional CFTR protein for adequate chloride transport. Therefore, they produce normal, watery secretions in their lungs and do not develop cystic fibrosis. Someone with two defective alleles will produce only proteins that don't work properly and will develop the disease.

Genetic diseases such as cystic fibrosis can't be "cured" in the way that an infection can be cured by killing offending bacteria or viruses. Typically, genetic diseases are treated by replacing the lost function, such as by giving insulin to diabetics, or by relieving the symptoms. In cystic fibrosis, the most common treatments relieve some of the symptoms. These treatments include antibiotics, medicines that open the airways, and physical therapy to drain the lungs.

What ultimately happens to a person with cystic fibrosis depends on how defective the mutant alleles are. Canadian triathlete Lisa Bentley, for example, has a relatively mild case of cystic fibrosis (Fig. 12-13). However, during a

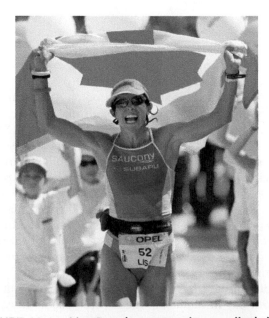

▲ FIGURE 12-13 **Lisa Bentley, sometimes called the Iron Queen, wins another triathlon.**

9-hour triathlon, she produces copious amounts of very salty sweat. It is a constant challenge for Bentley to keep her body supplied with salt during a race. Nevertheless, Bentley has won 11 triathlons, including the Australian Ironman Triathlon five straight years, from 2002 through 2006. Bentley carefully controls her diet, especially her salt intake. Vigorous exercise helps to clear out her lungs. She also scrupulously avoids situations where she might be exposed to contagious diseases. Her cystic fibrosis hasn't kept her from becoming one of the finest athletes in the world.

Consider This

BioEthics Most biomedical research in the United States is funded by government agencies, such as the National Institutes of Health (NIH). The NIH funds research on genetic disorders such as cystic fibrosis and muscular dystrophy; infectious diseases such as AIDS and tuberculosis; and a host of other conditions, including heart disease and cancer. The NIH also supports research on diseases, such as malaria, that are uncommon in the United States but claim hundreds of thousands of lives each year in impoverished countries. How do you think that NIH funds should be spent—in proportion to disease severity and incidence in the United States, which might mean that almost all NIH funds should be spent on heart disease and cancer; or according to the prospective life span of the victims, so that diseases of the young, such as cystic fibrosis, receive much more? Does the United States have a responsibility to develop treatments for people in other countries suffering from diseases that are rare in America?

CHAPTER REVIEW

Summary of Key Concepts

12.1 How Is the Information in DNA Used in a Cell?

Genes are segments of DNA that can be transcribed into RNA and, for most genes, translated into protein. Transcription produces the three types of RNA needed for translation: mRNA, tRNA, and rRNA. Messenger RNA carries the genetic information of a gene from the nucleus to the cytoplasm, where ribosomes use the information to synthesize a protein. Ribosomes are composed of rRNA and proteins, organized into large and small subunits. There are many different tRNAs. Each tRNA binds a specific amino acid and carries it to a ribosome for incorporation into a protein. The genetic code consists of codons, sequences of three bases in mRNA that specify the start of translation (start codon), the amino acids in the protein chain, or the end of protein synthesis (stop codons).

12.2 How Is the Information in a Gene Transcribed into RNA?

Within an individual cell, only certain genes are transcribed. When the cell requires the product of a gene, RNA polymerase binds to the promoter region of the gene and synthesizes a single strand of RNA. This RNA is complementary to the template strand in the gene's DNA double helix. Cellular proteins called transcription factors may bind to DNA near the promoter and enhance or suppress transcription of a given gene.

12.3 How Is the Base Sequence of mRNA Translated into Protein?

In prokaryotic cells, all of the nucleotides of a protein-coding gene code for amino acids; therefore, the RNA transcribed from the gene is the mRNA that will be translated on a ribosome. In eukaryotic cells, protein-coding genes consist of two parts: exons, which code for amino acids in a protein, and introns, which do not. The entire gene, including both introns and exons, is transcribed into a pre-mRNA molecule. The introns of the pre-mRNA are cut out and the exons are spliced together to produce a finished mRNA.

In eukaryotes, mRNA carries the genetic information from the nucleus to the cytoplasm, where ribosomes use this information to synthesize a protein. The two ribosomal subunits come together at the start codon of the mRNA molecule to form the complete protein-synthesizing assembly. Transfer RNAs deliver the appropriate amino acids to the ribosome for incorporation into the growing protein. Which tRNA binds and, consequently, which amino acid is delivered depend on base pairing between the anticodon of the tRNA and the codon of the mRNA. Two tRNAs, each carrying an amino acid, bind simultaneously to the ribosome; the large subunit catalyzes the formation of peptide bonds between the amino acids. As each new amino acid is attached, one tRNA detaches, and the ribosome moves over one codon, binding to another tRNA that carries the next amino acid specified by mRNA. Addition of amino acids to the growing protein continues until a stop codon is reached, causing the ribosome to disassemble and to release both the mRNA and the newly formed protein.

12.4 How Do Mutations Affect Protein Structure and Function?

A mutation is a change in the nucleotide sequence of a gene. Mutations can be caused by mistakes in base pairing during replication, by chemical agents, and by environmental factors such as radiation. Common types of mutations include inversions, translocations, deletions, insertions, and substitutions (point mutations). Mutations may be neutral or harmful, but in rare cases a mutation will promote better adaptation to the environment and thus will be favored by natural selection.

12.5 How Is Gene Expression Regulated?

The expression of a gene requires that it be transcribed and translated and that the resulting protein perform some action within the cell. Which genes are expressed in a cell at any given time is regulated by the function of the cell, the developmental stage of the organism, and the environment. Control of gene regulation can occur at many steps. The amount of mRNA synthesized from a particular gene can be regulated by increasing or decreasing the rate of its transcription, as well as by changing the stability of the mRNA itself. Rates of translation of mRNAs can also be regulated. Regulation of transcription and translation affects how many protein molecules are produced from a particular gene. Even after they are synthesized, many proteins must be modified before they can function. Proteins also vary in how rapidly they are degraded in a cell. In epigenetic regulation, adding methyl groups to DNA often suppresses gene transcription, whereas adding acetyl groups to histones increases gene transcription. Noncoding RNA may suppress transcription, speed up mRNA degradation, or inhibit translation of mRNA.

Key Terms

anticodon *211*	operon *222*
Barr body *227*	point mutation *221*
codon *210*	promoter *215*
deletion mutation *221*	regulatory gene *222*
epigenetics *225*	repressor protein *223*
exon *217*	ribonucleic acid (RNA) *210*
genetic code *212*	ribosomal RNA (rRNA) *210*
insertion mutation *221*	ribosome *210*
intron *217*	RNA polymerase *215*
inversion *221*	start codon *214*
lactose operon *223*	stop codon *214*
messenger RNA (mRNA) *210*	structural gene *222*
microRNA *226*	template strand *215*
mutation *220*	transcription *212*
neutral mutation *222*	transfer RNA (tRNA) *210*
nucleotide substitution *221*	translation *212*
operator *222*	translocation *221*

Learning Outcomes

In this chapter, you have learned to . . .

LO1 Describe the molecules and cellular structures that play central roles in the process by which information encoded in DNA is used to synthesize proteins.

LO2 Compare and contrast how information is encoded in DNA and in RNA.

LO3 Describe the functions of transcription and translation and identify the locations in the cell at which they occur.

LO4 Describe the main steps of transcription, including the molecules involved and how they interact.

LO5 Describe the main steps of translation, including the molecules involved and how they interact.

LO6 Describe the different types of mutations and explain their potential effects on protein synthesis.

LO7 Describe how gene expression is regulated.

Thinking Through the Concepts

Fill-in-the-Blank

1. Synthesis of RNA from the instructions in DNA is called _____. Synthesis of a protein from the instructions in mRNA is called _____. Which structure in the cell is the site of protein synthesis? _____ LO1 LO3

2. The three types of RNA that are essential for protein synthesis are_____, _____, and_____. Another type of RNA, which can interfere with translation, is called _____. LO2 LO3 LO7

3. The genetic code uses _____ (how many?) bases to code for a single amino acid. This short sequence of bases in mRNA is called a(n) _____. The complementary sequence of bases in tRNA is called a(n) _____. LO2

4. The enzyme _____ synthesizes RNA from the instructions in DNA. DNA has two strands, but for any given gene, only one strand, called the _____ strand, is transcribed. To begin transcribing a gene, this enzyme binds to a specific sequence of DNA bases located at the beginning of the gene. This DNA sequence is called the _____. Transcription ends when the enzyme encounters a DNA sequence at the end of the gene called the _____. LO4

5. Protein synthesis begins when mRNA binds to a ribosome. Translation begins with the _____ codon of mRNA and continues until a(n) _____ codon is reached. Individual amino acids are brought to the ribosome by _____. These amino acids are linked into protein by _____ bonds. LO5

6. There are several different types of mutations in DNA. If one nucleotide is substituted for another, this is called a(n) _____ mutation. _____ mutations occur if nucleotides are added in the middle of a gene. _____ mutations occur if nucleotides are removed from the middle of a gene. LO6

Review Questions

1. How does RNA differ from DNA? LO2

2. Name the three types of RNA that are essential to protein synthesis. What is the function of each? LO2 LO3 LO5

3. Define the following terms: *genetic code, codon,* and *anticodon.* What is the relationship among the bases in DNA, the codons of mRNA, and the anticodons of tRNA? LO2 LO5

4. How is mRNA formed from a eukaryotic gene? LO4

5. Diagram and describe protein synthesis. LO5

6. Explain how complementary base pairing is involved in both transcription and translation. LO4 LO5

7. Describe the principal mechanisms of regulating gene expression. LO7

8. Define *mutation.* Are most mutations likely to be beneficial or harmful? Explain your answer. LO6

Applying the Concepts

1. **BioEthics** As you have learned in this chapter, many factors influence gene expression, including hormones. The use of anabolic steroids and growth hormones among athletes has created controversy in recent years. Hormones certainly affect gene expression, but, in the broadest sense, so do vitamins and foods. What do you think are appropriate guidelines for the use of hormones? Should athletes take steroids or growth hormones? Should children at risk of being unusually short be given growth hormones? Should parents be allowed to request growth hormones for a child of normal height in the hope of producing a future basketball player?

2. Many years ago, some researchers reported that they could transfer learning from one animal (a flatworm) to another by feeding trained animals to untrained animals. Further, they claimed that RNA was the active molecule of learning. Given your knowledge of the roles of RNA and protein in cells, do you think that a *specific* memory (for example, remembering the base sequences of codons of the genetic code) could be encoded by a *specific* molecule of RNA and that this RNA molecule could transfer that memory to another person? In other words, in the future, could you learn biology by popping an RNA pill? If so, how would this work? If not, can you propose a reasonable hypothesis for the results with flatworms? How would you test your hypothesis?

3. Androgen insensitivity is inherited as a simple recessive trait, because one copy of the normal androgen receptor allele produces sufficient amounts of androgen receptors. Given this information and your knowledge of the chromosomal basis of inheritance, can androgen insensitivity be inherited, or must it arise as a new mutation each time it occurs? If it can be inherited, would inheritance be through the mother or through the father? Why?

Answers to Figure Caption questions and Fill-in-the-Blank questions can be found in the Answers section at the back of the book.

(MB) **Go to MasteringBiology for practice quizzes, activities, eText, videos, current events, and more.**

DNA profiling proved that Dennis Maher, shown here with attorney Aliza Kaplan, was innocent of the crimes for which he spent 19 years in prison.

CASE STUDY
Guilty or Innocent?

"IT'S OK TO CRY," Innocence Project attorney Aliza Kaplan told Dennis Maher, on his way to court in 2003. Maher seemed calm as District Attorney Martha Coakley asked the judge to dismiss the charges for which Maher had been imprisoned for over 19 years. The judge ordered Maher's immediate release. Maher and his family hugged and wept in the hall outside.

In 1984, Maher had been sentenced to life imprisonment for two counts of rape and one of attempted rape. As it turned out, his only crimes were living in the vicinity of the rapes, wearing a red sweatshirt, and looking like the real assailant. All three victims picked Maher

out of lineups. How can three people all identify the wrong man? It was dark, the assaults were swift, and, obviously, the victims were tremendously stressed. Contrary to popular belief, eyewitness testimony is very unreliable. Studies have found that eyewitness identification is wrong about 35% to 80% of the time, depending on the conditions used in the experiments.

You have probably already guessed what led to Maher's eventual exoneration—DNA evidence. In 1993, while watching the *Phil Donahue Show* in prison, Maher learned about the Innocence Project, which seeks to exonerate people who have been wrongly convicted of serious crimes. The Innocence Project agreed to help, but hit

a brick wall—no biological evidence was available for any of the cases.

Finally, 7 years later, an Innocence Project law student found the semen-stained underwear of one of the rape victims, lost in a box in a courthouse storage room. A few months later, a semen specimen from the second rape turned up as well. DNA profiling proved that Maher was not the assailant in either case.

In this chapter, we'll investigate the techniques of biotechnology that now pervade much of modern life. How do crime scene investigators decide that two DNA samples match? How can biotechnology diagnose inherited disorders? Should biotechnology be used to change the genetic makeup of crops, livestock, or even people?

AT A GLANCE

LEARNING GOALS

LG1 Describe natural processes that recombine DNA.

LG2 Define polymerase chain reaction, short tandem repeats, gel electrophoresis, and DNA probes, and describe how electrophoresis and the polymerase chain reaction work.

LG3 Describe how DNA profiles are generated, and explain how they can be used to identify individual people.

LG4 List the purposes for genetically modifying organisms, and describe the steps involved in creating a genetically modified organism.

LG5 Describe the potential drawbacks of genetically modified organisms.

LG6 Summarize the findings that resulted from the Human Genome Project, and describe the potential benefits of those findings.

LG7 Explain how biotechnology can be used to diagnose and treat inherited disorders.

13.1 WHAT IS BIOTECHNOLOGY?

Biotechnology is the use, and especially the alteration, of organisms, cells, or biological molecules to produce food, drugs, or other goods. Some aspects of biotechnology are ancient. For example, people have used yeast cells to produce bread, beer, and wine for the past 10,000 years. Prehistoric art and archaeological discoveries indicate that many plants and animals, including wheat, grapes, dogs, pigs, and cattle, were domesticated and selectively bred for desirable traits 6,000 to 15,000 years ago. For instance, selective breeding for desirable inherited traits rapidly transformed relatively slim wild boars, with long tusks and fierce temperaments, into much heavier, more placid domestic pigs. Selective breeding is still an important tool for improving livestock and crops.

In addition to selective breeding, modern biotechnology frequently uses **genetic engineering** to isolate and manipulate the genes that control inherited characteristics. Genetically engineered cells or organisms have genes deleted, added, or changed. Genetic engineering can be used to learn more about how cells and genes work; to develop better treatments for diseases; to produce valuable biological molecules, including hormones and vaccines; and to improve plants and animals for agriculture. A relatively familiar application of modern biotechnology is **cloning**—making identical copies of individual genes or even entire organisms. We describe how genes are cloned in Section 13.4. Natural and technological methods of cloning whole organisms are explored in "Science in Action: Carbon Copies—Cloning in Nature and the Lab."

A key tool in modern biotechnology is **recombinant DNA,** which is DNA that has been altered to contain genes or parts of genes from different organisms. Large amounts of recombinant DNA can be produced in bacteria, viruses, or yeast, and then transferred into other species. Plants and animals that contain DNA that has been modified or derived from other species are called **transgenic** or **genetically modified organisms (GMOs).**

Modern biotechnology includes many methods of analyzing and manipulating DNA, whether or not the DNA is subsequently put into a cell or an organism. For example, determining the nucleotide sequence of DNA is crucial for fields as diverse as forensic science, medicine, and evolutionary biology.

In this chapter, we will provide an overview of the applications of biotechnology and their impacts on society. We will also briefly describe some of the important methods used in those applications. We will organize our discussion around five major themes: (1) recombinant DNA mechanisms found in nature; (2) biotechnology in criminal forensics; (3) biotechnology in agriculture, specifically transgenic plants and animals; (4) analyzing the entire genomes of humans and other organisms; and (5) biotechnology in medicine, focusing on the diagnosis and treatment of inherited disorders.

CHECK YOUR LEARNING

Can you describe applications of genetic engineering and recombinant DNA?

13.2 HOW DOES DNA RECOMBINE IN NATURE?

The process of recombining DNA is not unique to modern laboratories. Many natural processes can transfer DNA from one organism to another, sometimes even to organisms of different species.

SCIENCE IN ACTION Carbon Copies—Cloning in Nature and the Lab

The word "cloning" may evoke images of Dolly the sheep or even *Star Wars: Attack of the Clones*, but nature has been quietly cloning for hundreds of millions of years. How are clones produced, either in nature or in the lab?

Cloning in Nature

Sexual reproduction relies on meiotic cell division, the production of gametes, and fertilization, and usually produces genetically unique offspring. In contrast, asexual reproduction (see Fig. 9-2) relies on mitotic cell division. Because mitotic cell division creates daughter cells that are genetically identical to the parent cell, offspring produced by asexual reproduction are genetically identical to their parents—they are clones. Many clusters of plants, including strawberries, grasses, and aspen groves (see Fig. 9-2) are clones.

Cloning Plants: A Familiar Application in Agriculture

Humans have been in the cloning business a lot longer than you might think. For example, consider navel oranges, which don't produce seeds. How do they reproduce? Navel orange trees are propagated by cutting a piece of stem from an adult navel tree and grafting it onto the top of the root of a seedling of another type of orange tree. The cells of the aboveground, fruit-bearing parts of the grafted tree are clones of the original navel orange stem. All navel oranges originated from a single mutant bud of an orange tree discovered in Brazil in the early 1800s, and propagated asexually ever since. Two navel orange trees were brought from Brazil to Riverside, California, in the 1870s—one of them is still there! All American navel orange trees are clones of these two trees.

Cloning Mammals

But, of course, the popular perception of the word "cloning" isn't about growing strawberries or making navel orange trees: It's about making whole new animals, usually by implanting a nucleus from one animal into a fertilized egg taken from another animal. In the 1950s, John Gurdon and his colleagues did this in frogs. They destroyed the nuclei of frog eggs, and then inserted new nuclei, taken from embryonic frog cells. Some of the resulting cells developed into complete frogs. By the 1990s, several labs had cloned mammals using nuclei from embryos, but it wasn't until 1996 that Ian Wilmut of the Roslin Institute in Edinburgh, Scotland, cloned a mammal using a nucleus taken from an adult. The resulting cloned sheep was the famous Dolly (Fig. E13-1).

Why bother to clone mammals? Suppose that a pharmaceutical company genetically engineered a cow that secreted a valuable molecule, such as an antibiotic, in its milk. Genetic engineering techniques are extremely expensive and somewhat hit or miss, so the company might successfully produce only one profitable cow. This cow could then be cloned, creating a whole herd of antibiotic-producing cows. Cloned cows that produce more milk or meat, and cloned pigs tailored to be organ donors for humans, already exist.

Cloning might also help rescue critically endangered species, many of which don't reproduce well in zoos. As Richard Adams of Texas A&M University put it, "You could repopulate the world [with an endangered species] in a matter of a couple of years. Cloning is not a trivial pursuit."

Cloning: An Imperfect Technology

Unfortunately, cloning mammals is beset with difficulties. An egg is subjected to severe trauma when its nucleus is sucked out or destroyed and a new nucleus is inserted. Often, the egg may simply die. Even if the egg survives and starts dividing, it may not develop properly. If the eggs do develop into viable embryos, the embryos must be implanted into the uterus of a surrogate mother. Many clones die or are aborted during gestation, often with serious or fatal consequences for the surrogate mother. Even if the clone survives gestation and birth, it may have defects, commonly a deformed head, lungs, or heart. Not surprisingly, these problems translate into a phenomenally high failure rate. It took 277 tries to produce Dolly. The first cloned dog, produced in 2005, was the sole survivor of 1,095 embryos implanted into 123 surrogate mothers, resulting in only three pregnancies, with two live puppies, one of which died within a month.

The Future of Cloning

Modern cloning technology has now successfully cloned dogs, cows, cats, sheep, horses, and a variety of other animals. As the process becomes more routine, it also brings ethical questions. While hardly anyone objects to cloning navel oranges, and few would refuse antibiotics or other medicinal products from cloned livestock, many people think that cloning pets is a frivolous luxury—especially when you consider that almost 10 million unwanted dogs and cats are euthanized in the United States every year. For the foreseeable future, it seems likely that mammalian cloning will be restricted to demonstrations of its feasibility (that is, to answer such questions as "Can we clone water buffalos and camels?" The answer is yes, we can) and to replicate particularly valuable animals, such as endangered species or champion horses.

What about cloning people? A horror story? Or a modern-day version of Shakespeare's "brave new world that has such people in it"? In principle, humans can probably be cloned. However, in the words of Ian Wilmut, who cloned Dolly: ". . . the possibility for harm far outweighs any currently conceivable benefits." Some people believe that human cloning is inevitable, eventually. Maybe so, but with huge technical and ethical hurdles to overcome, not anytime soon.

Sexual Reproduction Recombines DNA

Homologous chromosomes exchange DNA by crossing over during meiosis I (see Chapter 9). As a result, each chromosome in a gamete contains a mixture of alleles from the two parental chromosomes. Thus, every egg and sperm contains recombinant DNA, derived from the two parents. When a sperm fertilizes an egg, the resulting offspring also contains recombinant DNA.

Transformation May Combine DNA from Different Bacterial Species

In **transformation,** bacteria pick up pieces of DNA from the environment (Fig. 13-1). The DNA may be part of the chromosome from another bacterium (Fig. 13-1a), even from another species, or it may be tiny circular DNA molecules called **plasmids** (Fig. 13-1b). Many types of bacteria

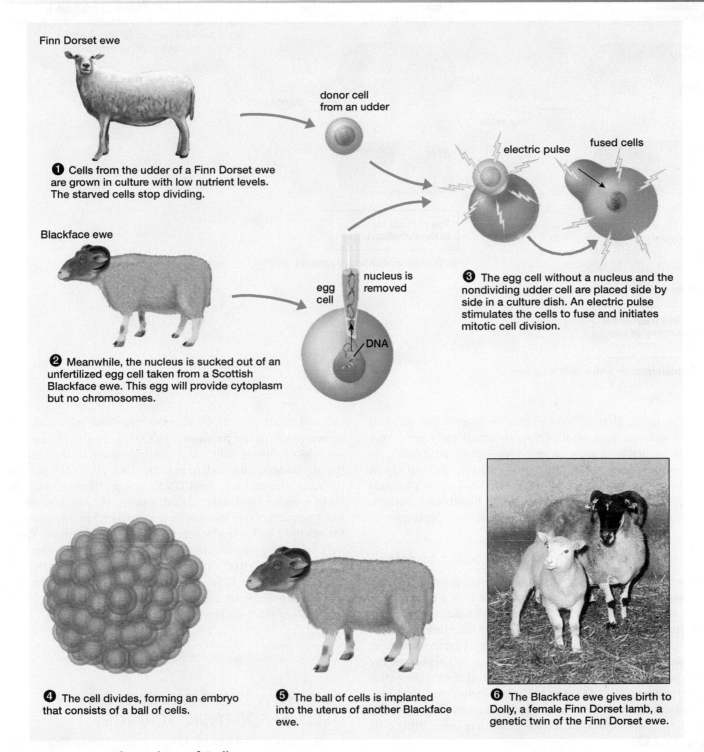

Finn Dorset ewe

1 Cells from the udder of a Finn Dorset ewe are grown in culture with low nutrient levels. The starved cells stop dividing.

donor cell from an udder

electric pulse   fused cells

Blackface ewe

egg cell

nucleus is removed

DNA

2 Meanwhile, the nucleus is sucked out of an unfertilized egg cell taken from a Scottish Blackface ewe. This egg will provide cytoplasm but no chromosomes.

3 The egg cell without a nucleus and the nondividing udder cell are placed side by side in a culture dish. An electric pulse stimulates the cells to fuse and initiates mitotic cell division.

4 The cell divides, forming an embryo that consists of a ball of cells.

5 The ball of cells is implanted into the uterus of another Blackface ewe.

6 The Blackface ewe gives birth to Dolly, a female Finn Dorset lamb, a genetic twin of the Finn Dorset ewe.

▲ FIGURE E13-1   **The making of Dolly**

contain plasmids, which range in length from about 1,000 to 100,000 nucleotides. (For comparison, the *E. coli* chromosome is around 4,600,000 nucleotides long.) A single bacterium may contain dozens or even hundreds of copies of a plasmid. When the bacterium dies, its plasmids are released into the environment, where they may be picked up by other bacteria of the same or different species. In addition, living

bacteria can often pass plasmids directly to other living bacteria. Plasmids may also move from bacteria to yeast, transferring genes from a prokaryotic cell to a eukaryotic cell.

What use are plasmids? A bacterium's chromosome contains all the genes the cell normally needs for basic survival. However, genes carried by plasmids may permit the bacteria to thrive in novel environments. Some plasmids

bacterial chromosome

bacterial chromosome

DNA fragments

plasmid

The plasmid replicates in the cytoplasm

(b) Transformation with a plasmid

A DNA fragment is incorporated into the chromosome

(a) Transformation with a DNA fragment

◄ **FIGURE 13-1 Transformation in bacteria** Bacterial transformation occurs when living bacteria take up **(a)** fragments of chromosomes or **(b)** plasmids.

contain genes that allow bacteria to metabolize unusual energy sources, such as oil. Other plasmids carry genes that enable bacteria to grow in the presence of antibiotics. In environments where antibiotic use is high, particularly in hospitals, bacteria carrying antibiotic-resistance plasmids can quickly spread among patients and health care workers, making antibiotic-resistant infections a serious problem.

Viruses May Transfer DNA Among Species

Viruses, which are often little more than genetic material encased in a protein coat, can reproduce only inside cells. A virus attaches to specific molecules on the surface of a suitable host cell (**Fig. 13-2 ❶**). Usually the virus then enters the cytoplasm of the host cell (**Fig. 13-2 ❷**), where it releases its genetic material (**Fig. 13-2 ❸**). The host cell replicates the viral genetic material (DNA or RNA) and synthesizes viral proteins (**Fig. 13-2 ❹**). The replicated genes and viral proteins assemble into new viruses inside the cell (**Fig. 13-2 ❺**). Eventually, the viruses are released and may infect other cells (**Fig. 13-2 ❻**).

Some viruses can transfer genes from one organism to another. In these instances, the viral DNA is inserted into one of the host cell's chromosomes (see Fig. 13-2 ❸). The viral DNA may remain there for days, months, or even years. Every time the cell divides, it replicates the viral DNA along with its own DNA. (Researchers believe that about 3% of the human genome consists of "fossil" viral genes, inserted into our DNA thousands to millions of years ago.) When new viruses are finally produced, some of the host cell's genes may be attached to the viral DNA. If such recombinant viruses infect another

cell and insert their DNA into the new host cell's chromosomes, pieces of the previous host's DNA are also inserted.

Most viruses infect and replicate only in the cells of specific bacterial, animal, or plant species. Therefore, most of the time, viruses move host DNA among different individuals of a single, or closely related, species. However, some viruses may infect species only distantly related to one another; for example, influenza infects birds, pigs, and humans. Gene transfer among viruses that infect multiple species can produce extremely lethal recombined viruses. This happened in 1957 and again in 1968, when recombination between bird and human flu viruses caused global epidemics that killed hundreds of thousands of people.

CHECK YOUR LEARNING

Can you describe natural processes that recombine DNA?

13.3 HOW IS BIOTECHNOLOGY USED IN FORENSIC SCIENCE?

Applications of DNA biotechnology vary, depending on the goals of those who use it. Forensic scientists need to identify victims and criminals; biotechnology firms need to identify specific genes and insert them into organisms such as bacteria, animals, or plants; and biomedical firms and physicians need to detect defective alleles and, ideally, devise ways to fix them or to insert normally functioning alleles into patients. We will begin by describing a few common methods of manipulating DNA and then discuss their application in forensic DNA analysis. Later, we will investigate how biotechnology is used in agriculture and medicine.

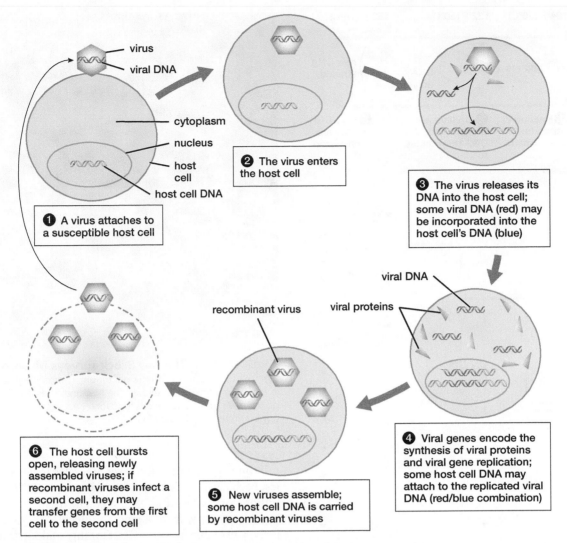

▲ FIGURE 13-2 **The life cycle of a typical virus** In some cases, viral infections may transfer DNA from one host cell to another.

The Polymerase Chain Reaction Amplifies DNA

Developed by Kary Mullis in 1986, the **polymerase chain reaction (PCR)** can be used to make billions, even trillions, of copies of selected pieces of DNA. PCR is so crucial to molecular biology that it earned Mullis a share in the Nobel Prize for Chemistry in 1993. PCR involves two major steps: (1) marking the DNA segment to be copied and (2) running repetitive reactions to make multiple copies. First, the desired DNA segment is bracketed with two short pieces of DNA, called *primers*. Primers are usually manufactured in a machine called a DNA synthesizer, which can be programmed to make short pieces of DNA with any desired sequence of nucleotides. The nucleotide sequence of one primer is complementary to the beginning of the target DNA segment on one strand of the double helix, and the sequence of the other primer is complementary to the beginning of the target DNA on the other strand. DNA polymerase recognizes the primers as the place where DNA replication should begin.

Second, the marked DNA is copied. DNA is mixed with primers, free nucleotides, and DNA polymerase in a small test tube. The primers bind to the desired DNA segment. The reaction mixture is then cycled through a series of temperature changes (**Fig. 13-3a**):

1. The test tube is heated to 194° to 203°F (90° to 95°C) (**Fig. 13-3a ❶**). High temperatures break the hydrogen bonds between complementary bases, separating the DNA into single strands.
2. The temperature is lowered to about 122°F (50°C) (**Fig. 13-3b ❷**), which allows the two primers to form complementary base pairs with the target DNA.
3. The temperature is raised to 158° to 162°F (70° to 72°C) (**Fig. 13-3a ❸**). DNA polymerase uses the free nucleotides to make copies of the DNA segment bounded by the primers. Most DNA polymerases do not function at temperatures much higher than 105°F (40°C). However, PCR uses a special DNA polymerase isolated from bacteria that live in hot springs

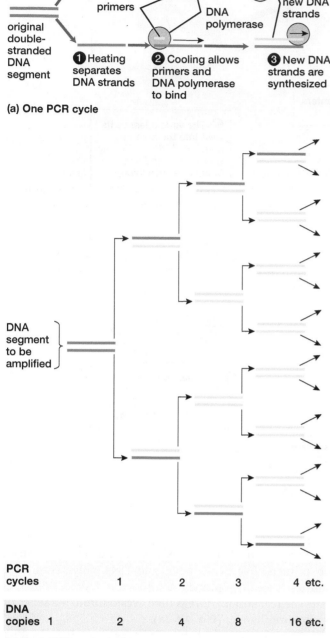

194°F (90°C)   122°F (50°C)   158°F (70°C)

primers

DNA polymerase

new DNA strands

original double-stranded DNA segment

❶ Heating separates DNA strands

❷ Cooling allows primers and DNA polymerase to bind

❸ New DNA strands are synthesized

(a) One PCR cycle

DNA segment to be amplified

PCR cycles	1	2	3	4 etc.
DNA copies	1	2	4	8	16 etc.

(b) Each PCR cycle doubles the number of copies of the DNA

▲ FIGURE 13-3 **PCR copies a specific DNA sequence**
(a) The polymerase chain reaction consists of a cycle of heating, cooling, and warming that is typically repeated 30 to 40 times. **(b)** Each cycle doubles the amount of target DNA. After a little more than 30 cycles, a billion copies of the target DNA have been synthesized.

(Fig. 13-4), which actually works best at these high temperatures.

4. This cycle is repeated, usually 30 to 40 times, until the free nucleotides have been used up.

In PCR, the amount of DNA doubles with every temperature cycle (Fig. 13-3b). Twenty PCR cycles make about a

▲ FIGURE 13-4 **Thomas Brock surveys Mushroom Spring** Brock discovered the bacterium *Thermus aquaticus* in Mushroom Spring in Yellowstone National Park. The DNA polymerase from *T. aquaticus* functions best at the high temperatures required by PCR.

million copies, and a little over 30 cycles make a billion copies. Each cycle takes only a few minutes, so PCR can produce billions of copies of a DNA segment in an afternoon, starting, if necessary, from a single molecule of DNA. The DNA is then available for forensics, cloning, making transgenic organisms, or many other purposes.

Differences in Short Tandem Repeats Are Used to Identify Individuals by Their DNA

In many criminal investigations, PCR is used to amplify the DNA so that there is enough to compare the DNA left at a crime scene with a suspect's DNA. How do crime labs compare DNA? After years of painstaking work, forensics experts have found that specific segments of DNA, called **short tandem repeats (STRs),** can be used to identify people with astonishing accuracy. Think of STRs as very small, stuttering genes (**Fig. 13-5**). STRs are *short* (about 20 to 250 nucleotides), *repeating* (consisting of the same sequence of 2 to 5 nucleotides repeated up to 50 times), and *tandem* (having all of the repetitions right alongside one another). As with any gene, there may be alternative forms, or alleles, of an STR. In any given STR, the different alleles simply have different numbers of repeats of the same short nucleotide sequence. To identify individuals from DNA samples, the U.S. Department of Justice established a standard set of 13 STRs that have highly variable numbers of repeats in different people. Most crime labs also examine a gene that shows whether the DNA sample came from a man or a woman.

▲ FIGURE 13-5 Short tandem repeats are common in noncoding regions of DNA This STR contains the sequence AGAT, repeated from 7 to 15 times in different individuals.

CASE STUDY c o n t i n u e d

Guilty or Innocent?

When a law student finally located semen samples in the Dennis Maher case, the Innocence Project team needed to find out if the samples collected from the rape victims came from Maher. Fortunately, DNA doesn't degrade very fast, so even old DNA samples, such as those in the Maher case, usually have STRs that are mostly intact. First, lab technicians amplified the DNA with PCR so that they had enough material to analyze. Then, they determined whether the DNA from the semen samples matched Maher's DNA.

Forensics labs use PCR primers that amplify only the STRs and the DNA immediately surrounding them. Because STR alleles vary in how many repeats they contain, they vary in size: An STR allele with more repeats is larger than one with fewer repeats. Therefore, a forensic lab needs to identify each STR in a DNA sample and then determine its size to find out which alleles occur in the sample.

Modern forensics labs use sophisticated and expensive machines to analyze STRs. Most of these machines, however, are based on two methods that are used in molecular biology labs around the world: first, separating DNA segments by size, and second, labeling specific DNA segments of interest.

Gel Electrophoresis Separates DNA Segments

A mixture of DNA pieces can be separated by a technique called **gel electrophoresis** (Fig. 13-6). First, a laboratory technician loads the DNA mixture into shallow grooves, or wells, in a slab of agarose, a carbohydrate purified from certain types of seaweed (**Fig. 13-6 ❶**). Agarose forms a gel, which is simply a meshwork of fibers with holes of various sizes between the fibers. The gel is put into a chamber with electrodes connected to each end. One electrode is made positive and the other negative; therefore, current will flow between the electrodes through the gel. How does this process separate pieces of DNA? Remember, the phosphate groups in the backbones of DNA are negatively charged. When electrical current flows through the gel, the negatively charged DNA fragments move toward the positively charged electrode. Because smaller fragments slip through the holes in the gel more easily than larger fragments do, they move

more rapidly toward the positively charged electrode. Eventually the DNA fragments are separated by size, forming distinct bands on the gel (**Fig. 13-6 ❷**).

DNA Probes Are Used to Label Specific Nucleotide Sequences

Unfortunately, the DNA bands are invisible. There are several dyes that stain DNA, but these are often not very useful in either forensics or medicine. Why not? Because there may be many DNA fragments of approximately the same size. For example, five or six different STRs with the same numbers of repeats might be mixed together in the same band. How can a technician identify a *specific* STR? Well, how does *nature* identify sequences of DNA? Right—by base pairing!

When the gel is finished running, the technician treats it with chemicals that break apart the double helices into single DNA strands. These DNA strands are transferred out of the gel onto a piece of paper made of nylon (**Fig. 13-6 ❸**). Because the DNA samples are now single-stranded, pieces of synthetic DNA, called **DNA probes,** can base-pair with specific DNA fragments in the sample. DNA probes are short pieces of single-stranded DNA that are complementary to the nucleotide sequence of a given STR (or any other DNA of interest in the gel). The DNA probes are labeled, either by radioactivity or by attaching colored molecules to them. Therefore, a given DNA probe will label certain DNA sequences, but not others (**Fig. 13-7**).

To locate a specific STR, the paper is bathed in a solution containing a DNA probe that will base-pair with, and therefore bind to, only that particular STR (**Fig. 13-6 ❹**). Any extra DNA probe is then washed off the paper. The result: The DNA probe shows where that specific STR ran in the gel (**Fig. 13-6 ❺**). (Visualizing the DNA fragments with radioactive or colored DNA probes is standard procedure in many research applications. In forensics labs, the STRs are directly labeled with colored molecules during PCR and are immediately visible in the gel, so DNA probes are not necessary.)

Unrelated People Almost Never Have Identical DNA Profiles

DNA samples run on STR gels produce a pattern, called a **DNA profile** (**Fig. 13-8**). The positions of the bands on the gel are determined by the numbers of repeats of the four-nucleotide sequence of each STR allele. If the same STRs are analyzed, then all samples of a person's DNA produce the same profile every time.

What does a DNA profile tell us? As with any gene, every person has two alleles of each STR, one on each homologous chromosome. The two alleles of a given STR might have the same number of repeats (the person would be homozygous for that STR) or a different number of repeats (the person would be heterozygous). For example, in the D16 STR samples shown on the right side of Figure 13-8, the first person's DNA has a single band at 12 repeats (this person is homozygous for the D16 STR), but the second person's DNA has two bands—at 13 and 12 repeats (this

1 DNA samples are pipetted into wells (shallow slots) in the gel. Electrical current is sent through the gel (negative at the end with the wells and positive at the opposite end).

power supply

pipetter

gel

wells

2 Electrical current moves the DNA segments through the gel. Smaller pieces of DNA move farther toward the positive electrode.

DNA "bands" (not yet visible)

3 The gel is placed on special nylon "paper." Electrical current drives the DNA out of the gel onto the nylon.

gel

nylon paper

4 The nylon paper with the DNA bound to it is bathed in a solution of labeled DNA probes (red) that are complementary to specific DNA segments in the original DNA sample.

solution of DNA probes (red)

nylon paper

5 Complementary DNA segments are labeled by the probes (red bands).

▲ FIGURE 13-6 **Gel electrophoresis and labeling with DNA probes separates and identifies segments of DNA.**

person is heterozygous for the D16 STR). If you look closely at all of the DNA samples in Figure 13-8, you will see that, although the DNA from some people had the same repeats for one of the STRs (e.g., the second, fourth, and fifth samples for D16), no one's DNA had the same repeats for all four STRs.

Are 13 STRs enough to uniquely identify people, given the huge human population? Worldwide, different people may have as few as 5 to as many 38 repeats in a given STR. Although there are some complicating factors that forensics labs need to take into account, let's take a simple case: Assume that a crime lab analyzes five STRs, each with 10 possible numbers of repeats (for example, all people have either 6, 7, 8, 9, 10, 11, 12, 13, 14, or 15 repeats). Let's also assume that all of the numbers of repeats occur with equal probability in the human population, that is, one in ten, or 1/10. Finally, STRs are independently assorted (see Chapter 10),

so the probability of two unrelated people sharing the same number of repeats of all five STRs is simply the product (multiplication) of the separate probabilities, or $1/10 \times 1/10 \times 1/10 \times 1/10 \times 1/10 = 1$ chance in 100,000.

With 13 STRs, containing up to 38 repeats each, the chances of a random match are incredibly small. A perfect match of both alleles for all 13 STRs used in the United States means that there is far less than one chance in a trillion that the two DNA samples matched purely by random chance. For complicated statistical reasons, there are probably a few unrelated people in the world who have the same DNA profile, but the odds of anyone who would be a likely suspect in a criminal case being misidentified are extremely low. Finally, a *mismatch* in DNA profiles is absolute proof that two samples did not come from the same source. In the Maher case, when DNA profiling showed that the STR alleles in the semen did not match Maher's, that ruled him out as the perpetrator.

STR #1: The probe base-pairs and binds to the DNA

STR #2: The probe cannot base-pair with the DNA, so it does not bind

▲ FIGURE 13-7 **DNA probes base-pair with complementary DNA sequences** A short, single-stranded piece of DNA is labeled with a colored molecule (red ball). This labeled DNA will base-pair with a target strand of DNA with a complementary base sequence (top), but not with a noncomplementary strand (bottom).

In the United States, anyone convicted of certain crimes (assault, burglary, attempted murder, etc.) must give a blood sample. Crime lab technicians then determine the criminal's DNA profile, and code the results as the number of repeats in each STR. The profile is stored in computer files at a state agency, at the FBI, or both. (On *CSI* and other TV crime shows, when the actors refer to "CODIS," that acronym stands for "Combined DNA Index System," a DNA profile database kept on FBI computers.) Because all U.S. forensic labs use the same 13 STRs, computers can easily determine if DNA left behind at another crime scene matches one of the profiles stored in the CODIS database. If the STRs match, then the odds are overwhelming that the crime scene DNA was left by the person with the matching profile. If there aren't any matches, the crime scene DNA profile will remain on file. Sometimes, years later, a new DNA profile will match an archived crime scene profile, and a "cold case" will be solved (see "Case Study Revisited" at the end of this chapter).

People aren't the only organisms that can be identified by the DNA sequences, of course. An international group of government and private organizations is putting together the "Barcode of Life" to enable rapid DNA identification of all of the species of life on Earth. DNA barcodes have both serious and entertaining applications, as we explain in "Earth Watch: What's Really in That Sushi?"

CHECK YOUR LEARNING

Can you explain the uses of electrophoresis, DNA probes, and the polymerase chain reaction, and how they work? Do you understand how DNA profiles are produced, and why a DNA profile is usually unique to each individual person?

▲ FIGURE 13-8 **DNA profiling** The lengths of short tandem repeats of DNA form characteristic patterns on a gel. This gel displays four different STRs (Penta D, CSF, etc.). The columns of evenly spaced yellow bands on the far left and far right sides of the gel show the number of repeats in the different STR alleles. DNA samples from 13 different people were run between these standards, resulting in one or two yellow bands in each vertical lane. The position of each band corresponds to the number of repeats in that STR allele (more repeats means more nucleotides, which in turn means that the allele is larger). (Photo courtesy of Dr. Margaret Kline, National Institute of Standards and Technology.)

QUESTION For any single person, a given STR always has either one or two bands. Why? Further, single bands are always about twice as bright as each band of a pair. For example, in the D16 STR on the right, the single bands of the first and third DNA samples are twice as bright as the pairs of bands of the second, fourth, and fifth samples. Why?

Earth|Watch

What's Really in That Sushi?

Walk into a Japanese restaurant or a sushi bar and chances are that the most expensive item on the menu is some type of tuna sushi. But is it really tuna? In 2008, two New York teenagers, Kate Stoeckle and Louisa Strauss, decided to find out (Fig. E13-2). Sounds difficult—after all, the fish are beheaded, cleaned, and skinned, and only a chunk of meat is presented to the diner—but biotechnology makes it simple, using DNA barcoding.

DNA barcoding sequences a small fragment of DNA from a gene found in the mitochondria of virtually all eukaryotic organisms—a fragment only 650 nucleotides long (Fig. E13-3). So far, no two species have been found to have the same nucleotide sequence in this particular piece of DNA. Thus, DNA barcoding is a simple, inexpensive way to identify species with absolute certainty.

Kate and Louisa visited restaurants and grocery stores, and brought home samples of raw fish. They cut off little pieces from each sample, preserved them in alcohol, and sent them off to a lab at the University of Guelph for barcoding. Surprise! About a quarter of the sushi samples were imposters. One specimen sold as red snapper was actually Acadian redfish, an endangered species. One "tuna" sushi turned out to be tilapia, a freshwater species often raised in fish farms. It turns out that some restaurants mislabel half their sushi.

DNA barcoding is useful for more than just checking up on your local sushi bar. Commercial laboratories will now barcode a sample for just a few dollars, with a one-day turnaround. Because of its high precision and low cost, barcoding is rapidly gaining acceptance as a way to identify agricultural pests such as fruit flies and public health threats such as disease-carrying mosquitoes. The U.S. Environmental Protection Agency is barcoding insect larvae to assess the health of streams—different species of insects live in clean vs. polluted streams. The Federal Aviation Administration barcodes feathers to find out what kinds of birds crash into planes.

In the future, DNA barcoding might help to stop illegal trafficking in endangered species, which is extremely lucrative (thought to be second only to illegal narcotics). Meat, skin, feathers, and many other animal parts are difficult to identify visually. And how many customs officials can tell the difference between greenhouse orchids and rare orchids plucked from a rain forest? Humans might be deceived, but barcoding can't be fooled. The hope is that, within a few years, small devices will be created that analyze suspect samples in an hour or so, perhaps even in minutes, and compare the barcode with publicly available databases. The day may come when barcoding not only verifies your sushi but puts a stop to the exploitation of endangered species.

▲ FIGURE E13-2 **Kate Stoeckle and Louisa Strauss with their research subjects**

Honeybee

Bumblebee

American Robin

Hermit Thrush

▲ FIGURE E13-3 **DNA barcoding** The different colors in the barcodes represent different bases in the DNA sequence of a fragment of a mitochondrial gene. Closely related organisms have more similar barcodes than distantly related organisms do, but every species has a unique barcode.

CASE STUDY continued

Guilty or Innocent?

Different countries use different STRs, and different numbers of STRs, for DNA profiling. Recently, the countries of the European Union pooled their databases, so that a DNA profile from a crime in, say, Italy, could be compared against profiles in Great Britain or France. Unfortunately, because they use different STRs, there may be as few as six STRs in common among the DNA profiles of member countries. As a result, comparing crime scene DNA with the European Union database can result in lots of false positives—matches that occur purely by chance. Fortunately, mismatches will still eliminate innocent suspects.

13.4 HOW IS BIOTECHNOLOGY USED TO MAKE GENETICALLY MODIFIED ORGANISMS?

The techniques of PCR, gel electrophoresis, and identifying DNA sequences with specific probes have applications far beyond forensic science. In combination with other procedures that we will discuss shortly, biotechnology can also be used to identify, isolate, and modify genes; combine genes from different organisms; and move genes from one species to another. Let's see how some of these techniques can be used to make genetically modified organisms (GMOs).

There are three major steps to making a GMO: (1) Obtain the desired gene, (2) clone the gene, and (3) insert the gene into the cells of the host organism. Various technologies can be used for each step, each involving complex procedures. We will provide only a brief overview of the general processes.

The Desired Gene Is Isolated or Synthesized

Two common methods are used to obtain a gene. For a long time, the only practical method was to isolate the target gene from the organism that possessed it. Chromosomes can be isolated from cells of the gene donor, cut up with enzymes (see below), and DNA fragments containing the desired gene can be separated from the rest of the DNA by gel electrophoresis (see Fig. 13-6). Today, biotechnologists can often synthesize the gene—or a modified version of it—in the lab, using DNA synthesizers.

The Gene Is Cloned

Once the gene has been obtained, it can be used to make transgenic organisms, shared with other scientists around the world, or used for medical treatments. Therefore, it is useful, or even essential, to have a huge number of copies of the gene. The simplest way to generate lots of copies of the gene is to let living organisms do it, by **DNA cloning.** In DNA cloning, the gene is usually inserted into single-celled organisms, such as bacteria or yeasts, that multiply very rapidly, manufacturing copies of the gene as they do.

The most common method of DNA cloning is to insert the gene into a bacterial plasmid (see Fig. 13-1), which will be replicated when bacteria containing the plasmid multiply. Inserting the gene into a plasmid, rather than the bacterial chromosome, also allows it to be easily separated from the majority of the bacterial DNA. The target gene may be further purified from the plasmid, or the whole plasmid may be used to make transgenic organisms, including plants, animals, or other bacteria.

Genes are inserted into plasmids using **restriction enzymes,** each of which cuts DNA at a specific nucleotide sequence. There are hundreds of different restriction enzymes. Many cut straight across the double helix of DNA. Others make a staggered cut, snipping the DNA in a different location on each of the two strands, so that single-stranded sections hang off the ends of the DNA. These single-stranded regions are commonly called "sticky ends," because they can base-pair with, and thus stick to, other single-stranded pieces of DNA with complementary bases (Fig. 13-9). Restriction enzymes that make a staggered cut are used in DNA cloning.

To insert a gene into a plasmid, the same restriction enzyme is used to cut the DNA on both sides of the gene and to split open the circle of plasmid DNA (Fig. 13-10 ❶). As a result, the ends of the DNA containing the gene and the opened-up plasmid both have complementary nucleotides in their sticky ends, and can base-pair with each other. When the cut genes and plasmids are mixed together, some of the genes will be temporarily inserted between the cut ends of the plasmids, held together by their complementary sticky ends. Adding DNA ligase (see Chapter 11) permanently bonds the genes into the plasmids (Fig. 13-10 ❷).

Bacteria are then transformed with these recombinant plasmids. Under the right conditions, when the bacteria multiply, they replicate the plasmids, too. Huge vats of bacteria can be easily grown, producing as many copies of the gene as anyone could ever need.

EcoRI restriction enzyme

double-stranded DNA { ...AATTGCTTAGAATTCGATTTG...
...TTAACGAATCTTAAGCTAAAC...

A specific restriction enzyme (EcoRI) binds to the GAATTC sequence and cuts the DNA, creating DNA fragments with "sticky ends."

...AATTGCTTAG
...TTAACGAATCTTAA

AATTCGATTTG...
GCTAAAC...

single-stranded "sticky ends"

▲ FIGURE 13-9 Restriction enzymes cut DNA at specific nucleotide sequences

QUESTION Restriction enzymes are isolated from bacteria. Why would bacteria synthesize enzymes that cut up DNA? (*Hint:* Bacteria can be infected by viruses called bacteriophages; see Chapter 11.) Why wouldn't a bacterium's restriction enzymes destroy the DNA of its own chromosome?

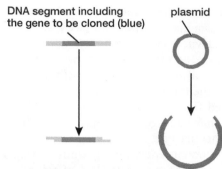

DNA segment including the gene to be cloned (blue)   plasmid

❶ The plasmid and the DNA segment containing the desired gene are cut with the same restriction enzyme.

recombinant plasmid

❷ The plasmids and the DNA segment containing the gene, both with the same complementary sticky ends, are mixed together; DNA ligase bonds the genes into the plasmids.

▲ FIGURE 13-10 **Inserting a gene into a plasmid for DNA cloning**

The Gene Is Inserted into a Host Organism

Now comes the hard part—**transfecting** the host organism. The gene must be inserted into the host and expressed in the appropriate cells, at the appropriate times, and at the desired level. Host organisms may be transfected by one of several different methods. In some cases, the recombinant plasmids or genes purified from them are inserted into harmless bacteria or viruses, called *vectors*, and then the host organism is infected with them. In the ideal case, the bacteria or viruses insert the new gene into the chromosomes of the host organism's cells, where it becomes a permanent part of the host's genome, and is replicated whenever the host's DNA is replicated. This is how some plants were transfected with genes for herbicide resistance and insect resistance (see Section 13.5).

A simpler method is to use a "gene gun." Microscopically small pellets of gold or tungsten are coated with DNA (either plasmids or purified genes) and then shot at cells or organisms. This process is literally "hit or miss," but is often quite effective for plants, cells in culture, and sometimes even whole animals (usually small ones, such as roundworms or fruit flies). Gene guns are often used when host organisms are easily available in large numbers, so that a low success rate doesn't really matter.

Finally, plasmids or purified genes can be directly injected into animal cells, usually fertilized eggs (**Fig. 13-11**). Tiny glass pipettes are loaded with a suitable solution containing the DNA. The pipettes have tips that are sharp enough to impale a cell without damaging it. Pressure applied to the back of the pipette pushes some of the DNA into the cell.

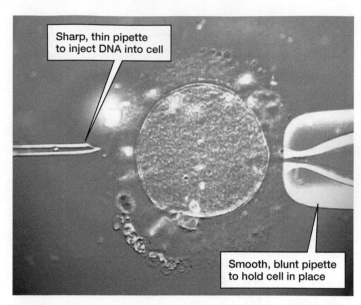

Sharp, thin pipette to inject DNA into cell

Smooth, blunt pipette to hold cell in place

▲ FIGURE 13-11 **Transfecting a fertilized egg by injecting foreign DNA** The large pipette on the right holds the egg stationary during the procedure. The small, sharp pipette on the left penetrates the egg and injects DNA.

CHECK YOUR LEARNING

Can you explain how genes are inserted into a plasmid, and why that is useful in making a genetically modified organism? Can you describe the procedures used to transfect an organism with a foreign gene?

13.5 HOW IS BIOTECHNOLOGY USED IN AGRICULTURE?

The main goals of agriculture are to grow as much food as possible, as cheaply as possible, with minimal loss from pests such as insects and weeds. Many commercial farmers and seed suppliers have turned to biotechnology to achieve these goals. Many people, however, feel that the risks of genetically modified food to human health or the environment are not worth the benefits. We will explore this controversy in Section 13.8.

Many Crops Are Genetically Modified

According to the U.S. Department of Agriculture (USDA), in 2011, 88% of the corn, 90% of the cotton, and 94% of the soybeans grown in the United States were transgenic; that is, they contained genes from other species (**Table 13-1**). Globally, 15.4 million farmers planted more than 365 million acres of land with transgenic crops in 2010.

Crops are most commonly modified to improve their resistance to insects, herbicides, or both. Herbicide-resistant crops allow farmers to kill weeds without harming their crops. Less competition from weeds means more water, nutrients, and light for the crops, and hence, larger harvests. Many herbicides kill plants by inhibiting an enzyme that is used by plants, fungi, and some bacteria—but not animals—to synthesize specific amino acids. Without these amino acids, the plants die because they cannot synthesize proteins.

TABLE 13-1 Genetically Engineered Crops with USDA Approval

Genetically Engineered Trait	Potential Advantage	Examples
Resistance to herbicide	Application of herbicide kills weeds but not crop plants, producing higher crop yields	Beet, canola, corn, cotton, flax, potato, rice, soybean, tomato
Resistance to pests	Crop plants suffer less damage from insects, producing higher crop yields	Corn, cotton, potato, rice, soybean
Resistance to disease	Plants are less prone to infection by viruses, bacteria, or fungi, producing higher crop yields	Papaya, potato, squash
Sterile	Transgenic plants cannot cross with wild varieties, making them safer for the environment and more economically productive for the seed companies that produce them	Chicory, corn
Altered oil content	Oils can be made healthier for human consumption or can be made similar to more expensive oils (such as palm or coconut)	Canola, soybean

Many herbicide-resistant transgenic crops have been given a bacterial gene encoding an enzyme that functions even in the presence of these herbicides, so the transgenic plants continue to synthesize normal amounts of amino acids and proteins.

The insect resistance of many crops has been enhanced by giving them a gene, called *Bt*, from the bacterium *Bacillus thuringiensis*. The protein encoded by the *Bt* gene damages the digestive tract of insects, but not mammals. Transgenic *Bt* crops often suffer far less damage from insects than do regular crops, so farmers can apply less pesticide to their fields (Fig. 13-12).

Genetically Modified Plants May Be Used to Produce Medicines

The tools of biotechnology can also be used to insert medically useful genes into plants, producing medicines down on the "pharm." For example, a plant can be engineered to produce harmless proteins that are normally found in disease-causing bacteria or viruses. If these proteins resist digestion in the stomach and intestine, simply eating such plants could act as a vaccination against the disease-causing organisms. Several years ago, such "edible vaccines" were touted as a great way to provide vaccinations—no need to produce purified vaccines, no refrigeration needed, and, of course, no needles. Recently, however, many biomedical researchers have warned that edible vaccine plants may not really be a good idea, because there is no simple way to control the dose: Too little and the user doesn't develop decent immunity; too much, and the vaccine proteins might be harmful. Nevertheless, producing vaccine proteins in plants is still worthwhile. To make typical vaccines, pharmaceutical companies would just have to extract and purify the proteins before use. Plant-produced vaccines against hepatitis B, measles, rabies, tooth decay, flu, infant diarrhea, and many other diseases are in animal or clinical trials.

Molecular biologists can also engineer plants to produce human antibodies to combat various diseases. When a disease-causing microbe invades your body, it takes several days for your immune system to respond and produce

▲ FIGURE 13-12 **Bt plants resist insect attack** Transgenic cotton plants expressing the *Bt* gene (right) resist attack by bollworms, which eat cotton seeds. The transgenic plants therefore produce far more cotton than nontransgenic plants do (left).

HAVE **YOU** EVER WONDERED …

If the Food You Eat Has Been Genetically Modified?

In addition to obvious things— tortilla chips, soy sauce, and margarine—corn and soy products are found in an amazing variety of foods. For example, corn syrup is an ingredient in foods as diverse as soda, ketchup, and bran flakes; soybean oil or protein is an important ingredient in cookies, cake mixes, and veggie burgers. Almost all of the corn and soy grown in the United States is genetically modified, with the result that about 80% of the packaged foods in American supermarkets contain substances made from GM plants. Many countries, including the European Union, require labeling of GM foods, but the U.S. Food and Drug Administration does not, so in America you can't tell if a food contains GM ingredients just by looking at the label. Therefore, unless you are extremely motivated and careful, you probably eat GM foods.

enough antibodies to overcome the infection. Meanwhile, you feel terrible, and might even die if the disease is serious enough. A direct injection of large quantities of the right antibodies might be able to cure the disease very quickly. Although none have yet entered medical practice, plant-derived antibodies against the bacteria that cause tooth decay and the virus that causes rabies have been developed.

Genetically Modified Animals May Be Useful in Agriculture and Medicine

Producing transgenic animals usually involves injecting the desired DNA, often incorporated into a disabled virus that cannot produce disease, into a fertilized egg. The egg is allowed to divide a few times in culture before being implanted into a surrogate mother. If the offspring are healthy and express the foreign gene, they are then bred with one another to produce homozygous transgenic animals. So far, it has proven difficult to create commercially valuable transgenic livestock, but several companies are working on it.

For example, biotechnology companies have made genetically modified sheep that produce more wool; cattle that produce more protein in their milk; and pigs that produce omega-3 fatty acids in their meat (omega-3 fatty acids are thought to provide a variety of health benefits). In 2010 researchers successfully produced transgenic chickens that cannot spread the H5N1 influenza virus, which causes avian flu. Worldwide, many millions of chickens have been killed to stop outbreaks of avian flu, so flu-resistant chickens could potentially be very valuable birds. There are even goats that secrete spider silk proteins in their milk. Spider silk is far stronger than steel or Kevlar®, the fiber usually used in bulletproof vests, so the hope is that lightweight, impenetrable vests could be made using silk protein from these goats.

Biotechnologists are also developing animals that produce medicines, such as human antibodies or other essential proteins. For example, there are genetically engineered sheep whose milk contains a protein, alpha-1-antitrypsin, that may prove valuable in treating cystic fibrosis and emphysema. Other GM sheep produce human clotting factors, which could be used to treat hemophilia. Other livestock have been engineered so that their milk contains erythropoietin (a hormone that stimulates red blood cell synthesis) or clot-busting proteins (to treat heart attacks caused by blood clots in the coronary arteries).

Finally, biomedical researchers have made a large number of transgenic animals, primarily mice, which carry genes associated with human diseases, such as Alzheimer's disease, Marfan syndrome, and cystic fibrosis. These animals are used to investigate the causes of disease and to develop possible treatments.

CHECK YOUR LEARNING

Can you describe the advantages of genetically modified crops and animals in agriculture, and provide some examples? Can you list some examples of how genetically modified animals might be useful in medicine?

13.6 HOW IS BIOTECHNOLOGY USED TO LEARN ABOUT THE GENOMES OF HUMANS AND OTHER ORGANISMS?

Genes influence virtually all the traits of human beings, including gender, size, hair color, intelligence, and susceptibility to disease organisms and toxic substances in the environment. To begin to understand how our genes influence our lives, the Human Genome Project was launched in 1990, with the goal of determining the nucleotide sequence of all the DNA in our entire set of genes, called the human genome.

By 2003, this joint project of molecular biologists in several countries had sequenced the human genome with an accuracy of about 99.99%. The human genome contains between 20,000 and 25,000 genes, comprising approximately 2% of the DNA. Some of the other 98% consists of promoters and regions that regulate how often individual genes are transcribed, but it's not really known what most of our DNA does.

Why do scientists want to sequence the genomes of people and other organisms? First, many genes were discovered whose functions are unknown. Using the genetic code to translate the DNA sequences of novel genes, biologists can predict the amino acid sequences of the proteins they encode. Comparing these proteins to familiar proteins whose functions are already known will enable us to find out what many of these newly discovered genes do.

Second, knowing the nucleotide sequences of human genes will have an enormous impact on medical practice. Over 2,000 genes are known to be associated with human inherited diseases. Defective alleles of these genes may cause or predispose people to develop medical conditions such as sickle-cell anemia, cystic fibrosis, breast cancer, alcoholism, schizophrenia, heart disease, Alzheimer's disease, and many others. Ongoing human genome research involves sequencing the DNA of many different people, looking for small differences in the DNA sequences of alleles that might increase a person's susceptibility to infectious diseases, toxic pollutants, or chemicals in tobacco smoke, or alter a person's responses to drugs. Someday, this knowledge will allow custom-tailored treatments for many diseases. Knowing the genomes of infectious viruses and bacteria should help in developing vaccines or treatments for the diseases they cause.

Third, the Human Genome Project, along with companion projects that have sequenced the genomes of organisms as diverse as bacteria, fungi, mice, and chimpanzees, helps us to appreciate our place in the evolution of life on Earth. For example, the DNA of humans and chimps differs by less than 5%. Comparing the similarities and differences may help biologists to understand what genetic differences help to make us human, and why we are susceptible to certain diseases that chimps are not. Recently, researchers have deciphered partial genomes for Neanderthals and recently discovered ancient hominids, called Denisovans. Modern human populations, depending on their origins, may have up to a few percent Neanderthal or Denisovan genes.

13.7 HOW IS BIOTECHNOLOGY USED FOR MEDICAL DIAGNOSIS AND TREATMENT?

For over two decades, biotechnology has been used to diagnose some inherited disorders, even in fetuses (see "Health Watch: Prenatal Genetic Screening," page 250). More recently, medical researchers have begun using biotechnology in an attempt to cure, or at least treat, genetic diseases.

DNA Technology Can Be Used to Diagnose Inherited Disorders

A person inherits a genetic disease because he or she inherits one or more defective alleles, which differ from normal, functional alleles because they have different nucleotide sequences. Most methods of diagnosing genetic disorders begin with PCR, to make multiple copies of specific genes, and sometimes specific alleles. Restriction enzymes or DNA probes may then be used to identify defective alleles.

Using PCR to Obtain Disease-Specific Alleles

Recall that PCR uses specific DNA primers to determine which DNA sequences to amplify. Thanks to many years of research by hundreds of researchers, the DNA sequences of the genes responsible for many genetic disorders are now known. PCR can be used to isolate and amplify disease-specific genes for various types of diagnostic procedures (see below). In some cases, medical testing companies have designed primers that amplify only the defective alleles that cause a given disorder and not the normal alleles that do not cause disease, so PCR itself can be a diagnostic tool.

Restriction Enzymes May Cut Different Alleles of a Gene at Different Locations

Sickle-cell anemia is an inherited form of anemia—not having enough red blood cells—caused by a point mutation in which thymine replaces adenine near the beginning of the globin gene (see Chapters 10 and 12). A common diagnostic test for sickle-cell anemia relies on the fact that restriction enzymes cut DNA only at specific nucleotide sequences. To diagnose the presence of the sickle-cell allele, DNA is extracted from cells of a patient, a parent who might be a carrier of the allele, or even a fetus (see "Health Watch: Prenatal Genetic Screening," page 250). PCR is used to amplify a section of DNA that includes the mutation site. A restriction enzyme called MstII can cut the normal sequence (CCTGAGGAG), but not the sickle-cell sequence (CCTGTGGAG). The result is that MstII cuts the normal globin allele in half, but the sickle-cell allele remains intact. Gel electrophoresis easily separates the intact sickle-cell allele from the pieces of the normal allele.

Different Alleles Bind to Different DNA Probes

Cystic fibrosis is a disease caused by a defect in a protein, called CFTR, that normally helps to move chloride ions across the plasma membranes of many cells, including those in the lungs, sweat glands, and intestines (see the case study in Chapter 12). In the lungs, lack of adequate chloride transport results in thick mucus lining the airways, frequent bacterial infections, and eventual death. There are more than 1,500 different *CFTR* alleles, all at the same locus, each encoding a different, defective CFTR protein. People with either one or two normal alleles synthesize enough functioning CFTR proteins that they do not develop cystic fibrosis. People with two defective alleles (they may be the same or different alleles) do not synthesize functional transport proteins, and therefore they develop cystic fibrosis.

How can anyone hope to diagnose a disorder that may be caused by any of 1,500 different alleles? Fortunately, 32 alleles account for about 90% of the cases of cystic fibrosis—the rest of the alleles are extremely rare. Nevertheless, it would probably be hopeless to try to find unique restriction enzyme cut sites for even 32 alleles, so the methodology used to diagnose sickle-cell anemia cannot be used for cystic fibrosis.

However, each defective allele has a different nucleotide sequence. As you know, a DNA strand will form perfect base pairs only with a perfectly complementary strand. Several companies now produce cystic fibrosis "arrays," which are pieces of specialized filter paper to which single-stranded DNA probes are bound (Fig. 13-13). Each probe is complementary to one strand of a different *CFTR* allele (Fig. 13-13a). A person's DNA is tested for cystic fibrosis by cutting it into small pieces, separating the pieces into single strands, and labeling the strands with a colored molecule (Fig. 13-13b). The array is then bathed in the resulting solution of labeled DNA fragments. Under the right conditions, only a perfect complementary strand of the person's DNA will bind to any given probe on the array, thereby showing which *CFTR* alleles the person possesses (Fig. 13-13c). A similar test using DNA probes is also available for the diagnosis of sickle-cell anemia.

In the near future, routine medical diagnosis might use greatly expanded versions of this type of analysis, called DNA microarrays, to determine which bacteria or viruses are causing an infection. In one application, called the Virochip, thousands of small DNA probes, each complementary to a part of a specific viral gene, are placed on a small chip. Nucleic acids are isolated from the patient and labeled with a fluorescent dye. The chip is bathed in the labeled nucleic acid solution. Different spots light up on the chip, depending on what virus has infected the patient. Similar arrays are under development for the diagnosis of bacterial infections.

DNA microarrays could also help to provide more effective, customized medical care. Different people have different alleles of hundreds of genes; these may cause them to be more or less susceptible to many diseases, or to respond more or less well to various treatments. Someday, physicians might be able to use a DNA microarray containing thousands of probes for disease-related alleles, to determine which susceptibility alleles each patient carries, and tailor medical care

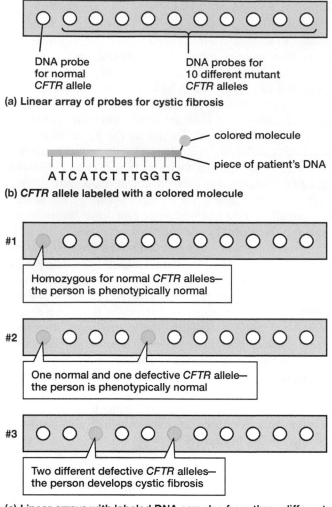

(a) Linear array of probes for cystic fibrosis

DNA probe for normal *CFTR* allele

DNA probes for 10 different mutant *CFTR* alleles

colored molecule

piece of patient's DNA

ATCATCTTTGGTG

(b) *CFTR* allele labeled with a colored molecule

#1

Homozygous for normal *CFTR* alleles—the person is phenotypically normal

#2

One normal and one defective *CFTR* allele—the person is phenotypically normal

#3

Two different defective *CFTR* alleles—the person develops cystic fibrosis

(c) Linear arrays with labeled DNA samples from three different people

▲ FIGURE 13-13 **A cystic fibrosis diagnostic array**
(a) A typical diagnostic array for cystic fibrosis consists of special paper to which DNA probes complementary to the normal *CFTR* allele (far left spot) and several of the most common defective *CFTR* alleles (the other 10 spots) are attached. (b) DNA from a patient is cut into small pieces, separated into single strands, and the *CFTR* alleles are labeled with colored molecules. (c) The array is bathed in a solution of the patient's labeled DNA. The labeled DNA binds to different spots on the array, depending on which *CFTR* alleles the patient possesses.

accordingly. Several companies already produce small arrays tailored to investigate gene activity in specific diseases, such as cancers of the breast, prostate, and immune system. Some hospitals use them to provide patients with treatments that are most likely to succeed with their specific cancer.

Finally, several companies offer individualized DNA screening to the public. These tests use DNA microarrays to look for alleles that might predispose an individual to develop heart disease, breast cancer, arthritis, or other diseases. The companies even offer health advice, presumably based on the individual DNA analysis, although most of the advice—to exercise, keep blood pressure and cholesterol levels down, keep weight under control, and refrain from smoking—would be a good idea for anyone, regardless of what alleles they carry.

DNA Technology Can Help to Treat Disease

There are two principal applications of DNA technology for treating disease: (1) producing medicines, mostly in bacteria, using recombinant DNA techniques and (2) **gene therapy,** which seeks to cure diseases by inserting, deleting, or altering genes in a patient's cells.

Using Biotechnology to Produce Medicines

Thanks to recombinant DNA technology, several medically important proteins are now routinely made in bacteria. The first human protein made by recombinant DNA technology was insulin. Prior to 1982, when recombinant human insulin was first licensed for use, the insulin needed by people with diabetes was extracted from the pancreases of cattle or pigs slaughtered for meat. Although the insulin from these animals is very similar to human insulin, the slight differences caused an allergic reaction in about 5% of people with diabetes. Recombinant human insulin does not cause allergic reactions.

Other human proteins, such as growth hormone and clotting factors, can also be produced in transgenic bacteria. Some of these proteins were formerly obtained from either human blood or human cadavers; these sources are expensive and sometimes dangerous. As you probably know, blood can be contaminated by the human immunodeficiency virus (HIV), which causes acquired immune deficiency syndrome (AIDS). Cadavers may also contain several hard-to-diagnose infectious diseases, such as Creutzfeldt-Jakob syndrome, in which an abnormal protein can be passed from the tissues of an infected cadaver to a patient and cause fatal brain degeneration (see the Chapter 3 case study). Engineered proteins grown in bacteria or other cultured cells avoid these dangers. Some of the types of human proteins produced by recombinant DNA technology are listed in **Table 13-2.**

Treating AIDS by Gene Therapy

The human immunodeficiency virus enters several kinds of immune cells (mostly white blood cells), including a type called *helper T cells* that play a crucial role in responses to infection. HIV kills helper T cells. When the body's supply of helper T cells becomes too low, the immune response falters, ordinarily trivial infections become life threatening, and full-blown AIDS develops. Untreated, AIDS is almost always fatal within a few years.

Why isn't AIDS always fatal? HIV binds to a receptor protein, called CCR5, found on the surface of susceptible immune cells. HIV then moves into the cells and begins its deadly infectious cycle. But a tiny number of people carry a mutation and don't make CCR5 receptors, so they can't be infected with the usual strains of HIV.

Biotechnology offers the possibility of eliminating the CCR5 receptor in patients with AIDS and curing, or at least greatly alleviating, their disease. Molecular biologists can manufacture specialized enzymes tailor-made to cut up specific genes, such as the one that encodes the CCR5 receptors. The treatment would work like this: Immune cells are removed from a patient, and the *CCR5* gene is damaged with the enzyme. Although the cells try to repair the damaged

TABLE 13-2   Examples of Medical Products Produced by Recombinant DNA Methods

Type of Protein	Purpose	Example	Method of Production
Human hormones	Used in the treatment of diabetes and growth deficiency	Humulin™ (human insulin)	Human gene inserted into bacteria
Human cytokines (regulate immune system function)	Used in bone marrow transplants and to treat cancers and viral infections, including hepatitis and genital warts	Leukine™ (granulocyte-macrophage colony stimulating factor)	Human gene inserted into yeast
Antibodies (immune system proteins)	Used to fight infections, cancers, diabetes, organ rejection, and multiple sclerosis	Herceptin™ (antibodies to a protein expressed in some breast cancer cells)	Recombinant antibody genes inserted into cultured hamster cells
Viral proteins	Used to generate vaccines against viral diseases and for diagnosing viral infections	Engerix-B™ (hepatitis B vaccine)	Viral gene inserted into yeast
Enzymes	Used in the treatment of heart attacks, cystic fibrosis, and other diseases, and in the production of cheeses and detergents	Activase™ (tissue plasminogen activator)	Human gene inserted into cultured hamster cells

DNA, about a quarter of them fail, and can never make CCR5 receptors again. These CCR5-deleted cells are transfused back into the patient. In two small clinical trials, the numbers of functioning immune cells were greatly increased in most of the patients receiving this treatment.

Mature immune cells don't live forever, so this treatment would probably have to be repeated at intervals for the rest of the patient's life. However, all the cells of the immune system originate from stem cells in the bone marrow. Stem cells are capable of dividing throughout a person's life, continuing to produce one or more (often many) different types of daughter cells (see Chapter 9 for more information about stem cells). Ideally, stem cells could be removed from a patient, genetically "repaired," and replaced into the patient. In the case of HIV, all of the helper T cells that derive from the CCR5-deleted stem cells would also lack CCR5 and resist HIV infection. In addition, natural selection should operate in the patient's body: HIV would continue to kill off the unrepaired cells, but not the CCR5-deleted cells. Eventually, the patient's entire population of helper T cells should consist of CCR5-deleted cells, and the cure should be permanent.

Treating Severe Combined Immune Deficiency by Gene Therapy

Severe combined immune deficiency (SCID) is a rare disorder in which a child fails to develop an immune system. About 1 in 80,000 children is born with some form of SCID. Infections that would be trivial in a normal child become life threatening. In some cases, if the child has an unaffected relative with a similar genetic makeup, a bone marrow transplant from the healthy relative can give the child functioning stem cells, so that he or she can develop a working immune system. Most children with SCID, however, die before their first birthday.

Most forms of SCID are caused by defective recessive alleles of one of several genes. In one type of SCID, affected children are homozygous recessive for a defective allele that normally codes for an enzyme called adenosine deaminase (this condition is often called ADA-SCID). In 1990, gene therapy was performed

on 4-year-old Ashanti DeSilva, who suffered from ADA-SCID. Some of her white blood cells were removed, genetically altered with a virus containing a functional version of her defective allele, and then returned to her bloodstream. The treatment was a partial success, but not a complete cure. Ashanti, now a healthy adult, continues to receive regular injections of a form of adenosine deaminase to boost her immune system. More recent clinical trials have used a somewhat different gene therapy to cure ADA-SCID. The researchers removed bone marrow stem cells from children with ADA-SCID, inserted a functional copy of the adenosine deaminase gene into the cells, and returned the repaired cells into the children. Because bone marrow stem cells continue to produce new white blood cells throughout life, the hope is that these children might be permanently cured. As of late 2011, all 27 children treated in this way are alive and healthy, and so far, 19 have needed no additional treatments to enhance their immune responses.

A second type of SCID, called X-linked SCID, is caused by a defective recessive allele of a gene located on the X chromosome. Twenty children have been given gene therapy to insert a functional copy of this gene into their bone marrow stem cells. Eighteen appear to be cured, some for as long as 10 years after treatment. However, gene therapy for X-linked SCID is not without risks: Several children developed leukemia, apparently because the gene insertion turned on an oncogene (see Chapter 9). More recent methods seem to have reduced, and perhaps eliminated, this danger.

Although the parents knew there were dangers associated with gene therapy, as one mother put it, "We didn't really have a choice." Now, instead of dying as infants, or living encapsulated within a sterile bubble, isolated from human contact, these children can live normal lives—going to school, playing soccer, and riding horses.

CHECK YOUR LEARNING

Can you explain how biotechnology is used to diagnose both inherited and infectious diseases? Can you describe the procedures and advantages of gene therapy to cure inherited diseases?

Health Watch

Prenatal Genetic Screening

Prenatal diagnosis of a variety of genetic disorders, including cystic fibrosis, sickle-cell anemia, muscular dystrophy, and Down syndrome, requires samples of fetal cells or chemicals produced by the fetus. Presently, three techniques are commonly used to obtain samples for prenatal diagnosis: amniocentesis, chorionic villus sampling, and maternal blood collection.

Amniocentesis

The human fetus, like all animal embryos, develops in a watery environment. A waterproof membrane called the amnion surrounds the fetus and holds the fluid. As the fetus develops, it releases various chemicals (often in its urine) and sheds some of its cells into the amniotic fluid. When a fetus is 15 weeks or older, amniotic fluid can be collected safely by a procedure called **amniocentesis.**

First, the physician determines the position of the fetus by ultrasound scanning. How does that work? You probably already know how bats find moths at night: They shriek extremely high-frequency sound (far above the limits of human hearing) and listen for echoes bouncing off the moth's body. To locate a fetus with ultrasound, high-frequency sound is broadcast into a pregnant woman's abdomen, and sophisticated instruments convert the resulting echoes into a real-time image of the fetus (**Fig. E13-4**). Using the ultrasound image as a guide, the physician carefully inserts a sterilized needle through the abdominal wall, the uterus, and the amnion (being sure to avoid the fetus and placenta), and withdraws 10 to 20 milliliters of amniotic fluid (**Fig. E13-5**). Amniocentesis carries a slight risk of miscarriage, about 0.5% or less.

Chorionic Villus Sampling

The chorion is a membrane that is produced by the fetus and becomes part of the placenta. The chorion produces many small projections, called villi. In **chorionic villus sampling (CVS)**, a physician inserts a small tube into the uterus through the mother's vagina and suctions off a few villi for analysis (see Fig. E13-5). The loss of a few villi does not harm the fetus. CVS has two major advantages over amniocentesis. First, it can be done much earlier in pregnancy—as early as the 8th week, but usually between the 10th and 12th weeks. This is especially important if the woman is contemplating a therapeutic abortion if her fetus has a major defect. Second, the sample contains far more fetal cells than can be obtained by amniocentesis. However, CVS appears to have a slightly greater risk of causing a miscarriage than amniocentesis does. Also, because the chorion is outside of the amniotic sac, CVS does not obtain a sample of the amniotic fluid. Finally, in some cases chorionic cells have chromosomal abnormalities that are in fact not present in the fetus, which complicates karyotyping. For these reasons, CVS is less commonly performed than amniocentesis.

▲ **FIGURE E13-4 A human fetus imaged with ultrasound**

Maternal Blood Collection

A tiny number of fetal cells cross the placenta and enter the mother's bloodstream as early as the sixth week of pregnancy. Separating fetal cells (perhaps as few as one per milliliter of blood) from the huge numbers of maternal cells is challenging, but it can be done. Surprisingly, there is also fetal DNA floating free in the mother's blood. In addition, a variety of proteins and other chemicals produced by the fetus may enter the mother's bloodstream.

Analyzing the Samples

Both amniotic fluid and maternal blood are briefly centrifuged to separate the cells from the fluids (amniotic fluid or plasma, respectively). Biochemical analysis may be performed to measure the concentrations of specific hormones, enzymes, or other proteins in the fluids. For example, if the amniotic fluid contains high concentrations of an embryonic protein called alpha-fetoprotein, this indicates that the fetus may have nervous system disorders, such as spina bifida, in which the spinal cord is incomplete, or anencephaly, in which major portions of the brain fail to develop. Specific combinations of alpha-fetoprotein, estrogen, and other chemicals in maternal plasma (detected by triple screen, quad screen, or penta screen tests, depending on whether three, four, or five chemicals are analyzed) indicate the likelihood of Down syndrome, spina bifida, or certain other disorders. However, these biochemical assays do not provide definitive diagnoses. Therefore, if they indicate that a disorder is present, then other tests, such as karyotyping, DNA analysis of fetal cells, or highly detailed

13.8 WHAT ARE THE MAJOR ETHICAL ISSUES OF MODERN BIOTECHNOLOGY?

Modern biotechnology offers the promise—some would say the threat—of greatly changing our lives, and the lives of many other organisms on Earth. Is humanity capable of handling the responsibility of biotechnology? Here we will explore two important issues: the use of genetically modified organisms in agriculture and the prospects for genetically modifying human beings.

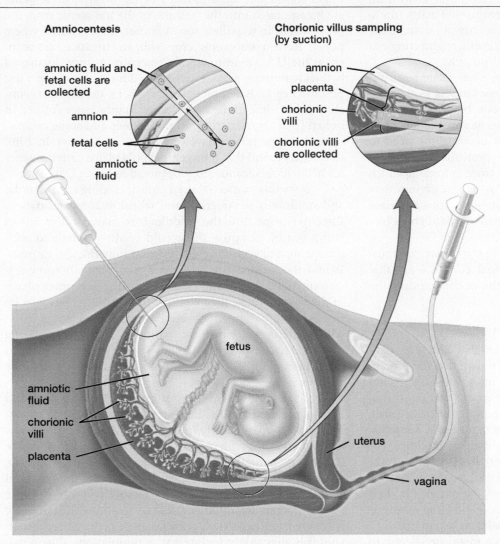

Amniocentesis

amniotic fluid and fetal cells are collected

amnion

fetal cells

amniotic fluid

Chorionic villus sampling (by suction)

amnion

placenta

chorionic villi

chorionic villi are collected

fetus

amniotic fluid

chorionic villi

placenta

uterus

vagina

◄ FIGURE E13-5 **Prenatal sampling techniques** The two most common ways of obtaining samples for prenatal diagnosis are amniocentesis and chorionic villus sampling. (In reality, CVS is usually performed when the fetus is much younger than the one depicted in this illustration.)

Biotechnology techniques can be used to analyze fetal DNA for many defective alleles, such as those that cause sickle-cell anemia or cystic fibrosis. Modified PCR techniques can also be used to diagnose Down syndrome, eliminating the need to culture fetal cells obtained by amniocentesis. In Great Britain, PCR is often used as a stand-alone method for diagnosing Down syndrome. In the United States, karyotyping remains the gold standard.

Prenatal diagnosis using fetal DNA obtained from maternal blood samples is advancing rapidly. Researchers in Hong Kong recently developed methods based on PCR and DNA sequencing to diagnose Down syndrome using fetal DNA found in maternal blood. Several companies now offer paternity testing based on fetal cells or fetal DNA isolated from maternal blood.

You may think that prenatal diagnosis is useful mainly when the parents are contemplating an abortion if the fetus has a serious genetic disorder. However, prenatal diagnosis

ultrasound examination of the fetus, are employed to find out whether or not the fetus actually has one of these conditions.

Fetal cells, or at least fetal DNA, are required for karyotyping or DNA analysis. Amniotic fluid contains very small numbers of fetal cells, so to obtain enough cells for karyotyping or DNA analysis, the usual procedure is to grow the cells in culture for a week or two. The large number of fetal cells obtained by CVS means that karyotyping and DNA analyses can usually be performed without culturing the cells first (although some labs do culture the cells for a few days). Karyotyping the fetal cells can show if there are too many or too few copies of the chromosomes, and if any chromosomes show structural abnormalities. Down syndrome, for example, results from the presence of three copies of chromosome 21 (see Chapter 10).

can also be used to provide better care for an affected infant. For example, if the fetus is homozygous for the sickle-cell allele, some therapeutic measures can be taken beginning at birth. In particular, regular doses of penicillin greatly reduce bacterial infections that otherwise kill about 15% of homozygous children. Further, knowing that a child has the disorder ensures correct diagnosis and rapid treatment during a "sickling crisis," when malformed red blood cells clump and block blood flow. Fetuses with spina bifida are often delivered by planned cesarean section, both to reduce damage to the spinal cord during birth and so that a surgical team can be standing by in case immediate surgery on the infant is necessary. Comparable medical or behavioral interventions can be planned for several other disorders as well.

Should Genetically Modified Organisms Be Permitted in Agriculture?

The aims of traditional and modern agricultural biotechnology are the same: to modify the genetic makeup of living organisms to make them more useful. However, there are

three principal differences. First, traditional biotechnology is slow; many generations of selective breeding are usually necessary to produce useful new strains of plants or animals. Genetic engineering, in contrast, can potentially introduce massive genetic changes in a single generation. Second, traditional biotechnology almost always recombines genetic material from the same, or at least very closely related, species, whereas genetic engineering can recombine DNA from very different species in a single organism. Finally, traditional biotechnology has no way to directly manipulate the DNA sequence of genes themselves. Genetic engineering can produce new genes never before seen on Earth.

The best transgenic crops have clear advantages for farmers. Herbicide-resistant crops allow farmers to rid their fields of weeds, which reduce harvests by 10% or more, through the use of powerful herbicides at virtually any stage of crop growth. Insect-resistant crops decrease the need to apply pesticides, saving the cost of the pesticides themselves, as well as tractor fuel and labor. Therefore, transgenic crops may produce larger harvests at less cost. These savings may be passed along to the consumer. Transgenic crops also have the potential to be more nutritious than standard crops (see "Health Watch: Golden Rice").

However, many people strenuously object to transgenic crops or livestock. The principal concerns are that GMOs may be harmful to human health or dangerous to the environment.

Are Foods from GMOs Dangerous to Eat?

In most cases, there is no reason to think that GMOs are dangerous to eat. For example, tests have shown that the protein encoded by the *Bt* gene is not toxic to mammals, so it should not be dangerous to human health. If growth-enhanced livestock are ever marketed, they will simply have more meat, composed of exactly the same proteins that exist in nontransgenic animals, so they shouldn't be dangerous either. For example, a company called AquaBounty has produced transgenic salmon containing extra genes for growth hormone. The fish grow faster, but will have the same proteins in their flesh as any other salmon. The U.S. Food and Drug Administration has declared the AquaBounty salmon safe to eat.

On the other hand, some people might be allergic to genetically modified plants. In the 1990s, a gene from Brazil nuts was inserted into soybeans in an attempt to improve the balance of amino acids in soybean protein. It was soon discovered that people allergic to Brazil nuts would probably also be allergic to the transgenic soybeans. These transgenic soybean plants never made it to the farm. The U.S. Food and Drug Administration now requires all new transgenic crop plants to be tested for allergenic potential.

Are GMOs Hazardous to the Environment?

The environmental effects of GMOs are much more debatable. One clear positive effect of *Bt* crops is that farmers apply less pesticide to their fields. This should translate into less pollution of the environment and less harm to the farmers. For example, in 2002 and 2003, Chinese farmers planting *Bt* rice reduced pesticide use by 80% compared to farmers planting conventional rice. Further, they suffered no instances of pesticide poisoning, compared to about 5% of farmers planting conventional rice. A 10-year study in Arizona showed that *Bt* cotton allowed farmers to use less pesticide while obtaining the same yields of cotton.

On the other hand, *Bt* or herbicide-resistance genes might spread outside a farmer's fields. Because these genes are incorporated into the genome of the transgenic crop, the genes will be in its pollen, too. A farmer cannot control where pollen from a transgenic crop will go. In 2006, researchers at the U.S. Environmental Protection Agency discovered herbicide-resistant grasses more than 2 miles away from a test plot in Oregon. Based on genetic analyses, the scientists concluded that some of the herbicide-resistance genes escaped in pollen (most grasses are wind pollinated) and some escaped in seeds (most grasses have very lightweight seeds). In 2010, researchers found that transgenic canola plants carrying genes for herbicide resistance are widespread in North Dakota.

Does this matter? Many crops, including corn, canola, and sunflowers in America, and wheat, barley, and oats in Eastern Europe and the Middle East, have wild relatives living nearby. Suppose these wild relatives interbred with transgenic crops and became resistant to herbicides or pests. Would the accidentally transgenic wild plants become significant weed problems? Would they displace other plants in the wild, because they would be less likely to be eaten by insects? Even if transgenic crops have no close relatives in the wild, bacteria and viruses sometimes transfer genes among unrelated plant species. Could viruses spread unwanted genes into wild plant populations? No one really knows the answers to these questions.

What about transgenic animals? Unlike pollen and lightweight seeds, most domesticated animals, such as cattle or sheep, are relatively immobile. Further, most have few wild relatives with which they might exchange genes, so the dangers to natural ecosystems appear minimal. However, some transgenic animals, especially fish, have the potential to pose more significant threats, because they can disperse rapidly and are nearly impossible to recapture. If transgenic fish were more aggressive, grew faster, or matured faster than wild fish, they might replace native populations. One possible way out of this dilemma, pioneered by AquaBounty, is to raise only sterile transgenic fish, so that any escapees would die without reproducing and thus have minimal impact on natural ecosystems. Skeptics worry that the sterilization process may not be 100% effective, leaving open the possibility of fertile transgenic fish escaping into the wild.

Should the Genome of Humans Be Changed by Biotechnology?

Many of the ethical implications of human applications of biotechnology are fundamentally the same as those connected with other medical procedures. For example, long before biotechnology enabled prenatal testing for cystic fibrosis or sickle-cell anemia, trisomy 21 (Down syndrome) could be diagnosed in embryos by simply counting the chromosomes in cells taken from amniotic fluid (see "Health Watch: Prenatal Genetic Screening"). Whether parents should use such information as a basis for choosing an abortion or to prepare to care for the affected child generates enormous controversy. Other ethical concerns, however, have arisen purely as a result of advances

Health|Watch

Golden Rice

Rice is the principal food for about two-thirds of the people on Earth. Rice provides carbohydrates and some protein, but is a poor source of many vitamins, including vitamin A. Unless people eat enough fruits and vegetables, they often lack sufficient vitamin A, and may suffer from poor vision, immune system defects, and damage to their respiratory, digestive, and urinary tracts. According to the World Health Organization, more than 100 million children suffer from vitamin A deficiency. As a result, each year 250,000 to 500,000 children become blind, principally in Asia, Africa, and Latin America; half of those children die. Vitamin A deficiency typically strikes the poor, because rice may be all they can afford to eat. In 1999, biotechnology provided a possible remedy: rice genetically engineered to contain beta-carotene, a pigment that makes daffodils bright yellow and that the human body easily converts into vitamin A.

Creating a rice strain with high levels of beta-carotene wasn't simple. However, funding from the Rockefeller Institute, the European Community Biotech Program, and the Swiss Federal Office for Education and Science enabled molecular biologists Ingo Potrykus and Peter Beyer to tackle the task. They inserted three genes into the rice genome, two from daffodils and one from a bacterium. As a result, "Golden Rice" grains synthesize beta-carotene.

The trouble was, the original Golden Rice didn't make very much beta-carotene, so people would have had to eat enormous amounts to get enough vitamin A. The Golden Rice community didn't give up. It turns out that daffodils aren't the best source for genes that direct beta-carotene synthesis. Golden Rice 2, with genes from corn, produces over 20 times more beta-carotene than the original Golden Rice does, and consequently is bright yellow (Fig. E13-6). About 2 cups of cooked Golden Rice 2 should provide enough beta-carotene to equal the full recommended daily amount of vitamin A. Golden Rice 2 was given, free, to the Humanitarian Rice Board for experiments and planting in Southeast Asia.

However, Golden Rice faces other hurdles. Many people strongly resist large-scale planting of Golden Rice (or other transgenic crops). Getting Golden Rice genes into the popular Asian strains required years of traditional genetic crosses. By 2007, the International Rice Research Institute succeeded in incorporating the carotene-synthesizing genes of Golden Rice into Asian rice strains, and the first field trials of these Golden

▲ FIGURE E13-6 **Golden rice** The high beta-carotene content of Golden Rice 2 gives it a bright yellow color. Normal rice lacks beta-carotene and is off-white.

Rice varieties began in the Philippines in April 2008. Locally adapted strains of Golden Rice 2 are expected to be available for farmers in the Philippines to plant in 2013.

Is Golden Rice the best way, or the only way, to solve the problems of malnutrition in poor people? Perhaps not. For one thing, many poor people's diets are deficient in many nutrients, not just vitamin A. To help solve that problem, the Bill and Melinda Gates Foundation is funding research to increase the levels of vitamin E, iron, and zinc in rice. Further, not all poor people eat mostly rice. In parts of Africa, sweet potatoes are the main source of calories. Eating orange, instead of white, sweet potatoes, has dramatically increased vitamin A intake for many of these people. Finally, in many parts of the world, governments and humanitarian organizations have started vitamin A supplementation programs. In some parts of Africa and Asia, as many as 80% of the children receive large doses of vitamin A a few times when they are very young. Some day, the combination of these efforts may result in a world in which no children suffer blindness from the lack of a simple nutrient in their diets.

---

in biotechnology. For instance, should people be allowed to select, or even change, the genomes of their offspring?

On July 4, 1994, a girl in Colorado was born with Fanconi anemia, an inherited disorder that is fatal without a transplant of stem cells from the bone marrow of a genetically compatible donor. Her parents wanted another child—a very special child. They wanted one without Fanconi anemia, of course, but they also wanted a child who could serve as a stem cell donor for their daughter. They went to Yury Verlinsky of the Reproductive Genetics Institute for help. Verlinsky used the parents' sperm and eggs to create dozens of embryos in culture. The embryos were tested both for the genetic defect and for tissue

compatibility with the couple's daughter. Verlinsky chose an embryo with the desired genotype and implanted it into the mother's uterus. Nine months later, a son was born. Blood from his umbilical cord provided stem cells to transplant into his sister's bone marrow. Today, the girl's bone marrow failure has been cured, although she will always have anemia and many accompanying symptoms. Were these appropriate uses of genetic screening? Should dozens of embryos be created, knowing that the vast majority will be discarded? Is this ethical if it is the only way to save the life of another child?

The same technologies used to insert genes into stem cells to cure SCID could be used to insert or change the genes

parents with a genetic disease

fertilized egg with a defective gene

embryo with a genetic defect

cell removed and cultured

treated culture

therapeutic gene

viral vector

genetically corrected cell from culture

egg cell without a nucleus

genetically corrected egg cell

genetically corrected clone of the original embryo

healthy baby

◄ FIGURE 13-14 **Using biotechnology to correct genetic defects in human embryos** In this hypothetical example, human embryos would be derived from eggs fertilized by sperm in culture, with one or both of the parents having a genetic disorder. When an embryo containing a defective gene grows into a small cluster of cells, a single cell would be removed from the embryo, and the defective gene in the cell replaced using an appropriate vector, usually a disabled virus. The nucleus of another egg cell (taken from the same mother) would be removed. The genetically repaired cell could then be injected into the egg whose nucleus had been removed. The now repaired egg cell would then be implanted in the woman's uterus for fetal development.

of fertilized eggs (**Fig. 13-14**). Suppose it were possible to insert functional *CFTR* alleles into human eggs, thereby preventing cystic fibrosis. Would this be an ethical change to the human genome? What about making bigger football players or more beautiful supermodels? If and when the technology is developed to cure diseases, it will be difficult to prevent it from being used for nonmedical purposes. Who will determine which uses are appropriate and which are trivial vanity?

CHECK YOUR LEARNING

Can you explain why people might be opposed to the use of genetically modified organisms in agriculture? Can you envision circumstances in which it would be ethical to modify the genome of a human fertilized egg?

CASE STUDY revisited

Guilty or Innocent?

DNA profiling is often considered the gold standard of evidence, because of its extremely low error rate. Thanks to the power of DNA profiling, Dennis Maher is now a free man. And he's not alone. DNA evidence has proved the innocence of more than 300 people in the United States who had been wrongfully convicted of major crimes—and 17 of those people had spent time on death row.

Many people exonerated after years in prison have a hard time adjusting to life "outside." Maher, however, is a real success story. Soon after his release, he got a job servicing trucks for Waste Management, a trash pickup and recycling company. He met his wife, Melissa, through an online dating service, using the name DNADennis. They have two children, one named Aliza after his Innocence Project attorney. Does Maher harbor any resentment against the system that cost him 19 years of his life? Sure. As he puts it, "I lost what I can never get back." But he also says, "I don't have time to be angry. If I'm an angry person, I won't have the things I have in my life."

If you're a fan of TV crime shows such as *CSI*, you know that DNA profiling also helps police to solve cases. Most police departments in large cities now have a "cold case unit" that takes a fresh look at stale evidence, sometimes leading to convictions many years after a perpetrator seemed to have gotten away with a crime. In Pasadena, California, for example, a 72-year-old woman was murdered in her home in 1987, before DNA profiling had been invented. Although police thought they knew the assailant, they didn't have enough evidence to prove it, so the man was freed. In 2007, however, Pasadena set up an Unsolved Homicide Case Unit. Their first success was to use DNA profiling to identify, arrest, and convict the murderer, now serving 15 years to life in prison.

Consider This

BioEthics Who are the heroes in these stories? There are the obvious ones, of course—Innocence Project attorney Aliza Kaplan, the law students who spent many hours slogging through poorly labeled boxes searching for evidence, the members of the Pasadena Police Department, and, of course, Dennis Maher. But what about molecular biologist Kary Mullis, who discovered PCR? Or Thomas Brock, whose discovery of *Thermus aquaticus* in Yellowstone hot springs provided the source of heat-stable DNA polymerase that is so essential to PCR (see Fig. 13-4)? Or the hundreds of biologists, chemists, and mathematicians who developed procedures for gel electrophoresis, DNA labeling, and statistical analysis of sample matching?

Scientists often say that science is worthwhile for its own sake, and that it is difficult or impossible to predict which discoveries will lead to the greatest benefits for humanity. Nonscientists, when asked to pay the costs of scientific projects, are sometimes skeptical of such claims. How do you think that public support of science should be allocated? Fifty years ago, would you have voted to give Thomas Brock public funds to see what types of organisms lived in hot springs?

CHAPTER REVIEW

Summary of Key Concepts

13.1 What Is Biotechnology?

Biotechnology is the use, and especially the alteration, of organisms, cells, or biological molecules to produce food, drugs, or other goods. Modern biotechnology generates altered genetic material by genetic engineering. Genetic engineering frequently involves the production of recombinant DNA by combining DNA from different organisms. When DNA is transferred from one organism to another, the recipients are called transgenic or genetically modified organisms (GMOs). Major applications of modern biotechnology include increasing our understanding of gene function, treating disease, improving agriculture, and solving crimes.

13.2 How Does DNA Recombine in Nature?

DNA recombination occurs naturally through processes such as sexual reproduction; bacterial transformation, in which bacteria acquire DNA from plasmids or other bacteria; and viral infection, in which viruses incorporate fragments of DNA from their hosts and transfer the fragments to members of the same or other species.

13.3 How Is Biotechnology Used in Forensic Science?

Specific regions of very small quantities of DNA, such as might be obtained at a crime scene, can be amplified by the polymerase chain reaction. The most common regions used in forensics are short tandem repeats (STRs). The STRs are separated by gel electrophoresis and made visible with DNA probes. The pattern of STRs, called a DNA profile, can be used to match DNA found at a crime scene with DNA from suspects with extremely high accuracy.

13.4 How Is Biotechnology Used to Make Genetically Modified Organisms?

There are three steps to making a genetically modified organism. First, the desired gene is obtained from another organism, or, less commonly, synthesized. Second, the gene is cloned, often into a bacterial plasmid, to provide multiple copies of the gene. Third, the gene is inserted into a host organism, often through the action of bacteria or viruses, with gene guns, or by injection into cells (especially fertilized eggs).

13.5 How Is Biotechnology Used in Agriculture?

Many crop plants have been modified by the addition of genes that promote herbicide resistance or insect resistance. Plants may also be modified to produce human proteins, vaccines, or antibodies. Transgenic animals may be produced as well, with properties such as faster growth, increased production of valuable products such as milk, or the ability to produce human proteins, vaccines, or antibodies.

13.6 How Is Biotechnology Used to Learn About the Genomes of Humans and Other Organisms?

Techniques of biotechnology were used to discover the complete nucleotide sequence of the human genome. This knowledge is being used to learn the identities and functions of new genes, to discover medically important genes, to explore genetic variability among individuals, and to better understand the evolutionary relationships between humans and other organisms.

13.7 How Is Biotechnology Used for Medical Diagnosis and Treatment?

Biotechnology may be used to diagnose genetic disorders such as sickle-cell anemia or cystic fibrosis. For example, in the diagnosis of sickle-cell anemia, specific restriction enzymes can cut the normal globin allele but not the sickle-cell allele. The resulting DNA fragments of different lengths may then be separated and identified by gel electrophoresis. In the diagnosis of cystic fibrosis, DNA probes complementary to various cystic fibrosis alleles are placed on a DNA array. Base-pairing of a patient's DNA to specific probes on the array identifies which alleles are present in the patient.

Inherited diseases are caused by defective alleles of crucial genes. Genetic engineering may be used to insert functional alleles of these genes into normal cells, stem cells, or even into eggs to correct the genetic disorder.

13.8 What Are the Major Ethical Issues of Modern Biotechnology?

The use of genetically modified organisms in agriculture is controversial for two major reasons: food safety and potentially harmful effects on the environment. In general, GMOs contain proteins that are harmless to mammals, are readily digested, or are already found in other foods. The transfer of potentially allergenic proteins to normally nonallergenic foods can be avoided by thorough testing. Environmental effects of GMOs are more difficult to predict. It is possible that foreign genes, such as those for pest or herbicide resistance, might be transferred to wild plants, with resulting damage to agriculture and/or disruption of ecosystems. If they escape, highly mobile transgenic animals might displace their wild relatives.

Genetically selecting or modifying human embryos is highly controversial. As technologies improve, society may be faced with decisions about the extent to which parents should be allowed to correct or enhance the genomes of their children.

Key Terms

amniocentesis   *250*
biotechnology   *233*
chorionic villus
    sampling (CVS)   *250*
cloning   *233*
DNA cloning   *243*
DNA probe   *239*
DNA profile   *239*
gel electrophoresis   *239*
gene therapy   *248*
genetic engineering   *233*

genetically modified
    organism (GMO)   *233*
plasmid   *234*
polymerase chain
    reaction (PCR)   *237*
recombinant DNA   *233*
restriction enzyme   *243*
short tandem repeat (STR)   *238*
transfect   *244*
transformation   *234*
transgenic   *233*

Learning Outcomes

In this chapter, you have learned to . . .

LO1   Describe natural processes that recombine DNA.

LO2   Define polymerase chain reaction, short tandem repeats, gel electrophoresis, and DNA probes, and describe how electrophoresis and the polymerase chain reaction work.

LO3   Describe how DNA profiles are generated, and explain how they can be used to identify individual people.

LO4   List the purposes for genetically modifying

organisms, and describe the steps involved in creating a genetically modified organism.

LO5   Describe the potential drawbacks of genetically modified organisms.

LO6   Summarize the findings that resulted from the Human Genome Project, and describe the potential benefits of those findings.

LO7   Explain how biotechnology can be used to diagnose and treat inherited disorders.

Thinking Through the Concepts

Fill-in-the-Blank

1. _____ are organisms that contain DNA that has been modified (usually through use of recombinant DNA technology) or derived from other species. **LO4**

2. _____ is the process whereby bacteria pick up DNA from their environment. This DNA may be part of a chromosome or it may be tiny circles of DNA called _____. **LO1**

3. The _____ is a technique for multiplying DNA in the laboratory. **LO2**

4. Matching DNA samples in forensics uses a specific set of small "genes" called _____. The alleles of these genes in different people vary in the _____ of the allele. The pattern of these alleles that a given person possesses is called his or her _____. **LO3**

5. Pieces of DNA can be separated according to size by a process known as _____. The identity of a

specific sample of DNA is usually determined by binding a synthetic piece of DNA called a(n) _____, which binds to the sample DNA by _____. **LO2**

Review Questions

1. Describe three natural forms of genetic recombination, and discuss the similarities and differences between recombinant DNA technology and these natural forms of genetic recombination. **LO1**

2. What is a plasmid? How are plasmids involved in bacterial transformation? **LO1**

3. What is a restriction enzyme? How can restriction enzymes be used to splice a piece of human DNA into a plasmid? **LO4**

4. Describe the polymerase chain reaction. **LO2**

5. What is a short tandem repeat? How are short tandem repeats used in forensics? **LO3**

6. How does gel electrophoresis separate pieces of DNA? **LO2**

7. How are DNA probes used to identify specific nucleotide sequences of DNA? How are they used in the diagnosis of genetic disorders? **LO2 LO7**

8. Describe several uses of genetic engineering in agriculture. **LO5**

9. Describe several uses of genetic engineering in human medicine. **LO7**

10. Describe amniocentesis and chorionic villus sampling, including the advantages and disadvantages of each. What are their medical uses? **LO7**

Applying the Concepts

1. **BioEthics**   In a 2004 Web survey conducted by the Canadian Museum of Nature, 84% of the people polled said they would eat a genetically modified banana that contained a vaccine against an infectious disease, whereas only 47% said they would eat a GM banana with extra vitamin C produced by the action of a rat gene. Do you think that this difference in acceptance of GMOs is scientifically valid? Why or why not?

2. **BioEthics**   As you may know, many insects have evolved resistance to common pesticides. Do you think that insects might evolve resistance to *Bt* crops? If this is a risk, do you think that *Bt* crops should be planted anyway? Why or why not?

3. **BioEthics**   Discuss the ethical issues that surround the release of genetically modified organisms (plants, animals, or bacteria) into the environment. What could go wrong? What precautions might prevent the problems you listed from occurring? What benefits do you think would justify the risks?

4. All children born with X-linked SCID are boys. Can you explain why?

Answers to Figure Caption questions and Fill-in-the-Blank questions can be found in the Answers section at the back of the book.

(MB) *Go to MasteringBiology for practice quizzes, activities, eText, videos, current events, and more.*

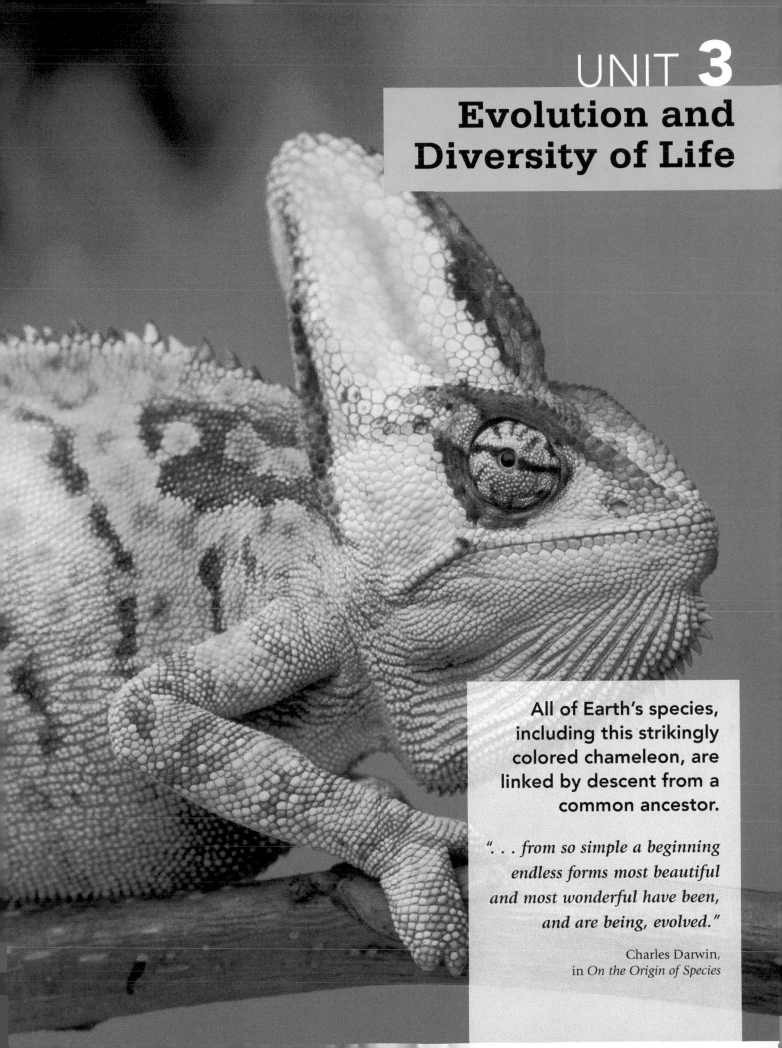

UNIT 3
Evolution and Diversity of Life

All of Earth's species, including this strikingly colored chameleon, are linked by descent from a common ancestor.

"...from so simple a beginning endless forms most beautiful and most wonderful have been, and are being, evolved."

Charles Darwin,
in *On the Origin of Species*

This massive, earthbound ostrich has wings, a legacy of its evolutionary heritage.

CASE STUDY

What Good Are Wisdom Teeth and Ostrich Wings?

HAVE YOU HAD YOUR WISDOM TEETH REMOVED YET? If not, it's probably only a matter of time. Almost all of us will visit an oral surgeon to have our wisdom teeth extracted. There's just not enough room in our jaws for these rearmost molars, and removing them is the best way to prevent the pain, infections, and gum disease that can accompany the development of wisdom teeth. Removal is harmless because we don't really need wisdom teeth.

If you've already suffered through a wisdom tooth extraction, you may have found yourself wondering why we even have these extra molars. Biologists hypothesize that we have them because our apelike ancestors had them and we inherited them, even though we don't need them. The presence in a living species of structures that have no current essential function, but that *are* useful in other living species, demonstrates shared ancestry among these species.

The connection between evolutionary ancestry and traits that have no essential function is illustrated by flightless birds. Consider the ostrich, a bird that can grow to 8 feet tall and weigh 300 pounds (see the photo at left). These massive creatures cannot fly. Nonetheless, they have wings, just as sparrows and ducks do. Why do ostriches have wings? Because the common ancestor of sparrows, ducks, and ostriches had wings, as do all of its descendants, even those that cannot fly. The bodies of today's organisms may contain now-useless hand-me-downs from their ancestors.

AT A GLANCE

LEARNING GOALS

LG1 Define *evolution*.

LG2 Describe pre-Darwin hypotheses and ideas that set the stage for the later emergence of the theory of evolution by natural selection.

LG3 Explain the mechanism of natural selection and the logic by which Darwin deduced it, and describe how natural selection affects populations.

LG4 Describe the main types of evidence that evolution has occurred, and provide an example of each type.

LG5 Compare and contrast similarities due to homology and similarities attributable to convergent evolution.

LG6 Describe the main lines of evidence that populations evolve by natural selection and provide examples of such evidence.

14.1 HOW DID EVOLUTIONARY THOUGHT DEVELOP?

When you began studying biology, you may not have seen a connection between your wisdom teeth and an ostrich's wings. But the connection is there, provided by the concept that unites all of biology: **evolution,** or change over time in the characteristics of a population. (A **population** consists of all the individuals of one species in a particular area.)

Modern biology is based on our understanding that life has evolved, but early scientists did not recognize this fundamental principle. The main ideas of evolutionary biology became widely accepted only after the publication of Charles Darwin's work in the nineteenth century. Nonetheless, the intellectual foundation on which these ideas rest developed gradually over the centuries before Darwin's time.

Early Biological Thought Did Not Include the Concept of Evolution

Pre-Darwinian science, heavily influenced by theology, held that all organisms were created simultaneously by God and that each distinct life-form remained fixed and unchanging from the moment of its creation. This explanation of how life's diversity arose was elegantly expressed by the ancient Greek philosophers, especially Plato and Aristotle. Plato (427–347 B.C.) proposed that each object on Earth is merely a temporary reflection of its divinely inspired "ideal form." Plato's student Aristotle (384–322 B.C.) categorized all organisms into a linear hierarchy that he called the "Ladder of Nature" (**Fig. 14-1**).

These ideas formed the basis of the view that the form of each type of organism is permanently fixed. This view reigned unchallenged for nearly 2,000 years. By the eighteenth century, however, several lines of newly emerging evidence began to undermine this static view of creation.

Exploration of New Lands Revealed a Staggering Diversity of Life

The Europeans who explored and colonized Africa, Asia, and the Americas were often accompanied by naturalists who observed and collected the plants and animals of these previously unknown (to Europeans) lands. By the 1700s, the accumulated observations and collections of the naturalists had begun to reveal the true scope of life's variety. The number of species, or different types of organisms, was much greater than anyone had suspected.

Stimulated by the new evidence of life's incredible diversity, some eighteenth-century naturalists began to take note of some fascinating patterns. They noticed, for example, that each geographic area had its own distinctive set of species. In addition, the naturalists saw that some of the species in a given location closely resembled one another, yet differed in some characteristics. To some scientists of the day, the differences between the species of different geographic areas and the existence of clusters of similar species within areas seemed inconsistent with the idea that species were fixed and unchanging. (You may wish to refer to the timeline in **Fig. 14-2** as you read the following historical account.)

A Few Scientists Speculated That Life Had Evolved

A few eighteenth-century scientists went so far as to speculate that species had, in fact, changed over time. For example, the French naturalist Georges Louis LeClerc (1707–1788), known by the title Comte de Buffon, suggested that the original creation provided a relatively small number of founding species, after which some might have "improved" or "degenerated," perhaps after moving to new geographic areas. That is, Buffon suggested that species had changed over time through natural processes.

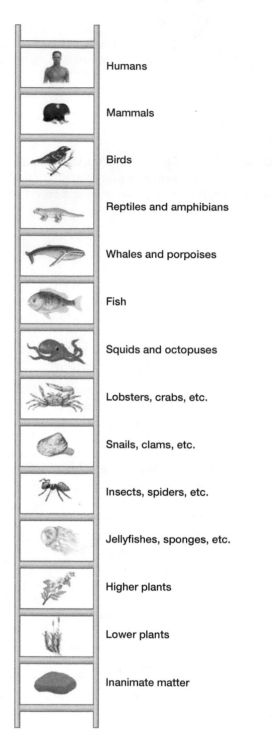

Humans

Mammals

Birds

Reptiles and amphibians

Whales and porpoises

Fish

Squids and octopuses

Lobsters, crabs, etc.

Snails, clams, etc.

Insects, spiders, etc.

Jellyfishes, sponges, etc.

Higher plants

Lower plants

Inanimate matter

▲ FIGURE 14-1 **Aristotle's Ladder of Nature** In Aristotle's view, fixed, unchanging species can be arranged in order of increasing closeness to perfection, with inferior types at the bottom and superior types above.

Fossil Discoveries Showed That Life Has Changed over Time

As Buffon and his contemporaries pondered the implications of new biological discoveries, developments in geology cast further doubt on the idea of permanently fixed species. Especially important was the discovery, during excavations for roads, mines, and canals, of rock fragments that resembled parts of living organisms. People had known of such objects since the fifteenth century, but most thought they were ordinary rocks that wind, water, or people had worked into lifelike forms. As more and more organism-shaped rocks were discovered, however, it became obvious that they were **fossils,** the preserved remains or traces of organisms that had died long ago (**Fig. 14-3**). Many fossils are bones, wood, shells, or their impressions in mud that have been petrified, or converted to stone. Fossils also include other kinds of preserved traces, such as tracks, burrows, pollen grains, eggs, and feces.

By the beginning of the nineteenth century, some pioneering investigators realized that the distribution of fossils in rock was also significant. Many rocks occur in layers, with newer layers positioned over older layers. The British surveyor William Smith (1769–1839), who studied rock layers and the fossils embedded in them, recognized that certain fossils were always found in the same layers of rock. Further, the organization of fossils and rock layers was consistent across different areas: Fossil type A could always be found in a rock layer resting beneath a younger layer containing fossil type B, which in turn rested beneath a still-younger layer containing fossil type C, and so on.

Scientists of the period also discovered that fossil remains showed a remarkable progression. Most fossils found in the oldest layers were very different from modern organisms, and the resemblance to modern organisms gradually increased in progressively younger rocks (**Fig. 14-4**). Many of the fossils were from plant or animal species that had gone *extinct*; that is, no members of the species still lived on Earth.

Putting all of these facts together, some scientists came to an inescapable conclusion: Different types of organisms had lived at different times in the past.

Some Scientists Devised Nonevolutionary Explanations for Fossils

Despite the growing fossil evidence, many scientists of the period did not accept the proposition that species changed and new ones arose over time. To account for extinct species while preserving the notion of a single creation by God, Georges Cuvier (1769–1832) advanced the idea of *catastrophism*. Cuvier, a French anatomist and paleontologist, hypothesized that a vast supply of species was created initially. Successive catastrophes (such as the Great Flood described in the Bible) produced layers of rock and destroyed many species, fossilizing some of their remains in the process. The organisms of the modern world, he speculated, are the species that survived the catastrophes.

Geology Provided Evidence That Earth Is Exceedingly Old

Cuvier's hypothesis of a world shaped by successive catastrophes was challenged by the work of the geologist Charles Lyell (1797–1875). Lyell, building on the earlier thinking of James Hutton (1726–1797), considered the forces of wind,

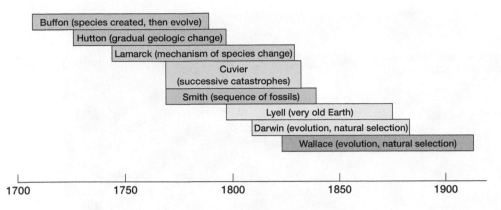

◄FIGURE 14-2 **A timeline of the roots of evolutionary thought** Each bar represents the life span of a scientist who played a key role in the development of modern evolutionary biology.

water, and volcanoes and concluded that there was no need to invoke catastrophes to explain the findings of geology. Don't flooding rivers lay down layers of sediment? Don't lava flows produce layers of basalt? Shouldn't we conclude, then, that layers of rock are evidence of ordinary natural processes, occurring repeatedly over long periods of time? This concept, that Earth's present landscape was produced by past action of the same gradual geological processes that we observe today, is called *uniformitarianism*. Acceptance of uniformitarianism by scientists of the time had a profound impact, because the idea implies that Earth is very old.

Before the 1830 publication of Lyell's evidence in support of uniformitarianism, few scientists suspected that Earth could be more than a few thousand years old. Counting generations in the Old Testament, for example, yields a maximum age of 4,000 to 6,000 years. An Earth this young poses problems for the idea that life has evolved. For example, ancient writers such as Aristotle described wolves, deer, lions, and other organisms that were identical to those present in Europe more than 2,000 years later. If organisms had changed so little over that time, how could whole new species possibly have arisen if Earth was created only a couple of thousand years before Aristotle's time?

But if, as Lyell suggested, rock layers thousands of feet thick were produced by slow, natural processes, then Earth must be old indeed, many millions of years old. Lyell, in fact, concluded that Earth was eternal. Modern geologists estimate that Earth is about 4.5 billion years old (see "Science in Action: How Do We Know How Old a Fossil Is?" on p. 317).

Lyell (and his intellectual predecessor Hutton) showed that there was enough time for evolution to occur. But what was the mechanism? What process could cause evolution?

Some Pre-Darwin Biologists Proposed Mechanisms for Evolution

One of the first scientists to propose a mechanism for evolution was the French biologist Jean Baptiste Lamarck (1744–1829). Lamarck was impressed by the sequences of organisms in rock layers. He observed that older fossils tend to be less like existing organisms than are more recent

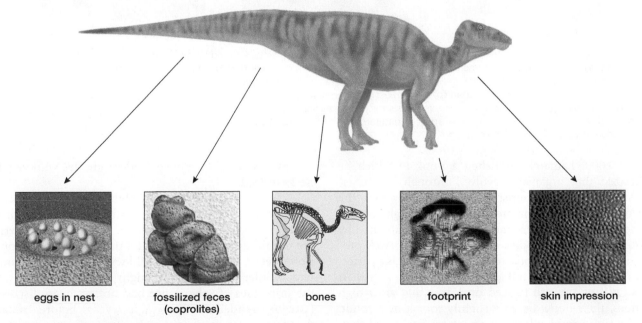

| eggs in nest | fossilized feces (coprolites) | bones | footprint | skin impression |

▲ FIGURE 14-3 **Types of fossils** Any preserved part or trace of an organism is a fossil.

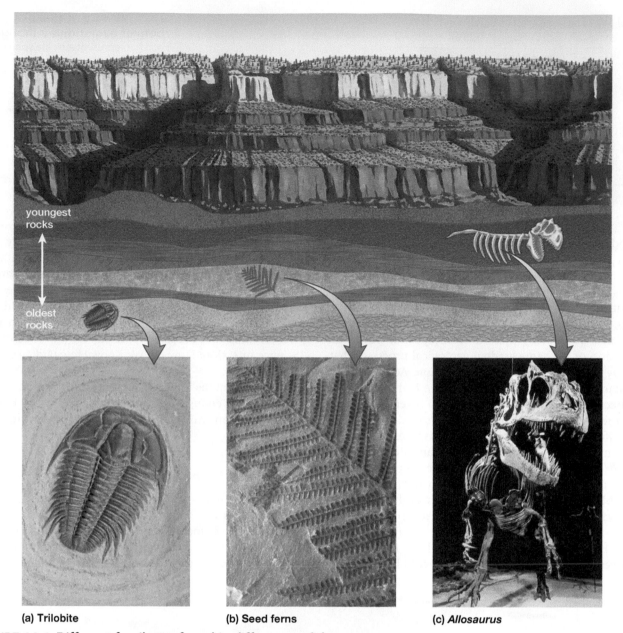

(a) Trilobite   **(b) Seed ferns**   **(c) *Allosaurus***

▲ FIGURE 14-4 **Different fossils are found in different rock layers** Fossils provide strong support for the idea that today's organisms were not created all at once but arose over time by the process of evolution. If all species had been created simultaneously, we would not expect **(a)** the earliest trilobites to be found in older rock layers than **(b)** the earliest seed ferns, which in turn would not be expected in older layers than **(c)** dinosaurs, such as *Allosaurus*. Trilobites first appeared about 520 million years ago, seed ferns (which were not actually ferns but had fern-like foliage) about 380 million years ago, and dinosaurs about 230 million years ago.

fossils. In 1809, Lamarck published a book in which he hypothesized that organisms evolved through the inheritance of acquired characteristics, a process in which the bodies of living organisms are modified through the use or disuse of parts, and these modifications are inherited by offspring. Why would bodies be modified? Lamarck proposed that all organisms possess an innate drive for perfection. For example, if ancestral giraffes tried to improve their lot by stretching upward to feed on leaves that grow high up in trees, their necks became slightly longer as a result. Their offspring would inherit these longer necks and then stretch even farther to reach still higher leaves. Eventually, this process would produce modern giraffes with very long necks indeed.

Today, we understand how inheritance works and can see that Lamarck's proposed evolutionary process could not work as he described it. Acquired characteristics are not inherited. The fact that a prospective father pumps iron doesn't mean that his child will look like a champion bodybuilder. Remember, though, that in Lamarck's time the principles of inheritance had not yet been discovered. (Gregor Mendel was born a few years before Lamarck's death, and his work with inheritance in pea plants was not widely recognized until 1900—see Chapter 10.) In any case, Lamarck's insight that inheritance plays an important role in evolution had an important influence on the later biologists who discovered the key mechanism of evolution.

Darwin and Wallace Proposed a Mechanism of Evolution

By the mid-1800s, a growing number of biologists had concluded that present-day species had evolved from earlier ones. But how? In 1858, Charles Darwin (1809–1882) and Alfred Russel Wallace (1823–1913), working separately, provided convincing evidence that evolution was driven by a simple yet powerful process.

Although their social and educational backgrounds were very different, Darwin and Wallace were quite similar in some respects. Both had traveled extensively in the tropics and had studied the plants and animals living there. Both found that some species differed in only a few features (Fig. 14-5). Both were familiar with the fossils that had been discovered, many of which showed a trend through time of increasing similarity to modern organisms. Finally, both were aware of the studies of Hutton and Lyell, who had proposed that Earth is extremely ancient. These facts suggested to both Darwin and Wallace that species change over time. Both men sought a mechanism that might cause such evolutionary change.

Of the two, Darwin was the first to propose a mechanism for evolution, which he sketched out in 1842 and described more fully in an essay in 1844. He sent the essay to a few colleagues, but did not submit it for publication, perhaps because he was fearful of the controversy that publication would cause. Some historians wonder if Darwin would ever have published his ideas had he not received, some 16 years after his initial draft, a paper by Wallace that outlined ideas remarkably similar to Darwin's own. Darwin realized that he could delay no longer.

In separate but similar papers that were presented to the Linnaean Society in London in 1858, Darwin and Wallace each described the same mechanism for evolution. Initially, their papers had little impact. The secretary of the society, in fact, wrote in his annual report that nothing very interesting happened that year. Fortunately, the next year, Darwin published his monumental book, *On the Origin of Species by Means of Natural Selection*, which attracted a great deal of attention to the new ideas about how species evolve. (To learn more about Darwin's life, see "Science in Action: Charles Darwin—Nature Was His Laboratory.")

CHECK YOUR LEARNING

Can you identify some of the thinkers whose ideas set the stage for the development of the theory of evolution? Can you describe the key ideas of those thinkers? Can you define *evolution*?

(a) Large ground finch, beak suited to large seeds

(b) Small ground finch, beak suited to small seeds

(c) Warbler finch, beak suited to insects

(d) Vegetarian tree finch, beak suited to leaves

◄ FIGURE 14-5 Darwin's finches, residents of the Galápagos Islands Darwin studied a group of closely related species of finches on the Galápagos Islands. Each species specializes in eating a different type of food and has a beak of characteristic size and shape because past individuals whose beaks were best suited to exploit each local food source produced more offspring than did individuals with less effective beaks.

SCIENCE IN ACTION Charles Darwin—Nature Was His Laboratory

In 1831, when Charles Darwin was 22 years old (Fig. E14-1), he secured a position as "gentleman companion" to Captain Robert Fitzroy of the HMS *Beagle*. The *Beagle* soon embarked on a 5-year surveying expedition along the coastline of South America and then around the world.

Darwin's voyage on the *Beagle* sowed the seeds for his theory of evolution. In addition to his duties as companion to the captain, Darwin served as the expedition's official naturalist, whose task was to observe and collect geological and biological specimens. The *Beagle* sailed to South America and made many stops along its coast. There Darwin observed the plants and animals of the tropics and was stunned by the huge diversity of species compared with the number found in Europe.

Although he had boarded the *Beagle* convinced of the permanence of species, Darwin's experiences soon led him to doubt it. He discovered a snake with rudimentary hind limbs, calling it "the passage by which Nature joins the lizards to the snakes" (Fig. E14-2). Darwin also noticed that penguins used their wings to paddle through the water rather than fly through the air, and he observed a snake that had no rattles but vibrated its tail like a rattlesnake. If a creator had individually created each animal in its present form, to suit its present environment, what could be the purpose behind these makeshift arrangements?

Perhaps the most significant stopover of the voyage was the month spent on the Galápagos Islands off the northwestern coast of South America. There, Darwin found huge tortoises. Different islands were home to distinctively different types of tortoises. Darwin also found several types of mockingbirds and, as with the tortoises, different islands had different mockingbird species. Could the differences in these organisms have arisen after they became isolated from one another on separate islands?

From his experience as a naturalist, Darwin realized that members of a species typically compete with one another for survival. He also recognized that the competition's winners and losers were determined not by chance, but by the characteristics and abilities of the individual competitors. Darwin understood that if these characteristics were inherited by their possessors' offspring, species would evolve by natural selection.

When Darwin finally published *On the Origin of Species* in 1859, his evidence for evolution by natural selection had become truly overwhelming. Although its full implications would not be realized for decades, Darwin's theory has become a unifying concept for virtually all of biology.

▲ FIGURE E14-2 **The vestigial remnants of hind legs in a snake** Some snakes have small "spurs" where their distant ancestors had rear legs. In some species, these vestigial structures even retain claws.

▲ FIGURE E14-1 **A painting of Charles Darwin as a young man**

14.2 HOW DOES NATURAL SELECTION WORK?

Darwin and Wallace proposed that life's huge variety arose by a process of descent with modification, in which individuals in each generation differ slightly from the members of the preceding generation. Over long stretches of time, these small differences accumulate to produce major transformations.

Darwin and Wallace's Theory Rests on Four Postulates

The chain of logic that led Darwin and Wallace to their proposed process of evolution turns out to be surprisingly simple and straightforward. It is based on four postulates about populations:

Postulate 1 Individual members of a population differ from one another in many respects.

Postulate 2 At least some of the differences among members of a population are due to characteristics that may be passed from parent to offspring.

Postulate 3 In each generation, some individuals in a population survive and reproduce successfully but others do not.

Postulate 4 The fate of individuals is not determined entirely by chance or luck. Instead, an individual's likelihood of survival and reproduction depends on its characteristics. Individuals with advantageous traits survive longest and leave the most offspring, a process known as **natural selection.**

Darwin and Wallace understood that if all four postulates were true, populations would inevitably change over time. If members of a population have different traits, and if the individuals that are best suited to their environment leave more offspring, and if those individuals pass their favorable traits to their offspring, then the favorable traits will become more common in subsequent generations. The characteristics of the population will change slightly with each generation. This process is evolution by natural selection.

Are the four postulates true? Darwin thought so, and devoted much of *On the Origin of Species* to describing supporting evidence. Let's briefly examine each postulate, in some cases with the advantage of knowledge that had not yet come to light during the lifetimes of Darwin and Wallace.

Postulate 1: Individuals in a Population Vary

The accuracy of postulate 1 is apparent to anyone who has glanced around a crowded room. People differ in size, eye color, skin color, and many other physical features. Similar variability is present in populations of other organisms, although it may be less obvious to the casual observer (**Fig. 14-6**).

Postulate 2: Traits Are Passed from Parent to Offspring

The principles of genetics had not yet been discovered when Darwin published *On the Origin of Species*. Therefore, although observation of people, pets, and farm animals

▲ FIGURE 14-6 **Variation in a population of snails** Although these snails are all members of the same population, no two are exactly alike.

QUESTION Is sexual reproduction required to generate the variability in structures and behaviors that is necessary for natural selection?

seemed to show that offspring generally resemble their parents, Darwin and Wallace did not have scientific evidence in support of postulate 2. Mendel's later work, however, demonstrated conclusively that particular traits can be passed to offspring. Since Mendel's time, genetics researchers have produced a detailed picture of how inheritance works.

Postulate 3: Some Individuals Fail to Survive and Reproduce

Darwin's formulation of postulate 3 was heavily influenced by Thomas Malthus's *Essay on the Principle of Population* (1798), which described the perils of unchecked growth of human populations. Darwin was keenly aware that organisms can produce far more offspring than are required merely to replace the parents. He calculated, for example, that a single pair of elephants would multiply to a population of 19 million in 750 years if each descendant had six offspring that lived to reproduce.

But we aren't overrun with elephants. The number of elephants, like the number of individuals in most natural populations, tends to remain relatively constant. Therefore, more organisms must be born than survive long enough to reproduce. In each generation, many individuals must die young. Even among those that survive, many must fail to reproduce, produce few offspring, or produce less-vigorous offspring that, in turn, fail to survive and reproduce. As you might expect, whenever biologists have measured reproduction in a population, they have found that some individuals have more offspring than others.

Postulate 4: Survival and Reproduction Are Not Determined by Chance

If unequal reproduction is the norm in populations, what determines which individuals leave the most offspring? A large amount of scientific evidence has shown that reproductive success depends on an individual's characteristics. For example, scientists found that larger male elephant seals in a California population had more offspring than smaller males (because females were more likely to mate with large males). In a Colorado population of snapdragons, plants with white flowers had more offspring than plants with yellow flowers (because pollinators found white flowers more attractive). These results, and hundreds of other similar ones, show that in the competition to survive and reproduce, winners are for the most part determined not by chance but by the traits they possess.

Natural Selection Modifies Populations over Time

Observation and experiment suggest that the four postulates of Darwin and Wallace are sound. Logic suggests that the resulting consequence ought to be change over time in the characteristics of populations. In *On the Origin of Species*, Darwin proposed the following example: "Let us take the case of a wolf, which preys on various animals, securing [them] by . . . fleetness. . . . The swiftest and slimmest wolves would have the best chance of surviving, and so be preserved or selected. . . . Now if any slight innate change of habit or structure benefited an individual wolf, it would have the best chance of surviving and of leaving offspring. Some of its young would probably inherit the same habits or structure, and by the repetition of this process, a new variety might be formed." The same logic applies to the wolf's prey; the fastest or most alert or best camouflaged would be most likely to avoid predation and would pass these traits to its offspring.

Notice that natural selection acts on individuals within a population. The influence of natural selection on the fates of individuals eventually has consequences for the population as a whole. Over generations, the population changes as the percentage of individuals inheriting favorable traits increases. An individual cannot evolve, but a population can.

Although it is easier to understand how natural selection would cause changes within a species, under the right circumstances, the process might produce entirely *new* species. We will discuss the circumstances that might give rise to new species in Chapter 16.

CHECK YOUR LEARNING

Can you explain how natural selection works and how it affects populations? Can you describe the logic, based on four postulates, by which Darwin deduced that populations must evolve by natural selection?

14.3 HOW DO WE KNOW THAT EVOLUTION HAS OCCURRED?

Today, evolution is an accepted scientific theory. A scientific theory is a general explanation of important natural phenomena, developed through extensive, reproducible observations (see Chapter 1). An overwhelming body of evidence supports the conclusion that evolution has occurred. The key lines of evidence come from fossils, comparative anatomy (the study of how body structures differ among species), embryology (the study of developing organisms in the period from fertilization to birth or hatching), biochemistry, and genetics.

Fossils Provide Evidence of Evolutionary Change over Time

If it is true that many fossils are the remains of species ancestral to modern species, we might expect to find fossils in a progressive series that starts with an ancient organism, progresses through several intermediate stages, and culminates in a modern species. Such series have indeed been found. For example, fossils of the ancestors of modern whales illustrate stages in the evolution of an aquatic species from land-dwelling ancestors (Fig. 14-7). Series of fossil giraffes, elephants, horses, and mollusks also show the evolution of body structures over time. These fossil series suggest that new species evolved from, and replaced, previous species.

Comparative Anatomy Gives Evidence of Descent with Modification

Fossils provide snapshots of the past that allow biologists to trace evolutionary changes, but careful examination of today's organisms can also uncover evidence of evolution. Comparing the bodies of organisms of different species can reveal similarities that can be explained only by shared ancestry and differences that could result only from evolutionary change during descent from a common ancestor. In this way, the study of comparative anatomy has supplied strong evidence that different species are linked by a common evolutionary heritage.

Homologous Structures Provide Evidence of Common Ancestry

A body structure may be modified by evolution to serve different functions in different species. The forelimbs of birds and mammals, for example, are variously used for flying, swimming, running over several types of terrain, and grasping objects, such as branches and tools. Despite this enormous diversity of function, the internal anatomy of all bird and mammal forelimbs is remarkably similar (Fig. 14-8). It seems inconceivable that the same bone arrangements would be used to serve such diverse functions if each animal had been created separately. Such similarity is exactly what we would expect, however, if bird and mammal forelimbs were derived from a common ancestor. Through natural selection, the ancestral forelimb has undergone different modifications

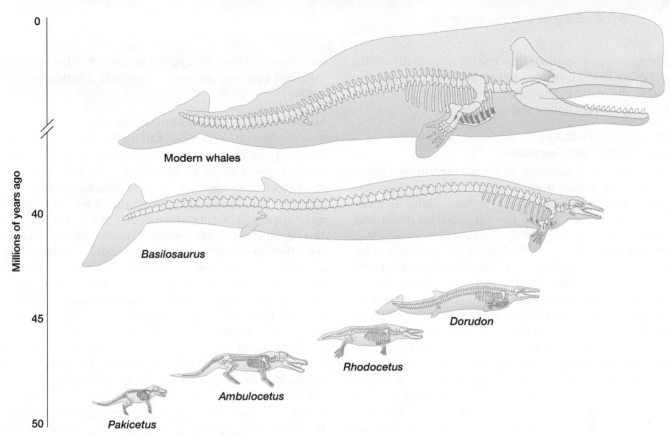

▲ FIGURE 14-7 **The evolution of the whale** During the past 50 million years, whales have evolved from four-legged land dwellers, to semi-aquatic paddlers, to fully aquatic swimmers with shrunken hind legs, to today's sleek ocean dwellers.

QUESTION The fossil history of some kinds of modern organisms, such as sharks and crocodiles, shows that their structure and appearance have changed very little over hundreds of millions of years. Is this lack of change evidence that such organisms have not evolved during that time?

▲ FIGURE 14-8 **Homologous structures** Despite wide differences in function, the forelimbs of all of these animals contain the same set of bones, inherited from a common ancestor. The different colors of the bones highlight the correspondences among the various species.

in different kinds of animals. The resulting internally similar structures are called **homologous structures,** meaning that they have the same evolutionary origin despite any differences in current function or appearance.

Functionless Structures Are Inherited from Ancestors

Evolution by natural selection also helps explain the curious circumstance of **vestigial structures** that have no apparent essential function. Examples include such things as molar teeth in vampire bats (which live on a diet of blood and, therefore, don't chew their food) and pelvic bones in whales and certain snakes (**Fig. 14-9**). Both of these vestigial structures are clearly homologous to structures that are found in—and used by—other vertebrates (animals with a backbone). The continued existence in animals of structures for which they have no use is best explained as a sort of "evolutionary baggage." For example, the ancestral mammals from which whales evolved had four legs and a well-developed set of pelvic bones (see Fig. 14-7). Whales do not have hind legs, yet they have small pelvic and leg bones embedded in their sides. During whale evolution, losing the hind legs provided an advantage, better streamlining the body for movement through water. The result is the modern whale with small,

useless pelvic bones that persist because they have shrunk to the point that they no longer constitute a survival-reducing burden.

Some Anatomical Similarities Result from Evolution in Similar Environments

The study of comparative anatomy has demonstrated the shared ancestry of life by identifying a host of homologous structures that different species have inherited from common ancestors, but comparative anatomists have also identified many anatomical similarities that do not stem from common ancestry. Instead, these similarities stem from **convergent evolution,** in which natural selection causes non-homologous structures that serve similar functions to resemble one another. For example, both birds and insects have wings, but this similarity did not arise from evolutionary modification of a structure that both birds and insects inherited from a common ancestor. Instead, the similarity arose from parallel modification of two different, non-homologous structures. Because natural selection favored flight in both birds and insects, the two groups evolved wings of roughly similar appearance, but the similarity is superficial. Such outwardly similar but non-homologous structures are called **analogous structures** (**Fig. 14-10**). Analogous structures are typically

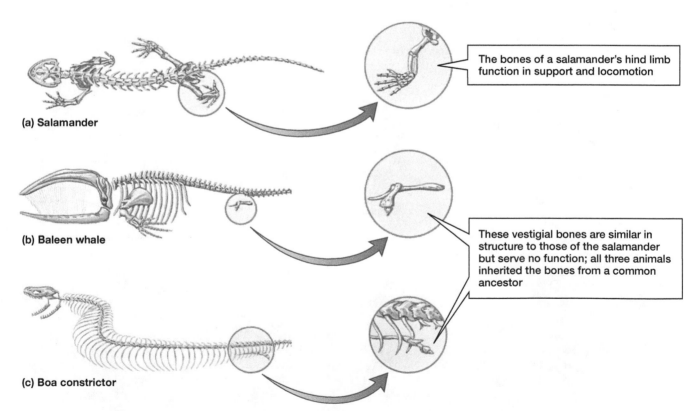

(a) Salamander

The bones of a salamander's hind limb function in support and locomotion

(b) Baleen whale

These vestigial bones are similar in structure to those of the salamander but serve no function; all three animals inherited the bones from a common ancestor

(c) Boa constrictor

▲ **FIGURE 14-9 Vestigial structures** Many organisms have vestigial structures that serve no apparent function. The **(a)** salamander, **(b)** baleen whale, and **(c)** boa constrictor all inherited hind limb bones from a common ancestor. These bones remain functional in the salamander but are vestigial in the whale and snake.

QUESTION Compile a list of human vestigial structures. For each structure, name the corresponding homologous structure in a nonhuman species.

?HAVE **YOU** EVER WONDERED ...

Why Backaches Are So Common?

Between 70% and 85% of people will experience lower back pain at some point in life and, for many people, the condition is chronic. This state of affairs is an unfortunately painful consequence of the evolutionary process. We walk upright on two legs, but our distant ancestors walked on all fours. Thus, natural selection formed our vertically oriented spine by remodeling one whose normal orientation was parallel to the ground. Our spinal anatomy evolved some modifications in response to its new posture but, as is often the case with evolution, the changes involved some trade-offs. The arrangements of bone and muscle that permit our smooth, bipedal gait also generate vertical compression of the spine, and the resulting pressure can, and frequently does, cause painful damage to muscle and nerve tissues.

(a) Damselfly

(b) Swallow

▲ FIGURE 14-10 **Analogous structures** Convergent evolution can produce outwardly similar structures that differ anatomically, such as the wings of **(a)** insects and **(b)** birds.

QUESTION Are a peacock's tail and a dog's tail homologous structures or analogous structures?

very different in internal anatomy, because the parts are not derived from common ancestral structures.

Embryological Similarity Suggests Common Ancestry

In the early 1800s, German embryologist Karl von Baer noted that all vertebrate embryos look quite similar to one another early in their development (**Fig. 14-11**). In their early embryonic stages, fish, turtles, chickens, mice, and humans all develop tails and gill slits (also called gill grooves). But among this group of animals, only fish retain gills as adults, and only fish, turtles, and mice retain substantial tails.

Why do vertebrates that are so different have similar developmental stages? The only plausible explanation is that ancestral vertebrates possessed genes that directed the development of gills and tails. All of their descendants still have those genes. In fish, these genes are active throughout development, resulting in adults with fully developed tails and gills. In humans and chickens, these genes are active only during early developmental stages, and the structures are lost or inconspicuous in adults.

Modern Biochemical and Genetic Analyses Reveal Relatedness Among Diverse Organisms

Biologists have been aware of anatomical and embryological similarities among organisms for centuries, but it took the emergence of modern technology to reveal similarities at the molecular level. Biochemical similarities among organisms provide perhaps the most striking evidence of their evolutionary relatedness. Just as relatedness is revealed by homologous anatomical structures, it is also revealed by homologous molecules.

Today's scientists have access to a powerful tool for revealing molecular homologies: DNA sequencing. It is now possible to quickly determine the sequence of nucleotides in a DNA molecule and to compare the DNA of different organisms. For example, consider the gene that encodes the protein cytochrome c (see Chapters 11 and 12 for information on DNA and how it encodes proteins). Cytochrome c is present in all plants and animals (and many single-celled organisms) and performs the same function in all of them. The sequence of nucleotides in the gene for cytochrome c is similar in these diverse species (**Fig. 14-12**). The widespread presence of the same complex protein, encoded by the same gene and performing the same function, is evidence that the common ancestor of plants and animals had cytochrome c in its cells. At the same time, though, the sequence of the cytochrome c gene differs slightly in different species,

(a) Lemur   **(b) Pig**   **(c) Human**

▲ **FIGURE 14-11 Embryological stages reveal evolutionary relationships** Early embryonic stages of a **(a)** lemur, **(b)** pig, and **(c)** human, showing strikingly similar anatomical features.

showing that variations arose during the independent evolution of Earth's multitude of plant and animal species.

Some biochemical similarities are so fundamental that they extend to all living cells. For example:

- All cells have DNA as the carrier of genetic information.
- All cells use RNA, ribosomes, and approximately the same genetic code to translate that genetic information into proteins.
- All cells use roughly the same set of 20 amino acids to build proteins.
- All cells use ATP as a cellular energy carrier.

The most plausible explanation for such widespread sharing of complex and specific biochemical traits is that the traits are homologies. That is, they arose only once, in the common ancestor of all living things, from which all of today's organisms inherited them.

CHECK YOUR LEARNING

Can you describe the evidence that evolution has occurred? Can you explain the difference between similarity due to homology and similarity due to convergent evolution?

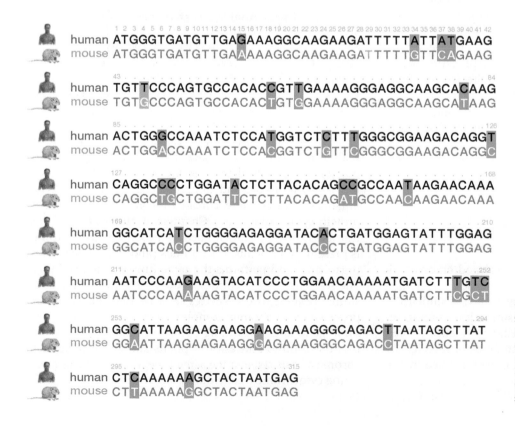

◄ **FIGURE 14-12 Molecular similarity shows evolutionary relationships** The DNA sequences of the genes that code for cytochrome c in a human and a mouse. Of the 315 nucleotides in the gene, only 30 (shaded blue) differ between the two species.

CASE STUDY continued

What Good Are Wisdom Teeth and Ostrich Wings?

Just as anatomical homology can lead to vestigial structures such as human wisdom teeth and the wings of flightless birds, genetic homology can lead to vestigial DNA sequences. For example, most mammal species produce an enzyme, L-gulonolactone oxidase, that catalyzes the last step in the production of vitamin C. The species that produce the enzyme are able to do so because they all inherited the gene that encodes it from a common ancestor. Humans, however, do not produce L-gulonolactone oxidase, so we can't produce vitamin C ourselves and must consume it in our diets. But even though we don't produce the enzyme, our cells do contain a stretch of DNA with a sequence very similar to that of the enzyme-producing gene present in rats and most other mammals. The human version, though, does not encode the enzyme (or any protein). We inherited this stretch of DNA from an ancestor that we share with other mammal species, but in us, the sequence has undergone a change that rendered it nonfunctional. (The change probably did not confer a strong disadvantage, because our ancestors got sufficient vitamin C in their diets.) The nonfunctional sequence remains as a vestigial trait, evidence of our shared ancestry.

14.4 WHAT IS THE EVIDENCE THAT POPULATIONS EVOLVE BY NATURAL SELECTION?

We have seen that evidence of evolution comes from many sources. But what is the evidence that evolution occurs by the process of natural selection?

Controlled Breeding Modifies Organisms

One line of evidence supporting evolution by natural selection is **artificial selection,** the breeding of domestic plants and animals to produce specific desirable features. The various dog breeds provide a striking example of artificial selection (**Fig. 14-13**). Dogs descended from wolves, and even today, the two will readily crossbreed. With few exceptions, however, modern dogs do not closely resemble wolves. Some breeds are so different from one another that they would be considered separate species if they were found in the wild. Humans produced these radically different dogs in a few thousand years by doing nothing more than repeatedly selecting individuals with desirable traits for breeding. Therefore, it is quite plausible that natural selection could, by an analogous process acting over hundreds of millions of years, produce the spectrum of living organisms. Darwin was so impressed by the connection between artificial selection and natural selection that he devoted a chapter of *On the Origin of Species* to the topic.

Evolution by Natural Selection Occurs Today

Additional evidence of natural selection comes from scientific observation and experimentation. The logic of natural selection gives us no reason to believe that evolutionary change is limited to the past. After all, inherited variation and

(a) Gray wolf

(b) Diverse dogs

▲ FIGURE 14-13 **Dog diversity illustrates artificial selection** A comparison of **(a)** the ancestral dog (the gray wolf, *Canis lupus*) and **(b)** various breeds of dog. Artificial selection by humans has caused great divergence in the size and shape of dogs in only a few thousand years.

competition for access to resources are certainly not limited to the past. If Darwin and Wallace were correct that those conditions lead inevitably to evolution by natural selection, then researchers ought to be able to detect evolutionary change as it occurs. And they have. Next, we will consider some examples that give us a glimpse of natural selection at work.

Brighter Coloration Can Evolve When Fewer Predators Are Present

On the island of Trinidad, guppies live in streams that are also inhabited by several species of larger, predatory fish that frequently dine on guppies (**Fig. 14-14**). In upstream portions of these streams, however, the water is too shallow for the predators, and guppies are free of danger from predators.

▲ FIGURE 14-14 **Guppies evolve to become more colorful in predator-free environments** Male guppies (top) are more brightly colored than females (bottom). Some male guppies are more colorful than others. In environments without predators, brighter males are selected; in environments with predators, duller males are selected.

When scientists compared male guppies in an upstream area with ones in a downstream area, they found that the upstream guppies were much more brightly colored than the downstream guppies. The scientists knew that the source of the upstream population was guppies that had found their way up into the shallower waters many generations earlier.

The explanation for the difference in coloration between the two populations stems from the sexual preferences of female guppies. The females prefer to mate with the most brightly colored males, so the brightest males have a large advantage when it comes to reproduction. In predator-free areas, male guppies with the bright colors that females prefer have more offspring than duller males. Bright color, however, makes guppies more conspicuous to predators and, therefore, more likely to be eaten. Thus, where predators are common, they act as agents of natural selection by eliminating the bright-colored males before they can reproduce. In these areas, the duller males have the advantage and produce more offspring. The color difference between the upstream and downstream guppy populations is a direct result of natural selection.

Natural Selection Can Lead to Herbicide and Pesticide Resistance

Natural selection is also evident in weed species that have evolved resistance to the herbicides with which we try to control them. Successful agriculture depends on farmers' ability to kill weeds that compete with crop plants, but many members of weed species can no longer be killed by a formerly lethal dose of glyphosate, the active ingredient in Roundup, the world's most widely used herbicide. How did these glyphosate-resistant "superweeds" arise? They arose because the herbicide has acted as an agent of natural selection. Consider, for example, giant ragweed, one of the highly destructive weed species that are now resistant to glyphosate in some

places. When a field is sprayed with Roundup, almost all of the giant ragweed plants there are killed, because glyphosate inactivates an enzyme that is essential to plants' survival. A few ragweed plants, however, survive, and researchers have discovered that some of these survivors carry a mutation that causes them to produce a tremendous amount of the enzyme that glyphosate attacks, more enzyme than the usual dose of glyphosate can destroy. In the face of repeated applications of Roundup, the formerly rare protective mutation has become common in many giant pigweed populations. (For additional examples of how humans influence evolution, see "Earth Watch: People Promote High-Speed Evolution.")

The evolution of glyphosate-resistant superweeds was a direct result of changes in agricultural practice. In the 1990s, the biotechnology company Monsanto began selling seeds that had been genetically engineered to produce crops that are not harmed by glyphosate. These "Roundup Ready" crops, which now account for the vast majority of soybean, corn, and cotton plantings in the United States and other countries, allow farmers to freely apply glyphosate to their fields without fear of harming crop plants. As a result, use of glyphosate has skyrocketed. Today, large-scale agriculture is extremely dependent on this single herbicide, even as its effectiveness declines steadily due to the evolution of resistant weeds.

Just as weeds have evolved to resist herbicides, many of the insects that attack crops have also evolved resistance to the pesticides that farmers use to control them. Such resistance has been documented in more than 500 species of crop-damaging insects, and virtually every pesticide has fostered the evolution of resistance in at least one insect species. We pay a heavy price for this evolutionary phenomenon. The additional pesticides that farmers apply in their attempts to control resistant insects cost almost $2 billion each year in the United States alone and add millions of tons of poisons to Earth's soil and water.

Experiments Can Demonstrate Natural Selection

In addition to observing natural selection in the wild, scientists have also devised numerous experiments that confirm the action of natural selection. For example, one group of evolutionary biologists released small groups of *Anolis sagrei* lizards onto 14 small Bahamian islands that were previously uninhabited by lizards (**Fig. 14-15**). The original lizards came from a population on Staniel Cay, an island with tall vegetation, including plenty of trees. In contrast, the islands to which the small colonial groups were introduced had few or no trees and were covered mainly with small shrubs and other low-growing plants.

The biologists returned to those islands 14 years after releasing the colonists and found that the original small groups of lizards had given rise to thriving populations of hundreds of individuals. On all 14 of the experimental islands, lizards had legs that were shorter and thinner than those of lizards from the original source population on Staniel Cay. In just over a decade, it appeared, the lizard populations had changed in response to new environments.

Why had the new lizard populations evolved shorter, thinner legs? Shorter, thinner legs allow for more agility and

▲ FIGURE 14-15 **Anole leg size evolves in response to a changed environment**

Selection Acts on Random Variation to Favor Traits That Work Best in Particular Environments

Two important points underlie the evolutionary changes just described:

- **The variations on which natural selection works are produced by chance mutations.** Bright coloration in Trinidadian guppies, extra enzyme in giant ragweed plants, and shorter legs in Bahamian lizards were not *produced* by the female mating preferences, Roundup herbicide, or thinner branches. The mutations that produced each of these beneficial traits arose spontaneously.
- **Natural selection favors organisms that are best adapted to a particular environment.** Natural selection is not a process for producing ever-greater degrees of perfection. Natural selection does not select for the "best" in any absolute sense, but only for what is best in the context of a particular environment, which varies from place to place and which may change over time. A trait that is advantageous under one set of conditions may become disadvantageous if conditions change. For example, in the presence of glyphosate herbicide, producing copious amounts of an essential enzyme yields an advantage to a giant ragweed plant, but under natural conditions producing unnecessary extra enzyme would be a huge waste of precious energy and nutrients.

CHECK YOUR LEARNING

Can you describe some observations and experiments that demonstrate that populations evolve by natural selection?

maneuverability on narrow surfaces, whereas longer, thicker legs permit greater running speed. On Staniel Cay, with its thick-branched trees, speed is more important than maneuverability for avoiding predators, so natural selection favored fast-running lizards whose legs were as long and thick as possible. But when the lizards were moved to an environment with only thin-branched bushes, individuals with long, thick legs were at a disadvantage. In the new environment, more agile individuals with shorter, thinner legs were better able to escape predators and survive to produce a greater number of offspring. Thus, members of subsequent generations had shorter, thinner legs on average.

CASE STUDY revisited

What Good Are Wisdom Teeth and Ostrich Wings?

Wisdom teeth are but one of many human anatomical structures that appear to no longer serve an important function (Fig. 14-16). Darwin himself noted many of these "useless, or nearly useless" traits in the very first chapter of *On the Origin of Species* and declared them to be prime evidence that humans had evolved from earlier species.

Body hair is another vestigial human trait. It seems to be an evolutionary relic of the fur that kept our distant ancestors warm (and that still warms our closest evolutionary relatives, the great apes). Not only do we retain useless body hair, we also still have arrector pili, the muscle fibers that allow other mammals to puff up their fur for better insulation. In humans, these vestigial structures just give us goose bumps.

Though humans don't have and don't need a tail, we nonetheless have a tailbone. The tailbone consists of a few tiny vertebrae fused into a small structure at the base of the backbone, where a tail would be if we had one. People born without a tailbone or who have theirs surgically removed suffer no ill effects.

Consider This

BioEthics Advocates of the view that all organisms were created simultaneously by God argue that there are no vestigial organs because if any function at all can be attributed to a structure, it cannot be considered functionless, even if its removal has no effect. Thus, according to this view, ostrich wings are not evidence of evolution, because they *can* be used to brush off biting insects. Is this a valid argument?

▲ FIGURE 14-16 **Wisdom teeth** Squeezed into a jaw that is too short to contain them, wisdom teeth often become impacted—unable to erupt through the surface of the gum. The leftmost upper and lower teeth in this X-ray image are impacted wisdom teeth.

Earth|Watch

People Promote High-Speed Evolution

You probably don't think of yourself as a major engine of evolution. Nonetheless, as you go about the routines of your daily life, you are contributing to what is perhaps today's most significant cause of rapid evolutionary change. Human activity has changed Earth's environments tremendously, and the biological logic of natural selection, spelled out so clearly by Darwin, tells us that environmental change leads inevitably to evolutionary change. Thus, by changing the environment, humans have become a major agent of natural selection.

Unfortunately, many of the evolutionary changes we have caused have turned out to be bad news for us. Our liberal use of pesticides has selected for resistant pests that frustrate efforts to protect our food supply. By overmedicating ourselves with antibiotics and other drugs, we have selected for resistant "supergerms" and diseases that are ever more difficult to treat (see Chapter 15). Heavy fishing in the world's oceans has favored smaller fish that can slip through nets more easily, thereby selecting for slow-growing fish that remain small even as mature adults. As a result, fish of many commercially important species are now so small that our ability to extract food from the sea is compromised.

Our use of pesticides, antibiotics, and fishing technology has caused evolutionary changes that threaten our health and welfare, but the scope of these changes may be dwarfed by those that will arise from human-caused modification of Earth's climate. Human activities, especially activities that use energy derived from fossil fuels, modify the climate by contributing to global warming. In coming years, species' evolution will be influenced by environmental changes associated with a warming climate, such as reduced ice and snow, longer growing seasons, and shifts in the life cycles of other species that provide food or shelter.

There is growing evidence that global warming is already causing evolutionary change. Warming-related evolution has been found in a number of plant and animal populations. For example, red squirrels in a Canadian colony closely monitored by scientists now produce litters 18 days earlier, on average, than they did 10 years ago. The change is tied to a warming climate, because spring now arrives earlier and spruce trees produce earlier crops of seeds, the squirrels' only food. Squirrels that breed earlier gain a competitive edge by better exploiting the warmer weather and more abundant food. And, because the time at which a squirrel gives birth is influenced by the animal's genetic makeup, early-breeding squirrels pass to their offspring the genes that confer this advantage. As a result, the genetic makeup of the squirrel population is changing, and early-breeding squirrels are becoming more common than later-breeding ones.

In Finland, tawny owls have changed color in response to a warmer climate (Fig. E14-3). Owls of this species come in two varieties, gray or brown. In the past, most owls were gray, and

▲ FIGURE E14-3 **Tawny owl populations have evolved in response to global climate change** The proportion of brown owls is increasing, because brown owls survive better than gray ones over winters with less snow.

the brown variety was rare. Today, however, about 40% of Finnish owls are brown, and researchers have shown that the increase in brown owls was probably caused by climate change. In particular, the researchers found that in snowy winters, gray owls survive much better than brown owls, perhaps because they are better camouflaged against the snow and therefore suffer less predation by eagles. In winters with less snow, brown owls are better camouflaged and more likely to survive. As temperatures have risen in recent decades, snowy winters have become increasingly rare and the resulting reduced snow cover has favored the survival of brown owls. Thus, a brown owl is more likely than a gray one to survive the winter and, because feather color is inherited, produce brown offspring. The proportion of brown owls in the population has grown in response to natural selection associated with warming temperatures.

The available evidence suggests that global climate change will have an enormous evolutionary impact, potentially affecting the evolution of almost every species. How will these evolutionary changes affect us and the ecosystems on which we depend? This question is not readily answerable, because the path of evolution is not predictable. We can hope, however, that careful monitoring of evolving species and increased understanding of evolutionary processes will help us take appropriate steps to safeguard our health and well-being as Earth warms.

CHAPTER REVIEW

Summary of Key Concepts

14.1 How Did Evolutionary Thought Develop?

Historically, the most common explanation for the origin of species was the divine creation of each species in its present form, and species were believed to remain unchanged after their creation. This view was challenged by evidence from fossils, geology, and biological exploration, most notably in the tropics. Since the middle of the nineteenth century, scientists have realized that species originate and evolve by the operation of natural processes that change the genetic makeup of populations.

14.2 How Does Natural Selection Work?

Charles Darwin and Alfred Russel Wallace independently proposed the theory of evolution by natural selection. Their theory expresses the logical consequences of four postulates about populations. If (1) populations are variable, (2) the variable traits can be inherited, (3) there is unequal reproduction, and (4) differences in reproductive success depend on the traits of individuals, then the characteristics of successful individuals will be "naturally selected" and become more common over time.

14.3 How Do We Know That Evolution Has Occurred?

Many lines of evidence indicate that evolution has occurred, including the following:

- Fossils of ancient species tend to be simpler in form than modern species. Sequences of fossils have been discovered that show a graded series of changes in form. Both of these observations would be expected if modern species evolved from older species.
- Species thought to be related through evolution from a common ancestor possess many similar anatomical structures. For example, amphibians, reptiles, birds, and mammals have very similar forearm bones.
- Stages in early embryological development are quite similar among very different types of vertebrates.
- Similarities in biochemical traits such as the use of DNA as the carrier of genetic information support the notion of descent of related species through evolution from common ancestors.

14.4 What Is the Evidence That Populations Evolve by Natural Selection?

Similarly, many lines of evidence indicate that natural selection is the chief mechanism driving changes in the characteristics of species over time, including the following:

- Inheritable traits have been changed rapidly in populations of domestic animals and plants by selectively breeding organisms with desired features (artificial selection). The immense variations in species produced in a few thousand years by artificial selection makes it almost inevitable that

much larger changes would be wrought by hundreds of millions of years of natural selection.
- Evolution can be observed today. Both natural and human activities can drastically change the environment over short periods of time. Inherited characteristics of species have been observed to change significantly in response to such environmental changes.

Key Terms

analogous structure 268	homologous structure 268
artificial selection 271	natural selection 265
convergent evolution 268	population 259
evolution 259	vestigial structure 268
fossil 260	

Learning Outcomes

In this chapter, you have learned to . . .

LO1 Define *evolution*.

LO2 Describe pre-Darwin hypotheses and ideas that set the stage for the later emergence of the theory of evolution by natural selection.

LO3 Explain the mechanism of natural selection and the logic by which Darwin deduced it, and describe how natural selection affects populations.

LO4 Describe the main types of evidence that evolution has occurred, and provide an example of each type.

LO5 Compare and contrast similarities due to homology and similarities attributable to convergent evolution.

LO6 Describe the main lines of evidence that populations evolve by natural selection and provide examples of such evidence.

Thinking Through the Concepts

Fill-in-the-Blank

1. The flipper of a seal is homologous with the _____ of a bird, and both of these are homologous with the _____ of a human. The wing of a bird and the wing of a butterfly are described as _____ structures that arose as a result of _____ evolution. Remnants of structures in animals that have no use for them, such as the small hind leg bones of whales, are described as _____ structures. **LO4 LO5**

2. The finding that all organisms share the same genetic code provides evidence that all descended from a(n) _____. Further evidence is provided by the fact that all cells use roughly the same set of _____ to build proteins, and all cells use the molecule _____ as an energy carrier. **LO4**

3. Georges Cuvier espoused a concept called _____ to explain layers of rock with embedded fossils. Charles

Lyell, building on the work of James Hutton, proposed an alternative explanation called _____, which states that layers of rock and many other geological features can be explained by gradual processes that occurred in the past just as they do in the present. This concept provided important support for evolution because it required that Earth be extremely _____. LO2

4. The process by which inherited characteristics of populations change over time is called _____. Variability among individuals is the result of chance changes called _____ that occur in the hereditary molecule _____. LO1 LO2

5. The process by which individuals with traits that provide an advantage in their natural habitats are more successful at reproducing is called _____. People who breed animals or plants can produce large changes in their characteristics in a relatively short time, a process called _____. LO3 LO6

6. Darwin's postulate 2 states that _____. The work of _____ provided the first experimental evidence for this postulate. LO3

Review Questions

1. Selection acts on individuals, but only populations evolve. Explain why this statement is true. LO3

2. Distinguish between catastrophism and uniformitarianism. How did these hypotheses contribute to the development of evolutionary theory? LO2

3. Describe Lamarck's theory of inheritance of acquired characteristics. Why is it invalid? LO2

4. What is natural selection? Describe how natural selection might have caused unequal reproduction among the ancestors of a fast-swimming predatory fish, such as the barracuda. LO3

5. Describe how evolution occurs. In your description, include discussion of the reproductive potential of species, the stability of natural population sizes, variation among individuals of a species, inheritance, and natural selection. LO3

6. What is convergent evolution? Give an example. LO5

7. How do biochemistry and molecular genetics contribute to the evidence that evolution has occurred? LO4

Applying the Concepts

1. In discussions of untapped human potential, it is commonly said that the average person uses only 10% of his or her brain. Is this conclusion likely to be correct? Explain your answer in terms of natural selection.

2. Both the theory of evolution by natural selection and the theory of special creation (which states that all species were simultaneously created by God) have had an impact on evolutionary thought. Discuss why one is considered to be a scientific theory and the other is not.

3. Does evolution through natural selection produce "better" organisms in an absolute sense? Are we climbing the "Ladder of Nature"? Defend your answer.

4. In what sense are humans currently acting as agents of selection on other species? Name some traits that are *favored* by the environmental changes humans cause.

5. Darwin and Wallace's discovery of natural selection is one of the great revolutions in scientific thought. Some scientific revolutions spill over and affect the development of philosophy and religion. Is this true of evolution? Does (or should) the idea of evolution by natural selection affect the way humans view their place in the world?

6. In an alternate universe in which the climate of a planet changes much more rapidly than has been the case on Earth, what differences would you expect to find in the planet's fossil record?

Answers to Figure Caption questions and Fill-in-the-Blank questions can be found in the Answers section at the back of the book.

(MB) *Go to MasteringBiology for practice quizzes, activities, eText, videos, current events, and more.*

Biological Vocabulary: Common Roots, Prefixes, and Suffixes

Biology has an extensive vocabulary often based on Greek or Latin rather than English words. Rather than memorizing every word as if it were part of a new, foreign language, you can figure out the meaning of many new terms if you learn a much smaller number of word roots, prefixes, and suffixes. We have provided common meanings in biology rather than literal translations from Greek or Latin. For each item in the list, the following information is given: meaning; part of word (prefix, suffix, or root); example from biology.

a–, an–: without, lack of (prefix); *abiotic*, without life

acro–: top, highest (prefix); *acrosome*, vesicle of enzymes at the tip of a sperm

ad–: to (prefix); *adhesion*, property of sticking to something else

allo–: other (prefix); *allopatric* (literally, "different fatherland"), restricted to different regions

amphi–: both, double, two (prefix); *amphibian*, a class of vertebrates that usually has two life stages (aquatic and terrestrial; e.g., a tadpole and an adult frog)

andro: man, male (root); *androgen*, a male hormone such as testosterone

ant–, anti–: against (prefix); *antibiotic* (literally "against life"), a substance that kills bacteria

antero–: front (prefix or root); *anterior*, toward the front of

aqu–, aqua–: water (prefix or root); *aquifer*, an underground water source, usually rock saturated with water

apic–: top, highest (prefix); *apical meristem*, the cluster of dividing cells at the tip of a plant shoot or root

arthr–: joint (prefix); *arthropod*, animals such as spiders, crabs, and insects, with exoskeletons that include jointed legs

–ase: enzyme (suffix); *protease*, an enzyme that digests protein

auto–: self (prefix); *autotrophic*, self-feeder (e.g., photosynthetic)

bi–: two (prefix); *bipedal*, having two legs

bio–: life (prefix or root); *biology*, the study of life

blast: bud, precursor (root); *blastula*, embryonic stage of development, a hollow ball of cells

bronch: windpipe (root); *bronchus*, a branch of the trachea (windpipe) leading to a lung

carcin, –o: cancer (root); *carcinogenesis*, the process of producing a cancer

cardi, –a–, –o–: heart (root); *cardiac*, referring to the heart

carn–, –i–, –o–: flesh (prefix or root); *carnivore*, an animal that eats other animals

centi–: one hundredth (prefix); *centimeter*, a unit of length, 1 one-hundredth of a meter

cephal–, –i–, –o–: head (prefix or root); *cephalization*, the tendency for the nervous system to be located principally in the head

chloro–: green (prefix or root); *chlorophyll*, the green, light-absorbing pigment in plants

chondr–: cartilage (prefix); *Chondrichthyes*, class of vertebrates including sharks and rays, with a skeleton made of cartilage

chrom–: color (prefix or root); *chromosome*, a threadlike strand of DNA and protein in the nucleus of a cell (*Chromosome* literally means "colored body," because chromosomes absorb some of the colored dyes commonly used in microscopy.)

–cide: killer (suffix); *pesticide*, a chemical that kills "pests" (usually insects)

–clast: break down, broken (root or suffix); *osteoclast*, a cell that breaks down bone

co–: with or together with (prefix); *cohesion*, property of sticking together

coel–: hollow (prefix or root); *coelom*, the body cavity that separates the internal organs from the body wall

contra–: against (prefix); *contraception*, acting to prevent conception (pregnancy)

cortex: bark, outer layer (root); *cortex*, outer layer of kidney

crani–: skull (prefix or root); *cranium*, the skull

cuti: skin (root); *cuticle*, the outermost covering of a leaf

–cyte, cyto–: cell (root or prefix); *cytokinin*, a plant hormone that promotes cell division

de–: from, out of, remove (prefix); *decomposer*, an organism that breaks down organic matter

dendr: treelike, branching (root); *dendrite*, highly branched input structures of nerve cells

derm: skin, layer (root); *ectoderm*, the outer embryonic germ layer of cells

deutero–: second (prefix); *deuterostome* (literally, "second opening"), an animal in which the coelom is derived from the gut

di–: two (prefix); *dicot*, an angiosperm with two cotyledons in the seed

diplo–: both, double, two (prefix or root); *diploid*, having paired homologous chromosomes

dys–: difficult, painful (prefix); *dysfunction*, an inability to function properly

eco–: house, household (prefix); *ecology*, the study of the relationships between organisms and their environment

ecto–: outside (prefix); *ectoderm*, the outermost tissue layer of animal embryos

–elle: little, small (suffix); *organelle* (literally, "little organ"), a subcellular structure that performs a specific function

end–, endo–, ento–: inside, inner (prefix); *endocrine*, pertaining to a gland that secretes hormones inside the body

epi–: outside, outer (prefix); *epidermis*, outermost layer of skin

equi–: equal (prefix); *equidistant*, the same distance

erythro–: red (prefix); *erythrocyte*, red blood cell

eu–: true, good (prefix); *eukaryotic*, pertaining to a cell with a true nucleus

ex–, exo–: out of (prefix); *exocrine*, pertaining to a gland that secretes a substance (e.g., sweat) outside of the body

extra–: outside of (prefix); *extracellular*, outside of a cell

–fer: to bear, to carry (suffix); *conifer*, a tree that bears cones

gastr–: stomach (prefix or root); *gastric*, pertaining to the stomach

–gen–: to produce (prefix, root, or suffix); *antigen*, a substance that causes the body to produce antibodies

glyc–, glyco–: sweet (prefix); *glycogen*, a starch-like molecule composed of many glucose molecules bonded together

gyn, –o: female (prefix or root); *gynecology*, the study of the female reproductive tract

haplo–: single (prefix); *haploid*, having a single copy of each type of chromosome

hem–, hemato–: blood (prefix or root); *hemoglobin*, the molecule in red blood cells that carries oxygen

hemi–: half (prefix); *hemisphere*, one of the halves of the cerebrum

herb–, herbi–: grass (prefix or root); *herbivore*, an animal that eats plants

hetero–: other (prefix); *heterotrophic*, an organism that feeds on other organisms

hom–, homo–, homeo–: same (prefix); *homeostasis*, to maintain constant internal conditions in the face of changing external conditions

hydro–: water (usually prefix); *hydrophilic*, being attracted to water

hyper–: above, greater than (prefix); *hyperosmotic*, having a greater osmotic strength (usually higher solute concentration)

hypo–: below, less than (prefix); *hypodermic*, below the skin

inter–: between (prefix); *interneuron*, a neuron that receives input from one (or more) neuron(s) and sends output to another neuron (or many neurons)

intra–: within (prefix); *intracellular*, pertaining to an event or substance that occurs within a cell

iso–: equal (prefix); *isotonic*, pertaining to a solution that has the same osmotic strength as another solution

–itis: inflammation (suffix); *hepatitis*, an inflammation (or infection) of the liver

kin–, kinet–: moving (prefix or root); *cytokinesis*, the movements of a cell that divide the cell in half during cell division

lac–, lact–: milk (prefix or root); *lactose*, the principal sugar in mammalian milk

leuc–, leuco–, leuk–, leuko–: white (prefix); *leukocyte*, a white blood cell

lip–: fat (prefix or root); *lipid*, the chemical category to which fats, oils, and steroids belong

–logy: study of (suffix); *biology*, the study of life

lyso–, –lysis: loosening, split apart (prefix, root, or suffix); *lysis*, to break open a cell

macro–: large (prefix); *macrophage*, a large white blood cell that destroys invading foreign cells

medulla: marrow, middle substance (root); *medulla*, inner layer of kidney

mega–: large (prefix); *megaspore*, a large, haploid (female) spore formed by meiotic cell division in plants

–mere: segment, body section (suffix); *sarcomere*, the functional unit of a vertebrate skeletal muscle cell

meso–: middle (prefix); *mesophyll*, middle layers of cells in a leaf

meta–: change, after (prefix); *metamorphosis*, to change body form (e.g., developing from a larva to an adult)

micro–: small (prefix); *microscope*, a device that allows one to see small objects

milli–: one-thousandth (prefix); *millimeter*, a unit of measurement of length; 1 one-thousandth of a meter

mito–: thread (prefix); *mitosis*, cell division (in which chromosomes appear as threadlike bodies)

mono–: single (prefix); *monocot*, a type of angiosperm with one cotyledon in the seed

morph–: shape, form (prefix or root); *polymorphic*, having multiple forms

multi–: many (prefix); *multicellular*, pertaining to a body composed of more than one cell

myo–: muscle (prefix); *myofibril*, protein strands in muscle cells

neo–: new (prefix); *neonatal*, relating to or affecting a newborn child

neph–: kidney (prefix or root); *nephron*, functional unit of mammalian kidney

neur–, neuro–: nerve (prefix or root); *neuron*, a nerve cell

neutr–: of neither gender or type (usually root); *neutron*, an uncharged subatomic particle found in the nucleus of an atom

non–: not (prefix); *nondisjunction*, the failure of chromosomes to distribute themselves properly during cell division

oligo–: few (prefix); *oligomer*, a molecule made up of a few subunits (see also *poly–*)

omni–: all (prefix); *omnivore*, an animal that eats both plants and animals

oo–, ov–, ovo–: egg (prefix); *oocyte*, one of the stages of egg development

opsi–: sight (prefix or root); *opsin*, protein part of light-absorbing pigment in eye

opso–: tasty food (prefix or root); *opsonization*, process whereby antibodies and/or complement render bacteria easier for white blood cells to engulf

–osis: a condition, disease (suffix); *atherosclerosis*, a disease in which the artery walls become thickened and hardened

oss–, osteo–: bone (prefix or root); *osteoporosis*; a disease in which the bones become spongy and weak

para–: alongside (prefix); *parathyroid*, referring to a gland located next to the thyroid gland

pater, patr–: father (usually root); *paternal*, from or relating to a father

path–, –i–, –o–: disease (prefix or root); *pathology*, the study of disease and diseased tissue

–pathy: disease (suffix); *neuropathy*, a disease of the nervous system

peri–: around (prefix); *pericycle*, the outermost layer of cells in the vascular cylinder of a plant root

phago–: eat (prefix or root); *phagocyte*, a cell (e.g., some types of white blood cell) that eats other cells

–phil, philo–: to love (prefix or suffix); *hydrophilic* (literally, "water loving"), pertaining to a water-soluble molecule

–phob, phobo–: to fear (prefix or suffix); *hydrophobic* (literally, "water fearing"), pertaining to a water-insoluble molecule

photo–: light (prefix); *photosynthesis*, the manufacture of organic molecules using the energy of sunlight

–phyll: leaf (root or suffix); *chlorophyll*, the green, light-absorbing pigment in a leaf

–phyte: plant (root or suffix); *gametophyte* (literally, "gamete plant"), the gamete-producing stage of a plant's life cycle

plasmo, –plasm: formed substance (prefix, root, or suffix); *cytoplasm*, the material inside a cell

ploid: chromosomes (root); *diploid*, having paired chromosomes

pneumo–: lung (root); *pneumonia*, a disease of the lungs

–pod: foot (root or suffix); *gastropod* (literally, "stomach-foot"), a class of mollusks, principally snails, that crawl on their ventral surfaces

poly–: many (prefix); *polysaccharide*, a carbohydrate polymer composed of many sugar subunits (see also *oligo–*)

post–, postero–: behind (prefix); *posterior*, pertaining to the hind part

pre–, pro–: before, in front of (prefix); *premating isolating mechanism*, a mechanism that prevents gene flow between species, acting to prevent mating (e.g., having different courtship rituals or different mating seasons)

prim–: first (prefix); *primary cell wall*, the first cell wall laid down between plant cells during cell division

pro–: before (prefix); *prokaryotic*, pertaining to a cell without (that evolved before the evolution of) a nucleus

proto–: first (prefix); *protocell*, a hypothetical evolutionary ancestor to the first cell

pseudo–: false (prefix); *pseudopod* (literally, "false foot"), the extension of the plasma membrane by which some cells, such as *Amoeba*, move and capture prey

quad–, quat–: four (prefix); *quaternary structure*, the "fourth level" of protein structure, in which multiple peptide chains form a complex three-dimensional structure

ren: kidney (root); *adrenal*, gland attached to the mammalian kidney

retro–: backward (prefix); *retrovirus*, a virus that uses RNA as its genetic material; this RNA must be copied "backward" to DNA during infection of a cell by the virus

sarco–: muscle (prefix); *sarcoplasmic reticulum*, a calcium-storing, modified endoplasmic reticulum found in muscle cells

scler–: hard, tough (prefix); *sclerenchyma*, a type of plant cell with a very thick, hard cell wall

semi–: one-half (prefix); *semiconservative replication*, the mechanism of DNA replication, in which one strand of the original DNA double helix becomes incorporated into the new DNA double helix

–some, soma–, somato–: body (prefix or suffix); *somatic nervous system*, part of the peripheral nervous system that controls the skeletal muscles that move the body

sperm, sperma–, spermato–: seed (usually root); *gymnosperm*, a type of plant producing a seed not enclosed within a fruit

–stasis, stat–: stationary, standing still (suffix or prefix); *homeostasis*, the physiological process of maintaining constant internal conditions despite a changing external environment

stoma, –to–: mouth, opening (prefix or root); *stoma*, the adjustable pore in the surface of a leaf that allows carbon dioxide to enter the leaf

sub–: under, below (prefix); *subcutaneous*, beneath the skin

sym–: same (prefix); *sympatric* (literally "same father"), found in the same region

tel–, telo–: end (prefix); *telophase*, the last stage of mitosis and meiosis

test–: witness (prefix or root); *testis*, male reproductive organ (derived from the custom in ancient Rome that only males had standing in the eyes of the law; *testimony* has the same derivation)

therm–: heat (prefix or root); *thermoregulation*, the process of regulating body temperature

trans–: across (prefix); *transgenic*, having genes from another organism (usually another species); the genes have been moved "across" species

tri–: three (prefix); *triploid*, having three copies of each homologous chromosome

–trop–, tropic: change, turn, move (suffix); *phototropism*, the process by which plants orient toward the light

troph: food, nourishment (root); *autotrophic*, self-feeder (e.g., photosynthetic)

ultra–: beyond (prefix); *ultraviolet*, light of wavelengths beyond the violet

uni–: one (prefix); *unicellular*, referring to an organism composed of a single cell

vita: life (root); *vitamin*, a molecule required in the diet to sustain life

–vor: eat (usually root); *herbivore*, an animal that eats plants

zoo–, zoa–: animal (usually root); *zoology*, the study of animals

Periodic Table of the Elements

atomic number (number of protons)

element (chemical symbol)

atomic mass (total mass of protons + neutrons + electrons)

1	2	3	4	5	6	7	8	9	10	11	12	13	14	15	16	17	18
1 H 1.008																	2 He 4.003
3 Li 6.941	4 Be 9.012											5 B 10.81	6 C 12.01	7 N 14.01	8 O 16.00	9 F 19.00	10 Ne 20.18
11 Na 22.99	12 Mg 24.31											13 Al 26.98	14 Si 28.09	15 P 30.97	16 S 32.07	17 Cl 35.45	18 Ar 39.95
19 K 39.10	20 Ca 40.08	21 Sc 44.96	22 Ti 47.87	23 V 50.94	24 Cr 52.00	25 Mn 54.94	26 Fe 55.85	27 Co 58.93	28 Ni 58.69	29 Cu 63.55	30 Zn 65.39	31 Ga 69.72	32 Ge 72.61	33 As 74.92	34 Se 78.96	35 Br 79.90	36 Kr 83.80
37 Rb 85.47	38 Sr 87.62	39 Y 88.91	40 Zr 91.22	41 Nb 92.91	42 Mo 95.94	43 Tc (98)	44 Ru 101.1	45 Rh 102.9	46 Pd 106.4	47 Ag 107.9	48 Cd 112.4	49 In 114.8	50 Sn 118.7	51 Sb 121.8	52 Te 127.6	53 I 126.9	54 Xe 131.3
55 Cs 132.9	56 Ba 137.3	57 *La 138.9	72 Hf 178.5	73 Ta 180.9	74 W 183.8	75 Re 186.2	76 Os 190.2	77 Ir 192.2	78 Pt 195.1	79 Au 197.0	80 Hg 200.6	81 Tl 204.4	82 Pb 207.2	83 Bi 209.0	84 Po (209)	85 At (210)	86 Rn (222)
87 Fr (223)	88 Ra (226)	89 †Ac (227)	104 Rf (261)	105 Db (262)	106 Sg (263)	107 Bh (264)	108 Hs (265)	109 Mt (268)	110 Ds (281)	111 Rg (280)	112 ** (277)	113 **	114 ** (285)	115 **			

*Lanthanide series

58 Ce 140.1	59 Pr 140.9	60 Nd 144.2	61 Pm (145)	62 Sm 150.4	63 Eu 152.0	64 Gd 157.3	65 Tb 158.9	66 Dy 162.5	67 Ho 164.9	68 Er 167.3	69 Tm 168.9	70 Yb 173.0	71 Lu 175.0
90 Th 232.0	91 Pa 231	92 U 238.0	93 Np (237)	94 Pu (244)	95 Am (243)	96 Cm (247)	97 Bk (247)	98 Cf (251)	99 Es (252)	100 Fm (257)	101 Md (258)	102 No (259)	103 Lr (262)

†Actinide series

The periodic table of the elements was first devised by Russian chemist Dmitri Mendeleev. The atomic numbers of the elements (the numbers of protons in the nucleus) increase in normal reading order: left to right, top to bottom. The table is "periodic" because all the elements in a column possess similar chemical properties, and such similar elements therefore recur "periodically" in each row. For example, elements that usually form ions with a single positive charge—including H, Li, Na, K, and so on—occur as the first element in each row.

The gaps in the table are a consequence of the maximum numbers of electrons in the most reactive, usually outermost, electron shells of the atoms. It takes only two electrons to completely fill the first shell, so the first row of the table contains only two elements, H and He. It takes eight electrons to fill the second and third shells, so there are eight elements in the second and third rows. It takes 18 electrons to fill the fourth and fifth shells, so there are 18 elements in these rows.

The lanthanide series and actinide series of elements are usually placed below the main body of the table for convenience—it takes 32 electrons to completely fill the sixth and seventh shells, so the table would become extremely wide if all of these elements were included in the sixth and seventh rows.

The important elements found in living things are highlighted in color. The elements in pale red are the six most abundant elements in living things. The elements that form the five most abundant ions in living things are in purple. The trace elements important to life are shown as dark blue (more common) and lighter blue (less common). For radioactive elements, the atomic masses are given in parentheses, and represent the most common or the most stable isotope. Elements indicated as double asterisks have not yet been named.

To Convert Metric Units:	Multiply by:	To Get English Equivalent:
Length		
Centimeters (cm)	0.394	Inches (in)
Meters (m)	3.281	Feet (ft)
Meters (m)	1.094	Yards (yd)
Kilometers (km)	0.621	Miles (mi)
Area		
Square centimeters (cm^2)	0.155	Square inches (in^2)
Square meters (m^2)	10.764	Square feet (ft^2)
Square meters (m^2)	1.196	Square yards (yd^2)
Square kilometers (km^2)	0.386	Square miles (mi^2)
Hectare (ha) (10,000 m^2)	2.471	Acres (a)
Volume		
Cubic centimeters (cm^3)	0.0610	Cubic inches (in^3)
Cubic meters (m^3)	35.315	Cubic feet (ft^3)
Cubic meters (m^3)	1.308	Cubic yards (yd^3)
Cubic kilometers (km^3)	0.240	Cubic miles (mi^3)
Liters (L)	1.057	Quarts (qt), U.S.
Liters (L)	0.264	Gallons (gal), U.S.
Mass		
Grams (g)	0.0353	Ounces (oz)
Kilograms (kg)	2.205	Pounds (lb)
Metric ton (tonne) (t)	1.102	Ton (tn), U.S.
Speed		
Meters/second (mps)	2.237	Miles/hour (mph)
Kilometers/hour (kmph)	0.621	Miles/hour (mph)

To Convert English Units:	Multiply by:	To Get Metric Equivalent:
Length		
Inches (in)	2.540	Centimeters (cm)
Feet (ft)	0.305	Meters (m)
Yards (yd)	0.914	Meters (m)
Miles (mi)	1.609	Kilometers (km)
Area		
Square inches (in^2)	6.452	Square centimeters (cm^2)
Square feet (ft^2)	0.0929	Square meters (m^2)
Square yards (yd^2)	0.836	Square meters (m^2)
Square miles (mi^2)	2.590	Square kilometers (km^2)
Acres (a)	0.405	Hectare (ha) (10,000 m^2)
Volume		
Cubic inches (in^3)	16.387	Cubic centimeters (cm^3)
Cubic feet (ft^3)	0.0283	Cubic meters (m^3)
Cubic yards (yd^3)	0.765	Cubic meters (m^3)
Cubic miles (mi^3)	4.168	Cubic kilometers (km^3)
Quarts (qt), U.S.	0.946	Liters (L)
Gallons (gal), U.S.	3.785	Liters (L)
Mass		
Ounces (oz)	28.350	Grams (g)
Pounds (lb)	0.454	Kilograms (kg)
Ton (tn), U.S.	0.907	Metric ton (tonne) (t)
Speed		
Miles/hour (mph)	0.447	Meters/second (mps)
Miles/hour (mph)	1.609	Kilometers/hour (kmph)

Metric Prefixes

Prefix			Meaning
giga-	G	$10^9 =$	1,000,000,000
mega-	M	$10^6 =$	1,000,000
kilo-	k	$10^3 =$	1,000
hecto-	h	$10^2 =$	100
deka-	da	$10^1 =$	10
		$10^0 =$	1
deci-	d	$10^{-1} =$	0.1
centi-	c	$10^{-2} =$	0.01
milli-	m	$10^{-3} =$	0.001
micro-	μ	$10^{-6} =$	0.000001

$$°C = \frac{°F - 32}{1.8} \qquad °F = (1.8 \times °C) + 32$$

Classification of Major Groups
of Eukaryotic Organisms*

Kingdom†	Phylum or Class	Common Name
Excavata	Parabasalia	parabasalids
	Diplomonadida	diplomonads
Euglenozoa	Euglenida	euglenids
	Kinetoplastida	kinetoplastids
Stramenopila	Oomycota	water molds
	Phaeophyta	brown algae
	Bacillariophyta	diatoms
Alveolata	Apicomplexa	sporozoans
	Pyrrophyta	dinoflagellates
	Ciliophora	ciliates
Rhizaria	Foraminifera	foraminiferans
	Radiolaria	radiolarians
Amoebozoa	Tubulinea	amoebas
	Myxomycota	acellular slime molds
	Acrasiomycota	cellular slime molds
Rhodophyta		red algae
Chlorophyta		green algae
Plantae	Marchantiophyta	liverworts
	Anthocerotophyta	hornworts
	Bryophyta	mosses
	Lycopodiopsida	club mosses
	Polypodiopsida	ferns, horsetails
	Gymnospermae	cycads, ginkgos, gnetophytes, conifers
	Anthophyta	flowering plants
Fungi	Chytridiomycota	chytrids
	Neocallimastigomycota	rumen fungi
	Blastocladiomycota	blastoclades
	Glomeromycota	glomeromycetes
	Ascomycota	sac fungi
	Basidiomycota	club fungi
Animalia	Porifera	sponges
	Cnidaria	hydras, sea anemones, sea jellies, corals
	Ctenophora	comb jellies
	Platyhelminthes	flatworms
	Annelida	segmented worms
	Oligochaeta	earthworms
	Polychaeta	tube worms
	Hirudinea	leeches
	Mollusca	mollusks
	Gastropoda	snails
	Pelecypoda	mussels, clams
	Cephalopoda	squid, octopuses
	Nematoda	roundworms
	Arthropoda	arthropods
	Insecta	insects
	Arachnida	spiders, ticks
	Crustacea	crabs, lobsters
	Myriapoda	millipedes, centipedes
	Chordata	chordates
	Urochordata	tunicates
	Cephalochordata	lancelets
	Myxini	hagfishes
	Petromyzontiformes	lampreys
	Chondrichthyes	sharks, rays
	Actinopterygii	ray-finned fishes
	Actinistia	coelacanths
	Dipnoi	lungfishes
	Amphibia	amphibians (frogs, salamanders)
	Reptilia	reptiles (turtles, crocodiles, birds, snakes, lizards)
	Mammalia	mammals

*This table lists only those taxonomic categories described in the textbook.
†Although the major protist groups are not generally called "kingdoms," they are approximately the same taxonomic rank as the kingdoms Plantae, Fungi, and Animalia.

Glossary

abiotic (ā-bī-ah'-tik): nonliving; the abiotic portion of an ecosystem includes soil, rock, water, and the atmosphere.

abscission layer: a layer of thin-walled cells, located at the base of the petiole of a leaf, that produces an enzyme that digests the cell walls holding the leaf to the stem, allowing the leaf to fall off.

accessory pigment: a colored molecule, other than chlorophyll *a*, that absorbs light energy and passes it to chlorophyll *a*.

acellular slime mold: a type of organism that forms a multinucleate structure that crawls in amoeboid fashion and ingests decaying organic matter; also called *plasmodial slime mold*. Acellular slime molds are members of the protist clade Amoebozoa.

acid: a substance that releases hydrogen ions (H^+) into solution; a solution with a pH less than 7.

acid deposition: the deposition of nitric or sulfuric acid, either in rain (acid rain) or in the form of dry particles, as a result of the production of nitrogen oxides or sulfur dioxide through burning, primarily of fossil fuels.

acidic: referring to a solution with an H^+ concentration exceeding that of OH^-; referring to a substance that releases H^+.

acrosome (ak'-rō-sōm): a vesicle, located at the tip of the head of an animal sperm, that contains enzymes needed to dissolve protective layers around the egg.

action potential: a rapid change from a negative to a positive electrical potential in a nerve cell. An action potential travels along an axon without a change in amplitude.

activation energy: in a chemical reaction, the energy needed to force the electron shells of reactants together, prior to the formation of products.

active site: the region of an enzyme molecule that binds substrates and performs the catalytic function of the enzyme.

active transport: the movement of materials across a membrane through the use of cellular energy, normally against a concentration gradient.

adaptation: a trait that increases the ability of an individual to survive and reproduce compared to individuals without the trait.

adaptive immune system: a widely distributed system of organs (including the thymus, bone marrow, and lymph nodes), cells (including macrophages, dendritic cells, B cells, and T cells), and molecules (including cytokines and antibodies) that work together to combat microbial invasion of the body; the adaptive immune system responds to and destroys specific invading toxins or microbes; see also *innate immune response*.

adaptive radiation: the rise of many new species in a relatively short time; may occur when a single species invades different habitats and evolves in response to different environmental conditions in those habitats.

adenine (A): a nitrogenous base found in both DNA and RNA; abbreviated as A.

adenosine diphosphate (a-den'-ō-sēn dī-fos'-fāt; ADP): a molecule composed of the sugar ribose, the base adenine, and two phosphate groups; a component of ATP.

adenosine triphosphate (a-den'-ō-sēn trī-fos'-fāt; ATP): a molecule composed of the sugar ribose, the base adenine, and three phosphate groups; the major energy carrier in cells. The last two phosphate groups are attached by "high-energy" bonds.

adhesion: the tendency of polar molecules (such as water) to adhere to polar surfaces (such as glass).

adrenal cortex: the outer part of the adrenal gland, which secretes steroid hormones that regulate metabolism and salt balance.

adrenal medulla: the inner part of the adrenal gland, which secretes epinephrine (adrenaline) and norepinephrine (noradrenaline) in the stress response.

adult stem cell (ASC): any stem cell not found in an early embryo; can divide and differentiate into any of several cell types, but usually not all of the cell types of the body.

aerobic: using oxygen.

age structure diagram: a graph showing the distribution of males and females in a population according to age groups.

aggression: antagonistic behavior, normally among members of the same species, that often results from competition for resources.

aggressive mimicry (mim'-ik-rē): the evolution of a predatory organism to resemble a harmless animal or a part of the environment, thus gaining access to prey.

albinism: a recessive hereditary condition caused by defective alleles of the genes that encode the enzymes required for the synthesis of melanin, the principal pigment in mammalian skin and hair; albinism results in white hair and pink skin.

alcoholic fermentation: a type of fermentation in which pyruvate is converted to ethanol (a type of alcohol) and carbon dioxide, using hydrogen ions and electrons from NADH; the primary function of alcoholic fermentation is to regenerate NAD^+ so that glycolysis can continue under anaerobic conditions.

alga (al'-ga; pl., algae, al'-jē): any photosynthetic protist.

allele (al-ēl'): one of several alternative forms of a particular gene.

allele frequency: for any given gene, the relative proportion of each allele of that gene in a population.

allopatric speciation (al-ō-pat'-rik): the process by which new species arise following physical separation of parts of a population (geographical isolation).

allosteric regulation: the process by which enzyme action is enhanced or inhibited by small organic molecules that act as regulators by binding to the enzyme at a regulatory site distinct from the active site, and altering the shape and/or function of the active site.

alternation of generations: a life cycle, typical of plants, in which a diploid sporophyte (spore-producing) generation alternates with a haploid gametophyte (gamete-producing) generation.

altruism: a behavior that benefits other individuals while reducing the fitness of the individual that performs the behavior.

alveolate (al-vē'-ō-lāt): a member of the Alveolata, a large protist clade. The alveolates, which are characterized by a system of sacs beneath the cell membrane, include ciliates, dinoflagellates, and apicomplexans.

amino acid: the individual subunit of which proteins are made, composed of a central carbon atom bonded to an amino group ($-NH_2$), a carboxyl group ($-COOH$), a hydrogen atom, and a variable group of atoms denoted by the letter *R*.

ammonia: NH_3; a highly toxic nitrogen-containing waste product of amino acid breakdown. In the mammalian liver, it is converted to urea.

amniocentesis (am-nē-ō-sen-tē'-sis): a procedure for sampling the amniotic fluid surrounding a fetus: A sterile needle is inserted through the abdominal wall, uterus, and amniotic sac of a pregnant woman, and 10 to 20 milliliters of amniotic fluid are withdrawn. Various tests may be performed on the fluid and the fetal cells suspended in it to provide information on the developmental and genetic state of the fetus.

amnion (am'-nē-on): one of the embryonic membranes of reptiles (including birds) and mammals; encloses a fluid-filled cavity that envelops the embryo.

amniotic egg (am-nē-ōt'-ik): the egg of reptiles, including birds; contains a membrane, the amnion, that surrounds the embryo, enclosing it in a watery environment and allowing the egg to be laid on dry land.

amoeba: an amoebozoan protist that uses a characteristic streaming mode of locomotion by extending a cellular projection called a *pseudopod*. Also known as *lobose amoebas*.

amoeboid cell: a protist or animal cell that moves by extending a cellular projection called a pseudopod.

amoebozoan: a member of the Amoebozoa, a protist clade. The amoebozoans, which generally lack shells and move by extending pseudopods, include the lobose amoebas and the slime molds.

amphibian: a member of the chordate clade Amphibia, which includes the frogs, toads, and salamanders, as well as the limbless caecilians.

amylase (am'-i-lās): an enzyme, found in saliva and pancreatic secretions, that catalyzes the breakdown of starch.

anaerobe (an-ə-rōb): an organism that can live and grow in the absence of oxygen.

anaerobic: not using oxygen.

analogous structure: structures that have similar functions and superficially similar appearance but very different anatomies, such as the wings of insects and birds. The similarities are the result of similar environmental pressures rather than a common ancestry.

anaphase (an'-a-fāz): in mitosis, the stage in which the sister chromatids of each chromosome separate from one another and are moved to opposite poles of the cell; in meiosis I, the stage in which homologous chromosomes, consisting of two sister chromatids, are separated; in meiosis II, the stage in which the sister chromatids of each chromosome separate from one another and are moved to opposite poles of the cell.

angina (an-jī'-nuh): chest pain associated with reduced blood flow to the heart muscle; caused by an obstruction of the coronary arteries.

angiosperm (an'-jē-ō-sperm): a flowering vascular plant.

annual ring: a pattern of alternating light (early) and dark (late) xylem in woody stems and roots; formed as a result of the unequal availability of water in different seasons of the year, normally spring and summer.

anterior pituitary: a lobe of the pituitary gland that produces prolactin and growth hormone as well as hormones that regulate hormone production in other glands.

antheridium (an-ther-id'-ē-um; pl., antheridia): a structure in which male sex cells are produced; found in nonvascular plants and certain seedless vascular plants.

antibody: a protein, produced by cells of the immune system, that combines with a specific antigen and normally facilitates the destruction of the antigen.

anticodon: a sequence of three bases in transfer RNA that is complementary to the three bases of a codon of messenger RNA.

antigen: a complex molecule, normally a protein or polysaccharide, that stimulates the production of a specific antibody.

antioxidant: any molecule that reacts with free radicals, neutralizing their ability to damage biological molecules. Vitamins C and E are examples of dietary antioxidants.

aphotic zone: the region of the ocean below 200 meters where sunlight does not penetrate.

apical meristem (ăp'-i-kul mer'-i-stem): the cluster of meristem cells at the tip of a shoot or root (or one of their branches).

apicomplexan (ā-pē-kom-pleks'-an): a member of the protist clade Apicomplexa, which includes mostly parasitic, single-celled eukaryotes such as *Plasmodium*, which causes malaria in humans. Apicomplexans are part of a larger group known as the alveolates.

aquaporin: a channel protein in the plasma membrane of a cell that is selectively permeable to water.

aquifer (ok'-wifer): an underground deposit of fresh water, often used as a source for irrigation.

archaea: prokaryotes that are members of the domain Archaea, one of the three domains of living organisms; only distantly related to members of the domain Bacteria.

Archaea: one of life's three domains; consists of prokaryotes that are only distantly related to members of the domain Bacteria.

archegonium (ar-ke-gō'-nē-um; pl., archegonia): a structure in which female sex cells are produced; found in nonvascular plants and certain seedless vascular plants.

artery (ar'-tuh-rē): a vessel with muscular, elastic walls that conducts blood away from the heart.

arthropod: a member of the animal phylum Arthropoda, which includes the insects, spiders, ticks, mites, scorpions, crustaceans, millipedes, and centipedes.

artificial selection: a selective breeding procedure in which only those individuals with particular traits are chosen as breeders; used mainly to enhance desirable traits in domesticated plants and animals; may also be used in evolutionary biology experiments.

ascomycete: a member of the fungus clade Ascomycota, whose members form sexual spores in a saclike case known as an ascus.

ascus (as'-kus; pl., asci): a saclike case in which sexual spores are formed by members of the fungus clade Ascomycota.

asexual reproduction: reproduction that does not involve the fusion of haploid gametes.

atom: the smallest particle of an element that retains the properties of the element.

atomic mass: the total mass of all the protons, neutrons, and electrons within an atom.

atomic nucleus: the central part of an atom that contains protons and neutrons.

atomic number: the number of protons in the nuclei of all atoms of a particular element.

ATP synthase: a channel protein in the thylakoid membranes of chloroplasts and the inner membrane of mitochondria that uses the energy of H^+ ions moving through the channel down their concentration gradient to produce ATP from ADP and inorganic phosphate.

atrioventricular (AV) node (ā'-trē-ō-ven-trik'-ū-lar nōd): a specialized mass of muscle at the base of the right atrium through which the electrical activity initiated in the sinoatrial node is transmitted to the ventricles.

atrium (ā'-trē-um; pl., atria): a chamber of the heart that receives venous blood and passes it to a ventricle.

auditory nerve: the nerve leading from the mammalian cochlea to the brain; it carries information about sound.

autoimmune disease: a disorder in which the immune system attacks the body's own cells or molecules.

autosome (aw'-tō-sōm): a chromosome that occurs in homologous pairs in both males and females and that does not bear the genes determining sex.

autotroph (aw'-tō-trōf): literally, "self-feeder"; normally, a photosynthetic organism; a producer.

axial skeleton: the skeleton forming the body axis, including the skull, vertebral column, and rib cage.

B cell: a type of lymphocyte that matures in the bone marrow, and that participates in humoral immunity; gives rise to plasma cells, which secrete antibodies into the circulatory system, and to memory cells.

bacteria (sing., bacterium): prokaryotes that are members of the domain Bacteria, one of the three domains of living organisms; only distantly related to members of the domain Archaea.

Bacteria: one of life's three domains; consists of prokaryotes that are only distantly related to members of the domain Archaea.

bacteriophage (bak-tir'-ē-ō-fāj): a virus that specifically infects bacteria.

bark: the outer layer of a woody stem, consisting of phloem, cork cambium, and cork cells.

Barr body: a condensed, inactivated X chromosome in the cells of female mammals that have two X chromosomes.

basal body: a structure derived from a centriole that produces a cilium or flagellum and anchors this structure within the plasma membrane.

base: (1) a substance capable of combining with and neutralizing H^+ ions in a solution; a solution with a pH greater than 7; (2) one of the nitrogen-containing, single- or double-ringed structures that distinguishes one nucleotide from another. In DNA, the bases are adenine, guanine, cytosine, and thymine.

basic: referring to a solution with an H^+ concentration less than that of OH^-; referring to a substance that combines with H^+.

basidiomycete: a member of the fungus clade Basidiomycota, which includes species that produce sexual spores in club-shaped cells known as basidia.

basidiospore (ba-sid'-ē-ō-spor): a sexual spore formed by members of the fungus clade Basidiomycota.

basidium (pl., basidia): a diploid cell, typically club-shaped, formed by members of the fungus clade Basidiomycota; produces basidiospores by meiosis.

behavior: any observable activity of a living animal.

behavioral isolation: reproductive isolation that arises when species do not interbreed because they have different courtship and mating rituals.

bilateral symmetry: a body plan in which only a single plane through the central axis will divide the body into mirror-image halves.

binocular vision: the ability to see objects simultaneously through both eyes, providing greater depth perception and more accurate judgment of the size and distance of an object than can be achieved by vision with one eye alone.

binomial system: the method of naming organisms by genus and species, often called the scientific name, usually using Latin words or words derived from Latin.

biocapacity: an estimate of the sustainable resources and waste-absorbing capacity actually available on Earth. Biocapacity calculations are subject to change as new technologies change the way people use resources.

biodegradable: able to be broken down into harmless substances by decomposers.

biodiversity: the diversity of living organisms; measured as the variety of different species, the variety of different alleles in species' gene pools, or the variety of different communities and nonliving environments in an ecosystem or in the entire biosphere.

biofilm: a community of prokaryotes of one or more species, in which the prokaryotes secrete and are embedded in slime that adheres to a surface.

biogeochemical cycle: the pathways of a specific nutrient (such as carbon, nitrogen, phosphorus, or water) through the living and nonliving portions of an ecosystem; also called a *nutrient cycle*.

biological magnification: the increasing accumulation of a toxic substance in progressively higher trophic levels.

biology: The study of all aspects of life and living things.

biomass: the total weight of all living material within a defined area.

biome (bī'-ōm): a terrestrial ecosystem that occupies an extensive geographical area and is characterized by a specific type of plant community; for example, deserts.

bioremediation: the use of organisms to remove or detoxify toxic substances in the environment.

biosphere (bī'-ō-sfēr): all life on Earth and the nonliving portions of Earth that support life.

Biosphere Reserve: designated by the United Nations, a Biosphere Reserve is a region intended to maintain biodiversity and evaluate techniques for sustainable human development while maintaining local cultural values.

biotechnology: any industrial or commercial use or alteration of organisms, cells, or biological molecules to achieve specific practical goals.

biotic (bī-ah'-tik): living.

biotic potential: the maximum rate at which a population is able to increase, assuming ideal conditions that allow a maximum birth rate and minimum death rate.

birth rate: the number of births per individual in a specified unit of time, such as a year.

blade: the flat part of a leaf.

blastoclade: a member of the fungus clade Blastocladiomycota, whose members have swimming spores with a single flagellum and ribosomes arranged to form a nuclear cap.

blastopore: the site at which a blastula indents to form a gastrula.

blind spot: the area of the retina at which the axons of the ganglion cells merge to form the optic nerve; because there are no photoreceptors in the blind spot, objects focused at the blind spot cannot be seen.

blood–brain barrier: relatively impermeable capillaries of the brain that protect the cells of the brain from potentially damaging chemicals that reach the bloodstream.

blood vessel: any of several types of tubes that carry blood throughout the body.

bone: a hard, mineralized connective tissue that is a major component of the vertebrate endoskeleton; provides support and sites for muscle attachment.

boom-and-bust cycle: a population cycle characterized by rapid exponential growth followed by a sudden massive die-off; seen in seasonal species, such as many insects living in temperate climates, and in some populations of small rodents, such as lemmings.

brain: the part of the central nervous system of vertebrates that is enclosed within the skull.

bronchiole (bron'-kē-ōl): a narrow tube, formed by repeated branching of the bronchi, that conducts air into the alveoli.

bud: in plants, an embryonic shoot, often dormant until stimulated by specific combinations of hormones. In asexually reproducing animals, a miniature copy of an animal that develops on some part of the adult animal's body; usually eventually separates from the adult and assumes independent existence.

budding: asexual reproduction by the growth of a miniature copy, or bud, of the adult animal on the body of the parent. The bud breaks off to begin independent existence.

buffer: a compound that minimizes changes in pH by reversibly taking up or releasing H^+ ions.

bulk flow: the movement of many molecules of a gas or liquid in unison (in bulk, hence the name) from an area of higher pressure to an area of lower pressure.

bundle sheath cells: cells that surround the veins of plants; in C_4 (but not in C_3) plants, bundle sheath cells contain chloroplasts.

C3 pathway: in photosynthesis, the cyclic series of reactions whereby carbon from carbon dioxide is fixed as phosphoglyceric acid, the simple sugar glyceraldehyde-3-phosphate is generated, and the carbon-capture molecule, RuBP, is regenerated.

C3 plant: a plant that relies on the C_3 pathway to fix carbon.

C4 pathway: the series of reactions in certain plants that fixes carbon dioxide into a four-carbon molecule, which is later broken down for use in the Calvin cycle of photosynthesis. This reduces wasteful photorespiration in hot, dry environments.

C4 plant: a plant that relies on the C_4 pathway to fix carbon.

calorie (kal'-ō-rē): the amount of energy required to raise the temperature of 1 gram of water by 1 degree Celsius.

Calvin cycle: in photosynthesis, the cyclic series of reactions whereby carbon from carbon dioxide is fixed as phosphoglyceric acid, the simple sugar glyceraldehyde-3-phosphate is generated, and the carbon-capture molecule, RuBP, is regenerated.

cambium (kam'-bē-um; pl., cambia): a lateral meristem, parallel to the long axis of roots and stems, that causes secondary growth of woody plant stems and roots. See *cork cambium; vascular cambium.*

camouflage (cam'-a-flaj): coloration and/or shape that renders an organism inconspicuous in its environment.

capillary: the smallest type of blood vessel, connecting arterioles with venules; capillary walls, through which the exchange of nutrients and wastes occurs, are only one cell thick.

carbohydrate: a compound composed of carbon, hydrogen, and oxygen, with the approximate chemical formula $(CH_2O)_n$; includes sugars, starches, and cellulose.

carbon cycle: the biogeochemical cycle by which carbon moves from its reservoirs in the atmosphere and oceans through producers and into higher trophic levels, and then back to its reservoirs.

carbon fixation: the process by which carbon derived from carbon dioxide is captured in organic molecules during photosynthesis.

cardiac muscle (kar'-dē-ak): the specialized muscle of the heart; able to initiate its own contraction, independent of the nervous system.

carnivore (kar'-neh-vor): literally, "meat eater"; a predatory organism that feeds on herbivores or on other carnivores; a secondary (or higher) consumer.

carotenoid (ka-rot'-en-oid): a red, orange, or yellow pigment, found in chloroplasts, that serves as an accessory light-gathering pigment in thylakoid photosystems.

carrier: an individual who is heterozygous for a recessive condition; a carrier displays the dominant phenotype but can pass on the recessive allele to offspring.

carrier protein: a membrane protein that facilitates the diffusion of specific substances across the membrane. The molecule to be transported binds to the outer surface of the carrier protein; the protein then changes shape, allowing the molecule to move across the membrane.

carrying capacity (K): the maximum population size that an ecosystem can support for a long period of time without damaging the ecosystem; determined primarily by the availability of space, nutrients, water, and light.

Casparian strip (kas-par'-ē-un): a waxy, waterproof band, located in the cell walls between endodermal cells in a root, that prevents the movement of water and minerals into and out of the vascular cylinder through the extracellular space.

catalyst (kat'-uh-list): a substance that speeds up a chemical reaction without itself being permanently changed in the process; a catalyst lowers the activation energy of a reaction.

cell: the smallest unit of life, consisting, at a minimum, of an outer membrane that encloses a watery medium containing organic molecules, including genetic material composed of DNA.

cell cycle: the sequence of events in the life of a cell, from one cell division to the next.

cell division: splitting of one cell into two; the process of cellular reproduction.

cell plate: in plant cell division, a series of vesicles that fuse to form the new plasma membranes and cell wall separating the daughter cells.

cell theory: the scientific theory stating that every living organism is made up of one or more cells; cells are the functional units of all organisms; and all cells arise from preexisting cells.

cell wall: A nonliving, protective, and supportive layer secreted outside the plasma membrane of fungi, plants, and most bacteria and protists.

cellular respiration: the oxygen-requiring reactions, occurring in mitochondria, that break down the end products of glycolysis into carbon dioxide and water while capturing large amounts of energy as ATP.

cellular slime mold: a type of organism consisting of individual amoeboid cells that can aggregate to form a slug-like mass, which in turn forms a fruiting body. Cellular slime molds are members of the protist clade Amoebozoa.

cellulose: an insoluble carbohydrate composed of glucose subunits; forms the cell wall of plants.

central vacuole (vak′-ū-ōl): a large, fluid-filled vacuole occupying most of the volume of many plant cells; performs several functions, including maintaining turgor pressure.

centriole (sen′-trē-ōl): in animal cells, a short, barrel-shaped ring consisting of nine microtubule triplets; a pair of centrioles is found near the nucleus and may play a role in the organization of the spindle; centrioles also give rise to the basal bodies at the base of each cilium and flagellum that give rise to the microtubules of cilia and flagella.

centromere (sen′-trō-mēr): the region of a replicated chromosome at which the sister chromatids are held together until they separate during cell division.

cephalization (sef-ul-ī-zā′-shun): concentration of sensory organs and nervous tissue in the anterior (head) portion of the body.

cerebral cortex (ser-ē′-brul kor-tex): a thin layer of neurons on the surface of the vertebrate cerebrum in which most neural processing and coordination of activity occurs.

cerebrum (ser-ē′-brum): the part of the forebrain of vertebrates that is concerned with sensory processing, the direction of motor output, and the coordination of most of the body's activities; consists of two nearly symmetrical halves (the hemispheres) connected by a broad band of axons, the corpus callosum.

channel protein: a membrane protein that forms a channel or pore completely through the membrane and that is usually permeable to one or to a few water-soluble molecules, especially ions.

chaparral: a biome located in coastal regions, with very low annual rainfall; is characterized by shrubs and small trees.

checkpoint: a mechanism in the eukaryotic cell cycle by which protein complexes in the cell determine whether the cell has successfully completed a specific process that is essential to successful cell division, such as the accurate replication of chromosomes.

chemical bond: an attraction between two atoms or molecules that tends to hold them together. Types of bonds include covalent, ionic, and hydrogen.

chemical energy: a form of potential energy that is stored in molecules and may be released during chemical reactions.

chemical reaction: a process that forms and breaks chemical bonds that hold atoms together in molecules.

chemiosmosis (ke-mē-oz-mō′-sis): a process of ATP generation in chloroplasts and mitochondria. The movement of electrons down an electron transport system is used to pump hydrogen ions across a membrane, thereby building up a concentration gradient of hydrogen ions; the hydrogen ions diffuse back across the membrane through the pores of ATP-synthesizing enzymes; the energy of their movement down their concentration gradient drives ATP synthesis.

chemosynthesis (kē-mō-sin-the-sis): the process of oxidizing inorganic molecules, such as hydrogen sulfide, to obtain energy. Producers in hydrothermal vent communities, where light is absent, use chemosynthesis instead of photosynthesis.

chemosynthetic (kēm′-ō-sin-the-tik): capable of oxidizing inorganic molecules to obtain energy.

chiasma (kī-as′-muh; pl., chiasmata): a point at which a chromatid of one chromosome crosses with a chromatid of the homologous chromosome during prophase I of meiosis; the site of exchange of chromosomal material between chromosomes.

chitin (kī′-tin): a compound found in the cell walls of fungi and the exoskeletons of insects and some other arthropods; composed of chains of nitrogen-containing, modified glucose molecules.

chlorophyll (klor-ō-fil): a pigment found in chloroplasts that captures light energy during photosynthesis; chlorophyll absorbs violet, blue, and red light but reflects green light.

chlorophyll a (klor′-ō-fil): the most abundant type of chlorophyll molecule in photosynthetic eukaryotic organisms and in cyanobacteria; chlorophyll a is found in the reaction centers of the photosystems.

chloroplast (klor′-ō-plast): the organelle in plants and plantlike protists that is the site of photosynthesis; is surrounded by a double membrane and contains an extensive internal membrane system that bears chlorophyll.

chondrocyte (kon′-drō-sīt): a living cell of cartilage. Together with their extracellular secretions of collagen, chondrocytes form cartilage.

chorionic gonadotropin (kor-ē-on′-ik gō-nādō-trō′-pin; CG): a hormone secreted by the chorion (one of the fetal membranes) that maintains the integrity of the corpus luteum during early pregnancy.

chorionic villus sampling (kōr-ē-on′-ik; CVS): a procedure for sampling cells from the chorionic villi produced by a fetus: A tube is inserted into the uterus of a pregnant woman, and a small sample of villi is suctioned off for genetic and biochemical analyses.

chromatid (krō′-ma-tid): one of the two identical strands of DNA and protein that forms a duplicated chromosome. The two sister chromatids of a duplicated chromosome are joined at the centromere.

chromatin (krō′-ma-tin): the complex of DNA and proteins that makes up eukaryotic chromosomes.

chromosome (krō′-mō-sōm): a DNA double helix and associated proteins that help to organize and regulate the use of the DNA.

chyme (kīm): an acidic, souplike mixture of partially digested food, water, and digestive secretions that is released from the stomach into the small intestine.

chytrid: a member of the fungus clade Chytridomycota, which includes species with flagellated swimming spores.

ciliate (sil′-ē-et): a member of a protist group characterized by cilia and a complex unicellular structure. Ciliates are part of a larger group known as the alveolates.

cilium (sil′-ē-um; pl., cilia): a short, hair-like, motile projection from the surface of certain eukaryotic cells that contains microtubules in a 9 + 2 arrangement. The movement of cilia may propel cells through a fluid medium or move fluids over a stationary surface layer of cells.

citric acid cycle: a cyclic series of reactions, occurring in the matrix of mitochondria, in which the acetyl groups from the pyruvic acids produced by glycolysis are broken down to CO_2, accompanied by the formation of ATP and electron carriers; also called the Krebs cycle.

clade: a group that includes all the organisms descended from a common ancestor, but no other organisms; a monophyletic group.

class: in Linnaean classification, the taxonomic rank composed of related orders. Closely related classes form a phylum.

climate: patterns of weather that prevail for long periods of time (from years to centuries) in a given region.

climate change: a long-lasting change in weather patterns, which may include significant changes in temperature, precipitation, the timing of seasons, and the frequency and severity of extreme weather events.

climax community: a diverse and relatively stable community that forms the endpoint of succession.

clonal selection: the mechanism by which the adaptive immune response gains specificity; an invading antigen elicits a response from only a few lymphocytes, which proliferate to form a clone of cells that attack only the specific antigen that stimulated their production.

clone: offspring that are produced by mitosis and are, therefore, genetically identical to each other.

cloning: the process of producing many identical copies of a gene; also the production of many genetically identical copies of an organism.

closed system: a hypothetical space where neither energy nor matter can enter or leave.

club fungus: a fungus of the clade Basidiomycota, whose members (which include mushrooms, puffballs, and shelf fungi) reproduce by means of basidiospores.

clumped distribution: the distribution characteristic of populations in which individuals are clustered into groups; the groups may be social or based on the need for a localized resource.

codominance: the relation between two alleles of a gene, such that both alleles are phenotypically expressed in heterozygous individuals.

codon: a sequence of three bases of messenger RNA that specifies a particular amino acid to be incorporated into a protein; certain codons also signal the beginning or end of protein synthesis.

coelom (sē'-lōm): in animals, a space or cavity, lined with tissue derived from mesoderm, that separates the body wall from the inner organs.

coenzyme: an organic molecule that is bound to certain enzymes and is required for the enzymes' proper functioning; typically, a nucleotide bound to a water-soluble vitamin.

coevolution: the evolution of adaptations in two species due to their extensive interactions with one another, such that each species acts as a major force of natural selection on the other.

cohesion: the tendency of the molecules of a substance to stick together.

coleoptile (kō-lē-op'-tĭl): a sheath surrounding the shoot in monocot seedlings that protects the shoot from abrasion by soil particles during germination.

collenchyma (kŏl-en'-ki-muh): an elongated plant cell type, with thickened, flexible cell walls, that is alive at maturity and that supports the plant body.

colostrum (kō-los'-trum): a yellowish fluid, high in protein and containing antibodies, that is produced by the mammary glands before milk secretion begins.

communication: the act of producing a signal that causes a receiver, normally another animal of the same species, to change its behavior in a way that is, on average, beneficial to both signaler and receiver.

community: populations of different species that live in the same area and interact with one another.

companion cell: a cell adjacent to a sieve-tube element in phloem; involved in the control and nutrition of the sieve-tube element.

competition: interaction among individuals who attempt to utilize a resource (for example, food or space) that is limited relative to the demand for that resource.

competitive exclusion principle: the concept that no two species can simultaneously and continuously occupy the same ecological niche.

competitive inhibition: the process by which two or more molecules that are somewhat similar in structure compete for the active site of an enzyme.

complementary base pair: in nucleic acids, bases that pair by hydrogen bonding. In DNA, adenine is complementary to thymine, and guanine is complementary to cytosine; in RNA, adenine is complementary to uracil, and guanine to cytosine.

compound eye: a type of eye, found in many arthropods, that is composed of numerous independent subunits called *ommatidia*. Each ommatidium contributes a piece of a mosaic-like image perceived by the animal.

concentration: the number of particles of a dissolved substance (solute) in a given volume of solvent.

concentration gradient: a difference in the concentration of a solute between different regions within a fluid or across a barrier such as a membrane.

conclusion: in the scientific method, a decision about the validity of a hypothesis, made on the basis of experiments or observations.

cone: a cone-shaped photoreceptor cell in the vertebrate retina; not as sensitive to light as are the rods. The three types of cones are most sensitive to different colors of light and provide color vision; see also *rod*.

conifer (kon-eh-fer): a member of a group of nonflowering vascular plants whose members reproduce by means of seeds formed inside cones; retains its leaves throughout the year.

conjugation: in prokaryotes, the transfer of DNA from one cell to another via a temporary connection; in single-celled eukaryotes, the mutual exchange of genetic material between two temporarily joined cells.

connection protein: a protein in the plasma membrane of a cell that attaches either to the cytoskeleton inside the cell, to other cells, or to the extracellular matrix.

conservation biology: the application of knowledge from ecology and other areas of biology to understand and conserve biodiversity.

constant-loss population: a population characterized by a relatively constant death rate; constant-loss populations have a roughly linear survivorship curve.

consumer: an organism that eats other organisms; a heterotroph.

contest competition: a mechanism for resolving intraspecific competition by using social or chemical interactions to limit access of some individuals to important limited resources, such as food, mates, or territories.

contractile vacuole: a fluid-filled vacuole in certain protists that takes up water from the cytoplasm, contracts, and expels the water outside the cell through a pore in the plasma membrane.

control: that portion of an experiment in which all possible variables are held constant; in contrast to the "experimental" portion, in which a particular variable is altered.

convergent evolution: the independent evolution of similar structures among unrelated organisms as a result of similar environmental pressures; see *analogous structures*.

convolution: a folding of the cerebral cortex of the vertebrate brain.

coral reef: an ecosystem created by animals (reef-building corals) and plants in warm tropical waters.

core reserve: a natural area protected from most human uses that encompasses enough space to preserve most of the biodiversity of the ecosystems in that area.

cork cell: a protective cell of the bark of woody stems and roots; at maturity, cork cells are dead, with thick, waterproof cell walls.

corona radiata (kuh-rō'-nuh rā-dē-a'-tuh): the layer of cells surrounding an egg after ovulation.

corpus luteum (kor'-pus loo-tē'-um): in the mammalian ovary, a structure that is derived from the follicle after ovulation and that secretes the hormones estrogen and progesterone.

cortisol (kor'-ti-sol): a steroid hormone released into the bloodstream by the adrenal cortex in response to stress. Cortisol helps the body cope with short-term stressors by raising blood glucose levels; it also inhibits the immune response.

countercurrent exchange: a mechanism for the transfer of some property, such as heat or a dissolved substance, from one fluid to another, generally without the two fluids actually mixing; in countercurrent exchange, the two fluids flow past one another in opposite directions, and they transfer heat or solute from the fluid with the higher temperature or higher solute concentration to the fluid with the lower temperature or lower solute concentration.

coupled reaction: a pair of reactions, one exergonic and one endergonic, that are linked together such that the energy produced by the exergonic reaction provides the energy needed to drive the endergonic reaction.

covalent bond (kō-vā'-lent): a chemical bond between atoms in which electrons are shared.

craniate: an animal that has a skull.

crassulacean acid metabolism (CAM): a biochemical pathway used by some plants in hot, dry climates to increase the efficiency of carbon fixation during photosynthesis. Mesophyll cells capture carbon dioxide at night and use it to produce sugar during the day.

critically endangered species: a species that faces an extreme risk of extinction in the wild in the immediate future.

cross-fertilization: the union of sperm and egg from two individuals of the same species.

crossing over: the exchange of corresponding segments of the chromatids of two homologous chromosomes during meiosis I; occurs at chiasmata.

cuticle (kū'-ti-kul): a waxy or fatty coating on the surfaces of the aboveground epidermal cells of many land plants; aids in the retention of water.

cytokine (sī'-tō-kīn): any of several chemical messenger molecules released by cells that facilitate communication with other cells and transfer signals within and among the various systems of the body. Cytokines are important in cellular differentiation and the adaptive immune response.

cytokinesis (sī-tō-ki-nē'-sis): the division of the cytoplasm and organelles into two daughter cells during cell division; normally occurs during telophase of mitotic and meiotic cell division.

cytoplasm (sī'-tō-plaz-um): all of the material contained within the plasma membrane of a cell, exclusive of the nucleus.

cytosine (C): a nitrogenous base found in both DNA and RNA; abbreviated as C.

cytoskeleton: a network of protein fibers in the cytoplasm that gives shape to a cell, holds and moves organelles, and is typically involved in cell movement.

cytosol: the fluid portion of the cytoplasm; the substance within the plasma membrane exclusive of the nucleus and organelles.

daughter cell: one of the two cells formed by cell division.

death rate: the number of deaths per individual in a specified unit of time, such as a year.

decomposer: an organism, usually a fungus or bacterium, that digests organic material by secreting digestive enzymes into the environment, in the process liberating nutrients into the environment.

deductive reasoning: the process of generating hypotheses about the results of a specific experiment or the nature of a specific observation.

deforestation: the excessive cutting of forests. In recent years, deforestation has occurred primarily in rain forests in the Tropics, to clear space for agriculture.

dehydration synthesis: a chemical reaction in which two molecules are joined by a covalent bond with the simultaneous removal of a hydrogen from one molecule and a hydroxyl group from the other, forming water; the reverse of hydrolysis.

deletion mutation: a mutation in which one or more pairs of nucleotides are removed from a gene.

demographic transition: a change in population dynamic in which a fairly stable population with both high birth rates and high death rates experiences rapid growth as death rates decline, and then returns to a stable (although much larger) population as birth rates decline.

demography: the study of the changes in human numbers over time, grouped by world regions, age, sex, educational levels, and other variables.

denature: to disrupt the secondary and/or tertiary structure of a protein while leaving its amino acid sequence intact. Denatured proteins can no longer perform their biological functions.

denatured: having the secondary and/or tertiary structure of a protein disrupted, while leaving the amino acid sequence unchanged. Denatured proteins can no longer perform their biological functions.

dendritic cell (den-drit'-ick): a type of phagocytic leukocyte that presents antigen to T and B cells, thereby stimulating an adaptive immune response to an invading microbe.

denitrifying bacteria (dē-nī'-treh-fī-ing): bacteria that break down nitrates, releasing nitrogen gas to the atmosphere.

density-dependent: referring to any factor, such as predation, that limits population size to an increasing extent as the population density increases.

density-independent: referring to any factor, such as floods or fires, that limits a population's size regardless of its density.

deoxyribonucleic acid (dē-ox-ē-rī-bō-noo-klā'-ik; DNA): a molecule composed of deoxyribose nucleotides; contains the genetic information of all living cells.

dermis (dur'-mis): the layer of skin beneath the epidermis; composed of connective tissue and containing blood vessels, muscles, nerve endings, and glands.

desert: a biome in which less than 10 inches (25 centimeters) of rain fall each year; characterized by cacti, succulents, and widely spaced, drought-resistant bushes.

desertification: the process by which relatively dry, drought-prone regions are converted to desert as a result of drought and overuse of the land, for example, by overgrazing or cutting of trees.

desmosome (dez'-mō-sōm): a strong cell-to-cell junction that attaches adjacent cells to one another.

detritivore (de-trī'-ti-vor): one of a diverse group of organisms, ranging from worms to vultures, that live off the wastes and dead remains of other organisms.

deuterostome (doo'-ter-ō-stōm): an animal with a mode of embryonic development in which the coelom is derived from outpocketings of the gut; characteristic of echinoderms and chordates.

developed country: a country such as Australia, Japan, and those in Europe and North America whose residents have relatively high average standards of living and good access to education, technology, and medical care.

developing country: a country (including most in Central and South America, Asia, and Africa) that has a relatively low average living standard and limited access to modern technology and medical care.

diabetes mellitus (di-uh-bē'-tēs mel-ī'-tus): a disease characterized by defects in the production, release, or reception of insulin; characterized by high blood glucose levels that fluctuate with sugar intake.

diastolic pressure (dī'-uh-stal-ik): the blood pressure measured during relaxation of the ventricles; the lower of the two blood pressure readings.

diatom (dī'-uh-tom): a member of a protist group that includes photosynthetic forms with two-part glassy outer coverings; important photosynthetic organisms in fresh water and salt water. Diatoms are part of a larger group known as the stramenopiles.

differentiate: the process whereby a cell becomes specialized in structure and function.

diffusion: the net movement of solute particles from a region of high solute concentration to a region of low solute concentration, driven by a concentration gradient; may occur within a fluid or across a barrier such as a membrane.

digestive system: a group of organs responsible for ingesting food, digesting food into simple molecules that can be absorbed into the circulatory system, and expelling undigested wastes from the body.

dinoflagellate (dī-nō-fla'-jel-et): a member of a protist group that includes photosynthetic forms in which two flagella project through armor-like plates; abundant in oceans; can reproduce rapidly, causing "red tides." Dinoflagellates are part of a larger group known as the alveolates.

diploid (dip'-loid): referring to a cell with pairs of homologous chromosomes.

diplomonad: a member of a protist group characterized by two nuclei and multiple flagella. Diplomonads, which include disease-causing parasites such as *Giardia*, are part of a larger group known as the excavates.

directional selection: a type of natural selection that favors one extreme of a range of phenotypes.

disaccharide (dī-sak'-uh-rīd): a carbohydrate formed by the covalent bonding of two monosaccharides.

disruptive selection: a type of natural selection that favors both extremes of a range of phenotypes.

dissolve: the process by which solvent molecules completely surround and disperse the individual atoms or molecules of another substance, the solute.

disturbance: any event that disrupts an ecosystem by altering its community, its abiotic structure, or both; disturbance precedes succession.

disulfide bond: the covalent bond formed between the sulfur atoms of two cysteines in a protein; typically causes the protein to fold by bringing otherwise distant parts of the protein close together.

DNA cloning: any of a variety of technologies that are used to produce multiple copies of a specific segment of DNA (usually a gene).

DNA helicase: an enzyme that helps unwind the DNA double helix during DNA replication.

DNA ligase: an enzyme that bonds the terminal sugar in one DNA strand to the terminal phosphate in a second DNA strand, creating a single strand with a continuous sugar-phosphate backbone.

DNA polymerase: an enzyme that bonds DNA nucleotides together into a continuous strand, using a preexisting DNA strand as a template.

DNA probe: a sequence of nucleotides that is complementary to the nucleotide sequence of a gene or other segment of DNA under study; used to locate the gene or DNA segment during gel electrophoresis or other methods of DNA analysis.

DNA profile: the pattern of short tandem repeats of specific DNA segments; using a standardized set of 13 short tandem repeats, DNA profiles identify individual people with great accuracy.

DNA replication: the copying of the double-stranded DNA molecule, producing two identical DNA double helices.

DNA sequencing: the process of determining the order of nucleotides in a DNA molecule.

domain: the broadest category for classifying organisms; organisms are classified into three domains: Bacteria, Archaea, and Eukarya.

dominance hierarchy: a social structure that arises when the animals in a social group establish individual ranks that determine access to resources; ranks are usually established through aggressive interactions.

dominant: an allele that can determine the phenotype of heterozygotes completely, such that they are indistinguishable from individuals homozygous for the allele; in the heterozygotes, the expression of the other (recessive) allele is completely masked.

dorsal root ganglion: a ganglion, located on the dorsal (sensory) branch of each spinal nerve, that contains the cell bodies of sensory neurons.

double fertilization: in flowering plants, the fusion of two sperm nuclei with the nuclei of two cells of the female gametophyte. One sperm nucleus fuses with the egg to form the zygote; the second sperm nucleus fuses with the two haploid nuclei of the central cell to form a triploid endosperm cell.

double helix (hē'-liks): the shape of the two-stranded DNA molecule; similar to a ladder twisted lengthwise into a corkscrew shape.

Down syndrome: a genetic disorder caused by the presence of three copies of chromosome 21; common characteristics include learning disabilities, distinctively shaped eyelids, a small mouth, heart defects, and low resistance to infectious diseases; also called *trisomy 21*.

duodenum: the first section of the small intestine, in which most food digestion occurs; receives chyme from the stomach, buffers and digestive enzymes from the pancreas, and bile from the liver and gallbladder.

duplicated chromosome: a eukaryotic chromosome following DNA replication; consists of two sister chromatids joined at the centromeres.

early loss population: a population characterized by a high birth rate, a high death rate among juveniles, and lower death rates among adults; early loss populations have a concave survivorship curve.

ecdysone (ek-dī'-sōn): a steroid hormone that triggers molting in insects and other arthropods.

ecological economics: the branch of economics that attempts to determine the monetary value of ecosystem services and to compare the monetary value of natural ecosystems with the monetary value of human activities that may reduce the services that natural ecosystems provide.

ecological footprint: the area of productive land needed to produce the resources used and absorb the wastes (including carbon dioxide) generated by an individual person, or by an average person of a specific part of the world (for example, an individual country), or of the entire world, using current technologies.

ecological isolation: reproductive isolation that arises when species do not interbreed because they occupy different habitats.

ecological niche (nitch): the role of a particular species within an ecosystem, including all aspects of its interaction with the living and nonliving environments.

ecology (ē-kol'-uh-jē): the study of the interrelationships of organisms with each other and with their nonliving environment.

ecosystem (ē'-kō-sis-tem): all the organisms and their nonliving environment within a defined area.

ecosystem services: the processes through which natural ecosystems and their living communities sustain and fulfill human life. Ecosystem services include purifying air and water, replenishing oxygen, pollinating plants, reducing flooding, providing wildlife habitat, and many more.

ectoderm (ek'-tō-derm): the outermost embryonic tissue layer, which gives rise to structures such as hair, the epidermis of the skin, and the nervous system.

effector (ē-fek'-tor): a part of the body (normally a muscle or gland) that carries out responses as directed by the nervous system.

electromagnetic spectrum: the range of all possible wavelengths of electromagnetic radiation, from wavelengths longer than radio waves, to microwaves, infrared, visible light, ultraviolet, x-rays, and gamma rays.

electron: a subatomic particle, found in an electron shell outside the nucleus of an atom, that bears a unit of negative charge and very little mass.

electron carrier: a molecule that can reversibly gain or lose electrons. Electron carriers generally accept high-energy electrons produced during an exergonic reaction and donate the electrons to acceptor molecules that use the energy to drive endergonic reactions.

electron shell: a region in an atom within which electrons orbit; each shell corresponds to a fixed energy level at a given distance from the nucleus.

electron transport chain (ETC): a series of electron carrier molecules, found in the thylakoid membranes of chloroplasts and the inner membrane of mitochondria, that extract energy from electrons and generate ATP or other energetic molecules.

element: a substance that cannot be broken down, or converted, to a simpler substance by ordinary chemical means.

embryo (em'-brē-ō): in animals, the stages of development that begin with the fertilization of the egg cell and end with hatching or birth; in mammals, the early stages in which the developing animal does not yet resemble the adult of the species.

embryonic stem cell (ESC): a cell derived from an early embryo that is capable of differentiating into any of the adult cell types.

emerging infectious disease: a previously unknown infectious disease (one caused by a microbe), or a previously known infectious disease whose frequency or severity has significantly increased in the past two decades.

emigration (em-uh-grā'-shun): migration of individuals out of an area.

endangered species: a species that faces a high risk of extinction in the wild in the near future.

endergonic (en-der-gon'-ik): pertaining to a chemical reaction that requires an input of energy to proceed; an "uphill" reaction.

endocrine disrupter: an environmental pollutant that interferes with endocrine function, often by disrupting the action of sex hormones.

endocrine hormone: a molecule produced by the cells of endocrine glands and released into the circulatory system. An endocrine hormone causes changes in target cells that bear specific receptors for the hormone.

endocytosis (en-dō-sī-tō'-sis): the process in which the plasma membrane engulfs extracellular material, forming membrane-bound sacs that enter the cytoplasm and thereby move material into the cell.

endoderm (en'-dō-derm): the innermost embryonic tissue layer, which gives rise to structures such as the lining of the digestive and respiratory tracts.

endomembrane system: internal membranes that create loosely connected compartments within the eukaryotic cell. It includes the nuclear envelope, the endoplasmic reticulum, vesicles, the Golgi apparatus, and lysosomes.

endoplasmic reticulum (en-dō-plaz'-mik re-tik'-ū-lum; ER): a system of membranous tubes and channels in eukaryotic cells; the site of most protein and lipid synthesis.

endoskeleton (en'-dō-skel'-uh-tun): a rigid internal skeleton with flexible joints that allow for movement.

endospore: a protective resting structure of some rod-shaped bacteria that withstands unfavorable environmental conditions.

endosymbiont hypothesis: the hypothesis that certain organelles, especially chloroplasts and mitochondria, arose as mutually beneficial associations between the ancestors of eukaryotic cells and captured bacteria that lived within the cytoplasm of the pre-eukaryotic cell.

energy: the capacity to do work.

energy-carrier molecule: high-energy molecules that are synthesized at the site of an exergonic reaction, where they capture one or two energized electrons and hydrogen ions. They include nicotinamide adenine dinucleotide (NADH) and its relative, flavin adenine dinucleotide ($FADH_2$).

energy pyramid: a graphical representation of the energy contained in succeeding trophic levels, with maximum energy at the base (primary producers) and steadily diminishing amounts at higher levels.

energy-requiring transport: the transfer of substances across a cell membrane using cellular energy; includes active transport, endocytosis, and exocytosis.

entropy (en'-trō-pē): a measure of the amount of randomness and disorder in a system.

environmental resistance: any factor that tends to counteract biotic potential, limiting population growth and the resulting population size.

enzyme (en'-zīm): a biological catalyst, usually a protein, that speeds up the rate of specific biological reactions.

epidermal tissue: dermal tissue in plants that forms the epidermis, the outermost cell layer that covers leaves, young stems, and young roots.

epidermis (ep-uh-der'-mis): in animals, specialized stratified epithelial tissue that forms the outer layer of the skin; in plants, the outermost layer of cells of a leaf, young root, or young stem.

epigenetics: the study of the mechanisms by which cells and organisms change gene expression and function without changing the base sequence of their DNA; usually, epigenetic controls over DNA expression involve modification of DNA, modification of chromosomal proteins, or alteration of transcription or translation through the actions of noncoding RNA molecules.

epinephrine (ep-i-nef'-rin): a hormone, secreted by the adrenal medulla, that is released in response to stress and that stimulates a variety of responses, including the release of glucose from the liver and an increase in heart rate.

equilibrium population: a population in which allele frequencies and the distribution of genotypes do not change from generation to generation.

erythropoietin (eh-rith'-rō-pō-ē'-tin): a hormone produced by the kidneys in response to oxygen deficiency; stimulates the production of red blood cells by the bone marrow.

essential amino acid: an amino acid that is a required nutrient; the body is unable to manufacture essential amino acids, so they must be supplied in the diet.

essential nutrient: any nutrient that cannot be synthesized by the body, including certain fatty acids and amino acids, vitamins, minerals, and water.

estuary (es'-choō-ār-ē): a wetland formed where a river meets the ocean; the salinity is quite variable, but lower than in seawater and higher than in fresh water.

ethology (ē-thol'-ō-jē): the study of animal behavior.

euglenid (ū'-gle-nid): a member of a protist group characterized by one or more whip-like flagella, which are used for locomotion, and by a photoreceptor, which detects light; are photosynthetic. Euglenids are part of a larger group known as euglenozoans.

euglenozoan: a member of the Euglenozoa, a protist clade. The euglenozoans, which are characterized by mitochondrial membranes that appear under the microscope to be shaped like a stack of disks, include the euglenids and the kinetoplastids.

Eukarya (ū-kar'-ē-a): one of life's three domains; consists of all eukaryotes (plants, animals, fungi, and protists).

eukaryote (ū-kar'-ē-ōt): an organism whose cells are eukaryotic; plants, animals, fungi, and protists are eukaryotes.

eukaryotic (ū-kar-ē-ot'-ik): referring to cells of organisms of the domain Eukarya (plants, animals, fungi, and protists). Eukaryotic cells have genetic material enclosed within a membrane-bound nucleus and they contain other membrane-bound organelles.

eutrophic lake: a lake that receives sufficiently large inputs of sediments, organic material, and inorganic nutrients from its surroundings to support dense communities, especially of plants and phytoplankton; contains murky water with poor light penetration.

evolution: (1) the descent of modern organisms, with modification, from preexisting life-forms; (2) the theory that all organisms are related by common ancestry and have changed over time; (3) any change in the genetic makeup (the proportions of different genotypes) of a population from one generation to the next.

excavate: a member of the Excavata, a protist clade. The excavates, which generally lack mitochondria, include the diplomonads and the parabasalids.

excretion: the elimination of waste substances from the body; can occur from the digestive system, skin glands, urinary system, or lungs.

exergonic (ex-er-gon'-ik): pertaining to a chemical reaction that releases energy (either as heat or in the form of increased entropy); a "downhill" reaction.

exocrine gland: a gland that releases its secretions into ducts that lead to the outside of the body or into a body cavity, such as the digestive or reproductive system; most exocrine glands are composed of epithelial cells.

exocytosis (ex-ō-sī-tō'-sis): the process in which intracellular material is enclosed within a membrane-bound sac that moves to the plasma membrane and fuses with it, releasing the material outside the cell.

exon: a segment of DNA in a eukaryotic gene that codes for amino acids in a protein; see also *intron*.

exoskeleton (ex'-ō-skel'-uh-tun): a rigid external skeleton that supports the body, protects the internal organs, and has flexible joints that allow for movement.

experiment: in the scientific method, the use of carefully controlled observations or manipulations to test the predictions generated by a hypothesis.

exponential growth: a continuously accelerating increase in population size; this type of growth generates a curve shaped like the letter "J."

external fertilization: the union of sperm and egg outside the body of either parent.

extinction: the death of all members of a species.

extraembryonic membrane: in the embryonic development of reptiles (including birds) and mammals, one of the following membranes: the chorion (functions in gas exchange), amnion (provision of the watery environment needed for development), allantois (waste storage), or yolk sac (storage of the yolk).

facilitated diffusion: the diffusion of molecules across a membrane, assisted by protein pores or carriers embedded in the membrane.

family: in Linnaean classification, the taxonomic rank composed of related genera. Closely related families make up an order.

fat (molecular): a lipid composed of three saturated fatty acids covalently bonded to glycerol; fats are solid at room temperature.

fatty acid: an organic molecule composed of a long chain of carbon atoms, with a carboxylic acid (–COOH) group at one end; may be saturated (all single bonds between the carbon atoms) or unsaturated (one or more double bonds between the carbon atoms).

feedback inhibition: in enzyme-mediated chemical reactions, the condition in which the product of a reaction inhibits one or more of the enzymes involved in synthesizing the product.

fermentation: anaerobic reactions that convert the pyruvic acid produced by glycolysis into lactic acid or alcohol and CO_2, using hydrogen ions and electrons from NADH; the primary function of fermentation is to regenerate NAD+ so that glycolysis can continue under anaerobic conditions.

fetal alcohol syndrome (FAS): a cluster of symptoms, including mental retardation and physical abnormalities, that occur in infants born to mothers who consumed large amounts of alcoholic beverages during pregnancy.

fever: an elevation in body temperature caused by chemicals (pyrogens) that are released by white blood cells in response to infection.

fibrin (fī'-brin): a clotting protein formed in the blood in response to a wound; binds with other fibrin molecules and provides a matrix around which a blood clot forms.

fibrinogen (fī-brin'-ō-jen): the inactive form of the clotting protein fibrin. Fibrinogen is converted into fibrin by the enzyme thrombin, which is produced in response to injury.

filament: in flowers, the stalk of a stamen, which bears an anther at its tip.

filtration: within Bowman's capsule in each nephron of a kidney, the process by which blood is pumped under pressure through permeable capillaries of the glomerulus, forcing out water and small solutes, including wastes and nutrients.

first law of thermodynamics: the principle of physics that states that within any closed system, energy can be neither created nor destroyed, but can be converted from one form to another; also called the law of conservation of energy.

fitness: the reproductive success of an organism, relative to the average reproductive success in the population.

flagellum (fla-jel'-um; pl., flagella): a long, hair-like, motile extension of the plasma membrane; in eukaryotic cells, it contains microtubules arranged in a 9 + 2 pattern. The movement of flagella propels some cells through fluids.

flavin adenine dinucleotide (FAD or FADH$_2$): an electron-carrier molecule produced in the mitochondrial matrix by the Krebs cycle; subsequently donates electrons to the electron transport chain.

florigen: one of a group of plant hormones that may stimulate or inhibit flowering in response to day length.

flower: the reproductive structure of an angiosperm plant.

fluid: any substance whose molecules can freely flow past one another; "fluid" can describe liquids, cell membranes, and gases.

fluid mosaic model: a model of cell membrane structure; according to this model, membranes are composed of a double layer of phospholipids in which various proteins are embedded. The phospholipid bilayer is a somewhat fluid matrix that allows the movement of proteins within it.

follicle-stimulating hormone (FSH): a hormone, produced by the anterior pituitary, that stimulates spermatogenesis in males and the development of the follicle in females.

food chain: a linear feeding relationship in a community, using a single representative from each of the trophic levels.

food vacuole: a membranous sac, within a single cell, in which food is enclosed. Digestive enzymes are released into the vacuole, where intracellular digestion occurs.

food web: a representation of the complex feeding relationships within a community, including many organisms at various trophic levels, with many of the consumers occupying more than one level simultaneously.

foraminiferan (for-am-i-nif'-er-un): a member of a protist group characterized by pseudopods and elaborate calcium carbonate shells. Foraminiferans are generally aquatic (largely marine) and are part of a larger group known as rhizarians.

fossil: the remains of a dead organism, normally preserved in rock; may be petrified bones or wood; shells; impressions of body forms, such as feathers, skin, or leaves; or markings made by organisms, such as footprints.

fossil fuel: a fuel, such as coal, oil, and natural gas, derived from the remains of ancient organisms.

founder effect: the result of an event in which an isolated population is founded by a small number of individuals; may result in genetic drift if allele frequencies in the founder population are by chance different from those of the parent population.

free nucleotide: a nucleotide that has not been joined with other nucleotides to form a DNA or RNA strand.

free radical: a molecule containing an atom with an unpaired electron, which makes it highly unstable and reactive with nearby molecules. By removing an electron from the molecule it attacks, it creates a new free radical and begins a chain reaction that can lead to the destruction of biological molecules crucial to life.

functional group: one of several groups of atoms commonly found in an organic molecule, including hydrogen, hydroxyl, amino, carboxyl, and phosphate groups, that determine the characteristics and chemical reactivity of the molecule.

gamete (gam'-ēt): a haploid sex cell, usually a sperm or an egg, formed in sexually reproducing organisms.

gametic incompatibility: a postmating reproductive isolating mechanism that arises when sperm from one species cannot fertilize eggs of another species.

ganglion (gang'-lē-un; pl., ganglia): a cluster of neurons.

gap junction: a type of cell-to-cell junction in animals in which channels connect the cytoplasm of adjacent cells.

gastric gland: one of numerous small glands in the stomach lining; contains cells that secrete mucus, hydrochloric acid, or pepsinogen (the inactive form of the protease pepsin).

gastrovascular cavity: a saclike chamber with digestive functions, found in some invertebrates such as cnidarians (sea jellies, anemones, and related animals); a single opening serves as both mouth and anus.

gastrulation (gas-troo-la'-shun): the process whereby a blastula develops into a gastrula, including the formation of endoderm, ectoderm, and mesoderm.

gel electrophoresis: a technique in which molecules (such as DNA fragments) are placed in wells in a thin sheet of gelatinous material and exposed to an electric field; the molecules migrate through the gel at a rate determined by certain characteristics, most commonly size.

gene: the unit of heredity; a segment of DNA located at a particular place on a chromosome that usually encodes the information for the amino acid sequence of a protein and, hence, a particular trait.

gene flow: the movement of alleles from one population to another owing to the migration of individual organisms.

gene linkage: the tendency for genes located on the same chromosome to be inherited together.

gene pool: the total of all alleles of all genes in a population; for a single gene, the total of all the alleles of that gene that occur in a population.

gene therapy: the attempt to cure a disease by inserting, deleting, or altering a patient's genes.

genetic code: the collection of codons of mRNA, each of which directs the incorporation of a particular amino acid into a protein during protein synthesis or causes protein synthesis to start or stop.

genetic drift: a change in the allele frequencies of a small population purely by chance.

genetic engineering: the modification of the genetic material of an organism, usually using recombinant DNA techniques.

genetic recombination: the generation of new combinations of alleles on homologous chromosomes due to the exchange of DNA during crossing over.

genetically modified organism (GMO): a plant or animal that contains DNA that has been modified or that has been obtained from another species.

genomic imprinting: a form of epigenetic control by which a given gene is expressed in an offspring only if the gene has been inherited from a specific parent; the copy of the gene that was inherited from the other parent is usually not expressed.

genotype (jēn'-ō-tip): the genetic composition of an organism; the actual alleles of each gene carried by the organism.

genus (jē'-nus): in Linnaean classification, the taxonomic rank composed of related species. Closely related genera make up a family.

geographic isolation: reproductive isolation that arises when species do not interbreed because a physical barrier separates them.

ghrelin (grel'-in): a peptide hormone secreted by the stomach that acts via the hypothalamus to stimulate hunger.

gill: in aquatic animals, a branched tissue richly supplied with capillaries around which water is circulated for gas exchange.

glia: cells of the nervous system that provide nutrients for neurons, regulate the composition of the interstitial fluid in the brain and spinal cord, modulate communication between neurons, and insulate axons, thereby speeding up the conduction of action potentials. Also called *glial cells*.

glomeromycete: a member of the fungus clade Glomeromycota, which includes species that form mycorrhizal associations with plant roots and that form bush-shaped branching structures inside plant cells.

glucagon (gloo'-ka-gon): a hormone, secreted by the pancreas, that increases blood sugar by stimulating the breakdown of glycogen (to glucose) in the liver.

glucose: the most common monosaccharide, with the molecular formula $C_6H_{12}O_6$; most polysaccharides, including cellulose, starch, and glycogen, are made of glucose subunits covalently bonded together.

glycerol (glis'-er-ol): a three-carbon alcohol to which fatty acids are covalently bonded to make fats and oils.

glycogen (glī'-kō-jen): a highly branched polymer of glucose that is stored by animals in the muscles and liver and metabolized as a source of energy.

glycolysis (glī-kol'-i-sis): reactions, carried out in the cytoplasm, that break down glucose into two molecules of pyruvic acid, producing two ATP molecules; does not require oxygen but can proceed when oxygen is present.

glycoprotein: a protein to which a carbohydrate is attached.

Golgi apparatus (gōl'-jē): a stack of membranous sacs, found in most eukaryotic cells, that is the site of processing and separation of membrane components and secretory materials.

gonadotropin-releasing hormone (gō-na-dō-trō'-pin; GnRH): a hormone produced by the neurosecretory cells of the hypothalamus, which stimulates cells in the anterior pituitary to release follicle-stimulating hormone (FSH) and luteinizing hormone (LH). GnRH is involved in the menstrual cycle and in spermatogenesis.

gradient: a difference in concentration, pressure, or electrical charge between two regions.

grassland: a biome, located in the centers of continents, that primarily supports grasses; also called a *prairie*.

gray matter: the outer portion of the brain and inner region of the spinal cord; composed largely of neuron cell bodies, which give this area a gray color in preserved tissue.

greenhouse effect: the process in which certain gases such as carbon dioxide and methane trap sunlight energy in a planet's atmosphere as heat; the glass in a greenhouse causes a similar warming effect. The result, global warming that causes climate change, is being enhanced by the production of these gases by humans.

greenhouse gas: a gas, such as carbon dioxide or methane, that traps sunlight energy in a planet's atmosphere as heat; a gas that participates in the greenhouse effect.

growth factor: small molecules, usually proteins or steroids, that bind to receptors on or in target cells and enhance their rate of cell division or differentiation.

growth rate: a measure of the change in population size per individual per unit of time.

guanine (G): a nitrogenous base found in both DNA and RNA; abbreviated as G.

gymnosperm (jim'-nō-sperm): a nonflowering seed plant, such as a conifer, gnetophyte, cycad, or gingko.

gyre (jīr): a roughly circular pattern of ocean currents, formed because continents interrupt the flow of the current; rotates clockwise in the Northern Hemisphere and counterclockwise in the Southern Hemisphere.

habitat fragmentation: the process by which human development and activities produce patches of wildlife habitat that may not be large enough to sustain minimum viable populations.

habituation (heh-bich-oo-ā'-shun): a type of simple learning characterized by a decline in response to a repeated stimulus.

hair follicle (fol'-i-kul): a cluster of specialized epithelial cells located in the dermis of mammalian skin, which produces a hair.

haploid (hap'-loid): referring to a cell that has only one member of each pair of homologous chromosomes.

Hardy–Weinberg principle: a mathematical model proposing that, under certain conditions, the allele frequencies and genotype frequencies in a sexually reproducing population will remain constant over generations.

heart attack: a severe reduction or blockage of blood flow through a coronary artery, depriving some of the heart muscle of its blood supply.

heartwood: older secondary xylem that usually no longer conducts water or minerals, but that contributes to the strength of a tree trunk.

heat of fusion: the energy that must be removed from a compound to transform it from a liquid into a solid at its freezing temperature.

heat of vaporization: the energy that must be supplied to a compound to transform it from a liquid into a gas at its boiling temperature.

helix (hē'-liks): a coiled, spring-like secondary structure of a protein.

hemocoel (hē'-mō-sēl): a cavity within the bodies of certain invertebrates in which a fluid, called hemolymph, bathes tissues directly; part of an open circulatory system.

hemodialysis (hē-mō-dī-al'-luh-sis): a procedure that simulates kidney function in individuals with damaged or ineffective kidneys; blood is diverted from the body, artificially filtered, and returned to the body.

hemolymph: in animals with an open circulatory system, the fluid that is located within the hemocoel and that bathes all the body cells, therefore serving as both blood and interstitial fluid.

hemophilia: a recessive, sex-linked disease in which the blood fails to clot normally.

hermaphrodite (her-maf'-ruh-dit'): an organism that possesses both male and female sexual organs. Some hermaphroditic animals can fertilize themselves; others must exchange sex cells with a mate.

hermaphroditic (her-maf'-ruh-dit'-ik): possessing both male and female sexual organs. Some hermaphroditic animals can fertilize themselves; others must exchange sex cells with a mate.

heterotroph (het'-er-ō-trōf'): literally, "other-feeder"; an organism that eats other organisms; a consumer.

heterozygous (het'-er-ō-zī'-gus): carrying two different alleles of a given gene; also called *hybrid*.

hinge joint: a joint at which the bones fit together in a way that allows movement in only two dimensions, as at the elbow or knee.

histamine (his'-ta-mēn): a substance released by certain cells in response to tissue damage and invasion of the body by foreign substances; promotes the dilation of arterioles and the leakiness of capillaries and triggers some of the events of the inflammatory response.

homeostasis (hōm-ē-ō-stā'-sis): the maintenance of the relatively constant internal environment that is required for the optimal functioning of cells.

hominin: a human or a prehistoric relative of humans; the oldest known hominin is *Sahelanthropus*, whose fossils are more than 6 million years old.

homologous chromosome: a chromosome that is similar in appearance and genetic information to another chromosome with which it pairs during meiosis; also called *homologue*.

homologous structure: structures that may differ in function but that have similar anatomy, presumably because the organisms that possess them have descended from common ancestors.

homologue (hō'-mō-log): a chromosome that is similar in appearance and genetic information to another chromosome with which it pairs during meiosis; also called *homologous chromosome*.

homozygous (hō-mō-zī'-gus): carrying two copies of the same allele of a given gene; also called *true-breeding*.

host: the prey organism on or in which a parasite lives; the host is harmed by the relationship.

human papillomavirus (pap-il-lo'-ma; HPV): a virus that infects the reproductive organs, often causing genital warts; causes most, if not all, cases of cervical cancer.

Huntington disease: an incurable genetic disorder, caused by a dominant allele, that produces progressive brain deterioration, resulting in the loss of motor coordination, flailing movements, personality disturbances, and eventual death.

hybrid: an organism that is the offspring of parents differing in at least one genetically determined characteristic; also used to refer to the offspring of parents of different species.

hybrid infertility: a postmating reproductive isolating mechanism that arises when hybrid offspring (offspring of parents of two different species) are sterile or have low fertility.

hybrid inviability: a postmating reproductive isolating mechanism that arises when hybrid offspring (offspring of parents of two different species) fail to survive.

hydrogen bond: the weak attraction between a hydrogen atom that bears a partial positive charge (due to polar covalent bonding with another atom) and another atom (oxygen, nitrogen, or fluorine) that bears a partial negative charge; hydrogen bonds may form between atoms of a single molecule or of different molecules.

hydrologic cycle (hī-drō-loj'-ik): the biogeochemical cycle by which water travels from its major reservoir, the oceans, through the atmosphere to reservoirs in freshwater lakes, rivers, and groundwater, and back into the oceans. The hydrologic cycle is driven by solar energy. Nearly all water remains as water throughout the cycle (rather than being used in the synthesis of new molecules).

hydrolysis (hī-drol'-i-sis): the chemical reaction that breaks a covalent bond by means of the addition of hydrogen to the atom on one side of the original bond and a hydroxyl group to the atom on the other side; the reverse of dehydration synthesis.

hydrophilic (hī-drō-fil'-ik): pertaining to molecules that dissolve readily in water, or to molecules that form hydrogen bonds with water; polar.

hydrophobic (hī-drō-fō'-bik): pertaining to molecules that do not dissolve in water or form hydrogen bonds with water; nonpolar.

hydrophobic interaction: the tendency for hydrophobic molecules to cluster together when immersed in water.

hydrothermal vent community: a community of unusual organisms, living in the deep ocean near hydrothermal vents, that depends on the chemosynthetic activities of sulfur bacteria.

hypertonic (hī-per-ton'-ik): referring to a solution that has a higher concentration of solute (and therefore a lower concentration of free water) than has the cytosol of a cell.

hypha (hī'-fuh; pl., hyphae): in fungi, a threadlike structure that consists of elongated cells, typically with many haploid nuclei; many hyphae make up the fungal body.

hypothalamus: (hī-pō-thal'-a-mus): a region of the brain that controls the secretory activity of the pituitary gland; synthesizes, stores, and releases certain peptide hormones; and directs autonomic nervous system responses.

hypothesis (hī-poth'-eh-sis): a proposed explanation for a phenomenon, often based on limited evidence, that leads to a prediction that can be tested.

hypotonic (hī-pō-ton'-ik): referring to a solution that has a lower concentration of solute (and therefore a higher concentration of free water) than has the cytosol of a cell.

immigration (im-uh-grā'-shun): migration of individuals into an area.

immune system: a system of cells, including macrophages, B cells, and T cells, and molecules, such as antibodies and cytokines, that work together to combat microbial invasion of the body.

implantation: the process whereby the early embryo embeds itself within the lining of the uterus.

imprinting: a type of learning in which an animal acquires a particular type of information during a specific sensitive phase of development.

incomplete dominance: a pattern of inheritance in which the heterozygous phenotype is intermediate between the two homozygous phenotypes.

indirect development: a developmental pathway in which an offspring goes through radical changes in body form as it matures.

induction: the process by which a group of cells causes other cells to differentiate into a specific tissue type.

inductive reasoning: the process of creating a generalization based on many specific observations that support the generalization, coupled with an absence of observations that contradict it.

ingestion: the movement of food into the digestive tract, usually through the mouth.

inheritance: the genetic transmission of characteristics from parent to offspring.

inhibitory postsynaptic potential (IPSP): an electrical signal produced in a postsynaptic cell that makes the resting potential more negative and, hence, makes the neuron less likely to fire an action potential.

innate (in-āt'): inborn; instinctive; an innate behavior is performed correctly the first time it is attempted.

inner cell mass: in human embryonic development, the cluster of cells, on the inside of the blastocyst, that will develop into the embryo.

inorganic: describing any molecule that does not contain both carbon and hydrogen.

insertion: the site of attachment of a muscle to the relatively movable bone on one side of a joint.

insertion mutation: a mutation in which one or more pairs of nucleotides are inserted into a gene.

insight learning: a type of learning in which a problem is solved by understanding the relationships among the components of the problem rather than through trial and error.

integration: the process of adding up all of the electrical signals in a neuron, including sensory inputs and postsynaptic potentials, to determine the output of the neuron (action potentials and/or synaptic transmission).

intensity: the strength of stimulation or response.

intermediate filament: part of the cytoskeleton of eukaryotic cells that is composed of several types of proteins and probably functions mainly for support.

intermembrane space: the fluid-filled space between the inner and outer membranes of a mitochondrion.

interneuron: in a neural network, a nerve cell that is postsynaptic to a sensory neuron and presynaptic to a motor neuron. In actual circuits, there may be many interneurons between individual sensory and motor neurons.

interphase: the stage of the cell cycle between cell divisions in which chromosomes are duplicated and other cell functions occur, such as growth, movement, and acquisition of nutrients.

interspecific competition: competition among individuals of different species.

interstitial fluid: fluid that bathes the cells of the body; in mammals, interstitial fluid leaks from capillaries and is similar in composition to blood plasma, but lacking the large proteins found in plasma.

intertidal zone: an area of the ocean shore that is alternately covered by water during high tides and exposed to the air during low tides.

intraspecific competition: competition among individuals of the same species.

intron: a segment of DNA in a eukaryotic gene that does not code for amino acids in a protein; see also *exon*.

invasive species: organisms with a high biotic potential that are introduced (deliberately or accidentally) into ecosystems where they did not evolve and where they encounter little environmental resistance and tend to displace native species.

inversion: a mutation that occurs when a piece of DNA is cut out of a chromosome, turned around, and reinserted into the gap.

invertebrate (in-vert'-uh-bret): an animal that lacks a vertebral column.

ion (ī-on): a charged atom or molecule; an atom or molecule that has either an excess of electrons (and, hence, is negatively charged) or has lost electrons (and is positively charged).

ionic bond: a chemical bond formed by the electrical attraction between positively and negatively charged ions.

islet cell: a cell in the endocrine portion of the pancreas that produces either insulin or glucagon.

isolating mechanism: a morphological, physiological, behavioral, or ecological difference that prevents members of two species from interbreeding.

isotonic (ī-sō-ton'-ik): referring to a solution that has the same concentration of solute (and therefore the same concentration of free water) as has the cytosol of a cell.

isotope (ī'-suh-tōp): one of several forms of a single element, the nuclei of which contain the same number of protons but different numbers of neutrons.

Jacob syndrome: a set of characteristics typical of human males possessing one X and two Y chromosomes (XYY); most XYY males are phenotypically normal, but XYY males tend to be taller than average and to have a slightly increased risk of learning disabilities.

J-curve: the J-shaped growth curve of an exponentially growing population in which increasing numbers of individuals join the population during each succeeding time period.

karyotype: a preparation showing the number, sizes, and shapes of all of the chromosomes within a cell.

kelp forest: a diverse ecosystem consisting of stands of tall brown algae and associated marine life. Kelp forests occur in oceans worldwide in nutrient-rich cool coastal waters.

keratin (ker'-uh-tin): a fibrous protein in hair, nails, and the epidermis of skin.

keystone species: a species whose influence on community structure is greater than its abundance would suggest.

kin selection: a type of natural selection that favors traits that enhance the survival or reproduction of an individual's relatives, even if the traits reduce the fitness of the individuals bearing them.

kinetic energy: the energy of movement; includes light, heat, mechanical movement, and electricity.

kinetochore (ki-net'-ō-kor): a protein structure that forms at the centromere regions of chromosomes; attaches the chromosomes to the spindle.

kinetoplastid: a member of a protist group characterized by distinctively structured mitochondria. Kinetoplastids are mostly flagellated and include parasitic forms such as *Trypanosoma*, which causes sleeping sickness. Kinetoplastids are part of a larger group known as euglenozoans.

kingdom: the second broadest taxonomic category, consisting of related phyla. Related kingdoms make up a domain.

Klinefelter syndrome: a set of characteristics typically found in individuals who have two X chromosomes and one Y chromosome; these individuals are phenotypically males but are sterile and may have several female-like traits, including broad hips and partial breast development.

Krebs cycle: a cyclic series of reactions, occurring in the matrix of mitochondria, in which the acetyl groups from the pyruvic acids produced by glycolysis are broken down to CO_2, accompanied by the formation of ATP and electron carriers; also called the citric acid cycle.

labor: a series of contractions of the uterus that result in birth.

lacteal (lak-tēl'): a lymph capillary; found in each villus of the small intestine.

lactic acid fermentation: anaerobic reactions that convert the pyruvic acid produced by glycolysis into lactic acid, using hydrogen ions and electrons from NADH; the primary function of lactic acid fermentation is to regenerate NAD^+ so that glycolysis can continue under anaerobic conditions.

lactose (lak'-tōs): a disaccharide composed of glucose and galactose; found in mammalian milk.

lactose intolerance: the inability to digest lactose (milk sugar) because lactase, the enzyme that digests lactose, is not produced in sufficient amounts; symptoms include bloating, gas pains, and diarrhea.

lactose operon: in prokaryotes, the set of genes that encodes the proteins needed for lactose metabolism, including both the structural genes and a common promoter and operator that control transcription of the structural genes.

larva (lar'-vuh; pl., larvae): an immature form of an animal that subsequently undergoes metamorphosis into its adult form; includes the caterpillars of moths and butterflies, the maggots of flies, and the tadpoles of frogs and toads.

late-loss population: a population in which most individuals survive into adulthood; late-loss populations have a convex survivorship curve.

lateral meristem: a meristem tissue that forms cylinders parallel to the long axis of roots and stems; normally located between the primary xylem and primary phloem (vascular cambium) and just outside the phloem (cork cambium); also called *cambium*.

law of conservation of energy: the principle of physics that states that within any closed system, energy can be neither created nor destroyed, but can be converted from one form to another; also called the first law of thermodynamics.

law of independent assortment: the independent inheritance of two or more traits, assuming that each trait is controlled by a single gene with no influence from gene(s) controlling the other trait; states that the alleles of each gene are distributed to the gametes independently of the alleles for other genes; this law is true only for genes located on different chromosomes or very far apart on a single chromosome.

law of segregation: the principle that each gamete receives only one of each parent's pair of alleles of each gene.

laws of thermodynamics: the physical laws that define the basic properties and behavior of energy.

leaf primordium (pri-mor'-dē-um; pl., pri-mor-dia): a cluster of dividing cells, surrounding a terminal or lateral bud, that develops into a leaf.

learning: the process by which behavior is modified in response to experience.

lens: a clear object that bends light rays; in eyes, a flexible or movable structure used to focus light on the photoreceptor cells of the retina.

leukocyte (loo'-kō-sīt): any of the white blood cells circulating in the blood.

lichen (lī'-ken): a symbiotic association between an alga or cyanobacterium and a fungus, resulting in a composite organism.

life table: a data table that groups organisms born at the same time and tracks them throughout their life span, recording how many continue to survive in each succeeding year (or other unit of time). Various parameters such as sex may be used in the groupings. Human life tables may include many other parameters (such as socioeconomic status) used by demographers.

light reactions: the first stage of photosynthesis, in which the energy of light is captured as ATP and NADPH; occurs in thylakoids of chloroplasts.

lignin: a hard material that is embedded in the cell walls of vascular plants and that provides support in terrestrial species; an early and important adaptation to terrestrial life.

limnetic zone: the part of a lake in which enough light penetrates to support photosynthesis.

linkage: the inheritance of certain genes as a group because they are parts of the same chromosome. Linked genes do not show independent assortment.

lipid (li'-pid): one of a number of organic molecules containing large nonpolar regions composed solely of carbon and hydrogen, which make lipids hydrophobic and insoluble in water; includes oils, fats, waxes, phospholipids, and steroids.

littoral zone: the part of a lake, usually close to the shore, in which the water is shallow and plants find abundant light, anchorage, and adequate nutrients.

lobefin: fish with fleshy fins that have well-developed bones and muscles. Lobefins include two living clades: the coelacanths and the lungfishes.

locus (pl., loci): the physical location of a gene on a chromosome.

logistic population growth: population growth characterized by an early exponential growth phase, followed by slower growth as the population approaches its carrying capacity, and finally reaching a stable population at the carrying capacity of the environment; this type of growth generates a curve shaped like a stretched-out letter "S."

long-term memory: the second phase of learning; a more-or-less permanent memory formed by a structural change in the brain, brought on by repetition.

lung: in terrestrial vertebrates, one of the pair of respiratory organs in which gas exchange occurs; consists of inflatable chambers within the chest cavity.

lymph (limf): a pale fluid found within the lymphatic system; composed primarily of interstitial fluid and white blood cells.

lymphatic capillary: the smallest vessel of the lymphatic system. Lymphatic capillaries end blindly in interstitial fluid, which they take up and return to the bloodstream.

lymphocyte (lim'-fō-sit): a type of white blood cell (natural killer cell, B cell, or T cell) that is important in either the innate or adaptive immune response.

macronutrient: a nutrient required by an organism in relatively large quantities.

major histocompatibility complex (MHC): a group of proteins, normally located on the surfaces of body cells, that identify the cell as "self"; also important in stimulating and regulating the immune response.

maltose (mal'-tōs): a disaccharide composed of two glucose molecules.

mammal: a member of the chordate clade Mammalia, which includes vertebrates with hair and mammary glands.

marsupial (mar-soo'-pē-ul): a member of the clade Marsupialia, which includes mammals whose young are born at an extremely immature stage and undergo further development in a pouch, where they remain attached to a mammary gland; kangaroos, opossums, and koalas are marsupials.

mass extinction: a relatively sudden extinction of many species, belonging to multiple major taxonomic groups, as a result of environmental change. The fossil record reveals five mass extinctions over geologic time.

mass number: The total number of protons and neutrons in the nucleus of an atom.

matrix: The fluid contained within the inner membrane of the mitochondrion.

mechanical incompatibility: a reproductive isolating mechanism that arises when differences in the reproductive structures of two species make the structures incompatible and prevent interbreeding.

medulla (med-ū'-luh): the part of the hindbrain of vertebrates that controls automatic activities such as breathing, swallowing, heart rate, and blood pressure.

megakaryocyte (meg-a-kar'-ē-ō-sit): a large cell type in the bone marrow, which pinches off pieces of itself that enter the circulation as platelets.

megaspore mother cell: a diploid cell, within the ovule of a flowering plant, that undergoes meiotic cell division to produce four haploid megaspores.

meiosis (mī-ō'-sis): in eukaryotic organisms, a type of nuclear division in which a diploid nucleus divides twice to form four haploid nuclei.

meiotic cell division: meiosis followed by cytokinesis.

memory B cell: a type of white blood cell that is produced by clonal selection as a result of the binding of an antibody on a B cell to an antigen on an invading microorganism. Memory B cells persist in the bloodstream and provide future immunity to invaders bearing that antigen.

menstrual cycle: in human females, a roughly 28-day cycle during which hormonal interactions among the hypothalamus, pituitary gland, and ovary coordinate ovulation and the preparation of the uterus to receive and nourish a fertilized egg. If pregnancy does not occur, the uterine lining is shed during menstruation.

meristem cell (mer'-i-stem): an undifferentiated cell that remains capable of cell division throughout the life of a plant.

mesophyll (mez'-ō-fil): loosely packed, usually photosynthetic cells located beneath the epidermis of a leaf.

messenger RNA (mRNA): a strand of RNA, complementary to the DNA of a gene, that conveys the genetic information in DNA to the ribosomes to be used during protein synthesis; sequences of three bases (codons) in mRNA that specify particular amino acids to be incorporated into a protein.

metabolic pathway: a sequence of chemical reactions within a cell in which the products of one reaction are the reactants for the next reaction.

metabolism: the sum of all chemical reactions that occur within a single cell or within all the cells of a multicellular organism.

metaphase (met'-a-fāz): in mitosis, the stage in which the chromosomes, attached to spindle fibers at kinetochores, are lined up along the equator of the cell; also the approximately comparable stages in meiosis I and meiosis II.

microfilament: part of the cytoskeleton of eukaryotic cells that is composed of the proteins actin and (in some cases) myosin; functions in the movement of cell organelles, locomotion by extension of the plasma membrane, and sometimes contraction of entire cells.

micronutrient: a nutrient required by an organism in relatively small quantities.

microRNA: small molecules of RNA that interfere with the translation of specific genes.

microspore mother cell: a diploid cell contained within an anther of a flowering plant; undergoes meiotic cell division to produce four haploid microspores.

microtubule: a hollow, cylindrical strand, found in eukaryotic cells, that is composed of the protein tubulin; part of the cytoskeleton used in the movement of organelles, cell growth, and the construction of cilia and flagella.

midbrain: during development, the central portion of the brain; contains most of an important relay center, the reticular formation.

mimicry (mim'-ik-rē): the situation in which a species has evolved to resemble something else, typically another type of organism.

mineralocorticoids: steroid hormones produced by the adrenal cortex that regulate salt retention in the kidney, thereby regulating the salt concentration in the blood and interstitial fluid.

minimum viable population (MVP): the smallest isolated population that can persist indefinitely and survive likely natural events such as fires and floods.

mitochondrion (mī-tō-kon'-drē-un; pl., mitochondria): an organelle, bounded by two membranes, that is the site of the reactions of aerobic metabolism.

mitosis (mī-tō'-sis): a type of nuclear division, used by eukaryotic cells, in which one copy of each chromosome (already duplicated during interphase before mitosis) moves into each of two daughter nuclei; the daughter nuclei are therefore genetically identical to each other.

mitotic cell division: mitosis followed by cytokinesis.

molecule (mol'-e-kūl): a particle composed of one or more atoms held together by chemical bonds; the smallest particle of a compound that displays all the properties of that compound.

molt: to shed an external body covering, such as an exoskeleton, skin, feathers, or fur.

monomer (mo'-nō-mer): a small organic molecule, several of which may be bonded together to form a chain called a polymer.

monosaccharide (mo-nō-sak'-uh-rīd): the basic molecular unit of all carbohydrates, normally composed of a chain of carbon atoms bonded to hydrogen and hydroxyl groups.

monotreme: a member of the clade Monotremata, which includes mammals that lay eggs; platypuses and spiny anteaters are monotremes.

motor neuron: a neuron that receives instructions from sensory neurons or interneurons and activates effector organs, such as muscles or glands.

mouth: the opening through which food enters a tubular digestive system.

multicellular: many-celled; most members of the kingdoms Fungi, Plantae, and Animalia are multicellular, with intimate cooperation among cells.

multiple alleles: many alleles of a single gene, perhaps dozens or hundreds, as a result of mutations.

muscle fiber: an individual muscle cell.

muscle tissue: tissue composed of one of three types of contractile cells (smooth, skeletal, or cardiac).

muscular dystrophy: an inherited disorder, almost exclusively found in males, in which defective dystrophin proteins cause the skeletal muscles to degenerate.

mutation: a change in the base sequence of DNA in a gene; often used to refer to a genetic change that is significant enough to alter the appearance or function of the organism.

mutualism (mū'-choo-ul-iz-um): a symbiotic relationship in which both participating species benefit.

mycelium (mī-sēl'-ē-um; pl., mycelia): the body of a fungus, consisting of a mass of hyphae.

mycorrhiza (mī-kō-rī'-zuh; pl., mycorrhizae): a symbiotic association between a fungus and the roots of a land plant that facilitates mineral extraction and absorption.

myofibril (mū-ō-fī'-bril): a cylindrical subunit of a muscle cell, consisting of a series of sarcomeres, surrounded by sarcoplasmic reticulum.

myosin (mī'-ō-sin): one of the major proteins of muscle, the interaction of which with the protein actin produces muscle contraction; found in the thick filaments of the muscle fiber; see also *actin*.

natural causality: the scientific principle that natural events occur as a result of preceding natural causes.

natural increase: the difference between births and deaths in a population. This number will be positive if the population is increasing or negative if it is decreasing.

natural laws: basic principles derived from the study of nature that have never been disproven by scientific inquiry. Natural laws include the laws of gravity, the behavior of light, and the way atoms interact with one another.

natural selection: unequal survival and reproduction of organisms due to heritable differences in their phenotypes, with the result that better adapted phenotypes become more common in the population.

nearshore zone: the region of coastal water that is relatively shallow but constantly submerged, and that can support large plants or seaweeds; includes bays and coastal wetlands.

negative feedback: a physiological process in which a change causes responses that tend to counteract the change and restore the original state. Negative feedback in physiological systems maintains homeostasis.

nephron (nef'-ron): the functional unit of the kidney; where blood is filtered and urine is formed.

nerve cord: a major nervous pathway consisting of a cord of nervous tissue extending lengthwise through the body, paired in many invertebrates and unpaired in chordates.

nerve tissue: the tissue that makes up the brain, spinal cord, and nerves; consists of neurons and glial cells.

net primary production: the energy stored in the autotrophs of an ecosystem over a given time period.

neuron (noor'-on): a single nerve cell.

neurotransmitter: a chemical that is released by a nerve cell close to a second nerve cell, a muscle, or a gland cell and that influences the activity of the second cell.

neutral mutation: a mutation that does not detectably change the function of the encoded protein.

neutron: a subatomic particle that is found in the nuclei of atoms, bears no charge, and has a mass approximately equal to that of a proton.

nicotinamide adenine dinucleotide (NAD+ or NADH): an electron carrier molecule produced in the cytoplasmic fluid by glycolysis and in the mitochondrial matrix by the Krebs cycle; subsequently donates electrons to the electron transport chain.

nitrogen cycle: the biogeochemical cycle by which nitrogen moves from its primary reservoir of nitrogen gas in the atmosphere via nitrogen-fixing bacteria to reservoirs in soil and water, through producers and into higher trophic levels, and then back to its reservoirs.

nitrogen-fixing bacterium: a bacterium that possesses the ability to remove nitrogen (N_2) from the atmosphere and combine it with hydrogen to produce ammonia (NH_3).

no-till: a method of growing crops that leaves the remains of harvested crops in place, with the next year's crops being planted directly in the remains of last year's crops without significant disturbance of the soil.

nodule: a swelling on the root of a legume or other plant that consists of cortex cells inhabited by nitrogen-fixing bacteria.

noncompetitive inhibition: the process by which an inhibitory molecule binds to a site on an enzyme that is distinct from the active site. As a result, the enzyme's active site is distorted, making it less able to catalyze the reaction involving its normal substrate.

nondisjunction: an error in meiosis in which chromosomes fail to segregate properly into the daughter cells.

nonpolar covalent bond: a covalent bond with equal sharing of electrons.

nonvascular plant: a plant that lacks lignin and well-developed conducting vessels. Nonvascular plants include mosses, hornworts, and liverworts.

northern coniferous forest: a biome with long, cold winters and only a few months of warm weather; dominated by evergreen coniferous trees; also called *taiga*.

notochord (nōt'-ō-kord): a stiff, but somewhat flexible, supportive rod that extends along the head-to-tail axis and is found in all members of the phylum Chordata at some stage of development.

nuclear envelope: the double-membrane system surrounding the nucleus of eukaryotic cells; the outer membrane is typically continuous with the endoplasmic reticulum.

nuclear pore complex: an array of proteins that line pores in the nuclear membrane and control which substances enter and leave the nucleus.

nucleic acid (noo-klā'-ik): an organic molecule composed of nucleotide subunits; the two common types of nucleic acids are ribonucleic acid (RNA) and deoxyribonucleic acid (DNA).

nucleoid (noo-klē-oid): the location of the genetic material in prokaryotic cells; not membrane enclosed.

nucleolus (noo-klē'-ō-lus; pl., nucleoli): the region of the eukaryotic nucleus that is engaged in ribosome synthesis; consists of the genes encoding ribosomal RNA, newly synthesized ribosomal RNA, and ribosomal proteins.

nucleotide: a subunit of which nucleic acids are composed; a phosphate group bonded to a sugar (deoxyribose in DNA), which is in turn bonded to a nitrogen-containing base (adenine, guanine, cytosine, or thymine in DNA). Nucleotides are linked together, forming a strand of nucleic acid, by bonds between the phosphate of one nucleotide and the sugar of the next nucleotide.

nucleotide substitution: a mutation in which a single base pair in DNA has been changed.

nucleus (atomic): the central region of an atom, consisting of protons and neutrons.

nucleus (cellular): the membrane-bound organelle of eukaryotic cells that contains the cell's genetic material.

nutrient: a substance acquired from the environment and needed for the survival, growth, and development of an organism.

nutrient cycle: the pathways of a specific nutrient (such as carbon, nitrogen, phosphorus, or water) through the living and nonliving portions of an ecosystem; also called a *biogeochemical cycle.*

observation: in the scientific method, the recognition of and a statement about a specific phenomenon, usually leading to the formulation of a question about the phenomenon.

oil: a lipid composed of three fatty acids, some of which are unsaturated, covalently bonded to a molecule of glycerol; oils are liquid at room temperature.

oligotrophic lake: a lake that is very low in nutrients and hence supports little phytoplankton, plant, and algal life; contains clear water with deep light penetration.

omnivore: an organism that consumes both plants and animals.

oogonium (ō-ō-gō'-nē-um; pl., oogonia): in female animals, a diploid cell that gives rise to a primary oocyte.

open ocean: that part of the ocean in which the water is so deep that wave action does not affect the bottom, even during strong storms.

operant conditioning: a laboratory training procedure in which an animal learns to perform a response (such as pressing a lever) through reward or punishment.

operator: a sequence of DNA nucleotides in a prokaryotic operon that binds regulatory proteins that control the ability of RNA polymerase to transcribe the structural genes of the operon.

operon (op'-er-on): in prokaryotes, a set of genes, often encoding the proteins needed for a complete metabolic pathway, including both the structural genes and a common promoter and operator that control transcription of the structural genes.

order: in Linnaean classification, the taxonomic rank composed of related families. Related orders make up a class.

organ: a structure (such as the liver, kidney, or skin) composed of two or more distinct tissue types that function together.

organelle (or-guh-nel'): a membrane-enclosed structure found inside a eukaryotic cell that performs a specific function.

organic: describing a molecule that contains both carbon and hydrogen.

organic molecule: a molecule that contains both carbon and hydrogen.

organism (or'-guh-niz-um): an individual living thing.

origin: the site of attachment of a muscle to the relatively stationary bone on one side of a joint.

osmoregulation: homeostatic maintenance of the water and salt content of the body within a limited range.

osmosis (oz-mō'-sis): the diffusion of water across a differentially permeable membrane, normally down a concentration gradient of free water molecules. Water moves into the solution that has a lower concentration of free water from a solution that has a higher concentration of free water.

osteoclast (os'-tē-ō-klast): a cell type that dissolves bone.

osteoporosis (os'-tē-ō-por-ō'-sis): a condition in which bones become porous, weak, and easily fractured; most common in elderly women.

oval window: the membrane-covered entrance to the cochlea.

overexploitation: hunting or harvesting natural populations at a rate that exceeds those populations' ability to replenish their numbers.

ovule: a structure within the ovary of a flower, inside which the female gametophyte develops; after fertilization, it develops into the seed.

ozone hole: a region of severe ozone loss in the stratosphere caused by ozone-depleting chemicals; maximum ozone loss occurs from September to early October over Antarctica.

ozone layer: the ozone-enriched layer of the upper atmosphere (stratosphere) that filters out much of the sun's ultraviolet radiation.

pacemaker: a cluster of specialized muscle cells in the upper right atrium of the heart that produce spontaneous electrical signals at a regular rate; the sinoatrial node.

pancreas (pan'-krē-us): a combined exocrine and endocrine gland located in the abdominal cavity next to the stomach. The endocrine portion secretes the hormones insulin and glucagon, which regulate glucose concentrations in the blood. The exocrine portion secretes pancreatic juice (a mixture of water, enzymes, and sodium bicarbonate) into the small intestine; the enzymes digest fat, carbohydrate, and protein; the bicarbonate neutralizes acidic chyme entering the intestine from the stomach.

parabasalid: a member of a protist group characterized by mutualistic or parasitic relationships with the animal species inside which they live. Parabasalids are part of a larger group known as the excavates.

parasite (par'-uh-sīt): an organism that lives in or on a larger organism (its host), harming the host but usually not killing it immediately.

parathyroid gland: one of four small endocrine glands, embedded in the surface of the thyroid gland, that produces parathyroid hormone, which (with calcitonin from the thyroid gland) regulates calcium ion concentration in the blood.

parenchyma (par-en'-ki-muh): a plant cell type that is alive at maturity, normally with thin cell walls, and carries out most of the metabolism of a plant. Most dividing meristem cells in a plant are parenchyma.

passive transport: the movement of materials across a membrane down a gradient of concentration, pressure, or electrical charge without using cellular energy.

pathogenic (path'-ō-jen-ik): capable of producing disease; referring to an organism with such a capability (a pathogen).

pedigree: a diagram showing genetic relationships among a set of individuals, normally with respect to a specific genetic trait.

pelagic (puh-la'-jik): free-swimming or floating.

peptide (pep'-tīd): a chain composed of two or more amino acids linked together by peptide bonds.

peptide bond: the covalent bond between the nitrogen of the amino group of one amino acid and the carbon of the carboxyl group of a second amino acid, joining the two amino acids together in a peptide or protein.

pericycle (per'-i-sī-kul): the outermost layer of cells of the vascular cylinder of a root.

peripheral nervous system (PNS): in vertebrates, the part of the nervous system that connects the central nervous system to the rest of the body.

peritubular capillaries: a capillary network surrounding each kidney tubule that allows the exchange of substances between the blood and the tubule contents during tubular reabsorption and tubular secretion.

permafrost: a permanently frozen layer of soil, usually found in tundra of the Arctic or high mountains.

petiole (pet'-ē-ōl): the stalk that connects the blade of a leaf to the stem.

pH scale: a scale, with values from 0 to 14, used for measuring the relative acidity of a solution; at pH 7 a solution is neutral, pH 0 to 7 is acidic, and pH 7 to 14 is basic; each unit on the scale represents a tenfold change in H^+ concentration.

phagocytosis (fa-gō-sī-tō'-sis): a type of endocytosis in which extensions of a plasma membrane engulf extracellular particles, enclose them in a membrane-bound sac, and transport them into the interior of the cell.

pharyngeal gill slit (far-in'-jē-ul): one of a series of openings, located just posterior to the mouth, that connects the throat to the outside environment; present (as some stage of life) in all chordates.

phenotype (fēn'-ō-tīp): the physical characteristics of an organism; can be defined as outward appearance (such as flower color), as behavior, or in molecular terms (such as glycoproteins on red blood cells).

pheromone (fer'-uh-mōn): a chemical produced by an organism that alters the behavior or physiological state of another member of the same species.

phospholipid (fos-fō-li'-pid): a lipid consisting of glycerol bonded to two fatty acids and one phosphate group, which bears another group of atoms, typically charged and containing nitrogen. A double layer of phospholipids is a component of all cellular membranes.

phospholipid bilayer: a double layer of phospholipids that forms the basis of all cellular membranes. The phospholipid heads, which are hydrophilic, face the watery interstitial fluid, a watery external environment, or the cytosol; the tails, which are hydrophobic, are buried in the middle of the bilayer.

phosphorus cycle (fos'-for-us): the biogeochemical cycle by which phosphorus moves from its primary reservoir—phosphate-rich rock—to reservoirs of phosphate in soil and water, through producers and into higher trophic levels, and then back to its reservoirs.

photic zone: the region of an ocean where light is strong enough to support photosynthesis.

photon (fō'-ton): the smallest unit of light energy.

photoreceptor: a receptor cell that responds to light; in vertebrates, rods and cones.

photorespiration: a series of reactions in plants in which O_2 replaces CO_2 during the Calvin cycle, preventing carbon fixation; this wasteful process dominates when C_3 plants are forced to close their stomata to prevent water loss.

photosynthesis: the complete series of chemical reactions in which the energy of light is used to synthesize high-energy organic molecules, usually carbohydrates, from low-energy inorganic molecules, usually carbon dioxide and water.

photosystem: in thylakoid membranes, a cluster of chlorophyll, accessory pigment molecules, proteins, and other molecules that collectively capture light energy, transfer some of the energy to electrons, and transfer the energetic electrons to an adjacent electron transport chain.

phylogeny (fī-lah'-jen-ē): the evolutionary history of a group of species.

phylum (fī-lum): in Linnaean classification, the taxonomic rank composed of related classes. Related phyla make up a kingdom.

phytoplankton (fī'-tō-plank-ten): photosynthetic protists that are abundant in marine and freshwater environments.

pigment molecule: a light-absorbing, colored molecule, such as chlorophyll, carotenoid, or melanin molecules.

pilus (pl., pili): a hairlike protein structure that projects from the cell wall of many bacteria. Attachment pili help bacteria adhere to structures. Sex pili assist in the transfer of plasmids.

pinna: a flap of skin-covered cartilage on the surface of the head that collects sound waves and funnels them to the auditory canal.

pinocytosis (pi-nō-sī-tō'-sis): the nonselective movement of extracellular fluids and their dissolved substances, enclosed within a vesicle formed from the plasma membrane, into a cell.

pioneer: an organism that is among the first to colonize an unoccupied habitat in the first stages of succession.

pith: cells forming the center of a root or stem.

placenta (pluh-sen'-tuh): in mammals, a structure formed by a complex interweaving of the uterine lining and the embryonic membranes, especially the chorion; functions in gas, nutrient, and waste exchange between embryonic and maternal circulatory systems, and also secretes the hormones estrogen and progesterone, which are essential to maintaining pregnancy.

placental (pluh-sen'-tul): referring to a mammal possessing a complex placenta (that is, species that are not marsupials or monotremes).

plankton: microscopic organisms that live in marine or freshwater environments; includes phytoplankton and zooplankton.

plaque (plak): a deposit of cholesterol and other fatty substances within the wall of an artery.

plasma cell: an antibody-secreting descendant of a B cell.

plasma membrane: the outer membrane of a cell, composed of a bilayer of phospholipids in which proteins are embedded.

plasmid (plaz'-mid): a small, circular piece of DNA located in the cytoplasm of many bacteria; usually does not carry genes required for the normal functioning of the bacterium, but may carry genes, such as those for antibiotic resistance, that assist bacterial survival in certain environments.

plasmodium (plaz-mō'-dē-um): a slug-like mass of cytoplasm containing thousands of nuclei that are not confined within individual cells.

plastid (plas'-tid): in plant cells, an organelle bounded by two membranes that may be involved in photosynthesis (chloroplasts), pigment storage, or food storage.

plate tectonics: the theory that Earth's crust is divided into irregular plates that are converging, diverging, or slipping by one another; these motions cause continental drift, the movement of continents over Earth's surface.

pleated sheet: a form of secondary structure exhibited by certain proteins, such as silk, in which many protein chains lie side by side, with hydrogen bonds holding adjacent chains together.

pleiotropy (ple'-ō-trō-pē): a situation in which a single gene influences more than one phenotypic characteristic.

point mutation: a mutation in which a single base pair in DNA has been changed.

polar covalent bond: a covalent bond with unequal sharing of electrons, such that one atom is relatively negative and the other is relatively positive.

pollen: the male gametophyte of a seed plant; also called a *pollen grain.*

pollination: in flowering plants, when pollen grains land on the stigma of a flower of the same species; in conifers, when pollen grains land within the pollen chamber of a female cone of the same species.

polygenic inheritance: a pattern of inheritance in which the interactions of two or more functionally similar genes determine phenotype.

polymer (pah'-li-mer): a molecule composed of three or more (perhaps thousands) smaller subunits called monomers, which may be identical (for example, the glucose monomers of starch) or different (for example, the amino acids of a protein).

polymerase chain reaction (PCR): a method of producing virtually unlimited numbers of copies of a specific piece of DNA, starting with as little as one copy of the desired DNA.

polypeptide: a long chain of amino acids linked by peptide bonds. A protein consists of one or more polypeptides.

polyploidy (pahl'-ē-ploid-ē): having more than two sets of homologous chromosomes.

polysaccharide (pahl-ē-sak'-uh-rīd): a large carbohydrate molecule composed of branched or unbranched chains of repeating monosaccharide subunits, normally glucose or modified glucose molecules; includes starches, cellulose, and glycogen.

population: all the members of a particular species within a defined area, found in the same time and place and actually or potentially interbreeding.

population bottleneck: the result of an event that causes a population to become extremely small; may cause genetic drift that results in changed allele frequencies and loss of genetic variability.

population cycle: regularly recurring, cyclical changes in population size.

post-anal tail: a tail that extends beyond the anus and contains muscle tissue and the most posterior part of the nerve cord; found in all chordates at some stage of development.

posterior pituitary: a lobe of the pituitary gland that is an outgrowth of the hypothalamus and that releases antidiuretic hormone and oxytocin.

postmating isolating mechanism: any structure, physiological function, or developmental abnormality that prevents organisms of two different species, once mating has occurred, from producing vigorous, fertile offspring.

postsynaptic potential (PSP): an electrical signal produced in a postsynaptic cell by transmission across the synapse; it may be excitatory (EPSP), making the cell more likely to produce an action potential, or inhibitory (IPSP), tending to inhibit an action potential.

potential energy: "stored" energy including chemical energy (stored in molecules), elastic energy (such as stored in a spring), or gravitational energy (stored in the elevated position of an object).

prairie: a biome, located in the centers of continents, that primarily supports grasses; also called *grassland.*

predation (pre-dā'-shun): the act of eating another living organism.

predator: an organism that eats other organisms.

prediction: in the scientific method, a statement describing an expected observation or the expected outcome of an experiment, assuming that a specific hypothesis is true.

premating isolating mechanism: any structure, physiological function, or behavior that prevents organisms of two different species from exchanging gametes.

presynaptic neuron: a nerve cell that releases a chemical (the neurotransmitter) at a synapse, causing changes in the electrical activity or metabolism of another (postsynaptic) cell.

prey: organisms that are eaten, and often killed, by another organism (a predator).

primary consumer: an organism that feeds on producers; an herbivore.

primary electron acceptor: A molecule in the reaction center of each photosystem that accepts an electron from one of the two reaction center chlorophyll *a* molecules and transfers the electron to an adjacent electron transport chain.

primary oocyte (ō'-ō-sīt): a diploid cell, derived from the oogonium by growth and differentiation, that undergoes meiotic cell division, producing the egg.

primary structure: the amino acid sequence of a protein.

primary succession: succession that occurs in an environment, such as bare rock, in which no trace of a previous community is present.

primate: a member of the mammalian clade Primates, characterized by the presence of an opposable thumb, forward-facing eyes, and a well-developed cerebral cortex; includes lemurs, monkeys, apes, and humans.

prion (prē'-on): a protein that, in mutated form, acts as an infectious agent that causes certain neurodegenerative diseases, including kuru and scrapie.

producer: a photosynthetic organism; an autotroph.

product: an atom or molecule that is formed from reactants in a chemical reaction.

profundal zone: the part of a lake in which light is insufficient to support photosynthesis.

prokaryote (prō-kar'-ē-ōt): an organism whose cells are prokaryotic (their genetic material is not enclosed in a membrane-bound nucleus and they lack other membrane-bound organelles); bacteria and archaea are prokaryotes.

prokaryotic (prō-kar-ē-ot'-ik): referring to cells of the domains Bacteria or Archaea. Prokaryotic cells have genetic material that is not enclosed in a membrane-bound nucleus; they also lack other membrane-bound organelles.

prokaryotic fission: the process by which a single bacterium divides in half, producing two identical offspring.

promoter: a specific sequence of DNA at the beginning of a gene, to which RNA polymerase binds and starts gene transcription.

prophase (prō'-fāz): the first stage of mitosis, in which the chromosomes first become visible in the light microscope as thickened, condensed threads and the spindle begins to form; as the spindle is completed, the nuclear envelope breaks apart, and the spindle microtubules invade the nuclear region and attach to the kinetochores of the chromosomes. Also, the first stage of meiosis: In meiosis I, the homologous chromosomes pair up, exchange parts at chiasmata, and attach to spindle microtubules; in meiosis II, the spindle re-forms and chromosomes attach to the microtubules.

prostate gland (pros'-tāt): a gland that produces part of the fluid component of semen; prostatic fluid is basic and contains a chemical that activates sperm movement.

protein: a polymer composed of amino acids joined by peptide bonds.

protist: a eukaryotic organism that is not a plant, animal, or fungus. The term encompasses a diverse array of organisms and does not represent a monophyletic group.

protocell: the hypothetical evolutionary precursor of living cells, consisting of a mixture of organic molecules within a membrane.

proton: a subatomic particle that is found in the nuclei of atoms; it bears a unit of positive charge and has a relatively large mass, roughly equal to the mass of a neutron.

protostome (prō'-tō-stōm): an animal with a mode of embryonic development in which the coelom is derived from splits in the mesoderm; characteristic of arthropods, annelids, and mollusks.

protozoan (prō-tuh-zō'-an; pl., protozoa): a nonphotosynthetic, single-celled protist.

pseudocoelom (soo'-dō-sēl'-ōm): in animals, a "false coelom," that is, a space or cavity, partially but not fully lined with tissue derived from mesoderm, that separates the body wall from the inner organs; found in roundworms.

pseudoplasmodium (soo'-dō-plaz-mō'-dē-um): an aggregation of individual amoeboid cells that form a slug-like mass.

pseudopod (sood'-ō-pod): an extension of the plasma membrane by which certain cells, such as amoebas, locomote and engulf prey.

pulmonary circuit: the pathway of blood from the heart to the lungs and back to the heart.

Punnett square method: a method of predicting the genotypes and phenotypes of offspring in genetic crosses.

pupa (pl., pupae): a developmental stage in some insect species in which the organism stops moving and feeding and may be encased in a cocoon; occurs between the larval and the adult phases.

quaternary structure (kwat'-er-nuh-rē): the complex three-dimensional structure of a protein consisting of more than one peptide chain.

question: in the scientific method, a statement that identifies a particular aspect of an observation that a scientist wishes to explain.

radial symmetry: a body plan in which any plane along a central axis will divide the body into approximately mirror-image halves. Cnidarians and many adult echinoderms exhibit radial symmetry.

radioactive: pertaining to an atom with an unstable nucleus that spontaneously disintegrates, with the emission of radiation.

radiolarian (rā-dē-ō-lar'-ē-un): a member of a protist group characterized by pseudopods and typically elaborate silica shells. Radiolarians are largely aquatic (mostly marine) and are part of a larger group known as rhizarians.

rain shadow: a local dry area, usually located on the downwind side of a mountain range that blocks the prevailing moisture-bearing winds.

random distribution: the distribution characteristic of populations in which the probability of finding an individual is equal in all parts of an area.

reactant: an atom or molecule that is used up in a chemical reaction to form a product.

reaction center: two chlorophyll *a* molecules and a primary electron acceptor complexed with proteins and located near the center of each photosystem within the thylakoid membrane. Light energy is passed to one of the chlorophylls, which donates an energized electron to the primary electron acceptor, which then passes the electron to an adjacent electron transport chain.

receptor-mediated endocytosis: the selective uptake of molecules from the interstitial fluid by binding to a receptor located at a coated pit on the plasma membrane and pinching off the coated pit into a vesicle that moves into the cytosol.

receptor protein: a protein, located in a membrane or the cytosol of a cell, that binds to specific molecules (for example, a hormone or neurotransmitter), triggering a response in the cell, such as endocytosis, changes in metabolic rate, cell division, or electrical changes.

recessive: an allele that is expressed only in homozygotes and is completely masked in heterozygotes.

recognition protein: a protein or glycoprotein protruding from the outside surface of a plasma membrane that identifies a cell as belonging to a particular species, to a specific individual of that species, and in many cases to one specific organ within the individual.

recombinant DNA: DNA that has been altered by the addition of DNA from a different organism, typically from a different species.

recombination: the formation of new combinations of the different alleles of each gene on a chromosome; the result of crossing over.

reflex: a simple, stereotyped movement of part of the body that occurs automatically in response to a stimulus.

regulatory gene: in prokaryotes, a gene encoding a protein that binds to the operator of one or more operons, controlling the ability of RNA polymerase to transcribe the structural genes of the operon.

releasing hormone: a hormone, secreted by the hypothalamus, that causes the release of specific hormones by the anterior pituitary.

renal cortex: the outer layer of the kidney, in which the largest portion of each nephron is located, including Bowman's capsule and the distal and proximal tubules.

renal pelvis: the inner chamber of the kidney, in which urine from the collecting ducts accumulates before it enters the ureter.

renin: in mammals, an enzyme that is released by the kidneys when blood pressure falls. Renin catalyzes the formation of angiotensin, which causes arterioles to constrict, thereby elevating blood pressure.

replacement level fertility (RLF): the average number of offspring per female that is required to maintain a stable population.

repressor protein: in prokaryotes, a protein encoded by a regulatory gene, which binds to the operator of an operon and prevents RNA polymerase from transcribing the structural genes.

reproductive isolation: the failure of organisms of one population to breed successfully with members of another; may be due to premating or postmating isolating mechanisms.

reptile: a member of the chordate group that includes the snakes, lizards, turtles, alligators, birds, and crocodiles.

reservoir: the major source and storage site of a nutrient in an ecosystem, normally in the abiotic portion.

resource partitioning: the coexistence of two species with similar requirements, each occupying a smaller niche than either would if it were by itself; a means of minimizing the species' competitive interactions.

respiratory center: a cluster of neurons, located in the medulla of the brain, that sends rhythmic bursts of nerve impulses to the respiratory muscles, resulting in breathing.

respiratory system: a group of organs that work together to facilitate gas exchange—the intake of oxygen and the removal of carbon dioxide—between an animal and its environment.

restriction enzyme: an enzyme, usually isolated from bacteria, that cuts double-stranded DNA at a specific nucleotide sequence; the nucleotide sequence that is cut differs for different restriction enzymes.

restriction fragment: a piece of DNA that has been isolated by cleaving a larger piece of DNA with restriction enzymes.

restriction fragment length polymorphism (RFLP): a difference in the length of DNA fragments that were produced by cutting samples of DNA from different individuals of the same species with the same set of restriction enzymes; fragment length differences occur because of differences in nucleotide sequences, and hence in the ability of restriction enzymes to cut the DNA, among individuals of the same species.

retina (ret'-in-uh): a multilayered sheet of nerve tissue at the rear of camera-type eyes, composed of photoreceptor cells plus associated nerve cells that refine the photoreceptor information and transmit it to the optic nerve.

rhizarian: a member of Rhizaria, a protist clade. Rhizarians, which use thin pseudopods to move and capture prey and which often have hard shells, include the foraminiferans and the radiolarians.

ribonucleic acid (RNA) (rī-bō-noo-klā'-ik; RNA): a molecule composed of ribose nucleotides, each of which consists of a phosphate group, the sugar ribose, and one of the bases adenine, cytosine, guanine, or uracil; involved in converting the information in DNA into protein; also the genetic material of some viruses.

ribosomal RNA (rī-bō-sō'-mul; rRNA): a type of RNA that combines with proteins to form ribosomes.

ribosome (rī'-bō-sōm): a complex consisting of two subunits, each composed of ribosomal RNA and protein, found in the cytoplasm of cells or attached to the endoplasmic reticulum, that is the site of protein synthesis, during which the sequence of bases of messenger RNA is translated into the sequence of amino acids in a protein.

ribozyme: an RNA molecule that can catalyze certain chemical reactions, especially those involved in the synthesis and processing of RNA itself.

RNA polymerase: in RNA synthesis, an enzyme that catalyzes the bonding of free RNA nucleotides into a continuous strand, using RNA nucleotides that are complementary to those of the template strand of DNA.

root: the part of a plant body, normally underground, that provides anchorage, absorbs water and dissolved nutrients and transports them to the stem, produces some hormones, and in some plants serves as a storage site for carbohydrates.

root hair: a fine projection from an epidermal cell of a young root that increases the absorptive surface area of the root.

root system: all of the roots of a plant.

rubisco: in the carbon fixation step of the Calvin cycle, the enzyme that catalyzes the reaction between ribulose bisphosphate (RuBP) and carbon dioxide, thereby fixing the carbon of carbon dioxide in an organic molecule; short for ribulose bisphosphate carboxylase.

rumen fungus: a member of the fungus clade Neocallimastigomycota, whose members have swimming spores with multiple flagella. Rumen fungi are anaerobic and most live in the digestive tracts of plant-eating animals.

S-curve: the S-shaped growth curve produced by logistic population growth, usually describing a population of organisms introduced into a new area; consists of an initial period of exponential growth, followed by a decreasing growth rate, and finally, relative stability around a growth rate of zero.

sac fungus: a member of the fungus clade Ascomycota, whose members form spores in a saclike case called an ascus.

sapwood: young secondary xylem that transports water and minerals in a tree trunk.

sarcoplasmic reticulum (sark'-ō-plas'-mik re-tik'-ū-lum; SR): the specialized endoplasmic reticulum in muscle cells; forms interconnected hollow tubes. The sarcoplasmic reticulum stores calcium ions and releases them into the interior of the muscle cell, initiating contraction.

saturated: referring to a fatty acid with as many hydrogen atoms as possible bonded to the carbon backbone (therefore, a saturated fatty acid has no double bonds in its carbon backbone).

savanna: a biome that is dominated by grasses and supports scattered trees; typically has a rainy season during which most of the year's precipitation falls, followed by a dry season during which virtually no precipitation occurs.

science: the organized and systematic inquiry, through observation and experiment, into the origins, structure, and behavior of our living and nonliving surroundings.

scientific method: a rigorous procedure for making observations of specific phenomena and searching for the order underlying those phenomena.

scientific name: the two-part Latin name of a species; consists of the genus name followed by the species name.

scientific theory: an explanation of natural phenomena developed through extensive and reproducible observations; more general and reliable than a hypothesis.

scientific theory of evolution: the theory that modern organisms descended, with modification, from preexisting life-forms.

sclerenchyma (skler-en'-ki-muh): a plant cell type with thick, hardened cell walls; sclerenchyma cells normally die as the last stage of differentiation; may support or protect the plant body.

scramble competition: a free-for-all scramble for limited resources among individuals of the same species.

second law of thermodynamics: the principle of physics that states that any change in a closed system causes the quantity of concentrated, useful energy to decrease and the amount of randomness and disorder (entropy) to increase.

secondary consumer: an organism that feeds on primary consumers; a type of carnivore.

secondary oocyte (ō'-ō-sīt): a large haploid cell derived from the diploid primary oocyte by meiosis I.

secondary structure: a repeated, regular structure assumed by a protein chain, held together by hydrogen bonds; for example, a helix.

secondary succession: succession that occurs after an existing community is disturbed—for example, after a forest fire; secondary succession is much more rapid than primary succession.

seed: the reproductive structure of a seed plant, protected by a seed coat; contains an embryonic plant and a supply of food for it.

segmentation (seg-men-tā'-shun): an animal body plan in which the body is divided into repeated, typically similar units.

selectively permeable: the quality of a membrane that allows certain molecules or ions to move through it more readily than others.

self-fertilization: the union of sperm and egg from the same individual.

semicircular canal: in the inner ear, one of three fluid-filled tubes, each with a bulge at one end containing a patch of hair cells; movement of the head moves fluid in the canal and consequently bends the hairs of the hair cells.

semiconservative replication: the process of replication of the DNA double helix; the two DNA strands separate, and each is used as a template for the synthesis of a complementary DNA strand. Consequently, each daughter double helix consists of one parental strand and one new strand.

seminal vesicle: in male mammals, a gland that produces a basic, fructose-containing fluid that forms part of the semen.

senescence: in plants, a specific aging process, typically including deterioration and the dropping of leaves and flowers.

sensory neuron: a nerve cell that responds to a stimulus from the internal or external environment.

sepal (sē'-pul): one of the group of modified leaves that surrounds and protects a flower bud; in dicots, usually develops into a green, leaflike structure when the flower blooms; in monocots, usually similar to a petal.

septum (pl., septa): a partition that separates the fungal hypha into individual cells; pores in septa allow the transfer of materials between cells.

severe combined immune deficiency (SCID): a disorder in which no immune cells, or very few, are formed; the immune system is incapable of responding properly to invading disease organisms, and the individual is very vulnerable to common infections.

sex chromosome: either of the pair of chromosomes that usually determines the sex of an organism; for example, the X and Y chromosomes in mammals.

sex-linked: referring to a pattern of inheritance characteristic of genes located on one type of sex chromosome (for example, X) and not found on the other type (for example, Y); in mammals, in almost all cases, the gene controlling the trait is on the X chromosome, so this pattern is often called X-linked. In X-linked inheritance, females show the dominant trait unless they are homozygous recessive, whereas males express whichever allele, dominant or recessive, is found on their single X chromosome.

sexual reproduction: a form of reproduction in which genetic material from two parent organisms is combined in the offspring; usually, two haploid gametes fuse to form a diploid zygote.

sexual selection: a type of natural selection that acts on traits involved in finding and acquiring mates.

shoot system: all the parts of a vascular plant exclusive of the root; usually aboveground. Consists of stem, leaves, buds, and (in season) flowers and fruits; functions include photosynthesis, transport of materials, reproduction, and hormone synthesis.

short tandem repeat (STR): a DNA sequence consisting of a short sequence of nucleotides (usually two to five nucleotides in length) repeated multiple times, with all of the repetitions side by side on a chromosome; variations in the number of repeats of a standardized set of 13 STRs produce DNA profiles used to identify people by their DNA.

sickle-cell anemia: a recessive disease caused by a single amino acid substitution in the hemoglobin molecule. Sickle-cell hemoglobin molecules tend to cluster together, distorting the shape of red blood cells and causing them to break and clog capillaries.

sieve-tube element: in phloem, one of the cells of a sieve tube.

simple diffusion: the diffusion of water, dissolved gases, or lipid-soluble molecules through the phospholipid bilayer of a cellular membrane.

sink: in plants, any structure that uses up sugars or converts sugars to starch, and toward which phloem fluids will flow.

skeletal muscle: the type of muscle that is attached to and moves the skeleton and is under the direct, normally voluntary, control of the nervous system; also called *striated muscle*.

small intestine: the portion of the digestive tract, located between the stomach and large intestine, in which most digestion and absorption of nutrients occur.

sodium-potassium (Na⁺-K⁺) pump: an active transport protein that uses the energy of ATP to transport Na^+ out of a cell and K^+ into a cell; produces and maintains the concentration gradients of these ions across the plasma membrane, such that the concentration of Na^+ is higher outside a cell than inside, and the concentration of K^+ is higher inside a cell than outside.

solute: a substance dissolved in a solvent.

solution: a solvent containing one or more dissolved substances (solutes).

solvent: a liquid capable of dissolving (uniformly dispersing) other substances in itself.

source: in plants, any structure that actively synthesizes sugar, and away from which phloem fluid will be transported.

speciation: the process of species formation, in which a single species splits into two or more species.

species (spē'-sēs): the basic unit of taxonomic classification, consisting of a population or group of populations that evolves independently of other populations. In sexually reproducing organisms, a species can be defined as a population or group of populations whose members

interbreed freely with one another under natural conditions but do not interbreed with members of other populations.

specific heat: the amount of energy required to raise the temperature of 1 gram of a substance by 1 °C.

spermatid: a haploid cell derived from the secondary spermatocyte by meiosis II; differentiates into the mature sperm.

spermatogonium (pl., spermatogonia): a diploid cell, lining the walls of the seminiferous tubules, that gives rise to a primary spermatocyte.

spermatophore: a package of sperm formed by the males of some invertebrate animals; the spermatophore can be inserted into the female reproductive tract, where it releases its sperm.

spinal cord: the part of the central nervous system of vertebrates that extends from the base of the brain to the hips and is protected by the bones of the vertebral column; contains the cell bodies of motor neurons that form synapses with skeletal muscles, the circuitry for some simple reflex behaviors, and axons that communicate with the brain.

spindle microtubule: microtubules organized in a spindle shape that separate chromosomes during mitosis or meiosis.

spleen: the largest organ of the lymphatic system, located in the abdominal cavity; contains macrophages that filter the blood by removing microbes and aged red blood cells, and lymphocytes (B and T cells) that reproduce during times of infection.

spontaneous generation: the proposal that living organisms can arise from nonliving matter.

sporangium (spor-an'-jē-um; pl., sporangia): a structure in which spores are produced.

spore: (1) in plants and fungi, a haploid cell capable of developing into an adult without fusing with another cell (without fertilization); (2) in bacteria and some other organisms, a stage of the life cycle that is resistant to extreme environmental conditions.

sporophyte (spor'-ō-fīt): the multicellular diploid stage in the life cycle of a plant; produces haploid, asexual spores through meiosis.

stabilizing selection: a type of natural selection that favors the average phenotype in a population.

starch: a polysaccharide that is composed of branched or unbranched chains of glucose molecules; used by plants as a carbohydrate-storage molecule.

start codon: the first AUG codon in a messenger RNA molecule.

startle coloration: a form of mimicry in which a color pattern (in many cases resembling large eyes) can be displayed suddenly by a prey organism when approached by a predator.

stem cell: an undifferentiated cell that is capable of dividing and giving rise to one or more distinct types of differentiated cell(s).

steroid: a lipid consisting of four fused carbon rings, with various functional groups attached.

stigma (stig'-muh): the pollen-capturing tip of a carpel.

stoma (stō'-muh; pl., stomata): an adjustable opening in the epidermis of a leaf or young stem, surrounded by a pair of guard cells, that regulates the diffusion of carbon dioxide and water into and out of the leaf or stem.

stop codon: a codon in messenger RNA that stops protein synthesis and causes the completed protein chain to be released from the ribosome.

stramenopile: a member of Stramenopila, a large protist clade. Stramenopiles, which are characterized by hair-like projections on their flagella, include the water molds, the diatoms, and the brown algae.

strand: a single polymer of nucleotides; DNA is composed of two strands wound about each other in a double helix; RNA is usually single stranded.

stroke: an interruption of blood flow to part of the brain caused by the rupture of an artery or the blocking of an artery by a blood clot. Loss of blood supply leads to rapid death of the area of the brain affected.

stroma (strō'-muh): the semifluid material inside chloroplasts in which the thylakoids are located; the site of the reactions of the Calvin cycle.

structural gene: in the prokaryotic operon, the genes that encode enzymes or other cellular proteins.

subclimax: a community in which succession is stopped before the climax community is reached; it is maintained by regular disturbance— for example, a tallgrass prairie maintained by periodic fires.

substrate: the atoms or molecules that are the reactants for an enzyme-catalyzed chemical reaction.

succession (suk-seh'-shun): a structural change in a community and its nonliving environment over time. During succession, species replace one another in a somewhat predictable manner until a stable, self-sustaining climax community is reached.

sucrose: a disaccharide composed of glucose and fructose.

sugar: a simple carbohydrate molecule, either a monosaccharide or a disaccharide.

sugar-phosphate backbone: a chain of sugars and phosphates in DNA and RNA; the sugar of one nucleotide bonds to the phosphate of the next nucleotide in a DNA or RNA strand. The bases in DNA or RNA are attached to the sugars of the backbone.

surface tension: the property of a liquid to resist penetration by objects at its interface with the air, due to cohesion between molecules of the liquid.

survivorship curve: the curve that results when the number of individuals of each age in a population is graphed against their age, usually expressed as a percentage of their maximum life span.

survivorship table: a data table that groups organisms born at the same time and tracks them throughout their life span, recording how many continue to survive in each succeeding year (or other unit of time). Various parameters such as gender may be used in the groupings. Human life tables may include many other parameters (such as socioeconomic status) used by demographers.

sustainable development: human activities that meet current needs for a reasonable quality of life without exceeding nature's limits and without compromising the ability of future generations to meet their needs.

sympatric speciation (sim-pat′-rik): the process by which new species arise in populations that are not physically divided; the genetic isolation required for sympatric speciation may be due to ecological isolation or chromosomal aberrations (such as polyploidy).

synaptic cleft: in a synapse, a small gap between the presynaptic and postsynaptic neurons.

synaptic terminal: a swelling at the branched ending of an axon; where the axon forms a synapse.

systematics: the branch of biology concerned with reconstructing phylogenies and with naming clades.

systolic pressure (sis′-tal-ik): the blood pressure measured at the peak of contraction of the ventricles; the higher of the two blood pressure readings.

T-cell receptor: a protein receptor, located on the surface of a T cell, that binds a specific antigen and triggers the immune response of the T cell.

taiga (tī′-guh): a biome with long, cold winters and only a few months of warm weather; dominated by evergreen coniferous trees; also called *northern coniferous forest*.

target cell: a cell on which a particular hormone exerts its effect.

taxonomy (tax-on′-uh-mē): the branch of biology concerned with naming and classifying organisms.

telomere (tē-le-mēr): the nucleotides at the end of a chromosome that protect the chromosome from damage during condensation, and prevent the end of one chromosome from attaching to the end of another chromosome.

telophase (tēl-ō-fāz): in mitosis and both divisions of meiosis, the final stage, in which the spindle fibers usually disappear, nuclear envelopes re-form, and cytokinesis generally occurs. In mitosis and meiosis II, the chromosomes also relax from their condensed form.

temperate deciduous forest: a biome having cold winters and warm summers, with enough summer rainfall for trees to grow and shade out grasses; characterized by trees that drop their leaves in winter (deciduous trees), an adaptation that minimizes water loss when the soil is frozen.

temperate rain forest: a temperate biome with abundant liquid water year-round, dominated by conifers.

template strand: the strand of the DNA double helix from which RNA is transcribed.

temporal isolation: reproductive isolation that arises when species do not interbreed because they breed at different times.

terminal bud: meristem tissue and surrounding leaf primordia that are located at the tip of a plant shoot or a branch.

territoriality: the defense of an area in which important resources are located.

tertiary consumer (ter′-shē-er-ē): a carnivore that feeds on other carnivores (secondary consumers).

tertiary structure (ter′-shē-er-ē): the complex three-dimensional structure of a single peptide chain; held in place by disulfide bonds between cysteines.

test cross: a breeding experiment in which an individual showing the dominant phenotype is mated with an individual that is homozygous recessive for the same gene. The ratio of offspring with dominant versus recessive phenotypes can be used to determine the genotype of the phenotypically dominant individual.

testosterone: in vertebrates, a hormone produced by the interstitial cells of the testis; stimulates spermatogenesis and the development of male secondary sex characteristics.

tetrapod: an organism descended from the first four-limbed vertebrate. Tetrapods include all extinct and living amphibians, reptiles (including birds), and mammals.

therapeutic cloning: the production of a clone for medical purposes. Typically, the nucleus from one of a patient's own cells would be inserted into an egg whose nucleus had been removed; the resulting cell would divide and produce embryonic stem cells that would be compatible with the patient's tissues and therefore would not be rejected by the patient's immune system.

thigmotropism: growth in response to touch.

threatened species: all species classified as critically endangered, endangered, or vulnerable.

thrombin: an enzyme produced in the blood as a result of injury to a blood vessel; catalyzes the production of fibrin, a protein that assists in blood clot formation.

thylakoid (thī′-luh-koid): a disk-shaped, membranous sac found in chloroplasts, the membranes of which contain the photosystems, electron transport chains, and ATP-synthesizing enzymes used in the light reactions of photosynthesis.

thymine (T): a nitrogenous base found only in DNA; abbreviated as T.

thymus (thī′-mus): an organ of the lymphatic system that is located in the upper chest in front of the heart and that secretes thymosin, which stimulates maturation of T lymphocytes of the immune system.

thyroid-stimulating hormone (TSH): a hormone, released by the anterior pituitary, that stimulates the thyroid gland to release hormones.

tight junction: a type of cell-to-cell junction in animals that prevents the movement of materials through the spaces between cells.

tissue: a group of (normally similar) cells that together carry out a specific function; a tissue may also include extracellular material produced by its cells.

tonsil: a patch of lymphatic tissue, located at the entrance to the pharynx, that contains macrophages and lymphocytes; destroys many microbes entering the body through the mouth and stimulates an adaptive immune response to them.

tracheae (tra′-ke-ē): the respiratory organ of insects, consisting of a set of air-filled tubes leading from openings in the body called spiracles and branching extensively throughout the body.

trans fat: a type of fat, produced during the process of hydrogenating oils, that may increase the risk of heart disease. The fatty acids of trans fats include an unusual configuration of double bonds that is not normally found in fats of biological origin.

transcription: the synthesis of an RNA molecule from a DNA template.

transfect: to introduce foreign DNA into a host cell; usually includes mechanisms to regulate the expression of the DNA in the host cell.

transfer RNA (tRNA): a type of RNA that binds to a specific amino acid, carries it to a ribosome, and positions it for incorporation into the growing protein chain during protein synthesis. A set of three bases in tRNA (the anticodon) is complementary to the set of three bases in mRNA (the codon) that codes for that specific amino acid in the genetic code.

transformation: a method of acquiring new genes, whereby DNA from one bacterium (normally released after the death of the bacterium) becomes incorporated into the DNA of another, living bacterium.

transgenic: referring to an animal or a plant that contains DNA derived from another species, usually inserted into the organism through genetic engineering.

translation: the process whereby the sequence of bases of messenger RNA is converted into the sequence of amino acids of a protein.

translocation: a mutation that occurs when a piece of DNA is removed from one chromosome and attached to another chromosome.

transport protein: a protein that regulates the movement of water-soluble molecules through the plasma membrane.

trial-and-error learning: a type of learning in which behavior is modified in response to the positive or negative consequences of an action.

triglyceride (trī-glis′-er-īd): a lipid composed of three fatty acid molecules bonded to a single glycerol molecule.

trisomy 21: see *Down syndrome*.

trisomy X: a condition of females who have three X chromosomes instead of the normal two; most such women are phenotypically normal and are fertile.

trophic level: literally, "feeding level"; the categories of organisms in a community, and the position of an organism in a food chain, defined by the organism's source of energy; includes producers, primary consumers, secondary consumers, and so on.

tropical deciduous forest: a biome, warm all year-round, with pronounced wet and dry seasons; characterized by trees that shed their leaves during the dry season (deciduous trees), an adaptation that minimizes water loss.

tropical rain forest: a biome with evenly warm, evenly moist conditions year-round, dominated by broadleaf evergreen trees; the most diverse biome.

tropical scrub forest: a biome, warm all year-round, with pronounced wet and dry seasons (drier conditions than in tropical deciduous forests); characterized by short, deciduous, often thorn-bearing trees with grasses growing beneath them.

true-breeding: pertaining to an individual all of whose offspring produced through self-fertilization are identical to the parental type. True-breeding individuals are homozygous for a given trait.

tubular reabsorption: the process by which cells of the tubule of the nephron remove water and nutrients from the filtrate within the tubule and return those substances to the blood.

tubule (toob'-ūl): the tubular portion of a nephron; includes a proximal portion, the loop of Henle, and a distal portion. Urine is formed from the blood filtrate as it passes through the tubule.

tundra: a biome with severe weather conditions (extreme cold and wind, and little rainfall) that cannot support trees.

turgor pressure: pressure developed within a cell (especially the central vacuole of plant cells) as a result of osmotic water entry.

Turner syndrome: a set of characteristics typical of a woman with only one X chromosome; women with Turner syndrome are sterile, with a tendency to be very short and to lack typical female secondary sexual characteristics.

unicellular: single-celled; most members of the domains Bacteria and Archaea and the kingdom Protista are unicellular.

uniform distribution: the distribution characteristic of a population with a relatively regular spacing of individuals, commonly as a result of territorial behavior.

unsaturated: referring to a fatty acid with fewer than the maximum number of hydrogen atoms bonded to its carbon backbone (therefore, an unsaturated fatty acid has one or more double bonds in its carbon backbone).

upwelling: an upward flow that brings cold, nutrient-laden water from the ocean depths to the surface.

ureter (ū'-re-ter): a tube that conducts urine from a kidney to the urinary bladder.

urinary system: the organ system that produces, stores, and eliminates urine. The urinary system is critical for maintaining homeostatic conditions within the bloodstream. In mammals, it includes the kidneys, ureters, bladder, and urethra.

uterine tube: the tube leading from the ovary to the uterus, into which the secondary oocyte (egg cell) is released; also called the *oviduct*, or, in humans, the *Fallopian tube*.

utricle: a patch of hair cells in the vestibule of the inner ear; bending of the hairs of the hair cells permits detection of the direction of gravity and the degree of tilt of the head.

vagina: the passageway leading from the outside of a female mammal's body to the cervix of the uterus; serves as the receptacle for semen and as the birth canal.

variable: a factor in a scientific experiment that is deliberately manipulated in order to test a hypothesis.

vas deferens (vaz de'-fer-enz): the tube connecting the epididymis of the testis with the urethra.

vascular cambium: a lateral meristem that is located between the xylem and phloem of a woody root or stem and that gives rise to secondary xylem and phloem.

vascular plant (vas'-kū-lar): a plant that has conducting vessels for transporting liquids; also called a tracheophyte.

vein: in vertebrates, a large-diameter, thin-walled vessel that carries blood from venules back to the heart; in plants, a vascular bundle in a leaf.

venule (ven'-ūl): a narrow vessel with thin walls that carries blood from capillaries to veins.

vertebral column (ver-tē'-brul): a column of serially arranged skeletal units (the vertebrae) that protect the nerve cord in vertebrates; the backbone.

vertebrate: an animal that has a vertebral column.

vesicle (ves'-i-kul): a small, temporary, membrane-bound sac within the cytoplasm.

vessel element: one of the cells of a xylem vessel; elongated, dead at maturity, with thick lateral cell walls for support but with end walls that are either heavily perforated or missing.

vestigial structure (ves-tij'-ē-ul): a structure that serves no apparent purpose but is homologous to functional structures in related organisms and provides evidence of evolution.

viroid (vī'-roid): a particle of RNA that is capable of infecting a cell and of directing the production of more viroids; responsible for certain plant diseases.

virus (vī'-rus): a noncellular parasitic particle that consists of a protein coat surrounding genetic material; multiplies only within a cell of a living organism (the host).

vitreous humor (vit'-rē-us): a clear, jelly-like substance that fills the large chamber of the eye between the lens and the retina; helps to maintain the shape of the eyeball.

vulnerable species: a species that is likely to become endangered unless conditions that threaten its survival improve.

waggle dance: a symbolic form of communication used by honeybee foragers to communicate the location of a food source to their hive mates.

warning coloration: bright coloration that warns predators that the potential prey is distasteful or even poisonous.

water mold: a member of a protist group that includes species with filamentous shapes that give them a superficially fungus-like appearance. Water molds, which include species that cause economically important plant diseases, are part of a larger group known as the stramenopiles.

wax: a lipid composed of fatty acids covalently bonded to long-chain alcohols.

weather: short-term fluctuations in temperature, humidity, cloud cover, wind, and precipitation in a region over periods of hours to days.

wetlands: a region (sometimes called a marsh, swamp, or bog) in which the soil is covered by, or saturated with, water for a significant part of the year.

wildlife corridor: a strip of protected land linking larger areas. Wildlife corridors allow animals to move freely and safely between habitats that would otherwise be isolated by human activities.

work: energy transferred to an object, usually causing the object to move.

working memory: the first phase of learning; short-term memory that is electrical or biochemical in nature.

X chromosome: the female sex chromosome in mammals and some insects.

Y chromosome: the male sex chromosome in mammals and some insects.

yolk sac: one of the embryonic membranes of reptiles (including birds) and mammals. In reptiles, the yolk sac is a membrane surrounding the yolk in the egg; in mammals, it forms part of the umbilical cord and the digestive tract but does not contain yolk.

zona pellucida (pel-oo'-si-duh): a clear, noncellular layer between the corona radiata and the egg.

zooplankton: nonphotosynthetic protists that are abundant in marine and freshwater environments.

zygomycete: a fungus species formerly placed in the now-defunct taxonomic group Zygomycota. Zygomycetes, which include the species that cause fruit rot and bread mold, do not constitute a true clade and are now distributed among several other taxonomic groups.

zygosporangium (zī'-gō-spor-an-jee-um): a tough, resistant reproductive structure produced by some fungi, such as bread molds; encloses diploid nuclei that undergo meiosis and give rise to haploid spores.

Answers to Figure Caption and Fill-in-the-Blank Questions

(Go to MasterBiology for answers to the Consider This, Review, and Applying the Concepts questions.)

Chapter 1
Figure Caption Questions

Figure 1-10 Global climate change will impact the entire biosphere. The growing human population—whose energy use is driving global climate change and whose demand for space and resources is causing widespread habitat destruction—would also be an appropriate answer.

Figure E1-1 Redi's experiment demonstrated that the maggots were caused by something that was excluded by a gauze cover, but the possibility remained that some agent other than flies produced the maggots. An effective follow-up experiment might involve a series of closed, meat-containing systems that were identical in all respects other than the addition of a single possible causal element. Perhaps one container would have flies added, one roaches, one dust or soot, and so on. And, of course, a control would have nothing added.

Fill-in-the-Blank

1. stimuli; energy, materials; complex, organized; evolve
2. atom; cell; tissues; population; community; ecosystem
3. scientific theory; hypothesis; scientific method
4. evolution; natural selection
5. deoxyribonucleic acid, DNA; genes

Chapter 2
Figure Caption Questions

Figure 2-2 Atoms with outer shells that are not full are unstable. They become stable by filling (or emptying) their outer shells. Except for hydrogen, atoms in biological molecules have outer shells that are stable when filled with eight electrons.

Figure 2-8 No, the salt would not dissolve. You can try this at home. The oil exerts no attraction for the ions in salt, so it remains in solid crystals.

Figure 2-9 Oil forms droplets when submerged in water because oil molecules are nonpolar and hydrophobic. Hydrogen bonds join surrounding water molecules, excluding the oil and causing oil molecules to group together.

Figure 2-10 The sunbathers' skin is reddening because their skin cells are being damaged by ultraviolet rays in sunlight (this causes extra blood flow to the damaged cells). This is dangerous because ultraviolet rays can damage DNA in skin cells, in some cases causing cancer.

Fill-in-the-Blank

1. protons, neutrons; atomic number; electrons, electron shells
2. ion; positive; negative; ionic
3. isotopes; subatomic; energy; elements; radioactive
4. inert; reactive; share
5. polar; hydrogen; cohesion

Chapter 3
Figure Caption Questions

Figure 3-8 During hydrolysis of sucrose, water would be split; a hydrogen atom from water would be added to the oxygen from glucose (that formerly linked the two subunits) and the remaining OH from water would be added to the carbon (formerly bonded to oxygen) of the fructose subunit.

Figure 3-12 The enzyme would hydrolyze the triglyceride into a glycerol and three fatty acids, using up three water molecules.

Figure 3-16 As lipids, steroids are soluble in the lipid-based cell membranes and can cross them to act inside the cell.

Figure 3-21 Heat energy can break hydrogen bonds and disrupt the proteins' three-dimensional structure. This prevents the protein from carrying out its usual function(s).

Fill-in-the-Blank

1. monomer, polymers; polysaccharides; hydrolysis; cellulose, starch, glycogen; sucrose, lactose, maltose
2. oil; wax; fat; steroids; cholesterol; phospholipid
3. dehydration, water; amino acids; primary; helix, pleated sheet; pleated sheet; denatured
4. double bonds (or double covalent bonds); hydrogen bonds; hydrogen bonds and disulfide bonds; hydrogen bonds; peptide bonds
5. ribose sugar, base, phosphate; adenosine triphosphate (ATP); adenine, guanine, cytosine, thymine; deoxyribonucleic acid (DNA), ribonucleic acid (RNA); phosphate

Chapter 4
Figure Caption Questions

Figure 4-7 Fluid would not move upward because the beating of the flagella would direct fluid straight out from the cell membranes. Mucus and trapped particles would accumulate in the trachea.

Figure 4-9 Condensation allows the chromosomes to become organized and separated from one another, so that a complete copy of genetic information can be distributed to each of the daughter cells that results from cell division.

Figure 4-14 The fundamentally similar composition of membranes allows them to merge with one another. This allows molecules in vesicles to be transferred from one membrane-enclosed structure (such as endoplasmic reticulum) to another (such as the Golgi apparatus). The material can be exported from the cell when the vesicle merges with the plasma membrane.

Fill-in-the-Blank

1. phospholipids, proteins; phospholipid; protein
2. cytoskeleton; microfilaments, intermediate filaments, microtubules; microtubules; microtubules; microfilaments; intermediate filaments
3. ribosomes; endoplasmic reticulum; nucleolus; Golgi apparatus; cell wall; messenger RNA
4. rough endoplasmic reticulum; vesicles, Golgi apparatus; carbohydrate; plasma membrane
5. mitochondria; chloroplasts; cell wall; nucleoid; cilia; cytoplasm
6. mitochondria, chloroplasts; double, ATP, size
7. cell walls; nucleoid; plasmids; sex pili

Chapter 5
Figure Caption Questions

Figure 5-7 The sac would be larger in all three cases.

Figure 5-8 The plant cell will not burst because its cell wall will resist the pressure of water entering by osmosis. Animal cells lack a cell wall, and when placed in a highly hypotonic solution will absorb water by osmosis until the cell membrane bursts.

Figure 5-9 The distilled water made the solution hypotonic to the blood cells, causing enough water to flow in to burst their fragile cell membranes.

Figure 5-14 Exocytosis uses cellular energy, whereas diffusion is passive. In addition, while materials move through a membrane during diffusion out of a cell, in exocytosis, materials are expelled without passing directly through the plasma membrane. Exocytosis allows materials that are too large to pass through membranes to be eliminated from the cell.

Fill-in-the-Blank

1. phospholipids; receptor, recognition, enzymes, attachment, transport
2. selectively permeable; diffusion; osmosis; aquaporins; active transport
3. channel, carrier; simple, lipids
4. desmosomes, tight junctions, gap junctions; plasmodesmata
5. simple diffusion, simple diffusion, facilitated diffusion, facilitated diffusion.
6. endocytosis; yes; pinocytosis, phagocytosis; vesicles

Chapter 6
Figure Caption Questions

Figure 6-1 This would be a boring roller coaster because each successive "hill" would need to be much lower than the previous one.

Figure 6-5 Burning glucose is an exergonic reaction.

Figure 6-7 Photosynthesis is an endergonic reaction.

Figure 6-10 No, only exergonic reactions can occur spontaneously after the activation energy is surmounted.

Figure 6-14 Competitive inhibition.

Fill-in-the-Blank

1. created, destroyed; kinetic, potential
2. more, less; organized; entropy
3. exergonic; endergonic; exergonic; endergonic; coupled
4. adenosine triphosphate; energy carrier; adenosine diphosphate, phosphate; energy
5. proteins; catalysts, activation energy; active site; substrates
6. inhibiting; competitive inhibitor; allosteric

Chapter 7
Figure Caption Questions

Figure 7-4 Chlorophyll *a* would appear more green because it absorbs fewer of the green wavelengths than chlorophyll *b*. Chlorophyll *b* would appear more yellowish and less green, because it absorbs more of the green wavelengths.

Figure E7-1 The C_4 pathway is less efficient than the Calvin cycle; C_4 uses one extra ATP per CO_2 molecule (for regenerating PEP). Thus, when CO_2 is abundant and photorespiration is not a problem, C_3 plants produce sugar at lower energy cost, and they outcompete C_4 plants.

Fill-in-the-Blank

1. stomata, oxygen (O_2), carbon dioxide (CO_2); water loss (evaporation); chloroplasts, mesophyll
2. red, blue, violet; green; carotenoids; photosystems, thylakoid
3. reaction center; primary electron acceptor; electron transport chain; hydrogen ions (H^+); chemiosmosis
4. water (H_2O), carbon dioxide (CO_2); Calvin cycle; carbon fixation
5. rubisco, oxygen (O_2); photorespiration; C_4 pathway, CAM (or crassulacean acid metabolism) pathway
6. ATP, NADH, Calvin; RuBP (or ribulose bisphosphate); G3P (glyceraldehyde-3-phosphate), glucose

Chapter 8
Figure Caption Questions

Figure 8-3 Glycolysis results in a net production of two ATP and two NADH for each glucose molecule.

Figure 8-6 Oxygen is the final acceptor in the electron transport chain; if it is not present, electrons cannot proceed through the chain, and production of ATP by chemiosmosis comes to a halt.

Figure 8-8 Glycolysis followed by fermentation results in a net production of two ATP molecules and no NADH.

Figure 8-9 In oxygen-rich environments, both types of bacteria can survive, but aerobic bacteria prevail because their respiration produces more ATP per glucose molecule. In oxygen-poor environments, however, aerobic bacteria are limited by the oxygen shortage, and anaerobes would prevail despite their inefficiency.

Fill-in-the-Blank

1. glycolysis, cellular respiration; cytosol, mitochondria; cellular respiration
2. anaerobic; glycolysis, two; fermentation, NAD^+
3. ethanol (alcohol), carbon dioxide; lactic acid; lactic acid
4. erythropoietin (EPO), red blood, oxygen; cellular respiration
5. matrix, intermembrane space, concentration gradient; chemiosmosis; ATP synthase
6. Krebs; pyruvate; two; NADH, $FADH_2$

Chapter 9
Figure Caption Questions

Figure 9-9 If the sister chromatids of one replicated chromosome failed to separate, then one daughter cell would not receive any copy of that chromosome, while the other daughter cell would receive both copies.

Figure 9-15 If one pair of homologues failed to separate at anaphase I, one of the resulting daughter cells (and the gametes produced from it) would have both homologues and the other daughter cell (and the gametes produced from it) would not have any copies of that homologue.

Fill-in-the-Blank

1. deoxyribonucleic acid (DNA); locus; alleles
2. asexual; sexual; Meiotic
3. prokaryotic fission
4. mitotic; differentiation; Stem
5. homologues OR homologous chromosomes; autosomes; sex chromosomes
6. prophase, metaphase, anaphase, telophase; cytokinesis; telophase
7. kinetochores; polar
8. four; meiosis I; gametes OR sperm and eggs
9. prophase; chiasmata; crossing over
10. shuffling of homologues OR random distribution of homologues; crossing over; fusion of gametes

Chapter 10
Figure Caption Questions

Figure 10-8 Half of the gametes produced by a *Pp* plant will have the *P* allele, and half will have the *p* allele. All of the gametes produced by a *pp* plant will have the *p* allele. Therefore, half of the offspring of a *Pp* × *pp* cross will be *Pp* (purple) and half will be *pp* (white), whereas all of the offspring of a *PP* × *pp* cross will be *Pp* (purple). See Figure 10-9.

Figure 10-11 A plant with wrinkled green seeds has the genotype *ssyy*. A plant with smooth yellow seeds could be *SSYY*, *SsYY*, *SSYy*, or *SsYy*. Set up four Punnett squares to see if the smooth yellow plant's genotype can be revealed by a test cross.

Figure 10-12 Chromosomes, not individual genes, assort independently during meiosis. Therefore, if the genes for seed color and seed shape were on the same chromosome, they would tend to be inherited together, and would not assort independently.

Figure 10-25 One of Victoria and Albert's sons, Leopold, had hemophilia. To be male, Leopold must have inherited Albert's Y chromosome. The X chromosome, not the Y chromosome, bears the gene for blood clotting, so Leopold must have inherited the hemophilia allele from his mother, Victoria.

Fill-in-the-Blank

1. locus; alleles; mutations
2. genotype, phenotype; heterozygous
3. independently; as a group; linked
4. an X and a Y, two X; sperm
5. sex-linked
6. incomplete dominance; codominance; polygenic inheritance

Chapter 11

Figure Caption Questions

Figure 11-5 It takes more energy to break apart a C–G base pair, because these are held together by three hydrogen bonds, compared with the two hydrogen bonds that bind A to T.

Figure E11-7 DNA polymerase always moves in the 3' to 5' direction on a parental strand. Because the two strands of a DNA double helix are oriented in opposite directions, the 5' direction on one strand leads toward the replication fork and the 5' direction on the other strand leads away from the fork. Therefore, DNA polymerase must move in opposite directions on the two strands.

Fill-in-the-Blank

1. nucleotides; sugar (deoxyribose), phosphate, base (order not important)
2. phosphate, sugar (order not important); double helix
3. thymine, cytosine; complementary
4. semiconservative
5. DNA helicase; DNA polymerase; DNA ligase
6. mutations; nucleotide substitution, point mutation

Chapter 12

Figure Caption Questions

Figure 12-3 RNA polymerase always travels in the 3' to 5' direction on the template strand. Because the two DNA strands run in opposite directions, if the other DNA strand were the template strand, then RNA polymerase must travel in the opposite direction (that is, right to left in this illustration).

Figure 12-4 Cells produce far larger amounts of some proteins than others. Obvious examples include cells that produce antibodies or protein hormones, which they secrete into the bloodstream in large quantities, with effects throughout the body. If a cell needs to produce more of certain proteins, it will probably synthesize more mRNA, which will then be translated into that protein.

Figure 12-7 Grouped into codons, the original mRNA sequence visible here is CGA AUC UAG UAA. Changing all G to U would produce the sequence CUA AUC UAU UAA. The two changes are in the first codon (CGA to CUA) and the third codon (UAG to UAU). Refer to the genetic code illustrated in Table 12-3. First, CGA encodes arginine, while CUA encodes leucine, so the first G → U change would substitute leucine for arginine in the protein. Second, UAG is a stop codon, but UAU encodes tyrosine. Therefore, the second G → U change would add tyrosine to the protein instead of stopping translation. The final codon in the illustration, UAA, is a stop codon, so the new protein would end with tyrosine.

Figure E12-1 The mold would be able to grow if any of ornithine, citrulline, or arginine were added to the medium.

Fill-in-the-Blank

1. transcription; translation; ribosome
2. mRNA, tRNA, rRNA (order not important); microRNA
3. three; codon; anticodon
4. RNA polymerase; template; promoter; termination signal
5. start, stop; transfer RNA; peptide
6. point; Insertion; Deletion

Chapter 13

Figure Caption Questions

Figure 13-8 As they do for other genes, each person normally has two copies of each STR gene, one on each of a pair of homologous chromosomes. A person may be homozygous (two copies of the same allele) or heterozygous (one copy of each of two alleles) for each STR. The bands on the gel represent individual alleles of an STR gene. Therefore, a single person can have one band (if homozygous) or two bands (if heterozygous). If a person is homozygous for an STR allele, then he has two copies of the same allele. The DNA from both (identical) alleles will run in the same place on the gel, and therefore that (single) band will have twice as much DNA as each of the two bands of DNA from a heterozygote. The more DNA, the brighter the band.

Figure 13-9 The genetic material of bacteriophages is DNA. Each bacterial restriction enzyme cuts DNA at a specific nucleotide sequence. A given bacterium is likely to have evolved restriction enzymes that cut DNA at sequences found in bacteriophages but not in their own chromosome.

Fill-in-the-Blank

1. Genetically modified organisms
2. Transformation; plasmids
3. polymerase chain reaction
4. short tandem repeats; length OR size OR number of repeats; DNA profile
5. electrophoresis OR gel electrophoresis; DNA probe; base pairing OR hydrogen bonds

Chapter 14

Figure Caption Questions

Figure 14-6 No. Mutations, the ultimate source of the variation on which natural selection acts, occur in all organisms, including those that reproduce asexually.

Figure 14-7 No. Evolution can include changes in traits that are not revealed in morphology (the physical form of an organism), such as physiological systems and metabolic pathways. More generally, evolution in the sense of changes in a species' genetic make-up is inevitable; genetic evolution is not necessarily reflected in morphological change.

Figure 14-9 Possibilities include:

coccyx (tailbone)—homologous with tail bones of a cat (or any tetrapod)

goose bumps—homologous with erectile hairs of a chimp (or any mammal; used for aggressive displays and insulation)

appendix—homologous with the cecum of a rabbit (and other herbivorous mammals; extension of large intestine used for storage)

wisdom teeth—homologous with grinding rear molars of a leaf-eating monkey (or other mammals)

ear-wiggling muscles (the muscles around the ear that some people can use to make their ears move)—homologous with muscles in a dog (and other mammals) that enable the external ear to orient toward sound

Figure 14-10 Analogous. Bird tails consist of feathers; dog tails do not (they consist of bone/muscle/skin). If the two structures were homologous, they would both consist of bone and muscle, or both consist of feathers

Fill-in-the-Blank

1. wing, arm; analogous, convergent; vestigial
2. common ancestor; amino acids, ATP
3. catastrophism; uniformitarianism; old
4. evolution; mutations, DNA
5. natural selection; artificial selection
6. many traits are inherited; Gregor Mendel

Credits

Index

Citations followed by *b* refer to material in boxes; citations followed by *f* refer to material in figures or illustrations; and citations followed by *t* refer to material in tables.

Pleiotropy, 176, 176f, 177
Pleistocene Park, 565b, 565f
Pneumonia, 277
Poaching, 560
Point mutations
    defined, 221–222, 221t
    DNA mutations, 205, 205f
Polar bears, 479f
Polar covalent bonds, 24t, 25f, 26–27, 28
Polar microtubules, 149–150, 149f, 150
Poliovirus, 16
Pollen
    early land plants, 316t, 321–322
    gene flow, 282
    herbicide resistance, 252
    seed plants, 391
Pollution
    biodiversity, threat to, 589
    open ocean, 573
    prokaryotes, 358
Polychaetes, 431, 431f
Polygenic inheritance, 176, 176f
Polymerase chain reaction (PCR),
    237–238, 238f, 247, 251b
Polymers, 36–37, 36f
Polypeptide, 37t, 45
Polyps, 426–427, 426f
Polyribosomes, 59f, 64, 64f
Polysaccharides, 37, 37t, 39–41, 40f, 41f
Ponds, succession in, 525, 526f
Population bottleneck, 285, 286f,
    288b, 288f
Population cycles, 495–496, 496f
Population growth
    biodiversity, conserving, 595, 595f
    limiting, ethics of, 506
Population growth and regulation,
    487–508
    Case Study, Easter Island, 487, 492,
        495, 506
    chapter review, 507–508
    environmental resistance, 490, 491,
        492–498, 492f, 493f, 494f, 496f, 497f
    exponential growth, 490–491, 491f, 492f
    human population change
        age structure, 503–505, 503f,
            504f, 505f
        demographic transition, 502, 502f
        fertility rates, 505, 505t
        growth and distribution, 502–503
        rapid growth, 500, 500f, 501b, 501f
        technical advances, 500, 502
        U.S. population, 506, 506f
    population distribution, 498–499,
        498f, 499f
    population size change, 488–490,
        489f, 490f
Populations. See also Evolution of
        populations
    defined, 4, 278
    evolution, 259
    level of biological organization, 8, 8f

natural selection, 265–266, 265f
    size change, 488–490, 489f, 490f
    variations in, 265, 265f
Porifera. See Sponges (Porifera)
Porphyra, 369t, 378b
Positron emission tomography (PET),
    22, 22f
Post-anal tail, 446
Posterior (tail) end, 420f, 421
Post-industrial stage of the demographic
    transition, 502, 502f
Postmating isolation mechanisms, 298t,
    300, 300f
Posture, and human evolution, 327, 329
Potassium, 20t
Potassium cyanide, 104
Potential energy, 94, 94f
Potrykus, Ingo, 253b
Power grip, 327
Practice hypothesis, 478
Precambrian era, 315, 316t, 320, 321f
Precipitation, and life on land, 551, 552f
Precision grip, 327
Predation
    animal diversity, 320
    evolution, 290
    extinction, 306
Predator-prey interactions
    appearance, 515–518, 515f, 516f, 517f,
        518f, 519f
    chemical warfare, 515, 515f
    counteracting adaptations, 513, 513f
    overview, 510t, 512–513, 513f, 514, 514f
Predators
    defined, 512
    density-dependent controls,
        495–496, 496f
Prediction, in scientific method, 11
Pre-industrial stage of the demographic
    transition, 502, 502f
Premating isolation mechanisms, 298–
    299, 298f, 298t, 299f, 300f
Prey, 495–496, 496f
Primary consumers, 532, 532f
Primary electron acceptor molecule,
    113, 114f
Primary structure, defined, 45–46, 46f
Primary succession, 522, 523f, 524, 524f
Primates, 326–327, 326f
Primers, PCR, 237, 238f
Prions
    case study, 34, 47, 49–50
    discovery of, 14, 361–362, 363
    replication of, 362–363
Probabilities
    genotype and phenotype prediction,
        170, 171f
    multiple traits, 173, 173f
Producers, 532, 532f
Products
    chemical reactions, 96, 96f, 97f
    second law of thermodynamics, 95

Profundal zone in lakes, 567f, 568
Prokaryotes
    classification systems, 351–352
    endospores, 353, 354f
    first organisms, 315, 316t
    genetic material exchange, 356, 357f
    habitats, 354, 354f, 355b, 355f
    humans and other organisms, effects
        on, 357–359, 357f
    metabolisms, 355–356, 356f
    motility, 352, 353f
    protective film, 352–353, 353f
    reproduction, 356, 356f
    shapes of, 351, 352f
    size of, 351
Prokaryotes and viruses, diversity of,
    350–365
    Archaea and Bacteria domains,
        351–352, 352f
    Case Study, foodborne illness, 350, 354,
        358, 361, 363
    chapter review, 364–365
    prokaryotes' effect on other organisms,
        357–359, 357f
    prokaryote survival and reproduction,
        352–356, 353f, 354f, 355f, 356f, 357f
    viruses, viroids, and prions, 359–363,
        359f, 360f, 361f, 362f, 363f
Prokaryotic cells
    cell cycle, 142–143, 143f
    cell type, 10, 10t
    features of, 69–71, 70f
    regulation of gene expression,
        222–223, 223f
    structures within, 58, 58t
    transcription and translation, 216, 217f
Prokaryotic (binary) fission, 142–143,
    143f, 356, 356f
Promoter, in transcription, 215, 216f
Prophase, in mitosis, 148–150, 148f, 158t
Prophase I, 154–155, 156f, 158t
Proteins
    amino acids, formation from, 44–45,
        45f, 46f
    cell membranes, 77f, 79–80, 79f, 88f
    cellular respiration, 132
    defined, 44
    functions of, 44, 44t, 45f, 48
    levels of structure, 45–47, 46f, 47f,
        50b, 50f
    manufacture and modification of, 66, 66f
    one gene, one protein, 212b, 213f
    prions, 34, 47, 49–50
    rough ER, 65
    subtypes and structures, 37t
    synthesis of, genetic information for,
        210–212, 211f, 211t, 213f
Protists
    defined, 367
    Eukarya domain, 9, 9f, 10t
    modern classification scheme, 344,
        344f, 345f